Financial Aid for Military Personnel & Military Family Members 2015 - 2017

DANTES SPECIAL EDITION

OTHER RSP FINANCIAL AID DIRECTORIES OF INTEREST TO MILITARY PERSONNEL, ROTC STUDENTS & MILITARY FAMILY MEMBERS

College Student's Guide to Merit and Other No-Need Funding
Selected as one of the "Outstanding Titles of the Year" by *Choice,* this directory describes 1,300 no-need funding opportunities for college students. 490 pages. ISBN 1588412121. $32.50, plus $7 shipping.

Directory of Financial Aids for Women
There are nearly 1,500 funding programs set aside for women described in this biennial directory, which has been called "the cream of the crop" by *School Library Journal* and the "best available reference source" by *Guide to Reference.* 504 pages. ISBN 1588412504. $45, plus $7 shipping.

Financial Aid for African Americans
More than 1,300 funding opportunities open to African American college students, professionals, and postdoctorates are described in this award-winning directory. 502 pages. ISBN 1588412423. $45, plus $7 shipping.

Financial Aid for Asian Americans
This is the source to use if you are looking for funding for Asian Americans, including college-bound high school seniors, undergraduates, graduate students, professionals, and postdoctorates; nearly 950 sources of free money are described here. 356 pages. ISBN 1588412431. $40, plus $7 shipping.

Financial Aid for Hispanic Americans
The 1,175 biggest and best sources of free money available to undergraduates, graduates students, professionals, and postdoctorates of Mexican, Puerto Rican, Central American, or other Latin American heritage are described here. 458 pages. ISBN 158841244X. $42.50, plus $7 shipping.

Financial Aid for Native Americans
Detailed information is provided on more than 1,400 funding opportunities open to American Indians, Native Alaskans, and Native Pacific Islanders for college, graduate school, or professional activities. 518 pages. ISBN 1588412458. $45, plus $7 shipping.

Financial Aid for Persons with Disabilities and Their Families
Formerly issued as *Financial Aid for the Disabled and Their Families,* this directory, which *Library Journal* named one of the "Best Reference Books of the Year," describes nearly 1,400 funding opportunities. 510 pages. ISBN 158841227X. $40, plus $7 shipping.

High School Senior's Guide to Merit and Other No-Need Funding
Here's your guide to 1,100 funding programs that *never* look at income level when making awards to college-bound high school seniors. 411 pages. ISBN 1588412369. $29.95, plus $7 shipping.

Money for Christian College Students
This is the only directory to describe 850 funding opportunities available to support Christian students working on an undergraduate or graduate degree. 264 pages. ISBN 1588412253. $30, plus $7 shipping.

Money for Graduate Students in the Arts & Humanities
Use this directory to identify 1,000 funding opportunities available to support graduate study and research in the arts/humanities. 287 pages. ISBN 1588412296. $42.50, plus $7 shipping

Money for Graduate Students in the Biological Sciences
This unique directory focuses solely on funding for graduate study/research in the biological sciences (800+ funding opportunities). 241 pages. ISBN 158841230X. $37.50, plus $7 shipping.

Money for Graduate Students in the Health Sciences
Described here are 1,000+ funding opportunities just for students interested in a graduate degree in dentistry, medicine, nursing, nutrition, pharmacology, etc. 313 pages. ISBN 1588412318. $42.50, plus $7 shipping.

Money for Graduate Students in the Physical & Earth Sciences
Nearly 900 funding opportunities for graduate students in the physical and earth sciences are described in detail here. 280 pages. ISBN 1588412326. $40, plus $7 shipping.

Money for Graduate Students in the Social & Behavioral Sciences
Looking for money for a graduate degree in the social/behavioral sciences? Here are 1,100 funding programs for you. 319 pages. ISBN 1588412334. $42.50, plus $7 shipping.

Financial Aid for Military Personnel & Military Family Members 2015 - 2017

DANTES SPECIAL EDITION

Gail A. Schlachter
R. David Weber

A Listing of Scholarships, Fellowships, and Other Sources of Funding Available Primarily or Exclusively to Military Personnel (including ROTC Students) and Military Family Members, Plus a Set of Seven Indexes: Program Title, Sponsoring Organization, Branch of Service, Residency, Tenability, Subject, and Deadline Date

Reference Service Press
Los Altos, California

ISBN 10: 1588412555
ISBN 13: 9781588412553
ISSN: 0896-7792

10 9 8 7 6 5 4 3 2 1

Reference Service Press (RSP) began in 1977 with a single financial aid publication *(Directory of Financial Aids for Women)* and now specializes in the development of financial aid resources in multiple formats, including books, print-on-demand reports, eBooks, and online sources. Long recognized as a leader in the field, RSP has been called, by the *Simba Report on Directory Publishing,* "a true success in the world of independent directory publishers." Both Kaplan Educational Centers and Military.com have hailed RSP as "the leading authority on scholarships."

DANTES Special Edition: DANTES (Defense Activity for Non-Traditional Education Support) is a Department of Defense agency that is committed to helping those with ties to the military pursue their educational goals. As part of that process, DANTES arranged with Reference Service Press to compile a directory of funding opportunities intended specifically for military personnel (including students with ROTC affiliation) and military family members. The result is this DANTES Special Edition, which describes in detail more than 1,130 scholarships, fellowships, and other sources of educational funding open to members of these target groups. This special edition is not available for general sale; it was prepared for and is sold solely to DANTES.

Reference Service Press
2310 Homestead, Suite C1 #219
Los Altos, CA 94024
(650) 861-3170
Fax: (650) 861-3171
E-mail: info@rspfunding.com
Visit our web site: www.rspfunding.com

Manufactured in the United States of America

Price: $40.00, plus $7 shipping.

Contents

Introduction

WHY THIS DIRECTORY IS NEEDED

More than one third of America's population today has either direct or indirect ties to the armed services, as active-duty military personnel, veterans, military family members (spouses, parents, children, grandchildren, and other descendants), and students affiliated with ROTC.

For decades, a number of organizations have attempted to reward the members of these groups in a variety of ways. In 1944, Congress established the Veterans Administration (now called the Department of Veterans Affairs) to develop programs for the benefit of the men and women who served in previous wars. Today, the DVA provides a wide variety of funding opportunities to veterans and their families. Many state governments have also established or expanded programs that complement federal benefits. In addition, voluntary and other private organizations (most notably the American Legion) have raised millions of dollars to provide financial aid to their members, other veterans or military personnel, or their family members. Similarly, to recruit, retain, and reward their personnel (especially since the advent of the all-volunteer military), the armed services have developed wide-ranging benefits for members and those who are related to them. In all, billions of dollars a year are now set aside in the form of publicly- and privately-funded scholarships, fellowships, grants-in-aid, and other sources of financial aid for those with direct or indirect ties to the military.

While numerous print and online resources have been prepared over the years to identify general financial aid opportunities (those open to all segments of society), only Reference Service Press has developed a comprehensive database of funding programs aimed primarily or exclusively at those with ties to the military. After years of purchasing Reference Service Press's off-the-shelf financial aid resources, DANTES requested that the company draw upon its unique database to compile a targeted directory covering funding opportunities aimed specifically at groups served by DANTES: military personnel (including students with ROTC affiliation) and military family members. The result is this DANTES Special Edition, which describes in detail more than 1,130 scholarships, fellowships, loans, and other sources of educational funding available specifically to members of these target groups.

WHAT'S COVERED IN THIS SPECIAL EDITION FOR DANTES?

Financial Aid for Military Personnel & Military Family Members (DANTES Special Edition) provides comprehensive information on more than 1,130 programs aimed specifically at current servicemembers (including ROTC students) and the spouses, children, parents, descendants, and other members of military families. The listings in this first special edition for DANTES cover every major field of study, are sponsored by more than 500 different private and public agencies and organizations, and are open to students (primarily or exclusively those with ties to the military) who are interested in pursuing postsecondary education at any level.

In addition to this extensive and focused coverage, this special DANTES edition offers several other unique features. First of all, hundreds of funding opportunities listed here are not covered in other sources. So, even if you have checked elsewhere, you will want to look at *Financial Aid for Military Personnel & Military Family Members* for additional leads. Further, all the funding described here is substantial; every program offers at least $1,000, and many award $20,000 or more or pay all college expenses.

Unlike other funding directories, which generally follow a straight alphabetical arrangement, *Financial Aid for Military Personnel and Military Family Members* groups entries by both educational level (undergraduate studies and graduate studies) and recipient groups (military servicemembers, ROTC students, and military family members)—thus making it easy to pinpoint appropriate programs. The same convenience is offered in the indexes, where the entries are also subdivided by educational level and recipient group. With this arrangement, users with one set of characteristics (e.g., military personnel) will be able to find all programs set aside specifically for them—and not be distracted or have to waste time sorting through descriptions of programs intended for members of the other recipient groups.

In fact, everything about the directory has been designed to make your search for funding as easy as possible. You can identify programs not only by recipient group, but by program title, sponsoring organizations, branch of service, where you live, where you want to spend the money, specific subject areas, and even deadline date (so fundseekers working within specific time constraints can locate programs that are still open). Plus, you'll find all the information you need to decide if a program is a match for you: purpose, eligibility requirements, financial data, duration, special features, limitations, number awarded, and application deadline. You even get fax numbers, toll-free numbers, e-mail addresses, and web site locations (when available), along with complete contact information, to make your requests for applications proceed smoothly.

WHAT'S EXCLUDED?

While this book is intended to be the most comprehensive source of information on funding available to military personnel (including ROTC students) and their family members, there are some programs we've specifically excluded from the directory:

- *Awards open equally to all segments of the population.* Only funding opportunities set aside specifically for military personnel (including ROTC students) or military families are covered here.

- *Programs administered by individual academic institutions solely for their own students.* The directory identifies "portable" programs—ones that can be used at any number of schools. Financial aid administered by individual schools specifically for their own students is not covered. Write directly to the schools you are considering to get information on their offerings.

- *Indirect aid programs,* where funds go to military-related agencies rather than directly to military personnel or military family members. To obtain that information, check with your state veteran's agency or your local DVA office.

- *Money for study outside the United States.* Since there are comprehensive and up-to-date directories that describe the funding available for study and research abroad (particularly Reference Service Press's biennial *Financial Aid for Study and Training Abroad),* only programs that support study or other degree-related activities in the United States are covered here.

- *Restrictive geographic coverage.* In general, programs are excluded if they are open only to residents of a narrow geographic area (anything below the state level). To get information on these geographically restrictive programs, contact Reference Service Press directly or use *RSP FundingFinder,* Reference Service Press's subscription-based online funding database.

- *Programs offering limited financial support.* Comprehensive coverage is provided in this directory only for programs that can substantively impact the financial situation of military personnel and their family members. Scholarships, fellowships, and other educationally-related funding programs must award at least $1,000 a year or they are not included here. Also excluded are programs that offer military personnel the opportunity to pursue college training but do not provide any financial support beyond their current salary. For information on these more limited programs, contact Reference Service Press directly or use *RSP FundingFinder.*

SAMPLE ENTRY

(1) **[639]**

(2) **Marine Corps Scholarships**

(3) Marine Corps Scholarship Foundation, Inc.
Attn: Scholarship Office
909 North Washington Street, Suite 400
Alexandria, VA 22314
Toll-free: (888) 668-1656   Fax: (703) 642-2054
E-mail: SVA@studentveterans.org
Web: www.studentveterans.org/?page=Programs

(4) **Summary** To provide financial assistance for college to the children of present or former members of the U.S. Marine Corps.

(5) **Eligibility** This program is open to the children of 1) Marines on active duty or in the Reserves; 2) veteran Marines who have received an honorable discharge or were killed while serving in the U.S. Marines; 3) active-duty or Reserve U.S. Navy Corpsmen who are serving or have served with a U.S. Marine unit; and 4) U.S. Navy Corpsmen who have served with a U.S. Marine unit and have received an honorable discharge or were killed while serving in the U.S. Navy. Applicants must be high school seniors, high school graduates, or current undergraduates in an accredited college, university, or postsecondary vocational/technical school. They must submit academic transcripts (GPA of 2.0 or higher); a written statement of service from their parent's commanding officer or a copy of their parent's honorable discharge; and a 500-word essay on a topic that changes periodically. Only undergraduate study is supported. The family income of applicants must be less than $93,000 per year.

(6) **Financial data** Stipends range from $1,500 to $10,000 per year.

(7) **Duration** 1 year; may be renewed upon reapplication.

(8) **Additional information** Students pursuing their second bachelor's degree, enrolling in graduate school of any kind, or attending Federal Service Academies are not eligible.

(9) **Number awarded** Varies each year; recently, 2,040 of these scholarships, worth more than $6,600,000, were awarded.

(10) **Deadline** February of each year.

DEFINITION

(1) **Entry number:** The consecutive number assigned to the references and used to index the entry.

(2) **Program title:** Title of scholarship, fellowship, loan, or other funding opportunity.

(3) **Sponsoring organization:** The name, address, and telephone number, toll-free, and fax numbers, e-mail address, and/or web site (when information was supplied) for the organization sponsoring the program.

(4) **Summary:** Identifies the basic program requirements; read the rest of the entry for additional detail.

(5) **Eligibility:** Qualifications required of the applicants, steps in the application process, and factors considered in the selection process.

(6) **Financial data:** Financial details of the program, including fixed sum, average amount, or range of funds offered, expenses for which funds may and may not be applied, and cash-related benefits supplied (e.g., room and board).

(7) **Duration:** Period for which support is provided; renewal prospects.

(8) **Additional information:** Any benefits, features, restrictions, or limitations (generally nonmonetary) associated with the program.

(9) **Number awarded:** Number of recipients each year or other specified period.

(10) **Deadline:** The month by which applications must be submitted.

HOW THE DIRECTORY IS COMPILED

The preparation of this special DANTES edition involved extensive research and review. To insure that the information included here is both reliable and current, the editors at Reference Service Press 1) identified, edited, and updated (through the first quarter of 2015) all relevant programs currently in Reference Service Press's funding database, and then 2) searched extensively for new program leads in a variety of sources, including printed directories, news reports, journals, newsletters, house organs, annual reports, and sites on the Internet.

Our policy is to include program descriptions that have been written directly from information supplied by the sponsoring organization in print or online (no information is ever taken from secondary sources). When that information cannot be found, we send up to four collection letters (followed by up to three telephone or email inquiries, if necessary) to those sponsors. Despite our best efforts, however, some sponsoring organizations still failed to respond and, as a result, their programs are not included in this special edition of the directory. The resulting listing presents the 1,130+ biggest and best sources of funding available to military personnel, ROTC students, and military family members.

HOW THE DIRECTORY IS ORGANIZED

This special DANTES edition is divided into two separate sections: 1) a descriptive list of financial aid programs aimed at military personnel, ROTC students, and military family members; and 2) a set of seven indexes to help you find the funding you need.

Funding Available to Military Personnel, ROTC Students, and Military Family Members.   The first section of the directory describes 1,136 financial aid programs set aside primarily or exclusively for those with ties to the military. Entries in this section are grouped into the following two educational categories, to guide readers in their search for a specific kind of financial assistance:

- **Undergraduate Studies:**   Programs that support studies at the postsecondary level in the United States. Money is available to entering or continuing students in any type of public or private (nonsecular or secular) postsecondary institution, ranging from technical schools and community colleges to major universities in the United States.

- **Graduate Studies:**   Programs that support study and other educational activities for students applying to, currently enrolled in, or returning to a master's, doctoral, professional, or specialist program in public or private graduate schools in the United States.

These two educational level chapters are each divided into three recipient groupings: military personnel, ROTC students, and military family members (children, spouses, parents, grandchildren, other relatives, etc.). Within these subdivisions, entries are arranged by program title. Programs that supply more than one type of assistance or assistance to more than one specific group are listed in all relevant subsections. For example, both undergraduate *and* graduate family members may apply for the Chan-Padgett Special Forces Memorial Scholarship, so that program is described in the "Military Family Members" section of both the Undergraduate Studies *and* Graduate Studies chapters.

Each program entry in the directory has been designed to provide a concise profile that includes information (when available) on program title, organization address, telephone numbers (including toll-free and fax numbers), e-mail addresses and web site, purpose, eligibility, money awarded, duration, special features, limitations, number of awards, and application deadline (see the sample entry on page 7).

The information reported for each of the programs in this section was gathered from research conducted through the first quarter of 2015. While the listing is intended to cover as comprehensively as possible the biggest and best sources of educational funding available to military personnel, ROTC students, and military family members, some sponsoring organizations did not post information online or respond to our research inquiries and, consequently, are not included in this edition of the directory.

Indexes.   To help you find the aid you need, we have constructed seven indexes; these will let you access the listings by program title, sponsoring organization, residency, tenability, branch of service, subject focus, and deadline date. These indexes use a word-by-word alphabetical arrangement. Note: numbers in the index refer to entry numbers, not to page numbers in the book.

Program Title Index. If you know the name of a particular funding program and want to find out where it is covered in the directory, use the Program Title Index. To assist you in your search, every program is listed by all its known names, former names, and abbreviations. Since one program can be listed in more than one subsection (e.g., a program providing assistance to military personnel at both the undergraduate and graduate levels is listed in two subsections), each entry number in the index has been coded to indicate educational level (e.g., U = Undergraduate Studies) and the intended recipient group (e.g., m = Military Personnel). By using this coding system, readers can turn directly to the programs that match their financial needs and eligibility characteristics.

Sponsoring Organization Index. This index provides an alphabetical listing of the more than 500 agencies that offer funding to military personnel, military family members, and ROTC students. As in the Program Title Index, entry numbers have been coded to indicate both educational level and recipient group.

Branch of Service Index. This index identifies funding programs that are open to applicants with ties to one or more of the five active branches of the Military (including their respective Guard and Reserve units): Air Force, Army, Coast Guard, Marine Corps, and Navy. To help you target your search for appropriate programs, we have subdivided each of the service branch index entries by both educational level (undergraduate or graduate studies) and recipient group (military personnel, ROTC students, and military family members).

Residency Index. Some programs listed in this book are restricted to military personnel, ROTC students, or military family members in a particular state or region. Others are open to those with ties to the military wherever they live. This index helps you identify both 1) programs available only to residents in your area as well as 2) programs that have no residency requirements. Further, to assist you in your search, we also indicated the educational levels and recipient groups required for the funding offered to residents in each of the areas listed in the index.

Tenability Index. This index identifies the geographic locations where the funding described in the directory may be used. Index entries (city, county, state, region) are arranged alphabetically and subdivided by educational level and recipient group. Use this index when you or your family members are looking for money to support study or other educational activities in a particular geographic area.

Subject Index. This index allows the reader to use more than 200 subject headings to identify the subject focus of each of the financial aid opportunities designed primarily or exclusively for military personnel, ROTC students, and military family members listed in the first section of the directory. Extensive "see" and "see also" references are provided to aid in the search for appropriate funding.

Calendar Index. Since most financial aid programs have specific deadline dates, some may have closed by the time you begin to look for funding. You can use the Calendar Index to determine which programs are still open. This index is arranged by educational level and divided by recipient groups (e.g., military personnel) and month during which the deadline falls. Filing dates can and quite often do vary from year to year; consequently, this index should be used only as a guide for deadlines beyond 2017.

HOW TO USE THE DIRECTORY

Here are some tips to help you get the most out of the funding opportunities listed in this special DANTES edition.

To Browse Quickly Through the Listings. Turn to the first part of the book, which is organized by educational level and recipient groups, and read the "Summary" paragraph in each entry there. In seconds, you'll know if this is an opportunity that might apply to you. If it is, read the rest of the information in the entry to make sure you meet all of the program requirements before writing or going online for an application form. Please, save your time and energy. Don't apply if you don't qualify!

To Locate Funding by Educational Level. If you want to get an overall picture of the funding opportunities that are available to support a particular degree level, turn to the appropriate chapter in the first section of the guide (undergraduate studies or graduate studies), go to the subsection that relates to you (military personnel, ROTC students, or military family members) and browse through the listings there. Originally, we thought we would further subdivide these two chapters by purpose (study and training versus research and creative activities). Once the compilation was complete, however, it became clear that many of the programs provided funding for both functions. Thus, further subdivision (beyond educational level) would have been unnecessarily repetitious.

To Find Information on a Specific Financial Aid Program.   If you know the name of a particular financial aid program, the educational level supported by the program (e.g., undergraduate studies) and the intended recipients (military personnel, or ROTC students, or family members), then go directly to the appropriate category in the first section of the directory, where you will find the program profiles arranged alphabetically first by educational level and then by recipient group. If you are looking for a specific program and do not find it in the subsection you have checked, be sure to refer to the Program Title Index to see if it is covered elsewhere in the directory. To save time, always check the Program Title Index first if you know the name of a specific award but are not sure under which subsection it would be listed.

To Locate Programs Sponsored by a Particular Organization.   The Sponsoring Organization Index makes it easy to determine specific organizations that provide financial assistance for undergraduate or graduate study to military personnel, ROTC students, or military families. Each entry number in the Sponsoring Organization Index is coded to identify both educational level and recipient group, so that you can quickly target appropriate entries.

To Locate Funding Available to Military Personnel or Military Family Members by Branch of Military Service.   To identify funding open to applicants with ties to one or more of the five active branches of the Military (Air Force, Army, Coast Guard, Marine Corps, and Navy), turn to the Branch of Service Index, where you will find listings subdivided by service branch, educational level, and recipient group (military personnel, ROTC students, and military family members).

To Locate Programs Open to Residents of or Tenable in a Particular Area.   The Residency Index identifies financial aid programs open to military personnel, ROTC students, or military family members who reside in a particular state, region, etc. The Tenability Index shows where the money can be spent. In both indexes, "see" and "see also" references are used liberally, and index entries for a particular geographic area are subdivided by both educational level and recipient group, to help you find the funding that's right for you. When using these indexes, always check the listings under the term "United States," since the programs indexed there have no geographic restrictions and can be used in any area.

To Locate Financial Aid Programs That Support Study in a Particular Subject Area.   Turn to the Subject Index first if you are interested in identifying financial aid programs for military personnel, ROTC students, of military family members that focus on a particular subject area. To help you structure your search, the educational level (undergraduate or graduate studies) and the recipient group (military personnel, ROTC students, or family members) are clearly identified. Extensive cross-references are provided. Since a large number of programs are not restricted by subject, be sure to check the references listed under the "General programs" heading in the index, in addition to the specific terms that directly relate to your interest areas. The listings under "General programs" can be used to fund activities in any subject area (although the programs may be restricted in other ways).

To Locate Financial Aid Programs by Deadline Date.   If you are working with specific time constraints and want to weed out the financial aid programs whose filing dates you won't be able to meet, turn first to the Calendar Index and check the program references listed under the educational level, recipient group, and month. Note: not all sponsoring organizations supplied deadline information; those programs are listed under the "Deadline not specified" entries in the index. To identify every relevant financial aid program, regardless of filing dates, read through all the entries in each of the educational level chapters (undergraduate or graduate studies) and recipient subsections (military personnel, military family members, and ROTC students) that apply.

To Locate Financial Aid Programs Open to All Segments of the Population.   Only programs available to individuals with ties to the military are listed in this publication. However, there are thousands of other funding programs that are open equally to all segments of the population. To identify these programs, talk to your local librarian, check with your financial aid office on campus, look at the list of RSP print resources on the page opposite the title page in this directory, check out the listings on Reference Service Press's website (www.rspfunding.com), or see if your library subscribes to Reference Service Press' interactive online funding database; for more information on that resource, go online to: www.rspfunding.com/esubscriptions.html.

OTHER RELATED PUBLICATIONS

In addition to this Special DANTES Edition, Reference Service Press publishes several other titles dealing with fundseeking, including the biennially-issued *Directory of Financial Aids for Women* and *College Student's Guide to Merit and Other No-Need Funding*. For more information on these and other related publications, you can 1) write to Reference Service Press' Marketing Department at 2310 Homestead Rd, Suite C1 #219, Los Altos, CA 94024; 2) call us at (650) 861-3170; 3) send us an e-mail message at info@rspfunding.com; 4) fax us at (650) 861-3171; or 5) visit us on the web: www.rspfunding.com.

ACKNOWLEDGEMENTS

A debt of gratitude is owed all the organizations that contributed information to this Special DANTES Edition. Their generous cooperation has helped to make this publication a current and comprehensive survey of awards.

ABOUT THE AUTHORS

Dr. Gail Ann Schlachter has worked for more than three decades as a library manager, a library educator, and an administrator of library-related publishing companies. Among the reference books to her credit are the biennially-issued *Directory of Financial Aids for Women* and two award-winning bibliographic guides: *Minorities and Women: A Guide to Reference Literature in the Social Sciences* (which was chosen as an "outstanding reference book of the year" by *Choice)* and *Reference Sources in Library and Information Services* (which won the first Knowledge Industry Publications "Award for Library Literature"). She was the reference book review editor for *RQ* (now *Reference and User Services Quarterly)* for 10 years, is a past president of the American Library Association's Reference and User Services Association, is the former editor-in-chief of the *Reference and User Services Association Quarterly,* is currently serving her seventh term on the American Library Association's governing council, and was recently elected to the association's Executive Board. In recognition of her outstanding contributions to reference service, Dr. Schlachter has been named the University of Wisconsin School of Library and Information Studies "Alumna of the Year" and has been awarded both the Isadore Gilbert Mudge Citation and the Louis Shores/Oryx Press Award.

Dr. R. David Weber taught history and economics at Los Angeles Harbor College (in Wilmington, California) for many years and continues to teach history as an emeritus professor. During his years of full-time teaching there, and earlier at East Los Angeles College, he directed the Honors Program and was frequently chosen the "Teacher of the Year." He has written a number of critically-acclaimed reference works, including *Dissertations in Urban History* and the three-volume *Energy Information Guide.* With Gail Schlachter, he is the author of Reference Service Press' *Financial Aid for Persons with Disabilities and Their Families,* which was selected by *Library Journal* as one of the "best reference books of the year," and a number of other award-winning financial aid titles, including the *College Student's Guide to Merit and Other No-Need Funding,* which was chosen as one of the "outstanding reference books of the year" by *Choice.*

Financial Aid Programs for Military Personnel and Military Family Members

Undergraduate Studies ●

Graduate Studies ●

Undergraduate Studies

Military Personnel ●

ROTC Students ●

Military Family Members ●

Described here are 907 funding programs available to 1) military personnel, 2) ROTC students, and 3) military family members (spouses, children, grandchildren, parents, and other relatives with family ties to the military) who are starting or continuing their undergraduate studies in public or private postsecondary institutions, ranging from technical schools and community colleges to major universities in the United States. Of these listings, 247 are available to military personnel, 81 to ROTC students, and 579 to military family members. If you are looking for a particular program and don't find it in this section, be sure to check the Program Title Index to see if it is covered elsewhere in the directory.

Military Personnel

[1]
10TH MOUNTAIN DIVISION (LIGHT INFANTRY) SCHOLARSHIPS

Northern New York Community Foundation, Inc.
120 Washington Street, Suite 400
Watertown, NY 13601
(315) 782-7110   Fax: (315) 782-0047
E-mail: info@nnycf.org
Web: www.nnycf.org/scholarships.asp?mm=6

Summary To provide financial assistance for college to current and former members of the 10th Mountain Division and their dependents.

Eligibility This program is open to current and former members of the 10th Mountain Division and their dependents (children and spouses). Applicants must be high school seniors applying for the freshmen year or traditional or non-traditional students enrolled as full-time undergraduates in any year of college or technical school. Along with their application, they must submit a 150-word essay on the character traits that have contributed the most to their success, how they have contributed to their success, and how each will contribute to their vision of a successful life. High school juniors who will graduate early because they are in an advanced placement program may also apply. Interviews are required. Selection is based on academic achievement, personal data, and financial need.

Financial data The stipend is $5,000.

Duration 1 year.

Number awarded Varies each year; recently, 8 were awarded.

Deadline March of each year.

[2]
ADMIRAL MIKE BOORDA LOAN PROGRAM

Navy-Marine Corps Relief Society
Attn: Education Division
875 North Randolph Street, Suite 225
Arlington, VA 22203-1757
(703) 696-4960   Fax: (703) 696-0144
E-mail: education@nmcrs.org
Web: www.nmcrs.org

Summary To provide educational loans to Navy or Marine Corps personnel selected for or enrolled in enlisted commissioning programs.

Eligibility This program is open to active-duty members of the Navy or Marine Corps selected for or enrolled in the Marine Enlisted Commissioning Education Program (MECEP) or the Navy's Medical Enlisted Commissioning Program (MECP). Participants in the Navy's Seaman to Admiral-21 program are not eligible. Applicants must be planning to enroll as a full-time undergraduate in a traditional classroom setting at a college or university. They must have a GPA of 2.0 or higher and be able to demonstrate financial need.

Financial data Loans range from $500 to $3,000 per year, depending on need. Funds are sent directly to the recipient's institution. No interest is charged. Loans are repaid by military payroll allotment within 3 months of commissioning date.

Duration 1 year; recipients may reapply.

Number awarded Varies each year.

Deadline May of each year.

[3]
AFCEA NOVA SCHOLARSHIPS

Armed Forces Communications and Electronics
  Association-Northern Virginia Chapter
Attn: Scholarship Chair
400 North Washington Street, Suite 300
Alexandria, VA 22314
(703) 778-4645   Fax: (703) 683-5480
E-mail: scholarships@afceanova.org
Web: www.afceanova.org/scholarships

Summary To provide financial assistance for undergraduate and graduate study in fields of science, technology, engineering, or mathematics (STEM) to military and civilian personnel affiliated with the Northern Virginia chapter of the Armed Forces Communications and Electronics Association (AFCEA NOVA).

Eligibility This program is open to residents of the greater Washington, D.C. area and to members of AFCEA NOVA and their children who live elsewhere. Applicants must be U.S. government service employees or military personnel (enlisted or junior grade officers) or their offspring; veterans are also given consideration. Applicants must be working on an undergraduate or graduate degree in a field of STEM (including information technology, computer science, and other technology fields supportive of national security). Selection is based on merit, although financial need and past and current military and government service may also be considered. U.S. citizenship is required.

Financial data The stipend is $2,000 for full-time students or $1,000 for part-time students.

Duration 1 year.

Additional information The greater Washington area is defined to include the District of Columbia; the Maryland counties of Calvert, Charles, Frederick, Montgomery, and Prince George's; the Virginia cities of Alexandria, Fairfax, Falls Church, Fredericksburg, Manassas, and Manassas Park; the Virginia counties of Arlington, Clarke, Culpeper, Fairfax, Fauquier, King George, Loudoun, Prince William, Spotsylvania, Stafford, and Warren; and the West Virginia counties of Berkeley and Jefferson.

Number awarded More than 30 each year.

Deadline February of each year.

[4]
AFGHANISTAN AND IRAQ WAR VETERANS SCHOLARSHIPS

Armed Forces Communications and Electronics
  Association
Attn: AFCEA Educational Foundation
4400 Fair Lakes Court
Fairfax, VA 22033-3899
(703) 631-6138   Toll Free: (800) 336-4583, ext. 6138
Fax: (703) 631-4693   E-mail: scholarship@afcea.org
Web: www.afcea.org

Summary To provide financial assistance to military personnel and veterans who served in Afghanistan or Iraq and are working on an undergraduate degree in fields related to the support of U.S. intelligence enterprises.

Eligibility This program is open to active-duty and honorably discharged U.S. military members (including Reservists and National Guard personnel) who served in Enduring Freedom (Afghanistan) or Iraqi Freedom operations. Applicants must be enrolled at a 2- or 4-year institution in the United States and working on an undergraduate degree in engineering (aerospace, computer, electrical, or systems), computer science, computer engineering technology, computer information systems, mathematics, physics, information systems management, science or mathematics education, or other fields related to the support of U.S. intelligence or homeland security enterprises. Selection is based on demonstrated academic excellence, leadership, and financial need.

Financial data The stipend is $2,500.

Duration 1 year.

Additional information This program began in 2005 with funding from the Northern Virginia Chapter of AFCEA.

Number awarded Up to 12 each year: 6 for the fall semester and 6 for the spring semester.

Deadline April of each year for fall semester; November of each year for spring semester.

[5]
AIR FORCE RESERVE TUITION ASSISTANCE

U.S. Air Force Reserve
Attn: Air Reserve Personnel Center
Directorate of Personnel Services
18420 East Silver Creek Avenue, Building 390, MS68
Buckley AFB, CO 80011
(303) 676-7037   Toll Free: (800) 525-0102
Fax: (478) 327-2215
E-mail: arpc.contactcenter@arpc.denver.af.mil
Web: www.arpc.afrc.af.mil

Summary To provide financial assistance for college or graduate school to members of the Air Force Reserve.

Eligibility This program is open to Air Force Reserve members interested in working on an undergraduate or graduate degree either through distance learning or on-campus courses from an accredited postsecondary institution. Applicants must be actively participating (for pay and points) and in good standing (not have a UIF, not placed on a control roster, not pending or issued an Article 15, and/or not pending court martial). They must submit a degree plan specifying all classes for which they are seeking assistance. Enlisted students must have retainability that extends beyond the last course approved for assistance or they must extend or reenlist; commissioned officers must have a mandatory separation date of not less than 48 months of service commitment starting at the end of the last course completed.

Financial data Airmen receive 100% of tuition for undergraduate or graduate study, to a maximum of $250 per semester hour or $4,500 per year.

Duration 1 year; may be renewed.

Number awarded Varies each year.

Deadline Applications may be submitted at any time.

[6]
AIR FORCE SERVICES CLUB MEMBERSHIP SCHOLARSHIP PROGRAM

Air Force Services Agency
Attn: HQ AFPC/SVOFT
10100 Reunion Place, Suite 501
San Antonio, TX 78216-4138
(210) 395-7351   E-mail: clubs@myairforcelife.com
Web: www.myairforcelife.com/Clubs/Scholarship.aspx

Summary To recognize and reward, with funding for undergraduate or graduate studies, Air Force Club members and their families who submit outstanding essays.

Eligibility This program is open to Air Force Club members and their spouses, children, and stepchildren who have been accepted by or are enrolled at an accredited college or university. Grandchildren are eligible if they are the dependent of a club member. Applicants may be undergraduate or graduate students enrolled full or part time. They must submit an essay of up to 500 words on a topic that changes annually; a recent topic was "My Contribution to the Air Force." Applicants must also include a 1-page summary of their long-term career and life goals and previous accomplishments, including civic, athletic, and academic awards.

Financial data Awards are $1,000 scholarships. Each winner also receives a laptop computer.

Duration The competition is held annually.

Additional information This competition, first held in 1997, is sponsored by Chase Military Credit Card Services.

Number awarded 25 each year.

Deadline April of each year.

[7]
AIR FORCE TUITION ASSISTANCE PROGRAM

U.S. Air Force
Attn: Air Force Personnel Center
Headquarters USAF/DPPAT
550 C Street West, Suite 10
Randolph AFB, TX 78150-4712
Fax: (210) 565-2328
Web: www.airforce.com/opportunities/enlisted/education

Summary To provide financial assistance for college or graduate school to active-duty Air Force personnel.

Eligibility Eligible to apply for this program are active-duty Air Force personnel who have completed 2 years of their service obligation.

Financial data Air Force personnel chosen for participation in this program continue to receive their regular Air Force pay. The Air Force will pay 100% of the tuition costs in an approved program, to a maximum of $4,500 per year or $250 per semester hour, whichever is less. Funding is available only for tuition, not fees or other associated expenses.

Duration Up to 4 years. Undergraduates must complete all courses with a grade of "C" or better; graduate students must complete classes with a grade of "B" of better. If recipients fail to achieve those grades, they must reimburse the Air Force for all funds received.

Additional information Applications and further information about this program are available from counselors at the education centers on Air Force bases. Most Air Force personnel who receive tuition assistance participate in the Community College of the Air Force; there, participants earn a 2-year associate degree by combining on-the-job technical training or attendance at Air Force schools with enrollment in college courses at a civilian institution during off-duty hours. In addition, each Air Force base offers at least 4 subject areas in which selected Air Force personnel can receive tuition assistance for study leading to a bachelor's degree, and 2 disciplines in which they can pursue graduate study.

Number awarded Varies each year.

Deadline Deadline not specified.

[8]
AIRMAN SCHOLARSHIP AND COMMISSIONING PROGRAM

U.S. Air Force
Attn: Headquarters AFROTC/RRUE
Jeanne M. Holm Center for Officer Accession and Citizen
  Development
551 East Maxwell Boulevard, Building 500
Maxwell AFB, AL 36112-6106
(334) 953-2091   Toll Free: (866) 4-AFROTC
Fax: (334) 953-6167   E-mail: enlisted@afrotc.com
Web: www.au.af.mil

Summary To allow selected enlisted Air Force personnel to separate from the Air Force and earn a bachelor's degree in approved majors by providing financial assistance for full-time college study.

Eligibility This program is open to active-duty enlisted members of the Air Force who have completed at least 1 year of continuous active duty and at least 1 year on station. Applicants normally must have completed at least 24 semester hours of graded college credit with a cumulative college GPA of 2.5 or higher. If they have not completed 24 hours of graded college credit, they must have an ACT score of 24 or higher or an SAT combined critical reading and mathematics score of 1100 or higher. They must also have scores on the Air Force Officer Qualifying Test (AFOQT) of 15 or more on the verbal scale and 10 or more on the quantitative scale and be able to pass the Air Force ROTC Physical Fitness Test. Applicants must have been accepted at a college or university (including cross-town schools) offering the AFROTC 4-year program. When they complete the program and receive their commission, they may not be 31 years of age or older. They must complete 24 semesters of mathematics and physical sciences or 4 semesters of a foreign language and major in an approved field; for a list of currently-approved majors, contact the program. U.S. citizenship is required.

Financial data Awards are type 2 AFROTC scholarships that provide for payment of tuition and fees, to a maximum of $18,000 per year, plus an annual book allowance of $900. All recipients are also awarded a tax-free subsistence allowance of $250 to $400 per month.

Duration 2 to 4 years, until completion of a bachelor's degree.

Additional information Selectees separate from the active-duty Air Force, join an AFROTC detachment, and become full-time students. Upon completing their degree, they are commissioned as officers and returned to active duty in the Air Force with a service obligation of 4 years of active duty and 4 years of Reserves. Further information is available from base education service officers or an Air Force ROTC unit.

Number awarded Varies each year.

Deadline October of each year.

[9]
ALABAMA NATIONAL GUARD EDUCATIONAL ASSISTANCE PROGRAM

Alabama Commission on Higher Education
Attn: Grants Coordinator
100 North Union Street
P.O. Box 302000
Montgomery, AL 36130-2000
(334) 242-2273   Fax: (334) 242-0268
E-mail: cheryl.newton@ache.alabama.gov
Web: www.ache.alabama.gov

Summary To provide financial assistance to members of the Alabama National Guard interested in attending college or graduate school in the state.

Eligibility This program is open to Alabama residents who are enrolled in an associate, baccalaureate, master's, or doctoral program at a public college, university, community college, technical college, or junior college in the state; are making satisfactory academic progress as determined by the eligible institution; and are members in good standing of the Alabama National Guard who have completed basic training and advanced individual training. Applicants may be receiving federal veterans benefits, but they must show a cost less aid amount of at least $25.

Financial data Scholarships cover tuition, educational fees, books, and supplies, up to a maximum of $1,000 per year. All Alabama Student Grant program proceeds for which the student is eligible are deducted from this award.

Duration Up to 12 years after the date of the first grant payment to the student through this program.

Number awarded Varies each year; recently, 653 were awarded. Awards are determined on a first-in, first-out basis as long as funds are available.

Deadline July of each year.

[10]
ALASKA NATIONAL GUARD STATE TUITION REIMBURSEMENT PROGRAM

Alaska National Guard
Attn: Education Services Office
P.O. Box 5800
Joint Base Elmendorf-Richardson, AK 99505-5800
(907) 428-6477   Fax: (907) 428-6929
E-mail: ngak-eduservicesoffice@ng.army.mil
Web: guardedu.alaska.gov

Summary To provide financial assistance to current and former members of the Alaska National Guard who wish to attend a college or university in the state.

Eligibility This program is open to members of the Alaska National Guard (Air and Army) and Naval Militia who have a rating of E-1 through O-5, including warrant officers, and are attending a university program in Alaska. Eligibility extends to members who 1) have satisfactorily completed their service contract and who served honorably in federal active service or federally-funded state active service after September 11, 2001; or 2) have been separated or discharged from the Guard because of a service-connected injury, disease, or disability. First priority is given to undergraduates; if funding is available, students working on a second bachelor's degree or a master's degree may be supported. Non-prior servicemembers must complete Initial Active Duty for Training (IADT); prior servicemembers are eligible immediately.

Financial data Recipients are entitled to reimbursement equivalent to 100% of the cost of tuition and fees at the University of Alaska, to a maximum of $7,500 per fiscal year.

Duration 1 semester; may be renewed for a total of 144 semester credits.

Number awarded Varies each year.

Deadline Applications may be submitted at any time, but they must be received at least 90 days after the last official day of the class or term.

[11]
AMEDD ENLISTED COMMISSIONING PROGRAM (AECP)

U.S. Army
Attn: Recruiting Command, RCHS-SVD-AECP
1307 Third Avenue
Fort Knox, KY 40121-2726
(502) 626-0381   Toll Free: (800) 223-3735, ext. 60381
Fax: (502) 626-0952   E-mail: aecp@usarec.army.mil
Web: www.goarmy.com

Summary To provide financial assistance to enlisted Army personnel who are interested in completing a bachelor's degree in nursing and becoming a commissioned officer.

Eligibility This program is open to enlisted Army personnel of grade E-4 or above in the active component or Reserves who have at least 3 but no more than 16 years of active federal service. Applicants must be interested in enrolling full time at an accredited school of nursing to work on a bachelor's degree and becoming a licensed registered nurse. They must be U.S. citizens, have a GPA of 2.5 or higher, have SAT scores of at least 450 in critical reading and 450 in mathematics, have an enrollment GT score of 110 or higher, be able to complete a bachelor's degree in nursing within 24 calendar months, be between 21 and 42 years of age, be eligible to become a commissioned officer in the active component following licensure, and agree to fulfill a 3-year additional service obligation.

Financial data The stipend is $9,000 per year for tuition and $1,000 for books. Participants are not allowed to attend a school whose tuition exceeds $9,000. They continue to draw their regular pay and allowances while attending nursing school.

Duration Participants must be able to complete all degree requirements in 24 consecutive months or less.

Number awarded Up to 100 each year.

Deadline January of each year.

[12]
ARKANSAS NATIONAL GUARD TUITION INCENTIVE PROGRAM

Arkansas National Guard
Attn: Education Services Officer
DCSPER-ED
Camp Robinson
North Little Rock, AR 72199-9600
(501) 212-4021   Fax: (501) 212-5449
E-mail: Education@ar.ngb.army.mil
Web: www.arguard.org/Education/GTIP.htm

Summary To provide financial assistance for college to members of the Arkansas National Guard.

Eligibility This program is open to members of the Arkansas National Guard who have 15 years or less of service.

Applicants must have a score of 50 or higher on the Armed Services Vocational Aptitude Battery (ASVAB) Test. They must be enrolled or accepted for full-time enrollment in an undergraduate program at a participating college or university in Arkansas.

Financial data The stipend is $2,500 per semester for fall or spring semester.

Duration 1 semester; may be renewed if the recipient maintains a GPA of 2.0 or higher.

Number awarded Varies each year.

Deadline August of each year for fall semester; December of each year for spring semester.

[13]
ARMY AVIATION ASSOCIATION OF AMERICA LOAN PROGRAM

Army Aviation Association of America
Attn: AAAA Scholarship Foundation
593 Main Street
Monroe, CT 06468-2806
(203) 268-2450   Fax: (203) 268-5870
E-mail: aaaa@quad-a.org
Web: www.quad-a.org

Summary To provide educational loans to members of the Army Aviation Association of America (AAAA) and their relatives.

Eligibility This program is open to AAAA members and their spouses, unmarried siblings, and unmarried children and grandchildren. Applicants must be enrolled or accepted for enrollment as an undergraduate or graduate student at an accredited college or university.

Financial data The maximum loan is $1,000 per year. All loans are interest free.

Duration Up to 4 years.

Number awarded Varies each year; recently, 1 of these loans was granted.

Deadline April of each year.

[14]
ARMY AVIATION ASSOCIATION OF AMERICA SCHOLARSHIPS

Army Aviation Association of America Scholarship
  Foundation
Attn: AAAA Scholarship Foundation
593 Main Street
Monroe, CT 06468-2806
(203) 268-2450   Fax: (203) 268-5870
E-mail: aaaa@quad-a.org
Web: www.quad-a.org

Summary To provide financial aid for undergraduate or graduate study to members of the Army Aviation Association of America (AAAA) and their relatives.

Eligibility This program is open to AAAA members (or deceased members) and their spouses, unmarried siblings, unmarried children, and unmarried grandchildren. Applicants must be enrolled or accepted for enrollment as an undergraduate or graduate student at an accredited college or university. Graduate students must include a 250-word essay on their life experiences, work history, and aspirations. Some scholarships are specifically reserved for enlisted, warrant officer, company grade, and Department of the Army civilian members. Selection is based on academic merit and personal achievement.

Financial data Stipends range from $1,000 to $2,500 per year.

Duration Scholarships may be for 1 year, 2 years, or 4 years.

Number awarded Varies each year; recently, $363,500 in scholarships was awarded to 236 students. Since the program began in 1963, the foundation has awarded more than $4.5 million to nearly 2,700 qualified applicants.

Deadline April of each year.

[15]
ARMY NATIONAL GUARD FEDERAL TUITION ASSISTANCE

U.S. Army National Guard
Education Support Center
Camp J.T. Robinson
Box 46
North Little Rock, AR 72199-9600
Toll Free: (866) 628-5999   E-mail: esc@ng.army.mil
Web: www.nationalguard.com

Summary To provide financial assistance for college or graduate school to members of the Army National Guard in each state.

Eligibility This program is open to members of the Army National Guard in every state who are interested in attending a college, community college, or university within the state. Applicants must have sufficient time to complete the course before their Expiration Time of Service (ETS) date. They must be interested in working on a high school diploma or equivalent (GED), certificate, associate degree, bachelor's degree, master's degree, or first professional degree, including those in architecture, Certified Public Accountant (C.P.A.), podiatry, dentistry (D.D.S. or D.M.D.), medicine (M.D.), optometry, osteopathic medicine, pharmacy (Pharm.D.), or theology (M.Div. or M.H.L.). Commissioned officers must agree to remain in the Guard for at least 4 years following completion of the course for which assistance is provided, unless they are involuntarily separated from the service.

Financial data Assistance provides up to 100% of tuition (to a maximum of $250 per semester hour or $4,500 per person per fiscal year).

Duration Participants in Officer Candidate School (OCS), Warrant Officer Candidate School (WOCS), and ROTC Simultaneous Membership Program (SMP) may enroll in up to 15 semester hours per year until completion of a baccalaureate degree. Warrant Officers are funded to complete an associate degree.

Additional information Tuition assistance may be used along with federal Pell Grants but not with Montgomery GI Bill benefits. State tuition assistance programs can be used concurrently with this program, but not to exceed 100% of tuition costs.

Number awarded Varies each year; recently, more than 22,000 Guard members received tuition assistance.

Deadline Deadline not specified.

[16]
ARMY NURSE CANDIDATE PROGRAM

U.S. Army
Attn: Recruiting Command, RCHS-SVD-AECP
1307 Third Avenue
Fort Knox, KY 40121-2726
(502) 626-0381   Toll Free: (800) 223-3735, ext. 60381
Fax: (502) 626-0952   E-mail: aecp@usarec.army.mil
Web: www.goarmy.com

Summary To provide financial assistance to nursing students who are interested in completing a bachelor's degree and becoming a commissioned officer in the U.S. Army.

Eligibility This program is open to nursing students enrolled full time in a CCNE- or NLN-accredited B.S.N. degree program. Applicants must be eligible to enlist in the U.S. Army Reserve and complete their degree within 6 to 24 months.

Financial data Participants receive a $5,000 bonus when they begin the program, another $5,000 bonus at graduation, and a stipend of $1,000 per month while they are attending classes.

Duration Up to 2 years or completion of the B.S.N. degree, whichever occurs first.

Additional information Following completion of their degree and passage of the NCLEX-RN examination, participants are commissioned as Army Nurse Corps officers with a 4-year service obligation if they receive support for 1 year or a 5-year service obligation if they receive support for 2 years.

Number awarded Varies each year.

Deadline January of each year.

[17]
ARMY NURSE CORPS ASSOCIATION SCHOLARSHIPS

Army Nurse Corps Association
Attn: Education Committee
P.O. Box 39235
San Antonio, TX 78218-1235
(210) 650-3534   Fax: (210) 650-3494
E-mail: education@e-anca.org
Web: e-anca.org/ANCAEduc.htm

Summary To provide financial assistance to students who have a connection to the Army and are interested in working on an undergraduate or graduate degree in nursing.

Eligibility This program is open to U.S. citizens attending colleges or universities that have accredited programs offering associate, bachelor's, master's, or doctoral degrees in nursing. Applicants must be 1) students currently enrolled in an accredited baccalaureate or advanced nursing or nurse anesthesia program who are serving or have served (and received an honorable discharge) in any branch and at any rank of a component of the U.S. Army; or 2) nursing or anesthesia students whose parent(s) or spouse are serving or have served in a component of the U.S. Army. Along with their application, they must submit a personal statement on their professional career objectives, reasons for applying for this scholarship, financial need, special considerations, personal and academic interests, and why they are preparing for a nursing career. Students who are receiving any support from any branch of the military, including ROTC scholarships, are not eligible.

Financial data The stipend is $3,000. Funds are sent directly to the recipient's school.

Duration 1 year.

Additional information Although the sponsoring organization is made up of current, retired, and honorably discharged officers of the Army Nurse Corps, it does not have an official affiliation with the Army. Therefore, students who receive these scholarships do not incur any military service obligation.

Number awarded 1 or more each year.

Deadline April of each year.

[18]
ARMY RESERVE TUITION ASSISTANCE

U.S. Army Reserve
Attn: Director, USAR Education
ARPC-PS
1 Reserve Way
St. Louis, MO 63132-5200
Toll Free: (800) 452-0201
Web: www.goarmyed.com

Summary To provide financial assistance for college or graduate school to specified members of the U.S. Army Reserve (USAR).

Eligibility This program is open to drilling USAR soldiers in good standing. Applicants must be working on their first bachelor's or master's degree and be able to declare an educational goal after completing 15 credit hours. Enlisted members and warrant officers must be able to complete the program under their current term of service or reenlist. Commissioned officers must have at last 4 years of remaining service obligation from the date or course completion.

Financial data Assistance is provided at the rate of $250 per credit hour, to a maximum of $4,500 per fiscal year.

Duration 1 year; may be renewed.

Number awarded Varies each year.

Deadline Applications may be submitted at any time.

[19]
ARMY SPECIALIZED TRAINING ASSISTANCE PROGRAM (STRAP)

U.S. Army National Guard
Education Support Center
Camp J.T. Robinson
Box 46
North Little Rock, AR 72199-9600
Toll Free: (866) 628-5999   E-mail: esc@ng.army.mil
Web: www.nationalguard.com

Summary To provide funding for service to members of the United States Army Reserve (USAR) or Army National Guard (ARNG) who are interested in obtaining additional training in designated health care fields that are considered critical for wartime medical needs.

Eligibility This program is open to members of the USAR or ARNG who are 1) medical residents (currently in orthopedic surgery, family practice, emergency medicine, general surgery, obstetrics/gynecology, or internal medicine); 2) dental residents (currently in general dentistry, oral surgery, prosthodontics, or comprehensive dentistry); 3) nursing students working on a master's degree (currently in community health, psychiatric nurse practitioner, or nurse anesthesia; or 4) associate degree or diploma nurses working on a bachelor's degree. Applicants must agree to a service obligation of 1 year for every 6 months of support received.

Financial data This program pays a stipend of $2,122 per month.

Duration 1 year; may be renewed.

Additional information During their obligated period of service, participants must attend Extended Combat Training (ECT) at least 12 days each year and complete the Officer Basic Leadership Course (OBLC) within the first year.

Number awarded Varies each year.

Deadline Applications may be submitted at any time.

[20]
ARMY TUITION ASSISTANCE BENEFITS

U.S. Army
Human Resources Command
AHRC-PDE-EI
Attn: Education Incentives and Counseling Branch
1500 Spearhead Division Avenue
Fort Knox, KY 40122-5408
Toll Free: (800) 872-8272
E-mail: usarmy.knox.hrc.mbx.tagd-pdeei@mail.mil
Web: www.goarmyed.com

Summary To provide financial assistance to Army personnel interested in working on an undergraduate or master's degree.

Eligibility This program is open to active-duty Army personnel, including members of the Army National Guard and Army Reserve on active duty, who have completed at least 1 year of service after graduation from AIT, OCS, or BOLC; graduate students must have completed 10 years of service. Applicants must first visit an education counselor to declare an educational goal and establish an educational plan. They may enroll in up to 16 semester hours of academic courses. Support is not provided for a second equivalent degree or for first professional degrees (e.g., Ph.D., M.D., or J.D.).

Financial data Those selected for participation in this program receive their regular Army pay and 100% of tuition at the postsecondary educational institution of their choice, but capped at $4,500 per year or $250 per semester hour, whichever is less. Funding is available only for tuition, not fees or other associated expenses.

Duration Up to 130 semester hours for completion of a bachelor's degree or up to 39 semester hours for completion of a master's degree. Undergraduates must complete all courses with a grade of "C" or better; graduate students must complete classes with a grade of "B" of better. If recipients fail to achieve those grades, they must reimburse the Army for all funds received.

Additional information This program is part of the Army Continuing Education System (ACES). Further information is available from counselors at the education centers at all Army installations with a troop strength of 750 or more. Officers incur a service obligation of 2 years for active duty or 4 years for Reserve and National Guard.

Number awarded Varies each year; recently, this program funded completion of 8,525 degree for active soldier, 1,359 for Guard soldiers, and 1,469 for Reserve soldiers.

Deadline Deadline not specified.

[21]
ASMC MEMBERS' CONTINUING EDUCATION GRANTS

American Society of Military Comptrollers
Attn: National Awards Committee
415 North Alfred Street
Alexandria, VA 22314
(703) 549-0360   Toll Free: (800) 462-5637
Fax: (703) 549-3181   E-mail: awards@asmconline.org
Web: asmc.nonprofitcms.org/a

Summary To provide financial assistance for continuing education to members of the American Society of Military Comptrollers (ASMC).

Eligibility Applicants for this assistance must have been members of the society for at least 2 full years and must have been active in the local chapter at some level (e.g., board member, committee chair or member, volunteer for chapter events), They must be enrolled or planning to enroll at an academic institution in a field of study directly related to military comptrollership, including business administration, economics, public administration, accounting, or finance. Selection is based on individual merit.

Financial data Stipends are $3,000 or $1,250.

Duration 1 year.

Additional information The ASMC is open to all financial management professionals employed by the U.S. Department of Defense and Coast Guard, both civilian and military. The applicant whose service to the society is judged the most exceptional is designated the Dick Vincent Scholarship winner.

Number awarded 11 each year: 1 at $3,000 (the Dick Vincent Scholarship) and 10 at $1,250.

Deadline March of each year.

[22]
ASSOCIATION OF OLD CROWS ENLISTED TUITION GRANTS

Association of Old Crows
Attn: AOC Educational Foundation
1000 North Payne Street, Suite 200
Alexandria, VA 22314-1652
(703) 549-1600   Fax: (703) 549-2589
Web: www.crows.org/aef/scholarship-a-grants.html

Summary To provide financial assistance to military enlisted personnel who are pursuing off-duty college-level education programs in fields related to electronics.

Eligibility This program is open to military enlisted personnel (rank of E-4 and above) who are utilizing the tuition assistance programs of the armed services to study physics, engineering, or other field related to electronic warfare or information superiority during their off-duty hours. Selection is based on academic excellence and financial need.

Financial data Support is provided to supplement the funding available through the tuition assistance programs.

Duration 1 semester; may be renewed.

Additional information Funding is provided by local chapters of this organization, which was founded by World War II veterans who had engaged in electronic warfare to disrupt enemy communications and radars. The program was code-named "Raven" and its operators became known as Old Crows. For information on a chapter in your area, contact the AOC Educational Foundation.

Number awarded Varies each year; recently, a total of $160,000 per year was available for this program.

Deadline Deadline not specified.

[23]
BART LONGO MEMORIAL SCHOLARSHIPS

National Chief Petty Officers' Association
c/o Marjorie Hays, Treasurer
1014 Ronald Drive
Corpus Christi, TX 78412-3548
Web: www.goatlocker.org/ncpoa/scholarship.htm

Summary To provide financial assistance for college or graduate school to members of the National Chief Petty Officers' Association (NCPOA) and their families.

Eligibility This program is open to members of the NCPOA and the children, stepchildren, and grandchildren of living or deceased members. Applicants may be high school seniors or graduates entering a college or university or students currently enrolled full time as undergraduate or graduate students. Selection is based on academic achievement and participation in extracurricular activities; financial need is not considered.

Financial data The stipend is $1,000.

Duration 1 year.

Additional information Membership in the NCPOA is limited to men and women who served or are serving as Chief Petty Officers in the U.S. Navy, U.S. Coast Guard, or their Reserve components for at least 30 days.

Number awarded 2 each year: 1 to a high school senior or graduate and 1 to an undergraduate or graduate student.

Deadline May of each year.

[24]
BECHTEL ENGINEERING AND SCIENCE SCHOLARSHIPS

Marines' Memorial Association
c/o Marines Memorial Club and Hotel
609 Sutter Street
San Francisco, CA 94102
(415) 673-6672, ext. 293   Fax: (415) 441-3649
E-mail: scholarship@marineclub.com
Web: www.marineclub.com/membership/scholarship.php

Summary To provide financial assistance to members of the Marines' Memorial Association from all branches of the armed forces and their descendants who are interested in studying a field of science, technology, engineering, or mathematics (STEM) in college.

Eligibility This program is open to active members of the association and their children and grandchildren. Applicants must be high school seniors or students currently enrolled full time in an undergraduate degree program in a field of STEM. Engineering programs must be ABET-accredited. Along with their application, they must submit an essay of 250 to 500 words on an ethical dilemma in relation to their field of study. Graduating high school seniors must submit a high school transcript and SAT or ACT scores; continuing college students must submit a college transcript. Selection is based on the essay, academic merit, references, and financial need.

Financial data The stipend is $5,000 per year.

Duration 1 year; recipients may reapply for up to 3 additional years.

Additional information Membership in the association is open to veterans of the Marines, Army, Navy, Air Force, or Coast Guard and to personnel currently serving in a branch of the armed forces. This program is funded by the S.D. Bechtel, Jr. Foundation.

Number awarded 5 each year.

Deadline April of each year.

[25]
BG BENJAMIN B. TALLEY SCHOLARSHIP

Society of American Military Engineers-Anchorage Post
Attn: BG B.B. Talley Scholarship Endowment Fund
P.O. Box 6409
Anchorage, AK 99506-6409
(907) 244-8063   E-mail: cturletes@gci.net
Web: www.sameanchorage.org/h_about/scholinfo.html

Summary To provide financial assistance to student members of the Society of American Military Engineers (SAME) from Alaska who are working on a bachelor's or master's degree in designated fields of engineering or the natural sciences.

Eligibility This program is open to members of the Anchorage Post of SAME who are residents of Alaska, attending college in Alaska, an active-duty military member stationed in Alaska, or a dependent of an active-duty military member stationed in Alaska. Applicants must be 1) sophomores, juniors, or seniors majoring in engineering, architecture, construction or project management, natural sciences, physical sciences, applied sciences, or mathematics at an accredited college or university; or 2) students working on a master's degree in those fields. They must have a GPA of 2.5 or higher. U.S. citizenship is required. Along with their application, they must submit an essay of 250 to 500 words on their career goals. Selection is based on that essay, academic achievement, participation in school and community activities, and work/family activities; financial need is not considered.

Financial data Stipends range up to $3,000.

Duration 1 year.

Additional information This program began in 1997.

Number awarded Several each year; at least 1 scholarship is reserved for a master's degree students.

Deadline December of each year.

[26]
BOSTON POST SAME SCHOLARSHIPS

Society of American Military Engineers-Boston Post
c/o Cristen M. Sardano, Scholarship Committee Chair
CB&I Federal Services
150 Royall Street
Canton, MA 02021
(617) 589-5111   Fax: (617) 589-2156
E-mail: Christen.sardano@cbifederalservices.com
Web: www.sameboston.org

Summary To provide financial assistance to residents of New England (particularly current military personnel, veterans, and students enrolled in ROTC) who are majoring in a program related to construction at a college in any state.

Eligibility This program is open to residents of New England who are currently enrolled in an accepted engineering or architecture program, preferably in civil engineering, environmental engineering, architecture, or other construction-related program, at a college or university in any state. Appli-

cants must have completed at least 1 academic year and have at least 1 year remaining. They must be nominated by their institution. Along with their application, they must submit a resume describing their academic and career objectives, extracurricular and community activities, work experience, and special interests or hobbies; transcripts; documentation of financial need; and a personal letter describing their qualifications and needs. An interview is required. Selection is based on academic achievement, financial need, extracurricular and community activities, the letter, and the interview. Preference is given to applicants who are enrolled in ROTC (preferably not a recipient of an ROTC scholarship), have current or prior service in the U.S. armed forces, are interested in the U.S. Public Health Service, and/or are interested in other public service with federal, state, or local government. U.S. citizenship is required.

Financial data The stipend is approximately $2,000 per year.

Duration 1 year.

Number awarded Approximately 25 each year.

Deadline February of each year.

[27]
BOWFIN MEMORIAL CONTINUING EDUCATION SCHOLARSHIPS

Pacific Fleet Submarine Memorial Association
c/o Sarah Santala, Chair
Bowfin Memorial Scholarship Committee
1568 Kupau Street
Kailua, HI 96734
(808) 423-1341   Fax: (808) 422-5201
E-mail: scholarship@pearlharborsosa.org
Web: www.bowfin.org/education

Summary To provide financial assistance to the submarine force personnel and their spouses who live in Hawaii and wish to attend college in the state.

Eligibility This program is open to submarine force personnel (active duty or retired), their spouses, and the spouses of deceased submarine force personnel. Applicants must live in Hawaii and be interested in attending school in the state. Selection is based on academic performance, community involvement, motivation, goals, and financial need.

Financial data A stipend is awarded (amount not specified).

Duration 1 year; may be renewed upon annual reapplication.

Additional information This program began in 1985 to honor the 3,505 submariners and 52 submarines lost during World War II. It is offered in conjunction with the Pearl Harbor Submarine Officers' Spouses' Association.

Number awarded Varies each year.

Deadline March of each year.

[28]
BRAXTON BRAGG CHAPTER AUSA SCHOLARSHIPS

Association of the United States Army-Braxton Bragg
  Chapter
Attn: Vice President for Scholarships
P.O. Box 70036
Fort Bragg, NC 28307
(910) 396-3755   E-mail: hbraxtonbraggc@nc.rr.com
Web: www.braggausa.org/?page_id=1425

Summary To provide financial assistance to members of the Braxton Bragg Chapter of the Association of the United States Army (AUSA) in North Carolina and their dependents who are interested in attending college or graduate school in any state.

Eligibility This program is open to chapter members and their families in North Carolina who are working on or planning to work on an undergraduate, graduate, or technical degree at a college or technical school in any state. Applicants must submit a 500-word essay on how the Army and Army values have influenced their life; letters of recommendation; a list of personal accomplishments; and a transcript that includes their ACT or SAT score. Selection is based on academic achievement, participation in extracurricular activities at school, and participation in community service activities. Membership in AUSA is open to current and retired Army personnel (including Reserves and National Guard), ROTC cadets, or civilian employees of the Army. Active-duty soldiers are especially encouraged to apply.

Financial data The stipend is $1,000.

Duration 1 year; recipients may reapply.

Additional information Membership in the Braxton Bragg Chapter is open to all Army active, National Guard, and Reserve members in North Carolina, along with Department of the Army civilians, retirees, concerned citizens, and family members.

Number awarded Varies each year; recently, 26 were awarded.

Deadline April of each year.

[29]
BRIGADIER GENERAL JOHN F. KINNEY FELLOWSHIP

Alpha Tau Omega Foundation
32 East Washington Street, Suite 1350
Indianapolis, IN 46204
(317) 472-0935   Toll Free: (800) 508-5131
Fax: (317) 472-0945
E-mail: jplummer@atofoundation.org
Web: www.ato.org/atofoundation/Scholarships.aspx

Summary To provide financial assistance to members of Alpha Tau Omega fraternity who are serving in the military or an ROTC unit while they attend college.

Eligibility This program is open to members of the fraternity who have a GPA of 3.5 or higher. Applicants must be serving in a National Guard or Reserve component of the military or enrolled in an ROTC training program. They must be planning to serve on active duty in the National Guard, the Reserves, or the active armed forces following graduation. Selection is based on academic achievement (40%), demonstrated leadership in the fraternity (30%), and demonstrated initiative on campus and in the community (30%).

Financial data A stipend is awarded (amount not specified).

Duration 1 year.

Number awarded 1 each year.

Deadline March of each year.

[30]
CALIFORNIA ENLISTED ASSOCIATION OF THE NATIONAL GUARD OF THE UNITED STATES SCHOLARSHIP PROGRAM

California Enlisted Association of the National Guard of
  the United States
c/o CSM Harry Courtney, President
P.O. Box 323
Seaside, CA 93955
(831) 242-7733   E-mail: president@caleangus.org
Web: www.caleangus.org/?page_id=1434

Summary To provide financial assistance to enlisted members of the California National Guard who are interested in obtaining additional education.

Eligibility This program is open to members of the California Army and Air National Guards who have completed at least 1 year of military service. The program supports 2 categories of applicants: Category A for those who hold a military rank of E-3 to E-6 and Category B for those who hold a military rank of E-7 to E-9. Applicants must be enrolled in an educational program whose goal is an associate or bachelor's degree or certification in a subject matter that will enhance their ability to support the unit's mission and goals. Along with their application, they must submit a personal statement that discusses how they plan to apply their educational accomplishments to their civilian and military professional and career goals; a current transcript, and a letter of endorsement from their commanding officer. Awards are granted first to Category A applicants; if funding is sufficient, applicants in Category B are considered.

Financial data A stipend is awarded (amount not specified).

Duration 1 year; may be renewed for 1 additional year.

Number awarded Varies each year.

Deadline August of each year.

[31]
CALIFORNIA LEGION AUXILIARY SCHOLARSHIPS FOR CONTINUING AND/OR REENTRY STUDENTS

American Legion Auxiliary
Department of California
205 13th Street, Suite 3300
San Francisco, CA 94103-2461
(415) 861-5092   Fax: (415) 861-8365
E-mail: calegionaux@calegionaux.org
Web: www.calegionaux.org/scholarships.htm

Summary To provide financial assistance to California residents who are active-duty military personnel, veterans, or children of veterans and require assistance to continue their education.

Eligibility This program is open to California residents who are 1) active-duty military personnel; 2) veterans of World War I, World War II, Korea, Vietnam, Grenada/Lebanon, Panama, or Desert Shield/Desert Storm; and 3) children of veterans who served during those periods of war. Applicants must be continuing or reentry students at a college, university, or business/trade school in California. Selection is based on the application (25%), scholarship (25%), character and leadership (25%), and financial need (25%).

Financial data The stipend is $1,000 or $500.

Duration 1 year.

Additional information This program includes 1 scholarship designated as the Mel Foronda Memorial Scholarship.

Number awarded 5 each year: 3 at $1,000 and 2 at $500.

Deadline March of each year.

[32]
CALIFORNIA NATIONAL GUARD EDUCATION ASSISTANCE AWARD PROGRAM

California State Military Department
Joint Force Headquarters
Attn: EEAP Coordinator
9800 Goethe Road, Box 37
Sacramento, CA 95826
(916) 854-4255   Fax: (916) 854-3739
E-mail: katrina.beck2@us.army.mil
Web: www.calguard.ca.gov/education/Pages/default.aspx

Summary To provide financial assistance to members of the California National Guard who are interested in attending college or graduate school in the state.

Eligibility This program is open to residents of California who have served at least 2 years as active members of the California National Guard (CNG) or the State Military Reserve (SMR). Applicants must be planning to attend a college, university, community college, or vocational/technical institute in the state to obtain a certificate, degree (associate, bachelor's, master's, or doctoral) or diploma that they do not currently hold. They must agree to remain an active member of the Guard, Reserve, or Militia as long as they participate in the program.

Financial data The maximum stipends are equal to those provided by Cal Grants A and B; recently, those were $12,192 at branches of the University of California or non-public institutions, $5,472 at branches of the California State University system, or $1,473 at community colleges. Graduate students receive an additional stipend of $500 for books and supplies.

Duration 1 year; may be renewed, provided the recipient maintains a GPA of 2.0 or higher.

Additional information This program operates in partnership with the California Student Aid Commission.

Number awarded Up to 1,000 each year.

Deadline The priority deadline for new applications is April of each year.

[33]
CALIFORNIA NON-RESIDENT COLLEGE FEE WAIVER PROGRAM FOR MILITARY PERSONNEL AND DEPENDENTS

California Department of Veterans Affairs
Attn: Division of Veterans Services
1227 O Street, Room 101
P.O. Box 942895
Sacramento, CA 94295
(916) 653-2573   Toll Free: (877) 741-8532
Fax: (916) 653-2563   TDD: (800) 324-5966
Web: www.calvet.ca.gov

Summary To waive non-resident fees at public institutions in California for undergraduate or graduate students from

other states who are active-duty military personnel, recently-discharged veterans, or dependents of active-duty military personnel.

Eligibility This program is open to residents of states outside California who are 1) veterans of the U.S. armed forces who spent more than 1 year on active duty in California immediately prior to being discharged; 2) members of the U.S. armed forces stationed in California on active duty; or 3) the natural or adopted child, stepchild, or spouse of a member of the U.S. armed forces stationed in California on active duty. Applicants must be attending or planning to attend a community college, branch of the California State University system, or campus of the University of California as an undergraduate or graduate student.

Financial data This program waives non-resident fees of qualifying military personnel, veterans, and families who attend publicly-supported community or state colleges or universities in California.

Duration 1 year; may be renewed until completion of an undergraduate degree or for 1 additional year for military personnel working on a graduate degree; nonrenewable for graduate students who are children or spouses.

Number awarded Varies each year.

Deadline Deadline not specified.

[34]
CAPTAIN SEAN P. GRIMES PHYSICIAN ASSISTANT EDUCATIONAL SCHOLARSHIP AWARD

Society of Army Physician Assistants
c/o Harold Slusher
6762 Candlewood Drive
P.O. Box 07490
Fort Myers, FL 33919
(239) 482-2162   Fax: (239) 482-2162
E-mail: hal.shusher@juno.com
Web: www.sapa.org/SeanScholarshipPage.htm

Summary To provide financial assistance to current and former Army personnel interested in seeking training as a physician assistant.

Eligibility This program is open to Army veterans, Army active-duty soldiers, Army National Guard soldiers, and Army Reservists. Soldiers may be of any enlisted or officer rank from E-5 through O-4. Applicants may be seeking initial training as a physician assistant or current physician assistants working on a baccalaureate, master's, or doctoral degree. They must have a GPA of 2.5 or higher. Candidates for initial training must be enrolled in an ARC-PA approved program. Other candidates must be enrolled at an accredited college or university. Financial need is considered in the selection process.

Financial data The stipend is $6,000.

Duration 1 year.

Additional information This program began in 2006.

Number awarded 1 each year.

Deadline January of each year.

[35]
CGMA EDUCATION LOAN PROGRAM

Coast Guard Mutual Assistance
4200 Wilson Boulevard, Suite 610
Arlington, VA 20598-7180
(202) 872-6716   Toll Free: (800) 881-2462
E-mail: ARL-DG-CGMA@uscg.mil
Web: www.cgmahq.org

Summary   To provide loans to members of Coast Guard Mutual Assistance (CGMA) and their families who are working on an undergraduate or graduate degree.

Eligibility   This program is open to 1) active-duty or retired Coast Guard personnel; 2) members of the Coast Guard Selected Reserve and retirement-eligible members of the IRR; 3) Coast Guard permanent and term civilian employees; 4) Coast Guard Auxiliary members; 5) U.S. Public Health Service officers serving with the Coast Guard; 6) unremarried widowed spouses of any of those; and 7) unmarried dependent children under 23 years of age and not enrolled in any military service of any of those. Applicants must be enrolled in an associate, bachelor's, or graduate degree program or an approved vocational/technical training program.

Financial data   The maximum loan is $2,000.

Duration   Loans must be repaid by the end of the month in which the course is completed.

Number awarded   Varies each year.

Deadline   Applications must be submitted no later than 30 days after the course begins.

[36]
CIVIL ENGINEER CORPS COLLEGIATE PROGRAM

U.S. Navy
Bureau of Navy Personnel
BUPERS-314E
5720 Integrity Drive
Millington, TN 38055-4630
(901) 874-4034   Toll Free: (866) CEC-NAVY
Fax: (901) 874-2681   E-mail: p4413d@persnet.navy.mil
Web: www.navycs.com/officer/civilengineerofficer.html

Summary   To provide financial assistance to undergraduate and graduate students in architecture and engineering who are interested in serving in the Navy's Civil Engineer Corps (CEC) following graduation.

Eligibility   This program is open to bachelor's and master's degree students who are U.S. citizens between 19 and 35 years of age. Applicants must be enrolled in an engineering program accredited by the Accreditation Board for Engineering and Technology (ABET) or an architecture program accredited by the National Architectural Accrediting Board (NAAB) and have a GPA of 2.7 or higher overall and 3.0 or higher in science and technical courses. They may be civilians, enlisted personnel of the regular Navy and the Naval Reserve, or enlisted personnel of other branches of the armed services with a conditional release from their respective service. Eligible majors include civil engineering, construction engineering, electrical engineering, environmental engineering, industrial engineering, mechanical engineering, ocean engineering, or architecture. Preference is given to applicants who have engineering or architecture work experience and registration as a Professional Engineer (P.E.) or Engineer-in-Training (EIT). Applicants must also be able to meet the Navy's physical fitness requirements.

Financial data   While attending classes, students are assigned to the Naval Reserve and receive the standard pay at E-3 level (approximately $2,575 per month) as an undergraduate or E-5 (approximately $4,700 per month) as a graduate student.

Duration   Up to 24 months.

Additional information   While in college, selectees have no uniforms, drills, or military duties. After graduation with a bachelor's or master's degree, they enter the Navy and attend 13 weeks at Officer Candidate School (OCS) in Pensacola, Florida, followed by 15 weeks at Civil Engineer Corps Officers School (CECOS) in Port Hueneme, California. They then serve 4 years in the CEC, rotating among public works, contract management, and the Naval Construction Force (Seabees).

Number awarded   Varies each year.

Deadline   Deadline not specified.

[37]
CIVIL ENGINEER CORPS OPTION OF THE SEAMAN TO ADMIRAL-21 PROGRAM

U.S. Navy
Attn: Commander, Naval Service Training Command
250 Dallas Street, Suite A
Pensacola, FL 32508-5268
(850) 452-9563   Fax: (850) 452-2486
E-mail: PNSC_STA21@navy.mil
Web: www.sta-21.navy.mil/program_options.asp

Summary   To allow outstanding enlisted Navy personnel to attend a college or university, affiliate with an NROTC unit, complete a bachelor's degree, and receive a commission in the Civil Engineer Corps (CEC).

Eligibility   This program is open to U.S. citizens who are currently serving on active duty in the Navy as enlisted personnel in any rating. Applicants must have completed at least 4 years of active duty, of which at least 3 years were in an other than formal training environment. They must be high school graduates (or GED recipients) who are able to complete requirements for a professional Accreditation Board for Engineering and Technology (ABET) engineering degree or National Architectural Accrediting Board (NAAB) architectural degree within 36 months or less. Preferred specialties are civil, electrical, mechanical, or ocean engineering. When applicants complete their degree requirements, they must be younger than 42 years of age. Within the past 3 years, they must have taken the SAT (and achieved scores of at least 500 on the mathematics section and 500 on the critical reading section) or the ACT (and achieved a score of at least 21 on the mathematics portion and 20 on the English portion).

Financial data   Awardees continue to receive their regular Navy pay and allowances while they attend college on a full-time basis. They also receive reimbursement for tuition, fees, and books up to $10,000 per year. If base housing is available, they are eligible to live there. Participants are not eligible to receive benefits under the Navy's Tuition Assistance Program (TA), the Montgomery GI Bill (MGIB), the Navy College Fund, or the Veterans Educational Assistance Program (VEAP).

Duration   Selectees are supported for up to 36 months of full-time, year-round study or completion of a bachelor's degree, as long as they maintain a GPA of 3.0 or higher.

Additional information This program began in 2001 as a replacement for the Civil Engineer Corps Enlisted Commissioning Program (CECECP). Upon acceptance into the program, selectees attend the Naval Science Institute (NSI) in Newport, Rhode Island for an 8-week program in the fundamental core concepts of being a naval officer (navigation, engineering, weapons, military history and justice, etc.). They then enter a college or university with an NROTC unit that is designated for the CEC to work full time on a bachelor's degree. They become members of and drill with the NROTC unit. When they complete their degree, they are commissioned as ensigns in the United States Naval Reserve and assigned to initial training as an officer in the CEC. After commissioning, 5 years of active service are required.

Number awarded Varies each year.

Deadline June of each year.

[38]
CMSGT GERALD R. GUILD MEMORIAL SCHOLARSHIPS

Enlisted Association National Guard of Arizona
Attn: Scholarship Chair
5636 East McDowell Road
Phoenix, AZ 85008-3495
(602) 267-2467 Fax: (602) 267-2509
E-mail: scholarship@eanga.org
Web: www.eanga.org

Summary To provide financial assistance to members of the Enlisted Association National Guard of Arizona (EANGA) and to members of their families who plan to attend college in any state.

Eligibility This program is open to EANGA members, the unmarried sons and daughters of EANGA members, the spouses of EANGA members, and the unremarried spouses and unmarried dependent sons and daughters of deceased EANGA members (who were in good standing at their time of death). Qualifying EANGA members must have at least 1 year remaining on their enlistment or have served 20 or more years of service. Applicants may be high school seniors or current college students who are enrolled or planning to enroll full time at a college or university in any state. Graduate students are not eligible. Selection is based on academic record, character, leadership, and financial need.

Financial data Stipends are $1,000 or $750. Funds are made payable to the recipient's school and sent directly to the recipient.

Duration 1 year; nonrenewable.

Number awarded Varies each year; recently, 3 were awarded: 1 at $1,000 and 2 at $750.

Deadline April of each year.

[39]
COAST GUARD FOUNDATION ENLISTED RESERVE SCHOLARSHIPS

U.S. Coast Guard
Attn: COMDT (CG-1311)
2703 Martin Luther King, Jr. Avenue, S.E., Stop 7907
Washington, DC 20593-7907
(202) 475-5459 E-mail: travis.p.thornell@uscg.mil
Web: www.uscg.mil/reserve/awards

Summary To provide financial assistance for college or graduate school to members of the Coast Guard Reserves and their dependents.

Eligibility This program is open to Coast Guard enlisted reservists (Selected Reserve or Individual Ready Reserve) and their dependents who are registered in the Defense Enrollment Eligibility Reporting System (DEERS). Applicants must be enrolled or accepted for enrollment at 1) an accredited institution in a program leading to an associate, bachelor's, master's, or doctoral degree; or 2) a 2- or 4-year course of study at an accredited technical or vocational training school. Along with their application, they must submit a 1-page essay on how the participation of themselves, their spouse, or their parent in the Coast Guard Reserve has contributed to their success. Selection is based on that essay and academic achievement.

Financial data The stipend is $1,000.

Duration 1 year.

Additional information This program is sponsored by the United States Automobile Association (USAA) Insurance Corporation.

Number awarded 6 each year.

Deadline July of each year.

[40]
COAST GUARD TUITION ASSISTANCE PROGRAM

U.S. Coast Guard Institute
Attn: Commanding Officer
5900 S.W. 64th Street, Room 233
Oklahoma City, OK 73169-6990
(405) 954-1360 Fax: (405) 954-7245
E-mail: CGI-PF-Tuition_Assistance@uscg.mil
Web: www.uscg.mil

Summary To provide financial assistance to members and employees of the Coast Guard who are interested in pursuing additional education during their off-duty hours.

Eligibility This program is open to Coast Guard members on active duty and Reservists on long-term orders greater than 180 days. Applicants must be interested in working on their first associate or bachelor's degree. Civilian employees with at least 90 days of Coast Guard service are also eligible. Enlisted members must complete the course before their enlistment ends or they retire. Active-duty officers must agree to fulfill a 2-year service obligation following completion of the course; officers of the selected reserve must agree to fulfill a 4-year service obligation following completion of the course. Civilian employees must agree to retain employment with the Coast Guard for 1 month for each completed course credit hour. For military personnel, the command education services officer (ESO) must certify that the course of instruction is Coast Guard mission or career related. The supervisor of civilian employees must certify that the education is career related. All courses must be related to the mission of the Coast Guard or the individual's career or professional development.

Financial data The program reimburses 75% of the cost of tuition, to a maximum of $250 per semester hour (of which the Coast Guard share is $187.50) or $3,000 per fiscal year (of which the Coast Guard share is $2,250). Funding is available only for tuition, not fees or other associated expenses.

Duration Until completion of an associate or bachelor's degree. Undergraduates must complete all courses with a grade of "C" or better; graduate students must complete classes with a grade of "B" of better. If recipients fail to achieve those grades, they must reimburse the Army for all funds received.

Number awarded Varies each year; recently, more than 10,000 Coast Guard personnel received tuition assistance worth approximately $14.5 million.

Deadline Applications may be submitted at any time.

[41]
COCA-COLA LEADERS OF PROMISE SCHOLARSHIP PROGRAM

Phi Theta Kappa
Attn: Scholarship Programs Department
1625 Eastover Drive
Jackson, MS 39211
(601) 987-5741   Toll Free: (800) 946-9995
Fax: (601) 984-3550
E-mail: scholarship.programs@ptk.org
Web: www.ptk.org/scholarships

Summary To provide financial assistance to members of Phi Theta Kappa, the international honor society for 2-year colleges (preference given to military personnel and veterans), who plan to continue work on an associate degree.

Eligibility This program is open to members of the society who have completed between 12 and 36 semester hours of course work for an associate degree at a community college in the United States. Applicants must have a cumulative GPA of 3.5 or higher. Along with their application, they must submit 250-word essays on questions about the work of the society and a 500-word essay on a topic that changes annually. Selection is based on those essays, college transcripts, and a letter of recommendation from a community college faculty member. Some of the scholarships are reserved for veterans and currently-serving military personnel.

Financial data The stipend is $1,000. The first $500 is disbursed upon documentation of enrollment at the community college and the second $500 upon documentation of continued participation in Phi Theta Kappa activities and a GPA of 3.25 or higher.

Duration 1 year.

Additional information This program, originally established in 2001, is currently sponsored by the Coca-Cola Foundation.

Number awarded 200 each year, of which 25 are reserved for veterans and currently-serving military personnel.

Deadline May of each year.

[42]
COLD WAR VETERANS ENGINEERING AND SCIENCE SCHOLARSHIPS

Marines' Memorial Association
c/o Marines Memorial Club and Hotel
609 Sutter Street
San Francisco, CA 94102
(415) 673-6672, ext. 293   Fax: (415) 441-3649
E-mail: scholarship@marineclub.com
Web: www.marineclub.com/membership/scholarship.php

Summary To provide financial assistance to members of the Marines' Memorial Association from all branches of the armed forces and their descendants who are interested in studying a field of science, technology, engineering, or mathematics (STEM) in college.

Eligibility This program is open to active members of the association and their children and grandchildren. Applicants must be high school seniors or students currently enrolled full time in an undergraduate degree program in a field of STEM. Along with their application, they must submit an essay of 250 to 500 words on the science of engineering and how they hope to contribute to its progression. Graduating high school seniors must submit a high school transcript and SAT or ACT scores; continuing college students must submit a college transcript. Selection is based on the essay, academic merit, references, and financial need.

Financial data The stipend is $2,500 per year.

Duration 1 year; recipients may reapply for up to 3 additional years.

Additional information Membership in the association is open to veterans of the Marines, Army, Navy, Air Force, or Coast Guard and to personnel currently serving in a branch of the armed forces. This program began in 2014.

Number awarded 2 each year.

Deadline April of each year.

[43]
COLLEGE STUDENT PRE-COMMISSIONING INITIATIVE

U.S. Coast Guard
Attn: Recruiting Command
2300 Wilson Boulevard, Suite 500
Arlington, VA 22201
(703) 235-1775   Toll Free: (877) NOW-USCG, ext. 205
Fax: (703) 235-1881
E-mail: Margaret.A.Jackson@uscg.mil
Web: www.gocoastguard.com

Summary To provide financial assistance to college students at minority or other designated institutions who are willing to serve in the Coast Guard following graduation.

Eligibility This program is open to students entering their junior or senior year at a college or university designated as an Historically Black College or University (HBCU), Hispanic Serving Institution (HSI), Tribal College or University (TCU), or the University of Guam, the University of Hawaii (at Manoa, Hilo, or West Oahu), Argosy University (Hawaii), or the Institute of American Indian and Alaska Native Culture (Santa Fe, New Mexico). Applicants must be U.S. citizens; have a GPA of 2.5 or higher; have scores of 1100 or higher on the critical reading and mathematics SAT, 23 or higher on the ACT, 4AQR/4PFAR on the ASTB, or 109 or higher on the SVAB GT; be between 19 and 27 years of age; and meet all physical requirements for a Coast Guard commission. They must agree to attend the Coast Guard Officer Candidate School following graduation and serve on active duty as an officer for at least 3 years.

Financial data Those selected to participate receive full payment of tuition, books, and fees; monthly housing and food allowances; medical and life insurance; special training in leadership, management, law enforcement, navigation, and marine science; 30 days of paid vacation per year; and a Coast Guard monthly salary of up to $2,200.

Duration Up to 2 years.

Number awarded Varies each year.

Deadline January of each year.

[44]
COLONEL RICHARD HALLOCK SCHOLARSHIPS

Marines' Memorial Association
c/o Marines Memorial Club and Hotel
609 Sutter Street
San Francisco, CA 94102
(415) 673-6672, ext. 293   Fax: (415) 441-3649
E-mail: scholarship@marineclub.com
Web: www.marineclub.com/membership/scholarship.php

Summary To provide financial assistance for college to members of the Marines' Memorial Association from all branches of the armed forces and their descendants.

Eligibility This program is open to active members of the association and their children and grandchildren. Applicants must be high school seniors or students currently enrolled full time in an undergraduate degree program at a college or university. Along with their application, they must submit an essay of 250 to 500 words on their conception of "fairness" and its impact on society and in their life. Graduating high school seniors must submit a high school transcript and SAT or ACT scores; continuing college students must submit a college transcript. Selection is based on the essay, academic merit, references, and financial need.

Financial data The stipend is $2,500 per year.

Duration 1 year; recipients may reapply for up to 3 additional years.

Additional information Membership in the association is open to veterans of the Marines, Army, Navy, Air Force, or Coast Guard and to personnel currently serving in a branch of the armed forces.

Number awarded 2 each year.

Deadline April of each year.

[45]
COLORADO NATIONAL GUARD STATE TUITION ASSISTANCE

Department of Military and Veterans Affairs
Attn: Colorado State Tuition Assistance Office
6848 South Revere Parkway
Centennial, CO 80112-6703
(720) 250-1550   Fax: (720) 250-1559
E-mail: tuition@dmva.state.co.us
Web: www.colorado.gov

Summary To provide financial assistance for college or graduate school to members of the Colorado National Guard.

Eligibility This program is open to members of the Colorado National Guard who have served at least 6 months. Applicants must be enrolled or planning to enroll at a public institution of higher education in Colorado to work on a vocational certificate or associate, bachelor's, or master's degree. They must have a GPA of 2.0 or higher. Enlisted personnel must complete courses before their expiration term of service date. Commissioned officers must agree to remain in the Guard for at least 4 years following completion of the course.

Financial data This program provides payment of up to 100% of the in-state tuition at public institutions in Colorado, to a maximum of $475 per credit hour or $4,250 per semester.

Duration 1 semester; may be renewed as long as the recipient remains an active member of the Guard and maintains a GPA of 2.0 or higher, to a maximum of 132 semester hours or 8 years.

Number awarded Varies each year.

Deadline June of each year for the fall semester; November of each year for the spring semester; April of each year for the summer term.

[46]
CONGRESSMAN DAVID L. HOBSON CIVIL ENGINEERING SCHOLARSHIP

Army Engineer Association
Attn: Program Coordinator
P.O. Box 30260
Alexandria, VA 22310-8260
(703) 428-7084   Fax: (703) 428-6043
E-mail: execasst@armyengineer.com
Web: www.armyengineer.com/scholarships.htm

Summary To provide financial assistance to members of the Army Engineer Association (AEA) and their families interested in studying civil engineering in college.

Eligibility This program is open to AEA members and their families who are U.S. citizens. Applicants must be enrolled full time at an accredited college or university and working on a bachelor's degree in civil engineering. Along with their application, they must submit a 600-word essay that lists their academic and professional goals, extracurricular activities, and military service (if applicable). Selection is based on that essay, scholastic aptitude, and letters of recommendation.

Financial data The stipend is $3,000.

Duration 1 year; nonrenewable.

Additional information This program is sponsored by the engineering firm, Trimble.

Number awarded 4 each year.

Deadline July of each year.

[47]
CONNECTICUT NATIONAL GUARD EDUCATIONAL ASSISTANCE PROGRAM

Connecticut National Guard
Attn: Education Service Officer
360 Broad Street
Hartford, CT 06105-3795
(860) 524-4816
Web: states.ng.mil

Summary To provide financial assistance for college to members of the Connecticut National Guard.

Eligibility This program is open to active members of the Connecticut National Guard who are interested in working on an undergraduate degree at any branch of the University of Connecticut, any of the 4 state universities, or any of the 13 community/technical colleges in Connecticut. Applicants must have been residents of the state and a satisfactory Guard participant for at least 12 months.

Financial data The program provides a full waiver of tuition at state colleges or universities in Connecticut.

Duration 1 year; may be renewed.

Number awarded Varies each year.

Deadline Deadline not specified.

[48]
CONNECTICUT NATIONAL GUARD FOUNDATION SCHOLARSHIPS

Connecticut National Guard Foundation, Inc.
Attn: Scholarship Committee
360 Broad Street
Hartford, CT 06105-3795
(860) 241-1550 Fax: (860) 293-2929
E-mail: ctngfi@sbcglobal.net
Web: www.ctngfoundation.org/Scholarship.asp

Summary To provide financial assistance for college to members of the Connecticut National Guard and their families.

Eligibility This program is open to members of the Connecticut Army National Guard and Organized Militia, their children, and their spouses. Applicants must be enrolled or planning to enroll in an accredited college or technical program. Along with their application, they must submit a letter of recommendation, a list of extracurricular activities, high school or college transcripts, and a 200-word statement on their educational and future goals. Selection is based on achievement and citizenship.

Financial data Stipends are $2,000 or $1,000.

Duration 1 year.

Number awarded 10 each year: 5 at $2,000 and 5 at $1,000.

Deadline March of each year.

[49]
CONNECTICUT TUITION WAIVER FOR VETERANS

Connecticut Board of Regents for Higher Education
39 Woodland Street
Hartford, CT 06105
(860) 723-0013 E-mail: fitzgerald2@ct.edu
Web: www.ct.edu/admission/veterans

Summary To provide financial assistance for college or graduate school to certain Connecticut military servicemembers, veterans, and their dependents.

Eligibility This program is open to 1) honorably-discharged Connecticut veterans who served at least 90 days during specified periods of wartime; 2) active members of the Connecticut Army or Air National Guard; 3) Connecticut residents who are a dependent child or surviving spouse of a member of the armed forces killed in action on or after September 11, 2001 who was also a Connecticut resident; and 4) Connecticut residents who are a dependent child or surviving spouse of a person officially declared missing in action or a prisoner of war while serving in the armed forces after January 1, 1960. Applicants must be attending or planning to attend a public college or university in the state.

Financial data The program provides a waiver of 100% of tuition for students working on an undergraduate or graduate degree at the University of Connecticut (including summer sessions and winter intersession), 100% of tuition for general fund courses at campuses of Connecticut State University, 50% of tuition for extension and summer courses at campuses of Connecticut State University, 100% of tuition at all Connecticut community colleges, and 50% or fees at Charter Oak State College.

Duration Up to 4 years.

Additional information This is an entitlement program; applications are available at the respective college financial aid offices.

Number awarded Varies each year.

Deadline Deadline not specified.

[50]
CREATE-A-GREETING-CARD SCHOLARSHIP CONTEST

Prudent Publishing Company, Inc.
The Gallery Collection
Attn: Scholarship Administrator
65 Challenger Road
P.O. Box 150
Ridgefield Park, NJ 07660
Toll Free: (800) 950-7064
E-mail: scholarshipadmin@gallerycollection.com
Web: www.gallerycollection.com/greetingcardscontests.htm

Summary To recognize and reward (with college scholarships) military personnel and students who submit artwork for use on a greeting card.

Eligibility This competition is open to legal residents (including international students who have a valid visa) of the United States and its territories. Applicants must be 1) high school, home school, college, or university students who are at least 14 years of age; or 2) military personnel who are younger than 35 years of age. They must submit an original photograph, artwork, or computer graphics appropriate for the front of a greeting card. Both digital and paper submissions are accepted. Selection is based on overall aesthetic appeal, quality of execution, creativity and originality, incorporation of design elements, appropriateness for use as a greeting card, attractiveness to the sponsor's corporate and consumer customers, and suitability as a design in the sponsor's greeting card line.

Financial data The award for high school and college students is $10,000. For students currently enrolled at a college or university, funds are sent directly to the institution as payment toward tuition, fees, books, and supplies. For students who are still minors, funds are paid to the winner's parent or guardian as custodian. The winner's school receives a grant of $1,000. The award for military personnel is $1,000.

Duration The competition is held annually.

Additional information This competition was first held in 2008. The winning design is used for a greeting card published by the sponsor.

Number awarded 2 each year: 1 for a high school or college student and 1 for a military member.

Deadline January of each year.

[51]
CSM HARRY AND MARY HENSELL SCHOLARSHIP PROGRAM

Enlisted Association National Guard of Arizona
Attn: Scholarship Chair
5636 East McDowell Road
Phoenix, AZ 85008-3495
(602) 267-2467 Fax: (602) 267-2509
E-mail: scholarship@eanga.org
Web: www.eanga.org

Summary To provide financial assistance to members of the Enlisted Association National Guard of Arizona (EANGA) and to members of their families who plan to attend college in any state.

Eligibility This program is open to EANGA members, the unmarried sons and daughters of EANGA members, the spouses of EANGA members, and the unremarried spouses and unmarried dependent sons and daughters of deceased EANGA members (who were in good standing at their time of death). Qualifying EANGA members must have at least 1 year remaining on their enlistment or have served 20 or more years of service. Applicants may be high school seniors or current college students who are enrolled or planning to enroll full time at a college or university in any state. Graduate students are not eligible. Selection is based on academic record, character, leadership, and financial need.

Financial data The stipend is $1,000. Funds are made payable to the recipient's school and sent directly to the recipient.

Duration 1 year; nonrenewable.

Additional information This program, sponsored by USAA Insurance Corporation, was established in 1998 and given its current name in 2009.

Number awarded 1 each year.

Deadline April of each year.

[52]
CSM JAMES NELSON JR. SCHOLARSHIPS

Enlisted Association of the National Guard of Georgia
Attn: Executive Director
P.O. Box 602
Ellenwood, GA 30294
(678) 644-9245   Fax: (770) 719-9791
E-mail: csmharper@comcast.net
Web: www.eangga.com

Summary To provide financial assistance to members of the Georgia Army National Guard of Georgia who are attending college.

Eligibility This program is open to members of the Georgia Army National Guard at grade level E-6 and below who are currently enrolled full time at an accredited college. Applicants must have a GPA of 3.0 or higher. Along with their application, they must submit a 1-page biography and a 500-word essay on why they deserve to have this scholarship.

Financial data The stipend is $1,000.

Duration 1 year.

Number awarded 2 each year.

Deadline May of each year.

[53]
CSM ROBERT W. ELKEY AWARD

Army Engineer Association
Attn: Program Coordinator
P.O. Box 30260
Alexandria, VA 22310-8260
(703) 428-7084   Fax: (703) 428-6043
E-mail: execasst@armyengineer.com
Web: www.armyengineer.com/scholarships.htm

Summary To provide financial assistance for college or graduate school to enlisted members of the Army Engineer Association (AEA).

Eligibility This program is open to AEA members serving in an active, Reserve, or National Guard component Army Engineer unit, school, or organization within the Corps of Engineers of the United States Army. Applicants must be enlisted personnel (PVT, PFC, SPC, CPL, SGT, or SSG). They must be working on or planning to work on an associate, bachelor's, or master's degree at an accredited college or university. Selection is based primarily on financial need, although potential for academic success and standards of conduct as supported by personal references are also considered.

Financial data The stipend is $1,000.

Duration 1 year.

Number awarded 3 each year.

Deadline June of each year.

[54]
CSM VINCENT BALDASSARI MEMORIAL SCHOLARSHIPS

Enlisted Association National Guard of New Jersey
Attn: Scholarship Chair
3650 Saylors Pond Road
Fort Dix, NJ 08640
(609) 432-9820   E-mail: npdsgt618@yahoo.com
Web: www.eang-nj.org/scholarships.html

Summary To provide financial assistance to New Jersey National Guard members and their children who are interested in attending college in any state.

Eligibility This program is open to 1) children of New Jersey National Guard members (active, inactive, or retired) who are also members of the Enlisted Association National Guard of New Jersey; and 2) drilling Guard members who are also members of the Association. Applicants must be attending or planning to attend a college or university in any state. Along with their application, they must submit 1) information on their church, school, and community activities; 2) a list of honors they have received; 3) letters of recommendation; 4) transcripts; and 5) a letter with specific facts about their desire to continue their education and specifying their career goals. Financial need is not considered in the selection process.

Financial data The stipend is $1,000.

Duration 1 year.

Number awarded Varies each year; recently, 2 were awarded.

Deadline May of each year.

[55]
CSM VIRGIL R. WILLIAMS SCHOLARSHIP PROGRAM

Enlisted Association of the National Guard of the United
  States
3133 Mount Vernon Avenue
Alexandria, VA 22305-2640
(703) 519-3846   Toll Free: (800) 234-EANG
Fax: (703) 519-3849   E-mail: eangus@eangus.org
Web: www.eangus.org/?page=GrantsScholarships

Summary To provide financial assistance to National Guard members and their dependents who are members of the Enlisted Association of the National Guard of the United States (EANGUS) and entering or continuing in college.

Eligibility This program is open to high school seniors and current college students who are enrolled or planning to enroll as full-time undergraduate students. They must be 1) National Guard members who belong to EANGUS; 2) unmarried sons and daughters of EANGUS members; 3) spouses of EANGUS members; or 4) unremarried spouses and unmarried dependent children of deceased EANGUS members who were in good standing at the time of their death. Honorary, associate, or corporate membership alone does not qualify. Applicants must submit a copy of their school transcript, 3 letters of recommendation, a letter of academic reference (from their principal, dean, or counselor), a photocopy of the qualifying state and/or national membership card (parent's, spouse's or applicant's), and a personal letter with specific facts as to their desire to continue their education and why financial assistance is necessary. Application packets must be submitted to the state EANGUS association; acceptable packets are then sent to the national offices for judging. Selection is based on academic achievement, character, leadership, and financial need.

Financial data The stipend is $2,000.

Duration 1 year; nonrenewable.

Additional information Recent sponsors of this program included USAA Insurance Corporation, GEICO Insurance, the Armed Forces Benefit Association, and the Armed Forces Insurance Company.

Number awarded Varies each year; recently, 10 were awarded.

Deadline Applications must first be verified by the state office and then submitted by June to the national office.

[56]
DELAWARE NATIONAL GUARD EDUCATION ASSISTANCE PROGRAM

Delaware National Guard
Attn: Education Services Officer
State Tuition Reimbursement Program
First Regiment Road
Wilmington, DE 19808-2191
(302) 326-7012   Fax: (302) 326-7029
Web: www.delawarenationalguard.com

Summary To provide financial assistance to members of the Delaware National Guard who plan to attend college in the state.

Eligibility This program is open to active members of the Delaware National Guard who are interested in working on an associate or bachelor's degree at a school in Delaware. Applicants must have made satisfactory progress in their assigned military career field, may not have missed more than 6 periods of scheduled unit training assembly periods in the preceding 12 months, and must have avoided all adverse personnel actions. They must earn a grade of 2.0 or higher in all courses to qualify for tuition reimbursement.

Financial data Participants receive reimbursement of 100% of the tuition at state-supported colleges and universities in Delaware, to a maximum of $1,236 per semester at Delaware Technical and Community college, $4,270 per semester at the University of Delaware, or $3,240.50 per semester at Delaware State University. Students who attend a Delaware private college are reimbursed up to $243 per credit hour. If total funding appropriated by the legislature is insufficient for all qualified applicants, the available funds are distributed among recipients according to a maximum allowable fair percentage formula. Recipients must complete 6 years of satisfactory membership in the Delaware National Guard (before, during, and after participation in the program) or repay the funds received.

Duration 1 semester; may be renewed. Guard members are eligible for this assistance only for 10 years after the date on which they begin the first course for which reimbursement was granted.

Number awarded Varies each year; recently, a total of $490,000 was available for this program.

Deadline September of each year for fall semester; January of each year for winter semester; March of each year for spring semester; June of each year for summer semester.

[57]
DISABLED WAR VETERANS SCHOLARSHIPS

Armed Forces Communications and Electronics Association
Attn: AFCEA Educational Foundation
4400 Fair Lakes Court
Fairfax, VA 22033-3899
(703) 631-6138   Toll Free: (800) 336-4583, ext. 6138
Fax: (703) 631-4693   E-mail: scholarship@afcea.org
Web: www.afcea.org

Summary To provide financial assistance to disabled military personnel and veterans who are majoring in specified scientific fields in college.

Eligibility This program is open to active-duty service personnel and honorably discharged U.S. military veterans, Reservists, and National Guard members who are disabled because of wounds received during service in Enduring Freedom (Afghanistan) or Iraqi Freedom operations. Applicants must be enrolled full or part time at an accredited 2- or 4-year college or university or in a distance learning or online degree program. They must be working toward a degree in engineering (aerospace, computer, electrical, or systems), computer science, computer engineering technology, computer information systems, mathematics, physics, information systems management, science or mathematics education, or other fields related to the support of U.S. intelligence or homeland security enterprises. Selection is based on demonstrated academic excellence, leadership, and financial need.

Financial data The stipend is $2,500.

Duration 1 year.

Additional information This program began in 2005 with funding from Microsoft and the Camp Pendleton Chapter of AFCEA.

Number awarded 2 each year: 1 for spring and 1 for fall.

Deadline April of each year for fall; November of each year for spring.

[58]
DISTRICT OF COLUMBIA NATIONAL GUARD TUITION ASSISTANCE

District of Columbia National Guard
Attn: Education Services Office
2001 East Capitol Street, S.E.
Washington, DC 20003-1719
(202) 685-9825   Fax: (202) 685-9815
E-mail: joanne.thweatt@dc.ngb.army.mil
Web: states.ng.mil/sites/DC/education/Pages/tuition.aspx

Summary To provide financial assistance for college or graduate school to current members of the District of Columbia National Guard.

Eligibility This program is open to traditional, technician, and AGR members of the District of Columbia Air and Army National Guard. Applicants must have a high school diploma or equivalency and currently be working on an associate, bachelor's, or master's degree at an accredited postsecondary education institution. In some instances, support may also be available for an M.D., D.O., P.A., or J.D. degree.

Financial data Army National Guard members are eligible for up to $4,500 per year in federal tuition assistance; they may supplement that with up to $1,500 per year in District tuition assistance. Air National Guard members do not have access to federal tuition assistance, so they may receive up to $6,000 in District tuition assistance. Funds must be used to pay for tuition, fees, and/or books.

Duration 1 semester; recipients may reapply.

Number awarded Varies each year.

Deadline July of each year for the fall session, October of each year for the spring session, or April of each year for the summer session.

[59]
DIVISION COMMANDER'S HIP POCKET SCHOLARSHIPS

U.S. Army
Attn: U.S. Army Cadet Command
G2 Incentives Division
1307 Third Avenue
Fort Knox, KY 40121-2725
(502) 624-7371   Toll Free: (888) 550-ARMY
Fax: (502) 624-6937
E-mail: usarmy.knox.usacc.mbx.train2lead@mail.mil
Web: www.goarmy.com

Summary To enable soldiers who are nominated by their Division Commanding General to obtain an early discharge from the Army and return to college to participate in the Army Reserve Officers' Training Corps (ROTC).

Eligibility Enlisted soldiers who have served at least 2 but less than 10 years on active duty are eligible for this program. They must be nominated by their Division Commanding General to obtain an early discharge in order to enroll in a baccalaureate degree program. Nominees must have a cumulative high school or college GPA of 2.5 or higher, a score of at least 21 on the ACT or 1100 on the combined mathematics and critical reading SAT, a General Technical (GT) score of 110 or higher, and a recent (within the past 6 months) Army Physical Fitness Test (APFT) score of 180 or higher (including 60 points in each event). They may not have a spouse who is also in the military or dependent children under 18 years of age (those requirements may be waived). At the time they graduate and are commissioned, they must be under 31 years of age. Selection is made by the Division Commanding General; no additional review is made by Cadet Command Headquarters.

Financial data Scholarship winners receive full payment of tuition, a grant of $1,200 per year for books and supplies, a monthly stipend of up to $500 per month (depending on academic status) for 10 months per year, and pay for attending the 6-week Leader Development and Assessment Course (LDAC) during the summer between the junior and senior year of college.

Duration 2, 3, or 4 years.

Additional information Recipients who had previously qualified for benefits from the Army College Fund and/or the Montgomery GI Bill are still entitled to receive those in addition to any benefits from this program. Upon graduation from college, scholarship winners are commissioned as second lieutenants and are required to serve in the military for 8 years. That obligation may be fulfilled by serving 4 years on active duty followed by 4 years in the Inactive Ready Reserve (IRR).

Number awarded Varies each year; recently, 117 were awarded.

Deadline March of each year.

[60]
DONALDSON D. FRIZZELL MEMORIAL SCHOLARSHIPS

First Command Educational Foundation
Attn: Scholarship Programs Manager
1 FirstComm Plaza
Fort Worth, TX 76109-4999
(817) 569-2634   Toll Free: (877) 872-8289
Fax: (817) 569-2970   E-mail: Scholarships@fcef.com
Web: www.fcef.com

Summary To provide financial assistance to students, especially those with ties to the military (including ROTC), who are entering or attending college or graduate school.

Eligibility This program is open to 1) members of a U.S. uniformed service and their spouses and dependents; 2) clients of First Command Financial Services and their family members; 3) dependent family members of First Command Advisors or field office staff members; or 4) non-contractual ROTC students. Applicants may be traditional students (high school seniors and students already enrolled at a college, university, or accredited trade school) or nontraditional students (those defined by their institution as nontraditional and adult students planning to return to a college, university, or accredited trade school). They must have a GPA of 3.0 or higher and be working on a trade school certification or associate, undergraduate, or graduate degree. Applicants must submit 1-page essays on 1) their active involvement in community service programs; 2) the impact of financial literacy on their future; and 3) why they need this scholarship. Selection is based primarily on the essays, academic merit, and financial need.

Financial data Stipends are $5,000 or $2,500. Funds are disbursed directly to the recipient's college, university, or trade school.

Duration 1 year.

Additional information The sponsoring organization was formerly known as the USPA & IRA Educational Foundation, founded in 1983 to provide scholarships to the children of active, retired, or deceased military personnel. In addition to these scholarships, for which students may apply directly, it supports scholarships offered by a number of partner organizations. Since its establishment, it has awarded scholarships worth nearly $4 million.

Number awarded 6 each year: 2 at $5,000 and 4 at $2,500. Awards are split evenly between the 2 categories.

Deadline The online application process begins in February of each year and continues until 200 applications have been received in each category.

[61]
DR. AILEEN WEBB TOBIN SCHOLARSHIP PROGRAM

U.S. Army Ordnance Corps Association
Attn: Scholarship
P.O. Box 5251
Fort Lee, VA 23801
(804) 733-5596   Fax: (804) 733-5599
E-mail: usaoca@usaocaweb.ort
Web: www.usaocaweb.org/scholarships.htm

Summary   To provide financial assistance for college to soldiers serving in the U.S. Army Ordnance Corps and members of the U.S. Army Ordnance Corps Association (OCA) and their families.

Eligibility   This program is open to Ordnance soldiers (active and reserve), OCA members, and immediate family of OCA members. Applicants must be entering or attending a college or university to work on an associate or baccalaureate degree. Along with their application, they must submit 1) an essay of 1,000 to 1,500 words on lifelong learning as it applies to the U.S. Army Ordnance Corps; and 2) an essay of 300 to 500 words on their educational and career goals. Selection is based on the essays, scholastic aptitude, and grades.

Financial data   The stipend is $1,000.

Duration   1 year.

Additional information   This program began in 2014.

Number awarded   1 each year.

Deadline   June of each year.

[62]
EANGUT SCHOLARSHIPS

Enlisted Association of the National Guard of Utah
Attn: Scholarship Committee
12953 South Minuteman Drive
Draper, UT 84020
(801) 699-1680   E-mail: eangut@hotmail.com
Web: www.eangut.org/Scholarship

Summary   To provide financial assistance to National Guard members belonging to the Enlisted Association National Guard of Utah (EANGUT) and their family members who are beginning or continuing their college studies in the state.

Eligibility   This program is open to members of EANGUT, their spouses, their children, and the spouses and unmarried dependent children of deceased members. Applicants must be attending or planning to attend a college, university, or vocational/technical school in Utah. EANGUT members must have at least 1 year remaining on their enlistment or have completed 20 or more years of service. Along with their application, they must submit 3 essays on 1) their educational and career goals; 2) their leadership and extracurricular activities; and 3) how the military has influenced their life.

Financial data   The stipend is $1,500 or $1,000.

Duration   1 year.

Additional information   This program receives support from the USAA Insurance Corporation.

Number awarded   2 each year: 1 at $1,500 and 1 at $1,000.

Deadline   March of each year.

[63]
EDMUND K. GROSS SCHOLARSHIP

Marines' Memorial Association
c/o Marines Memorial Club and Hotel
609 Sutter Street
San Francisco, CA 94102
(415) 673-6672, ext. 293   Fax: (415) 441-3649
E-mail: scholarship@marineclub.com
Web: www.marineclub.com/membership/scholarship.php

Summary   To provide financial assistance to members of the Marines' Memorial Association from all branches of the armed forces and their descendants who are interested in studying education in college.

Eligibility   This program is open to active members of the association and their children and grandchildren. Applicants must be enrolled or planning to enroll in an undergraduate degree program in education at a college or university. Along with their application, they must submit an essay of 250 to 500 words on what they value enough to promote to a wider audience. Graduating high school seniors must submit a high school transcript and SAT or ACT scores; continuing college students must submit a college transcript. Selection is based on the essay, academic merit, references, and financial need.

Financial data   The stipend is $2,500 per year.

Duration   1 year; recipients may reapply for up to 3 additional years.

Additional information   Membership in the association is open to veterans of the Marines, Army, Navy, Air Force, or Coast Guard and to personnel currently serving in a branch of the armed forces.

Number awarded   1 each year.

Deadline   April of each year.

[64]
EDUCATION FOUNDATION FOR THE COLORADO NATIONAL GUARD GRANTS

National Guard Association of Colorado
Attn: Education Foundation, Inc.
P.O. Box 440889
Aurora, CO 80044-0889
(303) 909-6369   Fax: (720) 535-5925
E-mail: BernieRogoff@comcast.net
Web: www.efcong.org/Grants

Summary   To provide financial assistance to members of the Colorado National Guard and their families who are interested in attending college or graduate school in any state.

Eligibility   This program is open to current and retired members of the Colorado National Guard and their dependent unmarried children and spouses. Applicants must be enrolled or planning to enroll full or part time at a college, university, trade school, business school, or graduate school in any state. Along with their application, they must submit an essay, up to 2 pages in length, on their desire to continue their education, what motivates them, their financial need, their commitment to academic excellence, and their current situation. Selection is based on academic achievement, community involvement, and financial need.

Financial data   Stipends are generally at least $1,000 per year.

Duration   1 year; may be renewed.

Number awarded Normally, 15 to 25 of these grants are awarded each semester.

Deadline August of each year for fall semester; January of each year for spring semester.

[65]
ENLISTED ASSOCIATION NATIONAL GUARD OF KANSAS SCHOLARSHIPS

Enlisted Association National Guard of Kansas
Attn: Executive Director
P.O. Box 841
Topeka, KS 66601-0841
(785) 242-5678   Fax: (785) 242-3765
E-mail: eangks@earthlink.net
Web: www.eangks.org/benefits/scholarships

Summary To provide financial assistance to members of the Enlisted Association National Guard of Kansas and their families who are interested in attending college in any state.

Eligibility This program is open to members of the association who are also currently serving in the Kansas National Guard and their families. Spouses and dependents of associate members are not eligible. Applicants must submit high school and/or college transcripts (including SAT and/or ACT scores); 4 letters of recommendation; information on their awards and recognition, community service, extracurricular activities, and work experience; documentation of financial need; and a brief essay on their goals and career objectives. They must be enrolled or planning to enroll full time at an accredited institution of higher learning in any state.

Financial data The stipend ranges up to $1,000.

Duration 1 year.

Additional information This program includes 1 scholarship supported by USAA Insurance Corporation.

Number awarded Varies each year.

Deadline May of each year.

[66]
EVELYN BUKOVAC HAMILTON HEALTH CARE SCHOLARSHIP

Marines' Memorial Association
c/o Marines Memorial Club and Hotel
609 Sutter Street
San Francisco, CA 94102
(415) 673-6672, ext. 293   Fax: (415) 441-3649
E-mail: scholarship@marineclub.com
Web: www.marineclub.com/membership/scholarship.php

Summary To provide financial assistance to members of the Marines' Memorial Association from all branches of the armed forces and their descendants who are interested in studying health care in college.

Eligibility This program is open to active members of the association and their children and grandchildren. Applicants must be high school seniors or students currently enrolled full time in an undergraduate degree program in a discipline within the field of health care. Along with their application, they must submit an essay of 250 to 500 words in which they compare and contrast scientific advances to literary education. Graduating high school seniors must submit a high school transcript and SAT or ACT scores; continuing college students must submit a college transcript. Selection is based on the essay, academic merit, references, and financial need.

Financial data The stipend is $2,500 per year.

Duration 1 year; recipients may reapply for up to 3 additional years.

Additional information Membership in the association is open to veterans of the Marines, Army, Navy, Air Force, or Coast Guard and to personnel currently serving in a branch of the armed forces.

Number awarded 1 each year.

Deadline April of each year.

[67]
EXPLOSIVE ORDNANCE DISPOSAL OPTION OF THE SEAMAN TO ADMIRAL-21 PROGRAM

U.S. Navy
Attn: Commander, Naval Service Training Command
250 Dallas Street, Suite A
Pensacola, FL 32508-5268
(850) 452-9563   Fax: (850) 452-2486
E-mail: PNSC_STA21@navy.mil
Web: www.sta-21.navy.mil/program_options.asp

Summary To allow outstanding enlisted Navy personnel to attend college, affiliate with an NROTC unit, complete a bachelor's degree, and receive a commission as an explosive ordnance disposal (EOD) officer.

Eligibility This program is open to U.S. citizens who are currently serving on active duty in the U.S. Navy or Naval Reserve, including Full Time Support (FTS), Selected Reserves (SELRES), and Navy Reservists on active duty, except for those on active duty for training (ACDUTRA). Applicants must have 1 of the following NECs: 5332, 5333, 5334, 5335, 5336, 5337, 5342, 5343 and 8493 or 8494. They must be high school graduates (or GED recipients) who are able to complete requirements for a baccalaureate degree in 36 months or less. When they complete their degree requirements, they must be younger than 29 years of age. That age limitation may be adjusted upward for active service on a month-for-month basis up to 24 months, and waivers are considered for enlisted personnel who possess particularly exceptional qualifications if they can complete their degree prior to their 35th birthday. Within the past 3 years, they must have taken the SAT (and achieved scores of at least 500 on the mathematics section and 500 on the critical reading section) or the ACT (and achieved a score of at least 21 on the mathematics portion and 20 on the English portion). They must also meet physical regulations that include qualification for diving duty and/or combat swimmer. Preference is given to applicants who plan to major in a technical field (e.g., chemistry, computer science, engineering, mathematics, oceanography, operations analysis, physical sciences, or physics).

Financial data Awardees continue to receive their regular Navy pay and allowances while they attend college on a full-time basis. They also receive reimbursement for tuition, fees, and books up to $10,000 per year. If base housing is available, they are eligible to live there. Participants are not eligible to receive benefits under the Navy's Tuition Assistance Program (TA), the Montgomery GI Bill (MGIB), the Navy College Fund, or the Veterans Educational Assistance Program (VEAP).

Duration Selectees are supported for up to 36 months of full-time, year-round study or completion of a bachelor's degree, as long as they maintain a GPA of 2.5 or higher.

Additional information This program began in 2001 as a replacement for the Seaman to Admiral Program (established in 1994), the Enlisted Commissioning Program, and other specialized programs for sailors to earn a commission. Upon acceptance into the program, selectees attend the Naval Science Institute (NSI) in Newport, Rhode Island for an 8-week program in the fundamental core concepts of being a naval officer (navigation, engineering, weapons, military history and justice, etc.). They then enter a college or university with an NROTC unit or affiliation to work full time on a bachelor's degree. They become members of and drill with the NROTC unit. When they complete their degree, they are commissioned as ensigns in the United States Naval Reserve and assigned to initial training as an EOD officer. After commissioning, 5 years of active service are required.

Number awarded Varies each year.

Deadline June of each year.

[68]
FAIRFAX-LEE AUSA SCHOLARSHIPS

Association of the United States Army-Fairfax-Lee
  Chapter
Attn: Scholarship Committee Chair
7542 Laurel Creek Lane
Springfield, VA 22150
E-mail: scholars@ausafairfaxlee.org
Web: www.ausafairfaxlee.org

Summary To provide financial assistance to residents of the National Capital Region who have an affiliation with the Fairfax-Lee Chapter of the Association of the United States Army (AUSA) and are interested in attending college in any state.

Eligibility This program is open to graduating high school seniors and current full- and part-time undergraduates who fall into 1 of the following categories: 1) National Capital Region active-duty, Army Reserve, and Army National Guard soldiers and their family members; 2) Warrior Transition Battalion soldiers and family members; 3) students enrolled in a senior ROTC or JROTC program; 4) National Capital Region Department of the Army civilian employees; 5) current Fairfax-Lee Chapter members and their families; or 6) students who fall into any of those categories and are majoring in a field of science, technology, engineering, or mathematics (STEM). Applicants must submit a 500-word essay on why they believe they are deserving of this scholarship, including any special family considerations.

Financial data Stipends range from $750 to $1,500.

Duration 1 year.

Additional information This program receives support from GEICO, Lockheed Martin, Peduzzi Associates, and other corporate sponsors. The National Capital Region is defined to include Washington, D.C.; the Maryland counties of Charles, Frederick, Montgomery, and Prince George's; the Virginia counties of Arlington, Fairfax, Loudoun, and Prince William; and the Virginia cities of Alexandria, Fairfax, Falls Church, Manassas, and Manassas Park.

Number awarded Varies each year; recently, 24 of these scholarships, with a total value of $20,000, were awarded.

Deadline April of each year.

[69]
FALCON FOUNDATION SCHOLARSHIPS

Falcon Foundation
3116 Academy Drive, Suite 200
USAF Academy, CO 80840-4400
(719) 333-4096   Fax: (719) 333-3669
Web: www.usafa.org/FalconFoundation/Scholarships

Summary To provide financial assistance to people who require additional training for possible admission to the U.S. Air Force Academy.

Eligibility This program is open to individuals who have applied for admission to the Air Force Academy and are considered qualified but not competitive. Applicants must be U.S. citizens, high school seniors or graduates, of good moral character, between 17 and 21 years of age on July 1 of the year of potential admission to the Academy, in good physical condition, unmarried, and with no dependent children. They must be interested in attending a selected junior college or preparatory school to enable them to meet Air Force Academy requirements. Selection is based on motivation to enter and graduate from the USAF Academy and then follow a career as an Air Force officer; scholastic achievements; qualities of maturity, truthfulness, courage, kindliness, unselfishness, fellowship, and devotion to duty; exhibition of moral force of character and leadership instincts, with an interest in others; and physical vigor, as shown by a fondness for, and participation and success in, sports.

Financial data Amounts of the scholarships depend on the availability of funds but are intended to provide a large portion of the cost of room, board, and tuition at a preparatory school or junior college selected by the foundation.

Duration 1 year.

Additional information Recently, scholarships were awarded for study at 7 junior colleges and preparatory schools: Greystone at Schreiner University (Kerrville, Texas), Kent School (Kent, Connecticut), Marion Military Institute (Marion, Alabama), New Mexico Military Institute (Roswell, New Mexico), Northwestern Preparatory School (Santa Barbara, California), Randolph-Macon Academy (Front Royal, Virginia), and Wentworth Military Academy (Lexington, Missouri).

Number awarded Up to 100 each year.

Deadline A precandidate questionnaire must be submitted by January of each year.

[70]
FIRST CAVALRY DIVISION ASSOCIATION SCHOLARSHIPS

First Cavalry Division Association
Attn: Foundation
302 North Main Street
Copperas Cove, TX 76522-1703
(254) 547-6537   Fax: (254) 547-8853
E-mail: firstcav@1cda.org
Web: www.1cda.org/Foundation_Overview.htm

Summary To provide financial assistance for undergraduate education to soldiers currently or formerly assigned to the First Cavalry Division and their families.

Eligibility This program is open to children of soldiers who died or have been declared totally and permanently disabled from injuries incurred while serving with the First Cavalry Division during any armed conflict; children of soldiers who died while serving in the First Cavalry Division during peacetime; and active-duty soldiers currently assigned or attached to the First Cavalry Division and their spouses and children.

Financial data   The stipend is $1,200 per year. The checks are made out jointly to the student and the school and may be used for whatever the student needs, including tuition, books, and clothing.

Duration   1 year; may be renewed up to 3 additional years.

Additional information   Requests for applications must be accompanied by a self-addressed stamped envelope.

Number awarded   Varies each year; since the program was established, it has awarded more than $760,000 to 481 children of disabled and deceased Cavalry members and more than $255,000 to 275 current members of the Division and their families.

Deadline   June of each year.

[71]
FLEET RESERVE ASSOCIATION MEMBER SCHOLARSHIPS

Fleet Reserve Association
Attn: FRA Education Foundation
125 North West Street
Alexandria, VA 22314-2754
(703) 683-1400   Toll Free: (800) FRA-1924
Fax: (703) 549-6610   E-mail: scholars@fra.org
Web: www.fra.org

Summary   To provide financial assistance for college or graduate school to members of the Fleet Reserve Association (FRA) and their families.

Eligibility   This program is open to members of the FRA and the dependent children, grandchildren, and spouses of living or deceased members. Applicants must be enrolled as full-time undergraduate or graduate students. Along with their application, they must submit an essay on why they want to go to college and what they intend to accomplish with their degree. Selection is based on academic record, financial need, extracurricular activities, leadership skills, and participation in community activities. U.S. citizenship is required.

Financial data   The stipend is $5,000 per year.

Duration   1 year; may be renewed.

Additional information   Membership in the FRA is restricted to active-duty, retired, and reserve members of the Navy, Marines, and Coast Guard. This program includes awards designated as the Robert M. Treadwell Annual Scholarship and the Donald Bruce Pringle Family Scholarship.

Number awarded   6 each year.

Deadline   April of each year.

[72]
FLEET RESERVE ASSOCIATION NON-MEMBER SCHOLARSHIPS

Fleet Reserve Association
Attn: FRA Education Foundation
125 North West Street
Alexandria, VA 22314-2754
(703) 683-1400   Toll Free: (800) FRA-1924
Fax: (703) 549-6610   E-mail: scholars@fra.org
Web: www.fra.org

Summary   To provide financial assistance for college or graduate school to sea service personnel and their families.

Eligibility   This program is open to 1) active-duty, Reserve, honorably-discharged veterans, and retired members of the U.S. Navy, Marine Corps, and Coast Guard; and 2) their spouses, children, and grandchildren. Applicants must be enrolled as full-time undergraduate or graduate students, but neither they nor their family member are required to be members of the sponsoring organization. Along with their application, they must submit an essay on why they want to go to college and what they intend to accomplish with their degree. Selection is based on academic record, financial need, extracurricular activities, leadership skills, and participation in community activities. U.S. citizenship is required.

Financial data   Stipends range up to $5,000 per year.

Duration   1 year; may be renewed.

Number awarded   1 or more each year.

Deadline   April of each year.

[73]
FLORIDA NATIONAL GUARD EDUCATIONAL DOLLARS FOR DUTY (EDD) PROGRAM

Department of Military Affairs
Attn: DCSPER-EDD
82 Marine Street
P.O. Box 1008
St. Augustine, FL 32085-1008
(904) 823-0417   Toll Free: (800) 342-6528
Web: dma.myflorida.com

Summary   To provide financial assistance for college or graduate school to members of the Florida National Guard.

Eligibility   This program is open to current members of the Florida National Guard. Applicants must be attending or planning to attend a college or university in Florida to work on an undergraduate or master's degree. College preparatory and vocational/technical programs also qualify. Guard members who already have a master's degree are not eligible.

Financial data   The program provides for payment of 100% of tuition and fees at a public college or university or an equivalent amount at a private institution.

Duration   1 year; may be renewed.

Number awarded   Varies each year; recently, approximately 765 Florida National Guard members utilized this program.

Deadline   Applications may be submitted at any time, but they must be received at least 90 days prior to the start of the class.

[74]
FLORIDA NAVY NURSE CORPS ASSOCIATION SCHOLARSHIPS

Florida Navy Nurse Corps Association
c/o Margaret Holder, Scholarship Committee
1033 Inverness Drive
St. Augustine, FL 32092
E-mail: maholder@me.com

Summary   To provide financial assistance to undergraduate and graduate nursing students, especially residents of Florida with ties to the military.

Eligibility   This program is open to students, including registered nursing continuing their studies, who are working on an undergraduate or graduate degree in nursing. Applicants must have completed at least 1 clinical nursing course and have a GPA of 3.0 or higher. They may be full- or part-time students. Preference is given to current active-duty and Reserve service members, veterans of military service, family members of current or former military service personnel, civil service employees, and residents of Florida. Financial need is considered in the selection process.

Financial data The stipend is $1,000. Funds are paid directly to the student.

Duration 1 year.

Additional information This program includes the Captain Miki Iwata Memorial Scholarship.

Number awarded Approximately 3 each year.

Deadline October of each year.

[75]
FORCE RECON ASSOCIATION SCHOLARSHIPS

Force Recon Association
c/o Al Sniadecki, Scholarship Committee Chair
P.O. Box 111000
Carrollton, TX 75011
E-mail: commchief@forcerecon.com
Web: www.forcerecon.com/join.htm

Summary To provide financial assistance for college to members of the Force Recon Association and their dependents.

Eligibility This program is open to members of the Force Recon Association and family members of a relative who served both in the U.S. Marine Corps and was or is assigned to a Force Reconnaissance Company. The relative must be either an active or deceased member of the Force Recon Association. Family members include wives and widows, sons and daughters (including adopted and stepchildren), grandchildren, and great-grandchildren. Applicants may be pursuing scholastic, vocational, or technical education. Along with their application, they must submit a personal statement on why they desire this scholarship, their proposed course of study, their progress in their current course of study, and their long-range career goals. Selection is based on academic achievement, letters of recommendation, demonstrated character, and the written statements.

Financial data A stipend is awarded (amount not specified).

Duration 1 year; may be renewed.

Number awarded 1 or more each year.

Deadline July of each year.

[76]
FRED AND SUSAN AUGSBURG SCHOLARSHIP

American Society of Military Comptrollers-Aviation
   Chapter
c/o Neal Wamsley, Scholarship Committee Co-Chair
4375 Chidlaw Road
Building 262, Room N225, Post 212B
Wright-Patterson AFB, OH 45433-0215
(937) 656-1274   E-mail: harold.wamsley.1@us.af.mil
Web: chapters.asmconline.org

Summary To provide financial assistance to members of the Aviation Chapter of the American Society of Military Comptrollers (ASMC) who are studying a field related to military comptrollership in college.

Eligibility This program is open to members of the ASMC Aviation Chapter who are enrolled at schools of higher education in southwestern Ohio while employed full time. Applicants must be majoring in a field related to military comptrollership, including (but not limited to) business administration, accounting, auditing, business law, banking, mathematics, budget, finance, economics, systems management, operations research, or public administration. Selection is based on individual merit.

Financial data The stipend is $1,000.

Duration 1 year.

Additional information The ASMC is open to all financial management professionals employed by the U.S. Department of Defense and Coast Guard, both civilian and military.

Number awarded 1 each year.

Deadline March of each year.

[77]
GEORGIA'S HERO SCHOLARSHIP PROGRAM

Georgia Student Finance Commission
Attn: Scholarships and Grants Division
2082 East Exchange Place, Suite 200
Tucker, GA 30084-5305
(770) 724-9000   Toll Free: (800) 505-GSFC
Fax: (770) 724-9089   E-mail: gacollege411@gsfc.org
Web: secure.gacollege411.org

Summary To provide financial assistance for college to members of the National Guard or Reserves in Georgia and their children and spouses.

Eligibility This program is open to Georgia residents who are active members of the Georgia National Guard or U.S. Military Reserves, were deployed outside the United States for active-duty service on or after February 1, 2003 to a location designated as a combat zone, and served in that combat zone for at least 181 consecutive days. Also eligible are 1) the children, younger than 25 years of age, of Guard and Reserve members who completed at least 1 term of service (of 181 days each) overseas on or after February 1, 2003; 2) the children, younger than 25 years of age, of Guard and Reserve members who were killed or totally disabled during service overseas on or after February 1, 2003, regardless of their length of service; and 3) the spouses of Guard and Reserve members who were killed in a combat zone, died as a result of injuries, or became 100% disabled as a result of injuries received in a combat zone during service overseas on or after February 1, 2003, regardless of their length of service. Applicants must be interested in attending a unit of the University System of Georgia, a unit of the Georgia Department of Technical and Adult Education, or an eligible private college or university in Georgia.

Financial data The stipend for full-time study is $2,000 per academic year, not to exceed $8,000 during an entire program of study. The stipend for part-time study is prorated appropriately.

Duration 1 year; may be renewed (if satisfactory progress is maintained) for up to 3 additional years.

Additional information This program, which stands for Helping Educate Reservists and their Offspring, was established in 2005.

Number awarded Varies each year.

Deadline June of each year.

[78]
GLADYS MCPARTLAND SCHOLARSHIPS

United States Marine Corps Combat Correspondents
Association
Attn: Executive Director
110 Fox Court
Wildwood, FL 34785
(352) 748-4698   E-mail: usmccca@cfl.rr.com
Web: www.usmccca.org/archives/4941

Summary To provide financial assistance to members of the U.S. Marine Corps Combat Correspondents Association (USMCCCA) or their dependents and to Marines in designated occupational fields who are interested in studying any field in college.

Eligibility This program is open to 1) members of USMCCCA, their dependents, and their spouses; and 2) active-duty Marines in Occupational Fields 4300 and 4600 and their dependents who are USMCCCA members or will agree to become members if awarded a scholarship. Applicants must be enrolled or planning to enroll in an undergraduate program in any field. Along with their application, they must submit 500-word essays on 1) their noteworthy achievements and long-range goals; and 2) the United States I want to see in 15 years and my role in the transformation. Financial need is not considered in the selection process.

Financial data Stipends range up to $3,000; funds are disbursed directly to the recipient's institution to be used exclusively for tuition, books, and/or fees.

Duration 1 year.

Number awarded 1 or more each year.

Deadline May of each year.

[79]
GREEN TO GOLD NON-SCHOLARSHIP PROGRAM

U.S. Army
Attn: U.S. Army Cadet Command
G2 Incentives Division
1307 Third Avenue
Fort Knox, KY 40121-2725
(502) 624-7371   Toll Free: (888) 550-ARMY
Fax: (502) 624-6937
E-mail: usarmy.knox.usacc.mbx.train2lead@mail.mil
Web: www.goarmy.com

Summary To provide financial assistance to soldiers who wish to obtain an early discharge from the Army and return to college to participate in the Army Reserve Officers' Training Corps (ROTC).

Eligibility This program is open to enlisted soldiers who have served at least 2 years on active duty and have also completed at least 2 years of college with a GPA of 2.0 or higher. Applicants must be under 30 years of age when they graduate (waivers up to 32 years of age are available). They apply for this program to obtain an early discharge from active duty in order to enroll in a baccalaureate degree program.

Financial data Cadets receive a stipend for 10 months of the year that is $450 per month during their junior year and $500 per month during their senior year, as well as pay for attending the 6-week Leader Development and Assessment Course (LDAC) during the summer between the junior and senior year of college.

Duration 2 years.

Additional information Cadets who had previously qualified for benefits from the Army College Fund and/or the Montgomery GI Bill are still entitled to receive those in addition to any benefits from this program. Cadets are also entitled to participate in the Simultaneous Membership Program and serve with pay in a drilling unit of the Army Reserve or Army National Guard. Upon graduation from college, cadets are commissioned as second lieutenants and are required to serve in the military for 8 years. That obligation may be fulfilled by serving 3 years on active duty and 5 years in the Inactive Ready Reserve (IRR).

Number awarded Varies each year.

Deadline March or September of each year.

[80]
GREEN TO GOLD SCHOLARSHIP PROGRAM

U.S. Army
Attn: U.S. Army Cadet Command
G2 Incentives Division
1307 Third Avenue
Fort Knox, KY 40121-2725
(502) 624-7371   Toll Free: (888) 550-ARMY
Fax: (502) 624-6937
E-mail: usarmy.knox.usacc.mbx.train2lead@mail.mil
Web: www.goarmy.com

Summary To provide scholarships and other payments to soldiers who wish to obtain an early discharge from the Army and return to college to participate in the Army Reserve Officers' Training Corps (ROTC).

Eligibility This program is open to enlisted soldiers who have served at least 2 years on active duty plus 3 months of active duty for each month of specialized training. Applicants must have a cumulative high school or college GPA of 2.5 or higher, a General Technical (GT) score of 110 or higher, and a recent (within the past 6 months) Army Physical Fitness Test (APFT) score of 180 or higher (including 60 points in each event). They may have no more than 3 dependents including a spouse (that requirement may be waived) and must be under 31 years of age when they graduate and are commissioned. They must have been accepted at a college or university offering Army ROTC. U.S. citizenship is required.

Financial data Scholarship winners receive up to $20,000 per year as support for tuition and fees or for room and board, whichever the recipient selects; additional support up to $1,200 per year for textbooks, supplies, and equipment; a stipend for 10 months of the year that is $350 per month during their sophomore year, $450 per month during their junior year, and $500 per month during their senior year; and pay for attending the 6-week Leader Development and Assessment Course (LDAC) during the summer between the junior and senior year of college.

Duration Scholarships are for 2, 3, or 4 years; soldiers without prior college credit or whose colleges accept them as academic freshmen are eligible for 4-year scholarships; soldiers with 1 year of college completed are eligible for 3-year scholarships; soldiers with 2 years of college completed are eligible for 2-year scholarships.

Additional information Recipients who had previously qualified for benefits from the Army College Fund and/or the Montgomery GI Bill are still entitled to receive those in addition to any benefits from this program. Upon graduation from college, scholarship winners are commissioned as second lieutenants and are required to serve in the military for 8 years. That obligation may be fulfilled by serving 4 years on active duty followed by 4 years in the Inactive Ready Reserve (IRR).

Number awarded Varies each year.

Deadline March or September of each year.

[81]
GUARANTEED RESERVE FORCES DUTY (GRFD) SCHOLARSHIPS

U.S. Army National Guard
Education Support Center
Camp J.T. Robinson
Box 46
North Little Rock, AR 72199-9600
Toll Free: (866) 628-5999   E-mail: esc@ng.army.mil
Web: www.nationalguard.com/tools/guard-scholarships

Summary To provide financial assistance to upper-division students who are willing to 1) enroll simultaneously in Army ROTC and either the Army National Guard or Army Reserve and then 2) serve in a Reserve component of the Army following graduation.

Eligibility This program is open to full-time students entering their junior year of college who have a GPA of 2.5 or higher and scores of 920 on the SAT or 19 on the ACT. Applicants must meet all other medical and moral character requirements for enrollment in Army ROTC and be able to complete the basic course requirements or basic training. They must be willing to enroll in the Simultaneous Membership Program (SMP) of an ROTC unit on their campus; the SMP requires simultaneous membership in Army ROTC and either the Army National Guard or Army Reserve.

Financial data Participants receive full reimbursement of tuition, a grant of $1,200 per year for books, plus an ROTC stipend for 10 months of the year at $450 per month during their junior year and $500 per month during their senior year. As a member of the Army National Guard or Army Reserve, they also receive weekend drill pay at the pay grade of a sergeant (approximately $225 per month) while participating in the SMP.

Duration 2 years.

Additional information After graduation, participants serve 3 to 6 months on active duty in the Officer Basic Course (OBC). Following completion of OBC, they are released from active duty and are obligated to serve 8 years in the Army National Guard or Army Reserve.

Number awarded Approximately 400 each year.

Deadline Deadline not specified.

[82]
HARDY WOLF & DOWNING SCHOLARSHIP AWARDS

Hardy Wolf & Downing
Attn: Scholarship Awards
477 Congress Street, 15th Floor
Portland, ME 04101
Toll Free: (800) 992-7333   E-mail: stepler@hwdlaw.com
Web: www.hardywolf.com/scholarships

Summary To provide financial assistance for college or law school to students who have a connection to the U.S. military or to law enforcement.

Eligibility This program is open to 1) high school seniors who plan to attend an accredited U.S. college; 2) college students attending an accredited U.S. college; and 3) law students currently entering or enrolled at an ABA-accredited law school. Applicants must be active, retired, or immediate family members of any branch of the U.S. military or any branch of law enforcement. They must have a GPA of 3.0 or higher. Along with their application, they must submit essays of 1,500 to 2,000 words on the following topics: for members and family members of the military, the greatest challenges facing veterans when they return home from serving their country; for members and family members of law enforcement, the greatest challenges facing law enforcement personnel today; for all law students, the area of law they intend to practice and why.

Financial data Stipends range from $100 to $2,500.

Duration 1 year.

Number awarded 13 each year: 1 at $2,500, 1 at $1,000, 1 at $500, and 10 at $100.

Deadline December of each year.

[83]
HELEN DYAR KING SCHOLARSHIP

Arizona Community Foundation
Attn: Director of Scholarships
2201 East Camelback Road, Suite 405B
Phoenix, AZ 85016
(602) 381-1400   Toll Free: (800) 222-8221
Fax: (602) 381-1575   E-mail: jmedina@azfoundation.org
Web: azfoundation.academicworks.com/opportunities/628

Summary To provide financial assistance to high school seniors and current college students, especially residents of Arizona, who are members or dependents of members of the armed services or a law enforcement agency and are interested in attending college in any state.

Eligibility This program is open to graduating high school seniors and current full-time students at colleges or universities in any state. Applicants must be an active-duty or retired member or dependent of such a member of the armed services (Air Force, Army, Coast Guard, Marine Corps, National Guard, Navy) or law enforcement agency. They must be U.S. citizens and have a GPA of 2.75 or higher. Preference is given to women and to residents of Arizona. Financial need is considered in the selection process.

Financial data The stipend is $2,000 for students at 2-year colleges or $4,000 for students at 4-year colleges and universities.

Duration 1 year.

Number awarded Varies each year.

Deadline April of each year.

[84]
HENRY G. HUESTIS MEMORIAL SCHOLARSHIP

AMVETS National Headquarters
Attn: Programs Department
4647 Forbes Boulevard
Lanham, MD 20706-3807
(301) 459-9600   Toll Free: (877) 7-AMVETS, ext. 3043
Fax: (301) 459-7924   E-mail: amvets@amvets.org
Web: www.amvets.org/programs/scholarships

Summary To provide financial assistance for college to military personnel and veterans of the armed forces.

Eligibility This program is open to veterans and current servicemembers, including the National Guard and Reserves. Applicants must be interested in working full or part time on an undergraduate degree or certification from an accredited technical/trade school. They must have exhausted all other government aid. U.S. citizenship is required. Selection is based on financial need, academic promise, military duty and awards, volunteer activities, community services, jobs held during the past 4 years, and an essay of 50 to 100 words on "This award will help me achieve my career/vocational goal, which is..."

Financial data The stipend is $1,000.

Duration 1 year; nonrenewable.

Number awarded 1 each year.

Deadline April of each year.

[85]
HNGEA SCHOLARSHIP

Hawaii National Guard Enlisted Association
c/o 1SG Jacob Magarro, Scholarship Committee Chair
96-1230 Waihona Street
Pearl City, HI 96782
E-mail: jacob.magarro@ng.army.mil
Web: www.hngea.net/organization.htm

Summary To provide financial assistance for college to members of the Hawaii National Guard Enlisted Association (HNGEA) and their dependents.

Eligibility This program is open to HNGEA members and their dependent spouses and children. Applicants must be attending or interested in attending a college or university in Hawaii as an undergraduate student. They must have a GPA of at least 2.5 for the current semester and 2.0 overall. Along with their application, they must submit a letter describing their educational goals and need for the scholarship.

Financial data Stipends range up to $2,000.

Duration 1 year.

Number awarded Varies each year.

Deadline May of each year.

[86]
HUMAN RESOURCES OPTION OF THE SEAMAN TO ADMIRAL-21 PROGRAM

U.S. Navy
Attn: Commander, Naval Service Training Command
250 Dallas Street, Suite A
Pensacola, FL 32508-5268
(850) 452-9563   Fax: (850) 452-2486
E-mail: PNSC_STA21@navy.mil
Web: www.sta-21.navy.mil/program_options.asp

Summary To allow outstanding enlisted Navy personnel to attend a college or university, affiliate with an NROTC unit, complete a bachelor's degree, and receive a commission as a human resources officer.

Eligibility This program is open to U.S. citizens who are currently serving on active duty in the U.S. Navy or Naval Reserve, including Full Time Support (FTS), Selected Reserves (SELRES), and Navy Reservists on active duty, except for those on active duty for training (ACDUTRA). Applicants must be high school graduates (or GED recipients) who are able to complete requirements for a baccalaureate degree in 36 months or less. They must be planning to work on a degree in human resources/personnel, financial man-

agement, manpower systems analysis, operations analysis, business administration, education/training management, or a related field. When they complete their degree requirements, they must be younger than 29 years of age. Within the past 3 years, they must have taken the SAT (and achieved scores of at least 500 on the mathematics section and 500 on the critical reading section) or the ACT (and achieved a score of at least 21 on the mathematics portion and 20 on the English portion).

Financial data Awardees continue to receive their regular Navy pay and allowances while they attend college on a full-time basis. They also receive reimbursement for tuition, fees, and books up to $10,000 per year. If base housing is available, they are eligible to live there. Participants are not eligible to receive benefits under the Navy's Tuition Assistance Program (TA), the Montgomery GI Bill (MGIB), the Navy College Fund, or the Veterans Educational Assistance Program (VEAP).

Duration Selectees are supported for up to 36 months of full-time, year-round study or completion of a bachelor's degree, as long as they maintain a GPA of 2.5 or higher.

Additional information Upon acceptance into the program, selectees attend the Naval Science Institute (NSI) in Newport, Rhode Island for an 8-week program in the fundamental core concepts of being a naval officer (navigation, engineering, weapons, military history and justice, etc.). They then enter a college or university with an NROTC unit or affiliation to work full time on a bachelor's degree. They become members of and drill with the NROTC unit. When they complete their degree, they are commissioned as ensigns in the United States Naval Reserve and assigned to initial training as a human resources officer. After commissioning, 5 years of active service are required.

Number awarded Varies each year.

Deadline June of each year.

[87]
IDAHO ENLISTED ASSOCIATION YOUNG PATRIOT SCHOLARSHIP

Idaho Enlisted Association of the National Guard of the
   United States
c/o Steve Vinsonhaler, President
7054 West Saxton Drive
Boise, ID 83714-2366
(208) 407-4887   E-mail: svinsonhaler@imd.idaho.gov
Web: www.eangusidaho.org/Scholarships.php

Summary To provide financial assistance to members of the Idaho Enlisted Association of the National Guard of the United States and their family who are interested in attending college in any state.

Eligibility This program is open to 1) members of the association; 2) dependent unmarried children of members; 3) spouses of members; and 4) unmarried spouses and unmarried dependent children of deceased members who were in good standing at the time of death. Association members must also be enlisted members of the Idaho National Guard with at least 1 year remaining on their enlistment or have 20 or more years of military service. Applicants must be enrolled or planning to enroll full time at a college, university, trade school, or business school in any state. Along with their application, they must submit a 2-page essay about an activity or interest that has been meaningful to them, a personal letter providing information about themselves and their families, 2 letters of recommendation, an academic letter of recommendation, and a copy of the sponsor's current membership card or number. Family income is considered in the selection process.

Financial data The stipend is $1,500.

Duration 1 year; nonrenewable.

Number awarded 2 each year.

Deadline August of each year.

[88]
ILLINOIS NATIONAL GUARD GRANT PROGRAM

Illinois Student Assistance Commission
Attn: Scholarship and Grant Services
1755 Lake Cook Road
Deerfield, IL 60015-5209
(847) 948-8550   Toll Free: (800) 899-ISAC
Fax: (847) 831-8549   TDD: (800) 526-0844
E-mail: isac.studentservices@isac.illinois.gov
Web: www.isac.org

Summary To provide financial assistance to current or former members of the Illinois National Guard who are interested in attending college or graduate school in the state.

Eligibility This program is open to members of the Illinois National Guard who 1) are currently active and have completed at least 1 full year of service; or 2) have been active for at least 5 consecutive years, have had their studies interrupted by being called to federal active duty for at least 6 months, and are within 12 months after their discharge date. Applicants must also be enrolled at an Illinois public 2- or 4-year college or university.

Financial data Recipients are eligible for payment of tuition and some fees for either undergraduate or graduate study at an Illinois state-supported college or university.

Duration This assistance extends for 4 academic years of full-time study (or the equivalent in part-time study) for Guard members with less than 10 years of active duty service. For Guard members with 10 years or more of active duty service, assistance is available for up to the equivalent of 6 academic years of full-time study.

Number awarded Varies each year.

Deadline September of each year for the academic year; February of each year for spring semester, winter quarter, or spring quarter; June of each year for summer term.

[89]
IMAGINE AMERICA MILITARY AWARD PROGRAM

Association of Private Sector Colleges and Universities
Attn: Imagine America Foundation
12001 Sunrise Valley Drive, Suite 203
Reston, VA 20191
(571) 267-3010   Fax: (866) 734-5812
E-mail: scholarships@imagine-america.org
Web: www.imagine-america.org/grantsformilitary

Summary To provide financial assistance to military personnel and veterans who are interested in attending a participating career college.

Eligibility This program is open to active-duty, reservist, honorably-discharged, and retired veterans of a U.S. military service branch. Applicants must be interested in attending 1 of more than 300 participating career colleges. All applications are submitted online to the college where the student

wishes to enroll. Selection is based on the likelihood of successfully completing postsecondary education and financial need.

Financial data The stipend is $1,000. Funds must be used for payment of tuition at a participating career college.

Duration 1 year.

Additional information The Imagine America Foundation (originally known as the Career College Foundation) established this program in 2004. Its membership includes 1,450 career colleges.

Number awarded Varies each year.

Deadline June of each year.

[90]
INDIANA NATIONAL GUARD SUPPLEMENTAL GRANT PROGRAM

Indiana Commission for Higher Education
Attn: Division of Student Financial Aid
W462 Indiana Government Center South
402 West Washington Street
Indianapolis, IN 46204
(317) 232-2355   Toll Free: (888) 528-4719 (within IN)
Fax: (317) 232-3260   E-mail: awards@sfa.che.in.gov
Web: www.in.gov/sfa/2339.htm

Summary To provide financial assistance to members of the Indiana National Guard who are interested in attending designated colleges in the state.

Eligibility This program is open to members of the Indiana Air and Army National Guard who are in active drilling status and have not been AWOL at any time during the preceding 12 months. Applicants must be high school graduates seeking their first associate or bachelor's degree. Allowances may be made for students who earned a GED certificate or were home schooled, but only on a case-by-case basis following a written appeal. As part of the application process, students must file the Free Application for Federal Student Aid (FAFSA). If they qualify as dependent students based on FAFSA data, their parents must be residents of Indiana; if the FAFSA standards define them as independent students, they must be Indiana residents.

Financial data The award provides payment of 100% of the tuition costs at state-funded colleges and universities in Indiana. No funding is provided for books, room, or board.

Duration 1 year; may be renewed.

Additional information This assistance may be used only at the following state funded colleges and universities: Ball State University, Indiana State University, Indiana University (all campuses), Indiana University/Purdue University-Indianapolis, Indiana University/Purdue University-Fort Wayne, Indiana University/Purdue University-Columbus, Ivy Tech Community College (all campuses), Purdue University (all campuses), University of Southern Indiana, Vincennes University, and Western Governors University-Indiana.

Number awarded Varies each year.

Deadline March of each year.

[91]
IOWA NATIONAL GUARD EDUCATION ASSISTANCE PROGRAM

Iowa National Guard
Joint Forces Headquarters Iowa
Attn: Education Services Officer
7105 N.W. 70th Avenue
Johnston, IA 50131-1824
(515) 252-4468   Toll Free: (800) 294-6607, ext. 4468
Fax: (515) 252-4025   E-mail: linda.s.perdue.mil@mail.mil
Web: www.iowanationalguard.com

Summary To provide financial assistance to members of the Iowa National Guard who wish to attend college.

Eligibility This program is open to residents of Iowa who are members of an Iowa Army or Air National Guard unit. Applicants must have satisfactorily completed Initial Entry Training (Basic Training and Advanced Individual Training), have maintained satisfactory performance of duty (including attending a minimum 90% of scheduled drill dates and scheduled annual training in the preceding 12 months), have maintained satisfactory academic progress as determined by their academic institution, and have not completed their baccalaureate degree. They may be seeking to attend a state-supported university, community college, or participating private accredited institution of postsecondary education located in Iowa.

Financial data Recently, available funding permitted payment of 100% of the tuition rate at Iowa Regents institutions, or a maximum of $3,329 per semester for full-time enrollment. Funds may be used for any educational expense, including tuition, room, board, supplies, books, fees, and other associated costs.

Duration 1 year; may be renewed.

Additional information This program began in 1999.

Number awarded Varies each year, depending on the availability of funds. Assistance is provided on a first-come, first-served basis.

Deadline June of each year for fall term or November of each year for spring term.

[92]
JACK E. BARGER, SR. MEMORIAL NURSING SCHOLARSHIPS

Nursing Foundation of Pennsylvania
3605 Vartan Way, Suite 204
Harrisburg, PA 17110
(717) 827-4369   Toll Free: (888) 707-7762
Fax: (717) 657-3796   E-mail: info@theNFP.org
Web: www.thenfp.webs.com/vfw-scholarship

Summary To provide financial assistance to military personnel, veterans, and their dependents who are studying nursing in Pennsylvania.

Eligibility This program is open to veterans, active-duty military personnel, and the children and spouses of veterans and active-duty military personnel. Applicants must be residents of Pennsylvania and currently enrolled in an undergraduate professional school of nursing in the state. Recipients are selected by lottery from among the qualified applicants.

Financial data The stipend is $1,000.

Duration 1 year.

Additional information This program is sponsored by the Department of Pennsylvania Veterans of Foreign Wars

(VFW). Recipients must attend the VFW Convention to accept the scholarship; travel, meals, and overnight expenses are paid by the VFW.

Number awarded 6 each year.

Deadline April of each year.

[93]
JAMES MONTAG, JR. SCHOLARSHIP

Tennessee Academy of Physician Assistants
Attn: Tennessee Physician Assistant Foundation
P.O. Box 150785
Nashville, TN 37215-0785
(615) 463-0026   Fax: (615) 463-0036
E-mail: info@tnpa.com
Web: www.tnpa.com/content/scholarship-applications

Summary To provide financial assistance to physician assistant students from Tennessee who are serving or have served in the military.

Eligibility This program is open to students in the first or second year of a physician assistant program who are either 1) enrolled at an approved program in Tennessee; or 2) residents of Tennessee enrolled at an approved school in another state. Applicants must be serving on active or Reserve duty in any branch of the military or the National Guard or have an honorable discharge; Air Force medics are particularly encouraged to apply. Along with their application, they must submit an essay of 2 to 3 pages on their professional career and lifetime goals. Financial need is not considered in the selection process.

Financial data The stipend is $1,000.

Duration 1 year.

Number awarded 1 each year.

Deadline August of each year.

[94]
JEWISH WAR VETERANS NATIONAL ACHIEVEMENT PROGRAM

Jewish War Veterans of the U.S.A.
Attn: National Achievement Program
1811 R Street, N.W.
Washington, DC 20009-1659
(202) 265-6280   Fax: (202) 234-5662
E-mail: jwv@jwv.org
Web: www.jwv.org

Summary To recognize and reward current servicemembers and veterans who are enrolled in college and submit outstanding essays on their military experience.

Eligibility This competition is open to veterans and current servicemembers who are enrolled or planning to enroll in an accredited associate, bachelor's, or nursing degree program. Applicants must submit an essay of 500 to 750 words on how their military experience will help them pursue their academic goals. Selection is based on answering the essay question (50%), logic and coherence of the essay's organization (25%), and description of relevant military experience (25%).

Financial data The awards are the Charles Kosmutza Memorial Grant of $2,500, the Max R. and Irene Rubenstein Memorial Grant of $1,500, and the Leon Brooks Memorial Grant of $1,000.

Duration The awards are presented annually.

Number awarded 3 each year.

Deadline May of each year.

[95]
JOE KING SCHOLARSHIPS

Council of College and Military Educators
c/o Kenneth D. McRae, Scholarship Committee Chair
Mississippi State University
G.V. "Sonny" Montgomery Center for America's Veterans
126 Magruder Street
P. O. Drawer 6283
Mississippi State, MS 39762
(662) 325-6719   Fax: (662) 325-6723
E-mail: scholarship@ccmeonline.aspx
Web: www.ccmeonline.org/scholarships

Summary To provide financial assistance to members of the armed services who are interested in working on an undergraduate or master's degree.

Eligibility This program is open to members of the uniformed services currently on active duty. Applicants must be currently enrolled full time at an accredited institution that is a member of the Council of College and Military Educators (CCME) and working on an associate, bachelor's, or master's degree. Undergraduates must have a GPA of 2.5 or higher and graduate students must have a GPA of 3.0 or higher. Along with their application, they must submit an essay of 400 to 750 words on how they would describe military leadership. Financial need is not considered in the selection process.

Financial data The stipend is $1,000. Funds are paid directly to the student.

Duration 1 year; nonrenewable.

Number awarded 5 each year.

Deadline September of each year.

[96]
JOHN CORNELIUS/MAX ENGLISH MEMORIAL SCHOLARSHIP AWARD

Marine Corps Tankers Association
c/o Stephen Chambers, Scholarship Chair
1922 Freeman Street
Oceanside, CA 92054
Web: www.usmarinetankers.org/scholarship-program

Summary To provide financial assistance for college or graduate school to children and grandchildren of members of the Marine Corps Tankers Association and to Marine and Navy personnel currently serving in tank units.

Eligibility This program is open to high school seniors and graduates who are children, grandchildren, or under the guardianship of an active, Reserve, retired, or honorably discharged Marine who served in a tank unit. Marine or Navy Corpsmen currently assigned to tank units are also eligible. Applicants must be enrolled or planning to enroll full time at a college or graduate school. Their parent or grandparent must be a member of the Marine Corps Tankers Association or, if not a member, must join if the application is accepted. Along with their application, they must submit an essay on their educational goals, future aspirations, and concern for the future of our society and for the peoples of the world. Selection is based on that essay, academic record, school activities, leadership potential, and community service.

Financial data The stipend is at least $2,000 per year.

Duration 1 year; recipients may reapply.

Number awarded Varies each year; recently, 15 were awarded.

Deadline March of each year.

[97]
JOHN J. GUENTHER MERIT SCHOLARSHIP

Marine Corps Intelligence Association, Inc.
Attn: Marine Corps Intelligence Educational Foundation
P.O. Box 1028
Quantico, VA 22134-1028
E-mail: scholarship@mcia-inc.org
Web: www.mcia-inc.org/MCIEFINC.html

Summary To provide financial assistance for college to members of the Marine Corps Intelligence Association (MCIA) and their dependent children.

Eligibility This program is open to current MCIA members, their dependent children, and their survivors. Applicants must be attending or planning to attend an accredited 4-year college or university as a full-time student. They must submit a 300-word essay on a risk that has led to a significant change in their personal or intellectual life, the most challenging obstacles they have had to overcome and what they learned from the experience, and where they envision themselves in 10 years. Selection is based on the essay, academic achievement, extracurricular activities, and work experience. Financial need is not considered.

Financial data The stipend is at least $1,000.

Duration 1 year.

Additional information Membership in the MCIA is open to Marine Corps intelligence personnel, including active duty, Reserve, and retired.

Number awarded At least 1 each year.

Deadline July of each year.

[98]
JOSEPH A. MCALINDEN DIVERS SCHOLARSHIP

Navy-Marine Corps Relief Society
Attn: Education Division
875 North Randolph Street, Suite 225
Arlington, VA 22203-1757
(703) 696-4960   Fax: (703) 696-0144
E-mail: education@nmcrs.org
Web: www.nmcrs.org

Summary To provide financial assistance to current and former Navy and Marine Corps divers and their families who are interested in completing diver training or working on an undergraduate degree in a field related to ocean agriculture.

Eligibility This program is open to 1) active-duty and retired sailors and Marines (including Reservists serving on active duty for more than 90 days) completing a program for advanced diver training, certification, or licensure; 2) the children and spouses of active-duty or retired sailors and Marines (including Reservists serving on active duty for more than 90 days) completing a program for advanced diver training, certification, or licensure; and 3) the children and spouses of active-duty or retired sailors and Marines (including Reservists serving on active duty for more than 90 days) working full time on their first undergraduate degree in oceanography, ocean agriculture, aquaculture, or a related field. Financial need is considered in the selection process.

Financial data The stipend ranges from $500 to $3,000, depending on the need of the recipient.

Duration 1 year.
Number awarded 1 or more each year.
Deadline Applications may be submitted at any time.

[99]
JOSEPH P. AND HELEN T. CRIBBINS SCHOLARSHIP

Association of the United States Army
Attn: Executive Assistant
2425 Wilson Boulevard
Arlington, VA 22201
(703) 841-4300, ext. 2652
Toll Free: (800) 336-4570, ext. 2652
E-mail: ausa-info@ausa.org
Web: www.ausa.org

Summary To provide financial assistance to active-duty and honorably-discharged enlisted soldiers interested in studying engineering in college.

Eligibility This program is open to 1) enlisted soldiers currently serving in the active Army, Army Reserve, or Army National Guard; and 2) honorably-discharged enlisted soldiers from any component of the total Army. Applicants must have been accepted at an accredited college or university to work on a degree in engineering or a related field (e.g., computer science, biotechnology). Along with their application, they must submit a 1-page autobiography, 2 letters of recommendation, and a transcript of high school or college grades (depending on which they are currently attending). Selection is based on academic merit and personal achievement. Financial need is not normally a selection criterion but in some cases of extreme need it may be used as a factor; the lack of financial need, however, is never a cause for non-selection.

Financial data The stipend is $2,000; funds are sent directly to the recipient's college or university.

Duration 1 year.
Number awarded 1 or more each year.
Deadline June of each year.

[100]
KANSAS MILITARY SERVICE SCHOLARSHIPS

Kansas Board of Regents
Attn: Student Financial Assistance
1000 S.W. Jackson Street, Suite 520
Topeka, KS 66612-1368
(785) 296-3518   Fax: (785) 296-0983
E-mail: loldhamburns@ksbor.org
Web: www.kansasregents.org/scholarships_and_grants

Summary To provide financial assistance for college to residents of Kansas who are currently serving or have served in the military.

Eligibility This program is open to students who graduated from high school in Kansas or received a GED credential and have been a resident of the state for at least 2 years. Applicants must have served in the U.S. armed forces in international waters or on foreign soil in support of military operations for at least 90 days after September 11, 2001 or for less than 90 days because of injuries received during such service. They must still be in military service or have received an honorable discharge with orders that indicate they served after September 11, 2001 in any operation for which they received hostile fire pay. Qualified veterans and military per-

sonnel may enroll at a public postsecondary institution in Kansas, including area vocational schools, area vocational/technical schools, community colleges, the municipal university, state educational institutions, or technical colleges. In the selection process, priority is given to applicants who can demonstrate financial need.

Financial data Qualifying students are permitted to enroll at an approved Kansas institution without payment of tuition or fees. If they receive any federal military tuition assistance, that money must be applied to their tuition and fees and they are eligible only for the remaining balance in scholarship assistance.

Duration 1 year; may be renewed for a total of 10 semesters as long as the recipient remains in good academic standing.

Additional information This program began in 2007.
Number awarded Varies each year.
Deadline April of each year.

[101]
KANSAS NATIONAL GUARD EDUCATIONAL ASSISTANCE

Kansas Board of Regents
Attn: Student Financial Assistance
1000 S.W. Jackson Street, Suite 520
Topeka, KS 66612-1368
(785) 296-3518   Fax: (785) 296-0983
E-mail: loldhamburns@ksbor.org
Web: www.kansasregents.org/scholarships_and_grants

Summary To provide financial assistance to members of the Kansas National Guard who wish to take additional college courses.

Eligibility This program is open to enlisted members of the Kansas National Guard (Air or Army) who are interested in working on a vocational, associate, or bachelor's degree. Applicants must have less than 20 years of service. They must agree to complete their current service obligation plus 3 months of additional service for each semester of assistance received. Full-time enrollment is not required.

Financial data The program reimburses up to 100% of tuition and fees at public and designated private institutions in Kansas.

Duration 1 semester; may be renewed.
Number awarded Varies each year; recently, approximately 300 were granted each semester.
Deadline April of each year for the academic year; February of each year for spring semester only.

[102]
KENTUCKIANA POST SAME SCHOLARSHIP

Society of American Military Engineers-Kentuckiana Post
c/o Kristen Crumpton, Scholarship Committee Co-Chair
URS Corporation
325 West Main Street, Suite 1200
Louisville, KY 40202
(502) 569-2301   Fax: (502) 569-2304
E-mail: kristen.crumpton@urs.com
Web: posts.same.org/kentuckiana

Summary To provide financial assistance to residents of Indiana and Kentucky who are majoring in engineering in college (especially those who are 1) currently serving in the military, 2) the family members of current service personnel, or ROTC students).

Eligibility This program is open to students who fall into 1 of the following categories: a dependent of a current Society of American Military Engineers (SAME) Kentuckiana Post member; an employee or dependent of an employee of a Kentuckiana Post sustaining member firm; an employee or dependent of an employee of the Louisville District Corps of Engineers; a current student member of the Kentuckiana Post; a student whose permanent home address is within the Kentuckiana Post's geographic boundary (Kentucky and Indiana) and who is enrolled in an ROTC program or military academy; or an individual on active duty or the dependent of an individual on active duty who is assigned to an installation within the Kentuckiana Post's geographic boundary. Applicants must be U.S. citizens accepted at an undergraduate ABET-accredited engineering program; undergraduates enrolled in engineering technology programs are not eligible. Along with their application, they must submit an essay of 300 to 500 words on a topic that changes annually; recently, applicants were invited to write on how winning this scholarship would promote a promising future for their engineering career and how they might envision that career supporting the mission of SAME. Financial need is not considered in the selection process.

Financial data The stipend is $4,000 per year.

Duration 1 year; may be renewed 1 additional year.

Additional information Recipients are required to attend the scholarship luncheon ceremony in Louisville in May.

Number awarded Varies each year; recently, 6 were awarded.

Deadline March of each year.

[103]
KENTUCKY NATIONAL GUARD TUITION AWARD PROGRAM

Kentucky Higher Education Assistance Authority
Attn: Student Aid Branch
100 Airport Road
P.O. Box 798
Frankfort, KY 40602-0798
(502) 696-7392   Toll Free: (800) 928-8926, ext. 7392
Fax: (502) 696-7373   TDD: (800) 855-2880
E-mail: studentaid@kheaa.com
Web: www.kheaa.com/website/kheaa/military_ky?main=7

Summary To provide financial assistance for college or graduate school to members of the Kentucky National Guard.

Eligibility This program is open to active enlisted members of the Kentucky National Guard who are interested in working full or part time on an undergraduate or graduate degree. Applicants must have maintained standards of satisfactory membership in the Guard, including passing the most recent physical fitness test, meeting the height-weight standard, meeting attendance standards, having no unsatisfactory performance or absence-without-leave records, and having no other restrictions on their personnel file. Preference is given to applicants working on their first undergraduate degree.

Financial data The program provides payment of full tuition and fees at any state-supported university, community college, or vocational or technical school in Kentucky.

Duration 1 semester; may be renewed.

Number awarded Varies each year.

Deadline March of each year for summer or fall terms; September of each year for spring term.

[104]
LARRY STRICKLAND LEADERSHIP AWARD AND SCHOLARSHIP

Association of the United States Army
Attn: Strickland Memorial Scholarship Fund
2425 Wilson Boulevard
Arlington, VA 22201
(703) 841-4300, ext. 2693
Toll Free: (800) 336-4570, ext. 2693
E-mail: jspencer@ausa.org
Web: www.ausa.org

Summary To recognize and reward, with funding for additional education, Army non-commissioned officers who demonstrate outstanding leadership.

Eligibility This award is presented to a non-commissioned officer who best exemplifies "the Army's vision and influences others in shaping future leaders." Candidates must also be interested in obtaining additional education.

Financial data The award consists of a plaque and $4,000 to assist in covering educational costs that Army tuition assistance does not pay, such as instructional fees, laboratory fees, and books.

Duration The award is presented annually.

Additional information This award was established in 2003 to honor SGM Larry L. Strickland, who was killed in the Pentagon on September 11, 2001.

Number awarded Up to 3 each year.

Deadline Deadline not specified.

[105]
LOUIS J. SCHOBER MEMORIAL SCHOLARSHIP

Society of American Military Engineers-Louisiana Post
c/o Chris Dunn, Young Members Committee Chair
U.S. Army Corps of Engineers, New Orleans District
7400 Leake Avenue
P.O. Box 60267
New Orleans, LA 70160
(504) 862-1799
E-mail: Christopher.L.Dunn@usace.army.mil
Web: posts.same.org/louisiana/YoungMembers.htm

Summary To provide financial assistance to students from Louisiana majoring in engineering, particularly those who are enrolled in ROTC, are serving or have served in the armed forces, or are children of members of the Society of American Military Engineers (SAME) Louisiana Post.

Eligibility This program is open to students currently working on an undergraduate degree in engineering. Applicants must be either 1) enrolled at a college or university in Louisiana; or 2) the children of a member of the SAME Louisiana Post (who may be studying at a college or university in any state). Graduate students are not eligible; high school seniors may be considered if no suitable college students apply. Selection is based primarily on academic record and demonstration of leadership characteristics; other factors considered are participation in SAME posts and activities, enrollment in an ROTC program, former or current military service, and participation in school and community activities.

Financial data The stipend is $2,000.

Duration 1 year; nonrenewable.
Number awarded 1 or more each year.
Deadline May of each year.

[106]
LOUISIANA NATIONAL GUARD STATE TUITION EXEMPTION PROGRAM

Louisiana National Guard
Attn: Education Service Officer
Military Development (DMP-XD)
Jackson Barracks
New Orleans, LA 70146-0330
(504) 278-8532   Toll Free: (800) 899-6355
E-mail: alfred.e.horridge.mil@mail.mil
Web: www.geauxguard.com

Summary To provide financial assistance to members of the Louisiana National Guard who are interested in attending college or graduate school in the state.

Eligibility This program is open to active drilling members of the Louisiana Army National Guard or Air National Guard. Guard members are ineligible if they have been disqualified by their unit commander for any adverse action, have already obtained a bachelor's degree, are placed on academic probation or suspension, test positive on a drug/alcohol test or declare themselves as a self-referral, are separated or transfer to the Inactive National Guard, or have 9 or more AWOLs. Applicants must have been accepted for admission or be enrolled in a Louisiana public institution of higher learning, either part time or full time, to work on an associate, bachelor's, or master's degree.

Financial data Recipients are exempt from all tuition charges at Louisiana state-funded colleges, universities, or community colleges.

Duration The exemption may be claimed for 5 separate academic years or until the receipt of a degree, whichever occurs first.

Additional information The state legislature established this program in 1974.

Number awarded Varies each year.

Deadline Deadline not specified.

[107]
MAJOR GENERAL DUANE L. "DUKE" CORNING MEMORIAL SCHOLARSHIP

South Dakota National Guard Enlisted Association
c/o Nancy Ausland, Scholarship Committee Chair
517 North Euclid Avenue
Sioux Falls, SD 57104
(605) 988-5946   E-mail: nancy.ausland@ang.af.mil
Web: www.sdngea.com/programs/scholarships

Summary To provide financial assistance to current and retired members of the South Dakota National Guard Enlisted Association (SDNGEA), the National Guard Association of South Dakota (NGASD), or their dependents who are interested in attending college in any state.

Eligibility This program is open to current and retired members of the SDNGEA and the NGASD and the dependents of current and retired members of those associations. Applicants must be graduating high school seniors or full-time undergraduate students at a college or university in any state. They must submit a 300-page autobiography that includes their experiences to date and their hopes and plans for the

future. Selection is based on the essay; awards, honors, and offices in high school, college, or trade school; GPA and ACT/SAT scores; letters of recommendation; and extracurricular and community activities and honors.

Financial data The stipend is $1,000.
Duration 1 year; nonrenewable.
Number awarded 1 each year.
Deadline March of each year.

[108]
MAJOR SAMUEL WOODFILL CHAPTER AUSA SCHOLARSHIP PROGRAM

Association of the United States Army-Major Samuel
 Woodfill Chapter
c/o LTC Robert F. Sprague, Retired
1326 Cayton Road
Florence, KY 41042-9335
(859) 525-1082   E-mail: spraguer@fuse.net
Web: www3.ausa.org/chapweb/wcc/index.html

Summary To provide financial assistance to Army personnel and their families, especially those from Indiana, Kentucky, and Ohio, who have served in the Global War on Terror and are interested in attending college in any state.

Eligibility This program is open to (in order of preference) 1) children and spouses of U.S. Army soldiers (active-duty, Reserve, or National Guard) who are currently serving, or have served in the Global War on Terrorism; 2) Army soldiers and veterans who are currently serving or have served in the Global War on Terrorism; and 3) children, grandchildren, and spouses of members of the Major Samuel Woodfill Chapter of the Association of the United States Army (AUSA). Priority is given to residents of Indiana, Kentucky, and Ohio. Applicants may be attending or accepted at an accredited college or university in any state. Along with their application, they must submit a 500-word essay on the greatest challenge they have faced and how it has impacted them. High school seniors must also submit information on their GPA, extracurricular activities, honors and/or awards, and SAT/ACT scores. Financial need is not considered in the selection process.

Financial data The stipend is $1,000. Funds are disbursed directly to the recipient's college or university.
Duration 1 year.
Number awarded Varies each year; recently, 5 were awarded.
Deadline March of each year.

[109]
MARINE CORPS TUITION ASSISTANCE PROGRAM

U.S. Marine Corps
c/o Naval Education and Training Professional
 Development and Technology Command
Code N814
6490 Saufley Field Road
Pensacola, FL 32509-5241
(850) 452-1001   Toll Free: (877) 838-1659
Fax: (850) 473-6401   E-mail: SFLY_TA.Marine@navy.mil
Web: www.marines.mil

Summary To provide financial assistance for undergraduate or graduate study to Marine Corps personnel.

Eligibility Eligible for assistance under this program are active-duty Marines who wish to take college courses for academic credit during off-duty time. Funding is available for vocational/technical, undergraduate, graduate, undergraduate development, independent study, and distance learning programs. Applicants must have completed at least 2 years of service, be eligible for promotion, and have completed designated military training courses. Commissioned officers must agree to remain on active duty for 2 years after the completion of any funded courses. Enlisted Marines must have an end of active duty status (EAS) of at least 60 days beyond the completion date of the course. All students must successfully complete their courses with a satisfactory grade.

Financial data Those selected for participation in this program receive their regular Marine Corps pay and 100% of tuition at the postsecondary educational institution of their choice, but capped at $4,500 per year or $250 per semester hour, whichever is less. Funding is available only for tuition, not fees or other associated expenses.

Duration Until completion of a bachelor's or graduate degree. Undergraduates must complete all courses with a grade of "C" or better; graduate students must complete classes with a grade of "B" of better. If recipients fail to achieve those grades, they must reimburse the Marine Corps for all funds received.

Number awarded Varies each year; in recent years, approximately 20,000 Marines availed themselves of this funding.

Deadline Applications must be submitted within 30 days of the start date of the class.

[110]
MARINES' MEMORIAL TRIBUTE SCHOLARSHIPS

Marines' Memorial Association
c/o Marines Memorial Club and Hotel
609 Sutter Street
San Francisco, CA 94102
(415) 673-6672, ext. 293   Fax: (415) 441-3649
E-mail: scholarship@marineclub.com
Web: www.marineclub.com/membership/scholarship.php

Summary To provide financial assistance to military personnel who are transitioning from active duty to civilian or Reserve status and wish to attend college.

Eligibility This program is open to military personnel who have separated from full-time active duty to civilian or Reserve status within the past 3 years. Applicants must be enrolled or planning to enroll full time in an undergraduate degree program at a college or university. Membership in the sponsoring organization is not required. Along with their application, they must submit an essay of 250 to 500 words in which they draw upon the values and experience they gained in the military to write on duty, patriotism, and failures as the pillars of success. Applicants entering college as freshmen must submit a high school transcript and SAT or ACT scores; continuing college students must submit a college transcript. Selection is based on the essay, academic merit, references, and financial need.

Financial data The stipend is $2,500 per year.

Duration 1 year; recipients may reapply for up to 3 additional years.

Number awarded 4 each year.

Deadline April of each year.

[111]
MARK YAMANE MILITARY SCHOLARSHIP

Nisei Veterans Committee
Attn: Military Scholarship
1212 South King Street
Seattle, WA 98144-2025
(206) 322-1122   E-mail: scholarship@nvcfoundation.org
Web: www.seattlenvc.org/education/scholarship

Summary To provide financial assistance for college to military personnel or ROTC students, especially those with ties to Washington, who are of Japanese ancestry.

Eligibility This program is open to individuals of Japanese ancestry who are regular military stationed at Fort Lewis, McChord Air Force Base, Whidbey Island Naval Air Station, Naval Station Everett, Naval Station Bangor, or Naval Station Bremerton; members of the U.S. Coast Guard under the command of the 13th District; residents of Washington who are members of the National Guard or Reserves and have served on active duty for a total of at least 2 years or are current on active duty; ROTC students at universities in the state of Washington; Washington state residents who are ROTC students at universities in any state; Washington state residents who are attending 1 of the military academies; or relatives of members of the Nisei Veterans Committee who are serving on active duty at any military base worldwide. Applicants must submit an essay on how the legacy of Japanese American soldiers who served during World War II has affected them and their military service to their country.

Financial data The stipend is $1,500. Funds may be used to buy a computer and software, pay off existing student loans, pay for books and tuition not covered by the military, or any combination of those.

Duration 1 year.

Number awarded 1 or more each year.

Deadline January of each year.

[112]
MARYLAND NATIONAL GUARD STATE TUITION ASSISTANCE REIMBURSEMENT (STAR)

Maryland National Guard
Attn: Education Services Office
Fifth Regiment Armory
29th Division Street, Room B-23
Baltimore, MD 21201-2288
(410) 576-1499   Toll Free: (800) 492-2526
Fax: (410) 576-6082
E-mail: mdng_education@md.ngb.army.mil
Web: www.md.ngb.army.mil

Summary To provide partial tuition reimbursement to members of the Maryland National Guard working on an undergraduate degree at a college in the state.

Eligibility This program is open to members of the Maryland National Guard in pay grades E-1 through O-4. Applicants must be attending or planning to attend designated "Partners in Education" institutions in the state (all 5 branches of the University of Maryland, 8 other public colleges and universities, 13 community colleges, 5 private universities, and 4 private career education institutions). They must have at least a 2-year obligation remaining from the course start date. Partial reimbursement of tuition is provided for courses completed with a grade of "C" or above.

Financial data This program provides reimbursement of all tuition charges not covered by other state or federal tuition assistance programs.

Duration 1 semester; recipients may reapply.

Additional information Individuals must submit their grades within 60 days after their course is completed.

Number awarded Varies each year.

Deadline Applications must be submitted within 45 days after the start of the semester.

[113]
MARYLAND NATIONAL GUARD STATE TUITION WAIVER (STW)

Maryland National Guard
Attn: Education Services Office
Fifth Regiment Armory
29th Division Street, Room B-23
Baltimore, MD 21201-2288
(410) 576-1499   Toll Free: (800) 492-2526
Fax: (410) 576-6082
E-mail: mdng_education@md.ngb.army.mil
Web: www.md.ngb.army.mil

Summary To waive tuition for members of the Maryland National Guard at colleges and universities in the state.

Eligibility This program is open to members of the Maryland National Guard who wish to attend designated "Partners in Education" institutions in the state. That includes all 5 branches of the University of Maryland, 8 other public colleges and universities, 13 community colleges, 5 private universities, and 4 private career education institutions that have agreed to waive part of the tuition charges for National Guard members. Applicants must have a 2-year obligation remaining from the course start date.

Financial data The amount of the waiver ranges from 25% to 50%. Most 4-year colleges waive 50% of tuition for up to 6 credits per semester.

Duration 1 semester; recipients may reapply.

Additional information Some schools also limit the number of credits for which a Guard member can receive waivers during any semester.

Number awarded Varies each year.

Deadline Deadline not specified.

[114]
MARYLAND SCHOLARSHIPS FOR VETERANS OF THE AFGHANISTAN AND IRAQ CONFLICTS

Maryland Higher Education Commission
Attn: Office of Student Financial Assistance
6 North Liberty Street, Ground Suite
Baltimore, MD 21201
(410) 767-3301   Toll Free: (800) 974-0203
Fax: (410) 332-0250   TDD: (800) 735-2258
E-mail: osfamail@mhec.state.md.us
Web: www.mhec.state.md.us

Summary To provide financial assistance for college to residents of Maryland who served in the armed forces in Afghanistan or Iraq and their children and spouses.

Eligibility This program is open to Maryland residents who are 1) a veteran who served at least 60 days in Afghanistan on or after October 24, 2001 or in Iraq on or after March 19, 2003; 2) an active-duty member of the armed forces who served at least 60 days in Afghanistan or Iraq on or after

those dates; 3) a member of a Reserve component of the armed forces or the Maryland National Guard who was activated as a result of the Afghanistan or Iraq conflicts and served at least 60 days; and 4) the children and spouses of such veterans, active-duty armed forces personnel, or members of Reserve forces or Maryland National Guard. Applicants must be enrolled or accepted for enrollment in a regular undergraduate program at an eligible Maryland institution. In the selection process, veterans are given priority over dependent children and spouses.

Financial data The stipend is equal to 50% of the annual tuition, mandatory fees, and room and board of a resident undergraduate at a 4-year public institution within the University System of Maryland, currently capped at $10,655 per year for students who live on campus, at $6,795 for students who live with their parents, or at %7,745 for students who live off campus.

Duration 1 year; may be renewed for an additional 4 years of full-time study or 7 years of part-time study, provided the recipient remains enrolled in an eligible program with a GPA of 2.5 or higher.

Additional information This program is scheduled to expire in 2016.

Number awarded Varies each year.

Deadline February of each year.

[115]
MASSACHUSETTS ARMED FORCES TUITION WAIVER PROGRAM

Massachusetts Office of Student Financial Assistance
454 Broadway, Suite 200
Revere, MA 02151
(617) 391-6070   Fax: (617) 727-0667
E-mail: osfa@osfa.mass.edu
Web: www.osfa.mass.edu

Summary To waive tuition at Massachusetts public colleges and universities for members of the armed forces.

Eligibility Applicants for this assistance must have been permanent legal residents of Massachusetts for at least 1 year and stationed in Massachusetts as members of the Army, Navy, Marine Corps, Air Force, or Coast Guard. They may not be in default on any federal student loan. They must enroll in at least 3 undergraduate credits per semester. U.S. citizenship or permanent resident status is required.

Financial data Eligible military personnel are exempt from any tuition payments toward an undergraduate degree or certificate program at public colleges or universities in Massachusetts.

Duration Up to 4 academic years, for a total of 130 semester hours.

Additional information Recipients may enroll either part or full time in a Massachusetts publicly-supported institution.

Number awarded Varies each year.

Deadline April of each year.

[116]
MASSACHUSETTS NATIONAL GUARD TUITION WAIVER PROGRAM

Massachusetts National Guard
Attn: Education Services Officer
50 Maple Street
Milford, MA 01757-3604
(508) 968-5889   Fax: (508) 968-5906
E-mail: ma-education@ng.army.mil
Web: states.ng.mil

Summary To provide financial assistance to members of the Massachusetts National Guard interested in working on an undergraduate or graduate degree at a college in the state.

Eligibility This program is open to actively participating members of the Army or Air National Guard in Massachusetts. Applicants must have less than 9 AWOLs (Absence Without Leave) at all times and must not ETS (Expiration of Term of Service) during the period enrolled. They must be accepted for admission or enrolled at 1 of 28 Massachusetts public colleges, universities, or community colleges and working on an associate, bachelor's, master's, or doctoral degree. The institution must have a vacancy after all tuition-paying students and all students who are enrolled under any scholarship or tuition waiver provisions have enrolled.

Financial data Eligible Guard members are exempt from any tuition payments at colleges or universities operated by the Commonwealth of Massachusetts and funded by the Massachusetts Board of Higher Education.

Duration Up to a total of 130 semester hours.

Additional information Recipients may enroll either part or full time in a Massachusetts state-supported institution. This program is funded through the Massachusetts Board of Higher Education.

Number awarded Varies each year.

Deadline Deadline not specified.

[117]
MEDICAL CORPS OPTION OF THE SEAMAN TO ADMIRAL-21 PROGRAM

U.S. Navy
Attn: Commander, Naval Service Training Command
250 Dallas Street, Suite A
Pensacola, FL 32508-5268
(850) 452-9563   Fax: (850) 452-2486
E-mail: PNSC_STA21@navy.mil
Web: www.sta-21.navy.mil/program_options.asp

Summary To allow outstanding enlisted Navy personnel to work on a bachelor's degree, affiliate with an ROTC unit, be accepted to medical school, earn an M.D. or D.O. degree, and be commissioned in the Navy Medical Corps.

Eligibility This program is open to U.S. citizens who are currently serving on active duty in the U.S. Navy or Naval Reserve, including Full Time Support (FTS), Selected Reserves (SELRES), and Navy Reservists on active duty, except for those on active duty for training (ACDUTRA). Applicants must be high school graduates (or GED recipients) who are able to 1) complete requirements for a baccalaureate degree within 36 months; 2) complete a medical degree through the Uniformed Services University of Health Services (USUHS) or the Health Professions Scholarship Program (HPSP); and 3) complete 20 years of active commissioned

service as a physician by age 62. Within the past 3 years, they must have taken the SAT (and achieved scores of at least 500 on the mathematics section and 500 on the critical reading section) or the ACT (and achieved a score of at least 21 on the mathematics portion and 20 on the English portion).

Financial data Awardees continue to receive their regular Navy pay and allowances while they attend college on a full-time basis. They also receive reimbursement for tuition, fees, and books up to $10,000 per year. If base housing is available, they are eligible to live there. Participants are not eligible to receive benefits under the Navy's Tuition Assistance Program (TA), the Montgomery GI Bill (MGIB), the Navy College Fund, or the Veterans Educational Assistance Program (VEAP).

Duration Selectees are supported for up to 36 months of full-time, year-round study or completion of a bachelor's degree, as long as they maintain a GPA of 3.0 or higher. They are then supported until completion of a medical degree.

Additional information Upon acceptance into the program, selectees attend the Naval Science Institute (NSI) in Newport, Rhode Island for an 8-week program in the fundamental core concepts of being a naval officer (navigation, engineering, weapons, military history and justice, etc.). They then enter an NROTC affiliated college or university with a pre-medical program that confers an accredited B.S. degree to pursue full-time study. They become members of and drill with the NROTC unit. After they complete their bachelor's degree, they are commissioned as an ensign in the Naval Reserve. They must apply to and be accepted at medical school, either the USUSH or a civilian medical school through the HPSP. Following completion of medical school, they are promoted to lieutenant and assigned to active duty in the Medical Corps. Selectees incur a service obligation of 5 years for their baccalaureate degree support plus whatever obligation they incur for medical degree support (usually 7 years if they attend USUSH or 4 years if they attend a civilian institution through HPSP).

Number awarded Varies each year.

Deadline June of each year.

[118]
MEDICAL SERVICE CORPS INSERVICE PROCUREMENT PROGRAM (MSC-IPP)

U.S. Navy
Attn: Navy Medicine Professional Development Center
8955 Wood Road, 16th Floor, Rooms 16141, 16148
Bethesda, MD 20889-5611
(301) 319-4520   Fax: (301) 295-1783
E-mail: mscipp@med.navy.mil
Web: www.med.navy.mil

Summary To provide funding to Navy and Marine enlisted personnel who wish to earn an undergraduate or graduate degree in selected health care specialties while continuing to receive their regular pay and allowances.

Eligibility This program is open to enlisted personnel who are serving on active duty in any rating in pay grade E-5 through E-9 of the U.S. Navy, U.S. Marine Corps, or the Marine Corps Reserve serving on active duty (including Full Time Support of the Reserve). Applicants must be interested in working on a degree to become commissioned in the following medical specialties: environmental health, health care administration, industrial hygiene, occupational therapy, pharmacy, physician assistant, radiation health, or social work. If they plan to work on a graduate degree, they must have scores of at least 1000 on the GRE or 500 on the GMAT; if they plan to work on a bachelor's or physician assistant degree, they must have scores of at least 1000 on the SAT (including 460 on the mathematics portion) or 42 on the ACT (21 on the English portion, 21 on the mathematics portion). They must be U.S. citizens who can be commissioned before they reach their 42nd birthday.

Financial data Participants receive payment of tuition, mandatory fees, a book allowance, and full pay and allowances for their enlisted pay grade. They are eligible for advancement while in college.

Duration 24 to 48 months of full-time, year-round study, until completion of a relevant degree.

Additional information Following graduation, participants are commissioned in the Medical Service Corps and attend Officer Indoctrination School. They incur an 8-year military service obligation, including at least 3 years served on active duty.

Number awarded Varies each year; recently, 36 were awarded: 2 in environmental health, 14 in health care administration, 1 in occupational therapy, 1 in pharmacy, 15 in physician assistant, 2 in radiation health, and 1 in social work.

Deadline August of each year.

[119]
MG BENJAMIN J. BUTLER "CENTURY DIVISION" SCHOLARSHIP AWARD

Association of the Century, Inc.
Attn: Scholarship Committee
P.O. Box 34393
Louisville, KY 40232
Web: www.the-century.org/scholarship.htm

Summary To provide financial assistance for college to members of the United States Army 100th Infantry Division and their descendants.

Eligibility This program is open to active, retired, or former members of the Army 100th Infantry Division (or any of its successor designations), their direct lineal descendants, and their adopted dependents. Applicants must be enrolled or planning to enroll at an accredited 4-year college or university. They must have a GPA of 2.5 or higher. Along with their application, they must submit a 250-word essay on how this scholarship will help them. Selection is based on academic excellence, qualities of good citizenship and patriotism, letters of recommendation, and financial need.

Financial data The stipend is $1,000.

Duration 1 year.

Additional information This program, which began in 2008, is managed by the Community Foundation of Louisville.

Number awarded Varies each year; recently, 5 were awarded.

Deadline May of each year.

[120]
MG LEIF J. SVERDRUP AWARD

Army Engineer Association
Attn: Program Coordinator
P.O. Box 30260
Alexandria, VA 22310-8260
(703) 428-7084   Fax: (703) 428-6043
E-mail: execasst@armyengineer.com
Web: www.armyengineer.com/scholarships.htm

Summary To provide financial assistance for college or graduate school to officers who are members of the Army Engineer Association (AEA).

Eligibility This program is open to AEA members serving in an active, Reserve, or National Guard component Army Engineer unit, school, or organization within the Corps of Engineers of the United States Army. Applicants must be commissioned officers (2LT, 1LT, or CPT) or warrant officers (WO1 or WO2). They must be working on or planning to work on an associate, bachelor's, or master's degree at an accredited college or university. Selection is based primarily on financial need, although potential for academic success and standards of conduct as supported by personal references are also considered.

Financial data The stipend is $1,000.

Duration 1 year.

Number awarded 2 each year: 1 to a commissioned officer and 1 to a warrant officer.

Deadline June of each year.

[121]
MICHIGAN NATIONAL GUARD UNIVERSITY AND COLLEGE TUITION GRANTS

Department of Military and Veterans Affairs
Attn: State Education Office
2500 South Washington Avenue
Lansing, MI 48913-5101
(517) 481-7646   Toll Free: (800) 292-1386
E-mail: enderlek@michigan.gov
Web: www.michigan.gov

Summary To provide financial assistance to members of the Michigan National Guard who are enrolled at designated universities in the state.

Eligibility This program is open to all members of the Michigan National Guard who are in good standing with their unit and have completed basic training. Applicants must be enrolled full time at 1 of the following institutions: Baker College, Cleary University, Cornerstone University, Eastern Michigan University, Ferris State University, Kalamazoo Valley Community College, Kirtland Community College, Lake Superior State University, Lansing Community College, Lawrence Technological University, Miller College, Northern Michigan University, Oakland University, Olivet College, Rochester College, Siena Heights University, Spring Arbor University, University of Detroit Mercy, or Walsh College.

Financial data The amount of the grant varies at each participating institution.

Duration 1 semester; may be renewed for a total of 4 years.

Additional information These grants are in addition to funds received through the Michigan National Guard State Education Reimbursement Program.

Number awarded Varies each year.
Deadline Deadline not specified.

[122]
MILITARY INTELLIGENCE CORPS ASSOCIATION SCHOLARSHIPS

Military Intelligence Corps Association
Attn: Scholarship Committee
P.O. Box 13020
Fort Huachuca, AZ 85670-3020
(520) 227-3894   E-mail: execdir@micorps.org
Web: www.micastore.com/Scholarships.html

Summary To provide financial assistance for college to members of the Military Intelligence Corps Association (MICA) and their immediate family.

Eligibility This program is open to active-duty, Reserve, National Guard, and retired military intelligence soldiers who are MICA members and to their immediate family (spouses, children, or other relatives living with and supported by the MICA member). Applicants must be attending or accepted for attendance at an accredited college, university, vocational school, or technical institution. Along with their application, they must submit a 1-page essay on their educational goals and program of study. Financial need is not considered in the selection process.

Financial data Stipend amounts vary depending on the availability of funds and the number of qualified applicants, but recently were $5,000. Funds are to be used for tuition, books, and classroom fees; support is not provided for housing, board, travel, or administrative purposes.

Duration 1 year; recipients may reapply.

Number awarded Varies each year; recently, 4 were awarded.

Deadline May of each year.

[123]
MILITARY NON-RESIDENT TUITION WAIVER FOR MEMBERS, SPOUSES OR CHILDREN ASSIGNED TO DUTY IN TEXAS

Texas Higher Education Coordinating Board
Attn: Grants and Special Programs
1200 East Anderson Lane
P.O. Box 12788
Austin, TX 78711-2788
(512) 427-6340   Toll Free: (800) 242-3062
Fax: (512) 427-6420   E-mail: grantinfo@thecb.state.tx.us
Web: www.collegeforalltexans.com

Summary To exempt military personnel stationed in Texas and their dependents from the payment of non-resident tuition at public institutions of higher education in the state.

Eligibility Eligible for these waivers are members of the U.S. armed forces and commissioned officers of the Public Health Service from states other than Texas, their spouses, and dependent children. Applicants must be assigned to Texas and attending or planning to attend a public college or university in the state.

Financial data Although persons eligible under this program are classified as non-residents, they are entitled to pay the resident tuition at Texas institutions of higher education, regardless of their length of residence in Texas.

Duration 1 year; may be renewed.

Number awarded Varies each year.
Deadline Deadline not specified.

[124]
MINNESOTA G.I. BILL PROGRAM

Minnesota Department of Veterans Affairs
Attn: Programs and Services Division
20 West 12th Street, Room 206
St. Paul, MN 55155
(651) 296-2562   Toll Free: (888) LINK-VET
TDD: (800) 627-3529   E-mail: MNGIBill@state.mn.us
Web: mn.gov/mdva/resources/education/minnesotagibill.jsp

Summary To provide financial assistance for college or graduate school in Minnesota to residents who 1) served in the military after September 11, 2001 or 2) are the family members of deceased or disabled military personnel.

Eligibility This program is open to residents of Minnesota enrolled at colleges and universities in the state as undergraduate or graduate students. Applicants must be 1) a veteran who is serving or has served honorably in a branch of the U.S. armed forces at any time; 2) a non-veteran who has served honorably for a total of 5 years or more cumulatively as a member of the Minnesota National Guard or other active or Reserve component of the U.S. armed forces, and any part of that service occurred on or after September 11, 2001; or 3) a surviving child or spouse of a person who has served in the military at any time on or after September 11, 2001 and who has died or has a total and permanent disability as a result of that military service. Financial need is also considered in the selection process.

Financial data The stipend is $1,000 per semester for full-time study or $500 per semester for part-time study. The maximum award is $3,000 per academic year or $10,000 per lifetime.

Duration 1 year; may be renewed, provided the recipient continues to make satisfactory academic progress.

Additional information This program was established by the Minnesota Legislature in 2007.

Number awarded Varies each year.
Deadline Deadline not specified.

[125]
MINNESOTA NATIONAL GUARD STATE TUITION REIMBURSEMENT

Department of Military Affairs
Attn: Education Services Officer
JFMN-J1-ARED
20 West 12th Street
St. Paul, MN 55155-2098
(651) 282-4589   Toll Free: (800) 657-3848
Fax: (651) 282-4694
E-mail: ng.mn.mnarng.mbx.assets-education@mail.mil
Web: www.minnesotanationalguard.org

Summary To provide financial assistance for college or graduate school to current members of the Minnesota National Guard.

Eligibility Eligible for this program are members of the Minnesota Army or Air National Guard who are currently serving in grades E-1 through O-5 (including warrant officers) and are enrolled as undergraduate or graduate students at colleges or universities in Minnesota. Reimbursement is provided only for undergraduate courses completed with a grade of "C" or better or for graduate courses completed with a grade of "B" or better. Applicants must be serving satisfactorily according to National Guard standards.

Financial data   The maximum reimbursement rate is 100% of the tuition rate at the University of Minnesota Twin Cities campus, with a maximum benefit of $13,000 per fiscal year for undergraduate course work or $22,000 per fiscal year for graduate course work.

Duration   1 semester, to a maximum of 18 credits per semester; may be renewed until completion of an associate, bachelor's, master's, or doctoral degree or 144 semester credits, whichever comes first.

Number awarded   Varies each year.

Deadline   Deadline not specified.

[126]
MISSISSIPPI NATIONAL GUARD STATE EDUCATIONAL ASSISTANCE PROGRAM

Mississippi Military Department
Attn: Education Services and Incentives Office
JFH-MS-J1-ED
1410 Riverside Drive
P.O. Box 5027
Jackson, MS 39296-5027
(601) 313-6248   Fax: (601) 313-6151
E-mail: msedu@ng.army.mil
Web: ms.ng.mil

Summary   To provide financial assistance to members of the Mississippi National Guard who are interested in attending college in the state.

Eligibility   This program is open to members of the Mississippi Army or Air National Guard who have completed basic training and are in good standing. Applicants must be registered to vote in Mississippi and be enrolled or accepted for enrollment at an accredited college or university (public or private) in the state. They may not currently be receiving federal tuition assistance.

Financial data   Stipends cover the actual cost of tuition, to a maximum of $4,500 per year or $250 per semester hour.

Duration   1 year; may be renewed until the Guard member earns a bachelor's degree, as long as the member maintains a minimum GPA of 2.0. The full benefit must be utilized within a 10-year period.

Number awarded   Varies each year.

Deadline   Applications must be submitted not later than 2 weeks after the start date of the semester.

[127]
MISSOURI NATIONAL GUARD ASSOCIATION SCHOLARSHIPS

Missouri National Guard Association
Attn: Scholarship
2303 Militia Drive
Jefferson City, MO 65101-1203
(573) 632-4240   Toll Free: (800) 972-1164
E-mail: executivedirector@mongaonline.com
Web: www.mongaonline.com/?page=Scholarship

Summary   To provide financial assistance to members of the Missouri National Guard Association (MoNGA) and their dependents who are interested in attending college in any state.

Eligibility   This program is open to annual, associate, and lifetime members of the association and their dependents. Applicants must be interested in working on a degree at an accredited junior college or 4-year college or university in any state. They must submit high school or college transcripts, 3 letters of recommendation, and a letter describing their desire to continue their education, why they need financial assistance, and how they have demonstrated the traits (scholarship, citizenship, and leadership) upon which selection is based.

Financial data   Stipends for MoNGA members are $1,000 or $750. Stipends for dependents are $750 or $500. In addition, USAA Insurance Corporation sponsors a $500 scholarship for enlisted MoNGA members. Funds are paid directly to the recipient's college or university.

Duration   1 year.

Number awarded   5 each year: 2 for MoNGA members (1 at $1,000 and 1 at $750), 2 for dependents (1 at $750 and 1 at $500), and 1 USAA scholarship.

Deadline   February of each year.

[128]
MISSOURI NATIONAL GUARD STATE TUITION ASSISTANCE PROGRAM

Office of the Adjutant General
Attn: NGMO-PER-INC (State TA)
2302 Militia Drive
Jefferson City, MO 65101-1203
(573) 638-9500, ext. 7023   Toll Free: (888) 526-MONG
Fax: (573) 638-9620
E-mail: ng.mo.moarng.mbx.per-inc-stateta@mail.mil
Web: www.moguard.com/moguard-tuition-assistance_.html

Summary   To provide financial assistance for college to members of the Missouri National Guard.

Eligibility   This program is open to members of the Missouri National Guard who are participating satisfactorily in required training. Applicants must be enrolled or accepted for enrollment as a full-time or part-time undergraduate at an approved public or private institution of higher learning. If they have already completed some college courses, they must have earned a GPA of 2.5 or higher. As recently structured, priority is given to personnel in the following order: 1) officers who do not have a bachelor's degree, regardless of their length of service; 2) non-prior service enlistees accessed to fill a valid unit vacancy; 3) prior service transfers access to fill a valid unit vacancy; and 4) prior service beyond first term with less than 10 years total military service.

Financial data   The program provide 100% tuition assistance for Guard members with 10 years or less of service and 50% tuition for those with more than 10 and less than 17 years of service. Tuition is paid at the rate of $274 per semester hour and may not exceed 39 hours per state fiscal year (15 hours in the fall, 15 hours in the spring, and 9 hours in the summer).

Duration   Support is provided for 10 semesters, 150 credit hours, or completion of a bachelor's degree, whichever comes first. Recipients must maintain a GPA of 2.5 or higher.

Additional information   This program began in 1998.

Number awarded   Varies each year, depending on the availability of funds.

Deadline   Applications must be submitted before the start date of class for standard 16-week semesters or within 30 days after the start date for classes shorter than the standard 16-weeks.

[129]
MONTANA NATIONAL GUARD SCHOLARSHIPS

Montana National Guard
Attn: Education Service Officer
P.O. Box 4789
Fort Harrison, MT 59636-4789
(406) 324-3236   E-mail: Julie.benson1@us.army.mil
Web: www.montanaguard.com/hro/html/educationpg2.cfm

Summary To provide financial assistance for college to members of the Montana National Guard.

Eligibility This program is open to members of the Montana National Guard who are enrolled or accepted for enrollment at a college, university, vocational/technical college, or other VA-approved training program in the state. Applicants must be in pay grades E-1 through E-7, W-1 through W-3, or O-1 through O-2; have completed Initial Active Duty for Training; have a high school diploma or GED; be eligible for Montgomery GI Bill Selected Reserve Benefits or be under a 6-year obligation to the Montana National Guard; and not have completed more than 16 years of military service. Funds are awarded on a first-come, first-served basis until exhausted.

Financial data Stipends are $1,500 per semester for study at a college or university or $400 per semester at a community college.

Duration 1 year; may be renewed.

Number awarded Varies each year.

Deadline Deadline not specified.

[130]
MONTGOMERY GI BILL (SELECTED RESERVE)

Department of Veterans Affairs
Attn: Veterans Benefits Administration
810 Vermont Avenue, N.W.
Washington, DC 20420
(202) 418-4343   Toll Free: (888) GI-BILL1
Web: www.benefits.va.gov/gibill/mgib_sr.asp

Summary To provide financial assistance for college or graduate school to members of the Reserves or National Guard.

Eligibility Eligible to apply are members of the Reserve elements of the Army, Navy, Air Force, Marine Corps, and Coast Guard, as well as the Army National Guard and the Air National Guard. To be eligible, a Reservist must 1) have a 6-year obligation to serve in the Selected Reserves signed after June 30, 1985 (or, if an officer, to agree to serve 6 years in addition to the original obligation); 2) complete Initial Active Duty for Training (IADT); 3) meet the requirements for a high school diploma or equivalent certificate before completing IADT; and 4) remain in good standing in a drilling Selected Reserve unit. Reservists who enlisted after June 30, 1985 can receive benefits for undergraduate degrees, graduate training, or technical courses leading to certificates at colleges and universities. Reservists whose 6-year commitment began after September 30, 1990 may also use these benefits for a certificate or diploma from business, technical, or vocational schools; cooperative training; apprenticeship or on-the-job training; correspondence courses; independent study programs; tutorial assistance; remedial, deficiency, or

refresher training; flight training; or state-approved alternative teacher certification programs.

Financial data The current monthly rate is $367 for full-time study, $274 for three-quarter study, $182 for half-time study, or $91.75 for less than half-time study. For apprenticeship and on-the-job training, the monthly stipend is $275.25 for the first 6 months, $201.85 for the second 6 months, and $128.45 for the remainder of the program. Other rates apply for cooperative education, correspondence courses, and flight training.

Duration Up to 36 months for full-time study, 48 months for three-quarter study, 72 months for half-time study, or 144 months for less than half-time study. Benefits end 10 years from the date the Reservist became eligible for the program.

Additional information This program is frequently referred to as Chapter 1606 (formerly Chapter 106).

Number awarded Varies each year.

Deadline Applications may be submitted at any time.

[131]
MSG LYNN H. STEINMAN MEMORIAL SCHOLARSHIP

Enlisted Association National Guard of New Jersey
Attn: Scholarship Chair
3650 Saylors Pond Road
Fort Dix, NJ 08640
(609) 432-9820   E-mail: npdsgt618@yahoo.com
Web: www.eang-nj.org/scholarships.html

Summary To provide financial assistance to New Jersey National Guard members interested in attending college in any state.

Eligibility This program is open to drilling members of the New Jersey National Guard. Membership in the Enlisted Association National Guard of New Jersey (EANGNJ) is not required. Applicants must be attending or planning to attend a college or university in any state. Along with their application, they must submit 1) information on their church, school, and community activities; 2) a list of honors they have received; 3) letters of recommendation; 4) transcripts; and 5) a letter with specific facts about their desire to continue their education and specifying their career goals. Financial need is not considered in the selection process.

Financial data The stipend is $1,000.

Duration 1 year.

Additional information This program is administered by EANGNJ and funded by USAA Insurance Corporation.

Number awarded 1 each year.

Deadline May of each year.

[132]
NATIONAL ASSOCIATION FOR UNIFORMED SERVICES SCHOLARSHIP PROGRAM

National Association for Uniformed Services
Attn: Scholarship Committee
5535 Hempstead Way
Springfield, VA 22151
(703) 750-1342   Toll Free: (800) 842-3451, ext. 1803
Fax: (703) 354-4380   E-mail: scholarship@naus.org
Web: www.naus.org/benefits-scholarship.html

Summary To provide financial assistance for college to members of the National Association for Uniformed Services (NAUS) and their families.

Eligibility This program is open to NAUS members, their spouses, and their children. Applicants must be high school seniors or undergraduates enrolled full or part time in a degree- or certificate-granting program. High school seniors must have a GPA of 3.0 or higher and undergraduates must have a GPA of 2.5 or higher. Along with their application, they must submit statements, up to 100 words each, on 1) their reasons for enrolling in a postsecondary education program; and 2) a list of academic achievements, personal achievements, extracurricular activities, and any community service performed in the past 2 years. Financial need is not considered in the selection process.

Financial data The stipend is $2,500.

Duration 1 year.

Additional information Membership in NAUS is open to members of the armed forces, veterans, retirees, their spouses, and their widow(er)s.

Number awarded Varies each year; recently, 8 were awarded.

Deadline April of each year.

[133]
NATIONAL CALL TO SERVICE PROGRAM

Department of Veterans Affairs
Attn: Veterans Benefits Administration
810 Vermont Avenue, N.W.
Washington, DC 20420
(202) 418-4343   Toll Free: (888) GI-BILL1
Web: www.benefits.va.gov

Summary To provide educational or other benefits to people who agree to serve in the military.

Eligibility This program is open to anyone who agrees to 1) serve on active duty in an approved military occupational specialty for 15 months; 2) continue by serving an additional period of active duty as assigned or 24 months in an active status in the selected reserve; and 3) continue by serving on active duty, in the selected reserve, in the individual ready reserve, or in Americorps or another domestic national service program.

Financial data Participants who complete the required service may choose to receive 1) a cash bonus of $5,000; 2) repayment of qualifying student loans up to $18,000; 3) entitlement to the full-time educational allowance established by the Montgomery GI Bill for 3-year enlistees (currently $1,717 per month); or 4) entitlement to the part-time educational allowance established by the Montgomery GI Bill for less than 3-year enlistees (currently $1,395 for full-time enrollment or proportional amounts for part-time enrollment).

Duration The cash bonus and loan repayment are 1-time benefits. Educational assistance is provided for up to 12 months for full-time enrollment or up to 36 months for part-time enrollment.

Additional information This program, which began in 2003, is a Department of Defense program but administered by the Department of Veterans Affairs.

Number awarded Varies each year.

Deadline Applications may be submitted at any time.

[134]
NATIONAL GUARD ASSOCIATION OF ARIZONA SCHOLARSHIPS

National Guard Association of Arizona
Attn: Scholarship Committee
5640 East McDowell Road
Phoenix, AZ 85008
(602) 275-8305   Fax: (602) 275-9254
E-mail: ngaofaz@aol.com
Web: www.ngaaz.org/scholarship.html

Summary To provide financial assistance to students at colleges and universities in Arizona who have a connection to the National Guard and the National Guard Association of Arizona (NGAAZ).

Eligibility This program is open to full-time students at colleges, universities, and community colleges in Arizona. Applicants must be a member of 1 of the following categories: 1) a current enlisted member of the Arizona National Guard; 2) a current officer member of the Arizona National Guard who is also a member of the NGAAZ; or 3) a child or spouse of an NGAAZ member. Applicants must submit 2 letters of recommendation and verification of good standing from the first commander in the chain of command of the Arizona National Guard. Selection is based on GPA (25%), community service (15%), letters of recommendation (15%), knowledge of National Guard philosophy (15%), and financial need (30%).

Financial data The stipend is $1,500.

Duration 1 year; nonrenewable.

Number awarded 3 each year: 1 to each category of applicant.

Deadline April of each year.

[135]
NATIONAL GUARD ASSOCIATION OF CALIFORNIA SCHOLARSHIPS

National Guard Association of California
Attn: Executive Director
3336 Bradshaw Road, Suite 230
Sacramento, CA 95827-2615
(916) 362-3411   Toll Free: (800) 647-0018
Fax: (916) 362-3707
Web: www.ngac.org

Summary To provide financial assistance to members of the National Guard Association of California (NGAC) and their dependents who are interested in attending college in any state.

Eligibility This program is open to 1) current members of the NGAC; 2) dependents of NGAC members; and 3) dependents of retired California National Guard servicemembers who are life members of the NGAC. Applicants must be attending or planning to attend a college, university, or trade school in any state. Along with their application, they must submit a 500-word essay on the greatest challenge they have faced and how it has impacted them. Selection is based on that essay; unweighted GPA; extracurricular activities, honors, and/or awards; letters of recommendation; and (if case of a tie after evaluation of those criteria) SAT or ACT scores.

Financial data Stipends range from $250 to $1,000. Funds are paid directly to the recipient.

Duration 1 year.

Number awarded Varies each year; recently, 19 were awarded.
Deadline May of each year.

[136]
NATIONAL GUARD ASSOCIATION OF CONNECTICUT SCHOLARSHIP PROGRAM

National Guard Association of Connecticut
Attn: Scholarship Committee
360 Broad Street
Hartford, CT 06105-3795
(860) 247-5000
E-mail: ngactexecutivedirector@gmail.com
Web: www.ngact.org/scholarships

Summary To provide financial assistance to members and the family of members of the National Guard Association of Connecticut (NGACT) who are interested in attending college in any state.
Eligibility This program is open to 1) NGACT members; 2) unmarried children and grandchildren of NGACT members; 3) spouses of NGACT members; and 4) unremarried spouses and unmarried dependent children and grandchildren of deceased NGACT members who were members in good standing at the time of their death. Applicants must be attending or planning to attend, on a part- or full-time basis, a college, university, trade school, or business school in any state. Graduate students are not eligible to apply. Along with their application, they must submit: an official transcript, a letter on their desire to continue their education and why financial assistance is required, 2 letters of recommendation, and 1 letter of academic reference. Selection is based on academic record, character, leadership, and need.
Financial data A stipend is awarded (amount not specified). Funds are sent to the recipient but are made payable to the recipient's choice of school. To receive the awards, proof of enrollment must be presented.
Duration 1 year.
Number awarded Varies each year.
Deadline May of each year.

[137]
NATIONAL GUARD ASSOCIATION OF INDIANA EDUCATIONAL GRANTS

National Guard Association of Indiana
Attn: Educational Grant Committee
2002 South Holt Road, Building 8
Indianapolis, IN 46241-4839
(317) 247-3196   Toll Free: (800) 219-2173
Fax: (317) 247-3575   E-mail: membership@ngai.net
Web: www.ngai.net/membership

Summary To provide financial assistance to members of the National Guard Association of Indiana (NGAI) and their dependents who plan to attend college in any state.
Eligibility This program is open to NGAI members and their dependents who are currently serving in the Indiana National Guard or are retired members of the Indiana National Guard. Applicants must be attending or planning to attend a college or university in any state. Along with their application, they must submit 2 letters of recommendation, a copy of high school or college transcripts, SAT or ACT scores (if taken), a letter of acceptance from a college or university (if not currently attending college), and a 2-page essay on the

educational program they intend to pursue and the goals they wish to attain. Selection is based on academic achievement, commitment and desire to achieve, extracurricular activities, accomplishments, goals, and financial need.
Financial data The stipend is $1,000.
Duration 1 year; recipients may reapply.
Number awarded 10 each year: 5 to military members and 5 to dependents.
Deadline March of each year.

[138]
NATIONAL GUARD ASSOCIATION OF MARYLAND SCHOLARSHIPS

National Guard Association of Maryland
Attn: Scholarship Committee
P.O. Box 16675
Baltimore, MD 21221-0675
(410) 557-2606   Toll Free: (800) 844-1394
Fax: (410) 893-7529
E-mail: executivedirector@ngam.net
Web: www.ngam.net/benefits/scholarships.html

Summary To provide financial assistance to members of the National Guard Association of Maryland (NGAM) and their family members who are interested in attending college in any state.
Eligibility This program is open to NGAM members (including current and former members of the National Guard) and their spouses and children. Applicants must be enrolled or planning to enroll in an accredited college, university, or vocational/technical school in any state on either a part-time or full-time basis. They must submit a resume in which they outline their academic background, activities in which they have participated, and honors they have received; 3 letters of recommendation; the name of the college; and information on financial need.
Financial data The stipend is $1,000. Funds are paid directly to the recipient's university to be used for tuition, fees, and books.
Duration 1 year; recipients may reapply.
Number awarded Varies each year; recently, 13 were awarded.
Deadline March of each year.

[139]
NATIONAL GUARD ASSOCIATION OF MICHIGAN EDUCATIONAL GRANTS

National Guard Association of Michigan
Attn: Scholarships
P.O. Box 810
Cadillac, MI 49601
Toll Free: (800) 477-1644   Fax: (231) 775-7906
E-mail: NGAM@charter.net
Web: www.ngam.org/site/?page_id=23

Summary To provide financial assistance to members of the National Guard Association of Michigan who are interested in attending college in any state.
Eligibility This program is open to members of the association who are also current members of the Michigan National Guard. Applicants may be enlisted members of any rank, warrant officers through CW3, or commissioned officers through the rank of captain. They must be attending or planning to attend a college, university, or trade school in any

state. Along with their application, they must submit a 100-word statement on their educational and military goals. Financial need is not considered in the selection process.

Financial data A stipend is awarded (amount not specified).

Duration 1 semester; may be renewed.

Number awarded Varies each year; recently, 6 were awarded.

Deadline June of each year for the fall term/semester; November of each year for the winter term/semester.

[140]
NATIONAL GUARD ASSOCIATION OF MINNESOTA SCHOLARSHIPS

National Guard Association of Minnesota
Attn: Executive Director
P.O. Box 47132
Plymouth, MN 55442
(763) 202-2151   E-mail: director@ngamn.org
Web: www.ngamn.org/node/56

Summary To provide financial assistance to current and retired members of the National Guard Association of Minnesota (NGAMN) and their families who are working on an undergraduate or graduate degree at a school in any state.

Eligibility This program is open to active members and retired life members of NGAMN and their spouses, children, and grandchildren. Applicants must be currently enrolled at least half time at an accredited institution of higher learning in any state and working on a 4-year bachelor's or graduate degree. They must have a GPA of 2.75 or higher. Along with their application, they must submit an essay on a topic that describes a value of the Army or Air Force, rotating among loyalty, duty, respect, selfless service, honor, integrity, personal courage, commitment, and excellence. Financial need is not considered in the selection process.

Financial data Stipends are $1,000 or $500. Funds are paid directly to the recipient.

Duration 1 year. Recipients may reapply after 3 years.

Additional information The $1,000 scholarship is sponsored by HiWay Federal Credit Union. This program began in 2008.

Number awarded 3 each year: 1 at $1,000 and 2 at $500 (1 to a member or retired member and 1 to a spouse, child, or grandchild).

Deadline July of each year.

[141]
NATIONAL GUARD ASSOCIATION OF NEW HAMPSHIRE SCHOLARSHIPS

National Guard Association of New Hampshire
Attn: Scholarship Committee
P.O. Box 22031
Portsmouth, NH 03802-2031
(603) 227-1597   E-mail: nganhscholarship@gmail.com
Web: www.nganh.org/Archive/Scholarship

Summary To provide financial assistance to members of the National Guard Association of New Hampshire and their dependents who are interested in attending college or graduate school in any state.

Eligibility This program is open to current members of the National Guard Association of New Hampshire (officer, enlisted, or retired), their spouses, and their dependent chil-

dren. Applicants must be enrolled or planning to enroll full or part time in an associate, bachelor's, graduate, professional, or doctoral degree program at an accredited college or university in any state. Along with their application, they must submit a 1-page essay on a topic that changes annually; recently, they were asked to describe what citizen service means to them.

Financial data The stipend is $1,000.

Duration 1 year.

Number awarded 1 each year.

Deadline April of each year.

[142]
NATIONAL GUARD ASSOCIATION OF NEW JERSEY SCHOLARSHIP PROGRAM

National Guard Association of New Jersey
Attn: Scholarship Committee
P.O. Box 266
Wrightstown, NJ 08562
(973) 541-6776   Fax: (973) 541-6909
E-mail: scholarship@nganj.org
Web: www.nganj.org/benefits.htm

Summary To provide financial assistance to members of the National Guard Association of New Jersey (NGANJ) or their dependents who are interested in attending college or graduate school in any state.

Eligibility This program is open to 1) active members of the NGANJ currently enrolled full time at an approved community college, school of nursing, or 4-year college in any state; and 2) the spouses, children, and grandchildren of active, retired, or deceased members entering or attending a 4-year college or university in any state. Applicants must submit transcripts, information on the civic and academic activities in which they have participated, and a list of offices, honors, awards, and special recognitions they have received. Selection is based on academic accomplishment, leadership, and citizenship.

Financial data Stipends up to $1,000 are available.

Duration 1 year; nonrenewable.

Number awarded Varies each year; recently, 10 were awarded.

Deadline April of each year.

[143]
NATIONAL GUARD ASSOCIATION OF RHODE ISLAND SCHOLARSHIPS

National Guard Association of Rhode Island
Attn: Scholarship Committee
645 New London Avenue
Cranston, RI 02920-3097
(401) 228-6586   Fax: (401) 541-9182
E-mail: ngarinews@gmail.com
Web: www.ngari.org/scholarships/

Summary To provide financial assistance to current and former members of the Rhode Island National Guard and their children who plan to attend college in any state.

Eligibility This program is open to active and retired members of the Rhode Island National Guard and their children. Applicants must be high school seniors, high school graduates, or undergraduate students. They must be attending or accepted at an accredited college, university, or vocational/technical school in any state. As part of their application, they must describe any needs, goals, and other factors that may help the selection committee.

Financial data The stipend is $1,000.

Duration 1 year; nonrenewable.

Number awarded Varies each year; recently, 4 were awarded.

Deadline May of each year.

[144]
NATIONAL GUARD ASSOCIATION OF SOUTH CAROLINA SCHOLARSHIPS

National Guard Association of South Carolina
Attn: NGASC Scholarship Foundation
132 Pickens Street
Columbia, SC 29205
(803) 254-8456   Toll Free: (800) 822-3235
Fax: (803) 254-3869   E-mail: nginfo@ngasc.org
Web: www.ngasc.org/services-view/scholorships

Summary To provide financial assistance to current and former South Carolina National Guard members and their dependents who are interested in attending college or graduate school in any state.

Eligibility This program is open to undergraduate students who are 1) current, retired, or deceased members of the South Carolina National Guard; 2) their dependents; and 3) members of the National Guard Association of South Carolina (NGASC). Graduate students are also eligible if they are members of the South Carolina National Guard. Applicants must be attending or interested in attending a college or university in any state as a full-time student. Several of the scholarships include additional restrictions on school or academic major; some are granted only for academic excellence, but most are based on both academics and financial need.

Financial data The stipend is $1,500 or $1,000.

Duration 1 year; may be renewed up to 3 additional years.

Number awarded Varies each year; recently, 55 were awarded.

Deadline January of each year.

[145]
NATIONAL GUARD ASSOCIATION OF TENNESSEE SCHOLARSHIP PROGRAM

National Guard Association of Tennessee
Attn: Scholarship Committee
4332 Kenilwood Drive
Nashville, TN 37204-4401
(615) 833-9100   Toll Free: (888) 642-8448 (within TN)
Fax: (615) 833-9173   E-mail: Christi@ngatn.org
Web: www.ngatn.org

Summary To provide financial assistance for college to members or dependents of members of the National Guard Association of Tennessee (NGATN).

Eligibility This program is open to active Tennessee National Guard members and to active annual or life members of the NGATN. If no active Guard or association member qualifies, the scholarships may be awarded to the child of a Guard or association member, including life members who have retired or are deceased. All applicants must be high school seniors or graduates who meet entrance or continuation requirements at a Tennessee college or university. Selection is based on leadership in school and civic activities, moti-

vation for continued higher education, academic achievement in high school and/or college, and financial need.

Financial data The stipends are $1,500.

Duration 1 year.

Number awarded 6 each year: 1 to an active National Guard member; 2 to current association members or their dependents; 2 to active National Guard members or their dependents; and 1 to a current Guard member who was mobilized for Operations Desert Storm, Noble Eagle, Enduring Freedom, or Iraqi Freedom.

Deadline May of each year.

[146]
NATIONAL GUARD ASSOCIATION OF TEXAS SCHOLARSHIP PROGRAM

National Guard Association of Texas
Attn: Education Committee
3706 Crawford Avenue
Austin, TX 78731-6803
(512) 454-7300   Toll Free: (800) 252-NGAT
Fax: (512) 467-6803   E-mail: rlindner@ngat.org
Web: www.ngat.org/educate.php

Summary To provide financial assistance to members and dependents of members of the National Guard Association of Texas who are interested in attending college or graduate school in any state.

Eligibility This program is open to annual and life members of the association and their spouses and children (associate members and their dependents are not eligible). Applicants may be high school seniors, undergraduate students, or graduate students, either enrolled or planning to enroll at an institution of higher education in any state. Along with their application, they must submit an essay on their desire to continue their education. Selection is based on scholarship, citizenship, and leadership.

Financial data Stipends range from $700 to $5,000.

Duration 1 year (nonrenewable).

Additional information This program includes 1 scholarship sponsored by USAA Insurance Corporation.

Number awarded Varies each year; recently, 9 were awarded: 1 at $5,000, 2 at $2,000, 1 at $1,500, 1 at $1,250, 3 at $1,000, and 1 at $750.

Deadline February of each year.

[147]
NATIONAL GUARD ASSOCIATION OF VERMONT SCHOLARSHIPS

National Guard Association of Vermont
Attn: Scholarships
P.O. Box 694
Essex Junction, VT 05453
(802) 338-3185   E-mail: timothy.gariboldi@us.army.mil
Web: www.ngavt.org/scholarInfo.shtml

Summary To provide financial assistance to members of the Vermont National Guard (VTNG) or the National Guard Association of Vermont (NGA-VT) and their children or spouses who are interested in attending college or graduate school in any state.

Eligibility This program is open to current members of the VTNG or the NGA-VT, their spouses, and their unmarried children. Applicants must be working, or planning to work, on an associate, undergraduate, technical, or graduate degree as a full-time student at a school in any state. Along with their application, they must submit an essay on their commitment to selfless public service or their plan for pursuing it in the future. In the selection process, first priority is given to applicants in grades E-1 through E-6, W-1 and W-2, and O-1 through O-3; second to E-7, E-8, and W3; third to E-9, W-4 and W-5, and O-4 and above. Other factors considered include the essay, academic performance, and community service. The program includes the COL James D. Kneeland Memorial Scholarship Award, reserved for a member of the Vermont Army National Guard Aviation Community.

Financial data Stipends range from $500 to $1,500. Funds are sent directly to the recipient.

Duration 1 year; recipients may reapply.

Number awarded 4 each year: 1 at $1,500 (the COL James D. Kneeland Memorial Scholarship Award), 1 at $1,000, and 2 at $500 (1 for a student affiliated with the Vermont Army National Guard and 1 for a student affiliated with the Vermont Air National Guard).

Deadline June of each year.

[148]
NATIONAL GUARD CHAPTER ASMC CONTINUING EDUCATION GRANTS

American Society of Military Comptrollers-National Guard Chapter
c/o CW3 Carl Jackson, Continuing Education Committee
United States Property and Fiscal Officer for Georgia
Resource Management Division
P.O. Box 17882
Atlanta, GA 30316-0882
(678) 569-6399   E-mail: carl.stefan.jackson@us.army.mil
Web: www.ng-asmc.org

Summary To provide financial assistance to members of the National Guard Chapter of the American Society of Military Comptrollers (ASMC) who are interested in attending a college or vocational school to obtain additional education in a field related to financial and resource management.

Eligibility This program is open to ASMC members who have been a member of its National Guard Chapter for at least 24 months. Applicants must be interested in enrolling at a college or vocational school for additional study related to financial and resource management (e.g., accounting, business administration, computer science, economics, finance, operations research related to financial management, public administration). They must be able to demonstrate financial need.

Financial data Stipends are $1,000 or $500.

Duration 1 year.

Additional information Membership in ASMC is open to military and civilian personnel involved in the field of military comptrollership. The National Guard Chapter serves ASMC members who are associated with the Army National Guard or Air National Guard in any state.

Number awarded 2 each year: 1 at $1,000 (designated the Robert E. Ruder Continuing Education Grant) and 1 at $500 (designated the Steve Emmons Continuing Education Grant).

Deadline February of each year.

[149]
NATIONAL GUARD OF GEORGIA SCHOLARSHIP FUND FOR COLLEGES OR UNIVERSITIES

Georgia Guard Insurance Trust
P.O. Box 889
Mableton, GA 30126
(770) 739-9651   Toll Free: (800) 229-1053
Fax: (770) 745-0673   E-mail: director@ngaga.org
Web: www.ngaga.org/scholarships.html

Summary To provide financial assistance to members of the Georgia National Guard and their spouses, children, and grandchildren who are interested in attending college in any state.

Eligibility This program is open to policyholders with the Georgia Guard Insurance Trust (GGIT) who are members of the National Guard Association of Georgia (NGAGA) or the Enlisted Association of the National Guard of Georgia (EANGGA); spouses, children, and grandchildren of NGAGA and EANGGA members are also eligible. Applicants must be enrolled or planning to enroll full time at a college or university in any state and have received an academic honor while in high school. Graduating high school seniors must have a combined mathematics and critical reading SAT score of at least 1000 or a GPA of 3.0 or higher. Students already enrolled at a college or university must have a cumulative GPA of 3.0 or higher. Along with their application, they must submit transcripts, a letter with personal specific facts regarding their desire to continue their education, 2 letters of recommendation, a letter of academic reference, and an agreement to retain insurance with the GGIT for at least 2 years following completion of the school year for which the scholarship is awarded. Selection is based on academics, character, and moral and personal traits.

Financial data The stipend is $1,000.

Duration 1 year.

Number awarded 1 or 2 each year.

Deadline April of each year.

[150]
NATIONAL GUARD OF GEORGIA SCHOLARSHIP FUND FOR VOCATIONAL OR BUSINESS SCHOOLS

Georgia Guard Insurance Trust
P.O. Box 889
Mableton, GA 30126
(770) 739-9651   Toll Free: (800) 229-1053
Fax: (770) 745-0673   E-mail: director@ngaga.org
Web: www.ngaga.org/scholarships.html

Summary To provide financial assistance to members of the Georgia National Guard and their spouses, children, and grandchildren who are interested in attending business or vocational school in any state.

Eligibility This program is open to policyholders with the Georgia Guard Insurance Trust (GGIT) who are members of the National Guard Association of Georgia (NGAGA) or the Enlisted Association of the National Guard of Georgia (EANGGA); spouses, children, and grandchildren of NGAGA and EANGGA members are also eligible. Applicants must be interested in enrolling full time in day or evening classes at a business or vocational school in any state. They must be able to meet program-specific admission standards and institutional requirements and complete all admission procedures for admission to a degree/diploma program in regular program status. Along with their application, they must submit transcripts, a letter with personal specific facts regarding their desire to continue their education, 2 letters of recommendation, and an agreement to retain insurance with the GGIT for at least 2 years following completion of the school year for which the scholarship is awarded. Selection is based on academics, character, and moral and personal traits.

Financial data The stipend is $1,000.

Duration 1 year.

Number awarded 1 or 2 each year.

Deadline April of each year.

[151]
NAVAL ENLISTED RESERVE ASSOCIATION SCHOLARSHIPS

Naval Enlisted Reserve Association
Attn: Scholarship Committee
6703 Farragut Avenue
Falls Church, VA 22042-2189
(703) 534-1329   Toll Free: (800) 776-9020
Fax: (703) 534-3617   E-mail: members@nera.org
Web: www.nera.org

Summary To provide financial assistance for college to members of the Naval Enlisted Reserve Association (NERA) and their families.

Eligibility This program is open to regular or associate NERA members, the spouses of regular members, and the unmarried children and grandchildren under 23 years of age of regular members. Applicants must be graduating high school seniors or undergraduates currently attending an accredited 2- or 4-year college or university as a full- or part-time student. Along with their application, they must submit a 500-word essay on either 1) their career goals and objectives for their education; or 2) why Reservists are important to America. Financial need is not considered in the selection process.

Financial data The stipend is $2,500.

Duration 1 year.

Additional information This program is funded in part by USAA Insurance Corporation.

Number awarded 4 each year.

Deadline June of each year.

[152]
NAVAL FLIGHT OFFICER OPTION OF THE SEAMAN TO ADMIRAL-21 PROGRAM

U.S. Navy
Attn: Commander, Naval Service Training Command
250 Dallas Street, Suite A
Pensacola, FL 32508-5268
(850) 452-9563   Fax: (850) 452-2486
E-mail: PNSC_STA21@navy.mil
Web: www.sta-21.navy.mil/program_options.asp

Summary To allow outstanding enlisted Navy personnel to attend college, affiliate with an NROTC unit, complete a bachelor's degree, and receive a commission as a naval flight officer (NFO).

Eligibility This program is open to U.S. citizens who are currently serving on active duty in the U.S. Navy or Naval Reserve, including Full Time Support (FTS), Selected Reserves (SELRES), and Navy Reservists on active duty, except for those on active duty for training (ACDUTRA). Appli-

cants must be high school graduates (or GED recipients) who are able to complete requirements for a baccalaureate degree in 36 months or less. When they complete their degree requirements, they must be younger than 27 years of age (may be adjusted to 31 years of age for prior active-duty service). Within the past 3 years, they must have taken the SAT (and achieved scores of at least 500 on the mathematics section and 500 on the critical reading section) or the ACT (and achieved a score of at least 21 on the mathematics portion and 20 on the English portion). They must also achieve a score of at least the following: AQR (4), FOFAR (5) on the Aviation Selection Test Battery.

Financial data Awardees continue to receive their regular Navy pay and allowances while they attend college on a full-time basis. They also receive reimbursement for tuition, fees, and books up to $10,000 per year. If base housing is available, they are eligible to live there. Participants are not eligible to receive benefits under the Navy's Tuition Assistance Program (TA), the Montgomery GI Bill (MGIB), the Navy College Fund, or the Veterans Educational Assistance Program (VEAP).

Duration Selectees are supported for up to 36 months of full-time, year-round study or completion of a bachelor's degree, as long as they maintain a GPA of 2.5 or higher.

Additional information This program began in 2001 as a replacement for the Aviation Enlisted Commissioning Program (AECP). Upon acceptance into the program, selectees attend the Naval Science Institute (NSI) in Newport, Rhode Island for an 8-week program in the fundamental core concepts of being a naval officer (navigation, engineering, weapons, military history and justice, etc.). They then enter a college or university with an NROTC unit or affiliation to work full time on a bachelor's degree. They become members of and drill with the NROTC unit. When they complete their degree, they are commissioned as ensigns in the United States Naval Reserve and assigned to flight training. After commissioning, participants incur an active-duty obligation of 6 years after designation as a Naval Flight Officer or 6 years from the date of disenrollment from flight training.

Number awarded Varies each year.

Deadline June of each year.

[153]
NAVAL HELICOPTER ASSOCIATION ACTIVE DUTY SCHOLARSHIPS

Naval Helicopter Association
Attn: Scholarship Fund
P.O. Box 180578
Coronado, CA 92178-0578
(619) 435-7139   Fax: (619) 435-7354
Web: nhascholarshipfund.org/scholarships-available.html

Summary To provide financial assistance for college or graduate school to active-duty personnel who are working or have worked in rotary wing activities of the sea services.

Eligibility This program is open to active-duty Navy, Marine Corps, or Coast Guard rotary wing aviators, aircrewmen, or support personnel. Applicants must be working on or planning to work on an undergraduate or graduate degree in any field. Along with their application, they must submit a personal statement on their academic and career aspirations. Selection is based on that statement, academic proficiency, scholastic achievements and awards, extracurricular activities, employment history, and letters of recommendation.

Financial data Stipends are approximately $2,000.

Duration 1 year.

Number awarded 4 each year: 2 to undergraduates and 2 to graduate students.

Deadline January of each year.

[154]
NAVAL HELICOPTER ASSOCIATION MEMORIAL SCHOLARSHIPS

Naval Helicopter Association
Attn: Scholarship Fund
P.O. Box 180578
Coronado, CA 92178-0578
(619) 435-7139   Fax: (619) 435-7354
Web: nhascholarshipfund.org/scholarships-available.html

Summary To provide financial assistance for college or graduate school to 1) active-duty personnel who are working or have worked in rotary wing activities of the sea services and 2) members of their families.

Eligibility This program is open to 1) active-duty Navy, Marine Corps, or Coast Guard rotary wing aviators, aircrewmen, or support personnel; and 2) the children and spouses of those personnel. Applicants must be working on or planning to work on an undergraduate or graduate degree in any field. Along with their application, they must submit a personal statement on their academic and career aspirations. Selection is based on that statement, academic proficiency, scholastic achievements and awards, extracurricular activities, employment history, and letters of recommendation.

Financial data Stipends are approximately $2,000.

Duration 1 year.

Additional information This program includes the following named awards: the Edward and Veronica Ream Memorial Scholarship, the CDR Mort McCarthy Memorial Scholarship, the Charles Karman Memorial Scholarship, the LT Christian "Horse" Hescock Memorial Scholarship, and the Captain Mark Starr Memorial Scholarship.

Number awarded Varies each year; recently, 4 were awarded.

Deadline January of each year.

[155]
NAVY ADVANCED EDUCATION VOUCHER PROGRAM

U.S. Navy
Naval Education and Training Command (N523)
Professional Development and Technology Center
Attn: AEV Program Office
250 Dallas Street
Pensacola, FL 32508-5220
(850) 452-7268   Fax: (850) 452-1272
E-mail: jason.szot@navy.mil
Web: www.navycollege.navy.mil/aev/aev_stu.aspx

Summary To provide financial assistance to senior Navy enlisted personnel who are interested in earning an undergraduate or graduate degree during off-duty hours.

Eligibility This program is open to senior enlisted Navy personnel in ranks E-7 through E-9. Applicants should be transferring to, or currently on, shore duty with sufficient time ashore to complete a bachelor's or master's degree. Person-

nel at rank E-7 may have no more than 17 years in service, E-8 no more than 19 years, and E-9 no more than 22 years. The area of study must be certified by the Naval Postgraduate School as Navy-relevant.

Financial data This program covers education costs (tuition, books, and fees), to a maximum of $6,700 per year or a total of $20,000 per participant for a bachelor's degree or $20,000 per year or a total of $40,000 per participant for a master's degree.

Duration Up to 36 months from the time of enrollment for a bachelor's degree; up to 24 months from the time of enrollment for a master's degree.

Additional information Recently approved majors for bachelor's degrees included human resources, construction management, information technology, emergency and disaster management, paralegal, engineering, business administration, leadership and management, nursing, strategic foreign languages, and electrical/electronic technology. Approved fields of study for master's degrees included business administration, education and training management, emergency and disaster management, engineering and technology, homeland defense and security, human resources, information technology, leadership and management, project management, and systems analysis. Recipients of this assistance incur an obligation to remain on active duty following completion of the program for a period equal to 3 times the number of months of education completed, to a maximum obligation of 36 months.

Number awarded Varies each year; recently, 20 of these vouchers were awarded: 15 for bachelor's degrees and 5 for master's degrees.

Deadline May of each year.

[156]
NAVY NURSE CANDIDATE PROGRAM

U.S. Navy
Attn: Navy Bureau of Medicine and Surgery
Accessions Department
8955 Wood Road, Suite 13132
Bethesda, MD 20889-5628
(301) 295-1217   Toll Free: (800) USA-NAVY
Fax: (301) 295-6865   E-mail: oh@med.navy.mil
Web: www.med.navy.mil

Summary To provide financial assistance for nursing education to students interested in serving in the Navy.

Eligibility This program is open to full-time students in a bachelor of science in nursing program who are U.S. citizens under 40 years of age. Prior to or during their junior year of college, applicants must enlist in the U.S. Navy Nurse Corps Reserve. Following receipt of their degree, they must be willing to serve on active duty as a nurse in the Navy.

Financial data This program pays a $10,000 initial grant upon enlistment (paid in 2 installments of $5,000 each) and a stipend of $1,000 per month. Students are responsible for paying all school expenses.

Duration Up to 24 months.

Additional information Students who receive support from this program for 1 to 12 months incur an active-duty service obligation of 4 years; students who receive support for 13 to 24 months have a service obligation of 5 years.

Number awarded Varies each year.

Deadline Deadline not specified.

[157]
NAVY SEAL FOUNDATION SCHOLARSHIPS

Navy Seal Foundation
Attn: Chief Financial Officer
1619 D Street, Building 5326
Virginia Beach, VA 23459
(757) 363-7490   Fax: (757) 363-7491
E-mail: info@navysealfoundation.org
Web: www.navysealfoundation.org

Summary To provide financial assistance for college or graduate school to Naval Special Warfare (NSW) personnel and their families.

Eligibility This program is open to active-duty Navy SEALS, Special Warfare Combatant-craft Crewmen (SWCC), and military personnel assigned to other NSW commands. Their dependent children and spouses are also eligible. Applicants must be entering or continuing full or part-time students working on an associate or bachelor's degree. Active-duty and spouses, but not dependent children, may also work on a graduate degree. Selection is based on GPA, SAT scores, class ranking, extracurricular activities, volunteer community involvement, leadership positions held, military service record, and employment (as appropriate).

Financial data Stipends are $15,000, $7,500, or $5,000 per year.

Duration 1 year; may be renewed.

Number awarded Varies each year; recently, the Navy Seal Foundation awarded 16 scholarships for all of its programs: 3 for 4 years at $15,000 per year to high school seniors and graduates, 3 for 1 year at $7,500 to high school seniors and graduates, 3 for 1 year at $15,000 to current college students, 3 for 1 year at $7,500 to current college students, and 4 for 1 year at $5,000 to spouses.

Deadline February of each year.

[158]
NAVY TUITION ASSISTANCE PROGRAM

U.S. Navy
Attn: Naval Education and Training Professional
  Development and Technology Command
Code N814
6490 Saufley Field Road
Pensacola, FL 32509-5241
(850) 452-1001   Toll Free: (877) 838-1659
Fax: (850) 473-6401   E-mail: SFLY_TA.Navy@navy.mil
Web: www.navycollege.navy.mil/ta_info.aspx

Summary To provide financial assistance for high school, vocational, undergraduate, or graduate studies to Navy personnel.

Eligibility This program is open to active-duty Navy officers and enlisted personnel, including Naval Reservists on continuous active duty, enlisted Naval Reservists ordered to active duty for 120 days or more, and Naval Reservist officers ordered to active duty for 2 years or more. Applicants must register to take courses at accredited civilian schools during off-duty time. They must be working on their first associate, bachelor's, master's, doctoral, or professional degree. Tuition assistance is provided for courses taken at accredited colleges, universities, vocational/technical schools, private schools, and through independent study/distance learning (but not for flight training).

Financial data Those selected for participation in this program receive their regular Navy pay and 100% of tuition at the postsecondary educational institution of their choice, but capped at $250 per semester hour and 16 semester hours per fiscal year, or a total of $4,500 per fiscal year. Funding is available only for tuition, not fees or other associated expenses.

Duration Until completion of a bachelor's or graduate degree. Undergraduates must complete all courses with a grade of "C" or better; graduate students must complete classes with a grade of "B" of better. If recipients fail to achieve those grades, they must reimburse the Navy for all funds received.

Additional information Officers must agree to remain on active duty for at least 2 years after completion of courses funded by this program.

Number awarded Varies each year.

Deadline Deadline not specified.

[159]
NEBRASKA NATIONAL GUARD TUITION ASSISTANCE PROGRAM

Nebraska Military Department
Attn: Nebraska National Guard
1300 Military Road
Lincoln, NE 68508-1090
(402) 309-7210
Web: ne.ng.mil/Pages/TARegister.aspx

Summary To provide an opportunity for enlisted members of the Nebraska National Guard to pursue additional education.

Eligibility Eligible for this benefit are enlisted members of the Nebraska National Guard who are enrolled in a Nebraska university, college, or community college. Commissioned and warrant officers are not eligible, nor are enlisted personnel who already have a baccalaureate degree. Guard members must apply for this assistance within 10 years of the date of initial enlistment. The credit is not available for graduate study or non-credit courses. Priority is given to Guard members who have previously received these benefits.

Financial data Students at state-supported institutions are exempted from payment of the tuition charges at their schools. Students at independent, nonprofit, accredited colleges and universities in Nebraska receive a credit equal to the amount they would receive if they attended the University of Nebraska at Lincoln. All funds are paid directly to the school.

Duration 1 year; may be renewed.

Additional information Any member of the Nebraska National Guard who receives this assistance must agree to serve in the Guard for 3 years after completion of the courses for which assistance was given.

Number awarded Up to 1,200 each year.

Deadline June of each year for academic terms beginning between July and September; September of each year for academic terms beginning between October and December; December of each year for academic terms beginning between January and March; March of each year for academic terms beginning between April and June.

[160]
NEBRASKA RESERVIST TUITION CREDIT
Department of Veterans' Affairs
State Office Building
301 Centennial Mall South, Sixth Floor
P.O. Box 95083
Lincoln, NE 68509-5083
(402) 471-2458   Fax: (402) 471-2491
E-mail: john.hilgert@nebraska.gov
Web: www.vets.state.ne.us/benefits.html

Summary To provide financial assistance for college to members of Nebraska units of the active Reserves.

Eligibility Nebraska residents who are enlisted members of a Nebraska-based unit of the active selected Reserve are eligible for this benefit. They must have at least 2 years remaining on their enlistment, have agreed to serve at least 3 years in the Reserves, not have completed the tenth year of total service in the U.S. armed forces (including active and Reserve time), and be working on a degree at a state-supported college or university or an equivalent level of study in a technical community college.

Financial data Reservists who meet the requirements may receive a credit for 50% of the tuition charges at any state-supported university or college in Nebraska, including any technical community college.

Duration 1 year; may be renewed until receipt of the degree or completion of the course of study.

Number awarded Varies each year; the program is limited to 200 new applications per calendar year.

Deadline Deadline not specified.

[161]
NERA MEMBER SCHOLARSHIPS
Naval Enlisted Reserve Association
Attn: Scholarship Committee
6703 Farragut Avenue
Falls Church, VA 22042-2189
(703) 534-1329   Toll Free: (800) 776-9020
Fax: (703) 534-3617   E-mail: members@nera.org
Web: www.nera.org

Summary To provide financial assistance for college to sea service enlisted Reservists who are also members of the Naval Enlisted Reserve Association (NERA).

Eligibility This program is open to drilling Reservists of the Coast Guard, Navy, and Marines who are regular members of the association. Applicants must be attending an accredited 2- or 4-year college or university as a full- or part-time student. Along with their application, they must submit a 500-word essay on either 1) their career goals and objectives for their education; or 2) why Reservists are important to America. Financial need is not considered in the selection process.

Financial data The stipend is $3,000.

Duration 1 year.

Additional information This program is funded in part by USAA Insurance Corporation.

Number awarded 2 each year.

Deadline June of each year.

[162]
NEVADA NATIONAL GUARD STATE TUITION WAIVER PROGRAM
Nevada National Guard
Attn: Education Officer
2460 Fairview Drive
Carson City, NV 89701-6807
(775) 887-7326   Fax: (775) 887-7279
E-mail: NV-TSC@ng.army.mil
Web: www.nv.ngb.army.mil

Summary To provide financial assistance to Nevada National Guard members who are interested in attending college or graduate school in the state.

Eligibility This program is open to active members of the Nevada National Guard who are interested in attending a public community college, 4-year college, or university in the state. Applicants must be residents of Nevada. Independent study, correspondence courses, and study at the William S. Boyd School of Law, the University of Nevada School of Medicine, and the UNLV School of Dental Medicine are not eligible.

Financial data This program provides a waiver of 100% of tuition at state-supported community colleges, colleges, or universities in Nevada.

Duration 1 year; may be renewed.

Additional information This program was established on a pilot basis in 2003 and became permanent in 2005. Recipients must attain a GPA of at least 2.0 or refund all tuition received.

Number awarded Varies each year.

Deadline Applications must be received at least 3 weeks prior to the start of classes.

[163]
NEW HAMPSHIRE NATIONAL GUARD TUITION WAIVER PROGRAM
Office of the Adjutant General
Attn: Education Office
State Military Reservation
4 Pembroke Road
Concord, NH 03301-5652
(603) 225-1312   Fax: (603) 225-1257
TDD: (800) 735-2964
E-mail: education@nharmyguard.com
Web: www.nh.ngb.army.mil/members/education

Summary To provide financial assistance to members of the New Hampshire National Guard who are interested in attending college or graduate school in the state.

Eligibility This program is open to active members of the New Hampshire National Guard who have completed advanced individual training or commissioning and have at least a 90% attendance rate at annual training and drill assemblies. Applicants may be working on any type of academic degree at public institutions in New Hampshire. They must apply for financial aid from their school, for the New Hampshire National Guard Scholarship Program, and for federal tuition assistance.

Financial data The program provides full payment of tuition.

Duration 1 year; may be renewed.

Additional information This program began in 1996.

Number awarded Varies each year, depending on availability of space.

Deadline Deadline not specified.

[164]
NEW JERSEY NATIONAL GUARD TUITION PROGRAM

New Jersey Department of Military and Veterans Affairs
Attn: New Jersey Army National Guard Education Center
3650 Saylors Pond Road
Fort Dix, NJ 08640-7600
(609) 562-0654   Toll Free: (888) 859-0352
Fax: (609) 562-0201
Web: www.state.nj.us/military/education/NJNGTP.htm

Summary To provide financial assistance for college or graduate school to New Jersey National Guard members and the surviving spouses and children of deceased members.

Eligibility This program is open to active members of the New Jersey National Guard who have completed Initial Active Duty for Training (IADT). Applicants must be New Jersey residents who have been accepted into a program of undergraduate or graduate study at any of 31 public institutions of higher education in the state. The surviving spouses and children of deceased members of the Guard who had completed IADT and were killed in the performance of their duties while a member of the Guard are also eligible if the school has classroom space available.

Financial data Tuition for up to 15 credits per semester is waived for full-time recipients in state-supported colleges or community colleges in New Jersey.

Duration 1 semester; may be renewed.

Number awarded Varies each year.

Deadline Deadline not specified.

[165]
NEW MEXICO NATIONAL GUARD TUITION SCHOLARSHIP PROGRAM

New Mexico National Guard
Attn: Education Services Officer
47 Bataan Boulevard
Santa Fe, NM 87508
(505) 474-1245   Fax: (505) 474-1243
E-mail: educationNM@nm.ngb.army.mil
Web: www.nm.ngb.army.mil/education.html

Summary To provide financial assistance to members of the New Mexico National Guard who are working on an undergraduate degree at a school in the state.

Eligibility This program is open to members of the New Mexico National Guard who are working on their first degree at the undergraduate or vocational school level. Applicants must be attending a state-supported school in New Mexico.

Financial data This program provides payment of 100% of the cost of tuition, including instructional fees in lieu of tuition and laboratory shop fees that are specifically required.

Duration 1 semester; may be renewed for up to 130 semester hours of undergraduate or vocational study.

Number awarded Varies each year, depending on the availability of funds.

Deadline June of each year for fall semester; November of each year for spring semester; April of each year for summer school.

[166]
NEW YORK RECRUITMENT INCENTIVE AND RETENTION PROGRAM

New York State Division of Military and Naval Affairs
Attn: New York National Guard Education Office
NYARNG MNP-ED
1 Buffington Street, Building 25, Suite 334
Watervliet, NY 12189-4000
(518) 272-4051
E-mail: ng.ny.nyarng.list.education-ny@mail.mil
Web: dmna.ny.gov/education/?id=rirp

Summary To provide financial assistance to members of the New York State Military Forces who are interested in attending college in the state.

Eligibility This program is open to members of the New York Army National Guard, New York Air National Guard, and New York Naval Militia in good military and academic standing. Applicants must have been enrolled in a degree program for a minimum of 6 credit hours per semester, have been legal residents of New York for at least 186 days prior to using the program for the first time and 186 days per year (excluding periods of active federal service), and be enrolled in their first baccalaureate degree program. They must have completed Initial Active Duty for Training (IADT), naval enlisted code (NEC) training, or a commissioning program.

Financial data The program pays for the cost of tuition (up to $4,350 or the maximum cost of the State University of New York undergraduate tuition) for credit bearing courses, or courses that are required as a prerequisite within the declared degree program.

Duration Up to 8 semesters of full-time study, or the equivalent of 4 academic years, are supported; if the undergraduate program normally requires 5 academic years of full-time study, then this program will support 10 semesters of full-time study or the equivalent of 5 academic years. For part-time (from 6 to 11 semester hours per semester) study, the program provides up to 16 semesters of support.

Additional information This program became effective in 1997.

Number awarded Varies each year.

Deadline August of each year for fall semester; December of each year for spring semester.

[167]
NGAMA SCHOLARSHIPS

National Guard Association of Massachusetts
Attn: Education Services Office
2 Randolph Road, Building 1505
Hanscom AFB, MA 01731-3001
E-mail: contact@ngama.org
Web: www.ngama.org/scholarships/

Summary To provide financial assistance to members of the Massachusetts National Guard and their dependents who are interested in attending college in any state.

Eligibility This program is open to 1) current members of the Massachusetts National Guard; 2) children and spouses of current members of the National Guard Association of Massachusetts (NGAMA); and 3) children and spouses of current members of the Massachusetts National Guard. Applicants must be enrolled in or planning to enroll in an accredited college or technical program in any state. Along with their application, they must submit a letter of recommendation, a list of extracurricular activities and other significant accomplishments, high school or college transcripts, and an essay on a topic that changes annually but relates to the National Guard.

Financial data   The stipend is $2,000.

Duration   1 year.

Number awarded   2 each year.

Deadline   March of each year.

[168]
NGAUT AND EANGUT "MINUTEMAN" SCHOLARSHIPS

National Guard Association of Utah
12953 South Minuteman Drive, Room 19835
P.O. Box 435
Draper, UT 84020
(801) 631-6312   E-mail: ngautah@ngaut.org
Web: www.ngaut.org/Scholarship.php

Summary   To provide financial assistance to members and dependents of members of the National Guard Association of Utah (NGAAUT) and the Enlisted Association of the National Guard of Utah (EANGUT) who are interested in attending college in the state.

Eligibility   This program is open to members and dependents of members of NGAUT and EANGUT who are high school seniors or students enrolled for at least 6 credit hours at a college or university in the state. Applicants must submit 1) a 150-word description of their educational and career goals; 2) a 200- to 300-word description of leadership and extracurricular activities that they may have had or currently enjoy; 3) a 300-word essay on how the military has influenced their life; 4) a 1-page cover letter or resume; and 5) 2 letters of reference.

Financial data   Stipends are $1,500 or $1,000. Funds are sent to the recipient's school and must be used for tuition, laboratory fees, and curriculum-required books and supplies.

Duration   1 year.

Number awarded   12 each year: 1 at $1,500 and 4 at $1,000 sponsored by NGAUT, 1 at $1,500 and 1 at $1,000 sponsored by EANGUT, 1 at $1,000 sponsored by Boeing, and 4 at $1,000 sponsored by other corporate members.

Deadline   March of each year.

[169]
NGAW SCHOLARSHIP PROGRAM

National Guard Association of Washington
Attn: Scholarship Committee
P.O. Box 5144
Camp Murray
Tacoma, WA 98430-5144
(253) 584-5411   Toll Free: (800) 588-6420
Fax: (253) 582-9521   E-mail: ngaw@ngaw.org
Web: www.ngaw.org/programs/scholarships-and-awards

Summary   To provide financial assistance to members of the Washington National Guard and their dependents who are interested in attending college in the state.

Eligibility   This program is open to members of the Washington National Guard and their dependents who are enrolled at an accredited college, university, or trade school in the state. Guard members may be full-time or part-time students; dependents must be enrolled full time. Applicants do not need to be members of the National Guard Association of

Washington (NGAW) although members are eligible for larger awards. Along with their application, they must submit a statement that covers their educational goals, academic credits completed, honors and awards, participation in National Guard, plans for the future in the National Guard, participation in school extracurricular activities, participation in volunteer civic and community events, and financial need.

Financial data   The stipend ranges from $500 to $1,000.

Duration   1 year.

Number awarded   7 each year: 1 at $1,000 (designated the Lowenberg Scholarship and reserved for a Guard member) and 6 at either $750 (if the recipient is an NGAW member) or $500 (if the recipient is not a member).

Deadline   March of each year.

[170]
NGOA-FL AND ENGAF SCHOLARSHIP PROGRAM

National Guard Association of Florida
Attn: Scholarship Committee
P.O. Box 3446
St. Augustine, FL 32085-3446
(904) 823-0628   Fax: (904) 839-2068
E-mail: ngafl1903@floridaguard.org
Web: www.floridaguard.org/index.php/scholarships

Summary   To provide financial assistance to members of the Florida National Guard and their families who are also members of either the National Guard Association of Florida (NGOA-FL) or the Enlisted National Guard Association of Florida (ENGAF) and interested in attending college in the state.

Eligibility   This program is open to active members of the Florida National Guard (enlisted, officer, and warrant officer), their spouses, and children, but preference is given to Guard members. Applicants must be residents of Florida attending or planning to attend an accredited college, university, or vocational/technical school in the state. They must also be a member, spouse of a member, or child of a member of their respective association. Selection is based on academic achievement, civic and moral leadership, character, and financial need.

Financial data   Scholarships are $1,000 for full-time students or $500 for part-time students; funds are paid directly to the recipient's institution.

Duration   1 year; may be renewed.

Additional information   This program is jointly sponsored by the respective associations.

Number awarded   15 each year.

Deadline   June of each year.

[171]
NORTH CAROLINA NATIONAL GUARD ASSOCIATION ACADEMIC EXCELLENCE/ LEADERSHIP AWARD

North Carolina National Guard Association
Attn: Educational Foundation, Inc.
7410 Chapel Hill Road
Raleigh, NC 27607-5047
(919) 851-3390, ext. 5
Toll Free: (800) 821-6159 (within NC)
Fax: (919) 859-4990
E-mail: peggyncngaef@bellsouth.net
Web: sites.google.com/site/ncngassociation/documents

Summary To provide financial assistance to members and dependents of members of the North Carolina National Guard Association who demonstrate academic excellence and are attending college in any state.
Eligibility This program is open to active and associate members of the association as well as the spouses, children, grandchildren, and legal dependents of active, associate, or deceased members. Applicants must be attending a 4-year college or university in any state and have a GPA of 3.5 or higher. Selection is based on academic achievement, citizenship, leadership, and other application information.
Financial data The stipend is $1,000.
Duration 1 year; may be renewed.
Number awarded 1 or 2 each year.
Deadline January of each year.

[172]
NORTH CAROLINA NATIONAL GUARD ASSOCIATION SCHOLARSHIPS

North Carolina National Guard Association
Attn: Educational Foundation, Inc.
7410 Chapel Hill Road
Raleigh, NC 27607-5047
(919) 851-3390, ext. 5
Toll Free: (800) 821-6159 (within NC)
Fax: (919) 859-4990
E-mail: peggyncngaef@bellsouth.net
Web: sites.google.com/site/ncngassociation/documents

Summary To provide financial assistance to members and dependents of members of the North Carolina National Guard Association who plan to attend college in any state.
Eligibility This program is open to active and associate members of the association as well as the spouses, children, grandchildren, and legal dependents of active, associate, or deceased members. Applicants must be high school seniors, high school graduates, or students currently enrolled at a college or university in any state. Selection is based on financial need, academic achievement, citizenship, leadership, and other application information. The most outstanding applicants receive scholarships provided by the SECU Foundation. Applicants who meet specified additional requirements qualify for various memorial and special scholarships.
Financial data Stipends are $10,000 or $5,000 for the SECU Foundation Scholarships, $1,000 for memorial and special scholarships, $1,000 for citizenship awards, $800 for general scholarships, or $400 for community college scholarships.
Duration 1 year; may be renewed.
Additional information This program, which began in 1968, includes a number of named memorial and special scholarships. Other scholarships are funded by the SECU Foundation of the State Employees' Credit Union and the USAA Insurance Corporation.
Number awarded Varies each year; recently, 37 were awarded: 2 SECU Foundation Scholarships (1 at $10,000 and 1 at $5,000), 18 memorial and special scholarships at $1,000, 2 citizenship awards are $1,000, 10 general scholarships at $800, and 5 community college scholarships at $400.
Deadline January of each year for high school graduates and college students; February of each year for high school seniors.

[173]
NORTH CAROLINA NATIONAL GUARD ASSOCIATION SPECIAL POPULATION SCHOLARSHIP

North Carolina National Guard Association
Attn: Educational Foundation, Inc.
7410 Chapel Hill Road
Raleigh, NC 27607-5047
(919) 851-3390, ext. 5
Toll Free: (800) 821-6159 (within NC)
Fax: (919) 859-4990
E-mail: peggyncngaef@bellsouth.net
Web: sites.google.com/site/ncngassociation/documents

Summary To provide financial assistance to members and dependents of members of the North Carolina National Guard Association who have a disability and are interested in attending college in any state.
Eligibility This program is open to active and associate members of the association as well as the spouses, children, grandchildren, and legal dependents of active, associate, or deceased members. Applicants must be learning disabled and/or physically disabled. They may be high school seniors, high school graduates, or students currently enrolled at a college or university in any state. Selection is based on financial need, academic achievement, citizenship, leadership, and other application information.
Financial data The stipend is $1,000.
Duration 1 year; may be renewed.
Number awarded 1 each year.
Deadline January of each year for high school graduates and college students; February of each year for high school seniors.

[174]
NORTH CAROLINA NATIONAL GUARD TUITION ASSISTANCE PROGRAM

North Carolina National Guard
Attn: Education and Employment Center
1636 Gold Star Drive
Raleigh, NC 27607
(919) 664-6649   Toll Free: (800) 621-4136
Fax: (919) 664-6520
E-mail: stacy.m.steinmetz.nfg@mail.mil
Web: www.nc.ngb.army.mil/Services/Pages/Edu.aspx

Summary To provide financial assistance to members of the North Carolina National Guard who plan to attend college or graduate school in the state.
Eligibility This program is open to active members of the North Carolina National Guard (officer, warrant officer, or enlisted) who have at least 2 years of enlistment remaining after the end of the academic period for which tuition assistance is provided. Applicants must be enrolled in an eligible business or trade school, private institution, or public college/university in North Carolina. They may be working on a vocational, undergraduate, graduate, or doctoral degree.
Financial data The maximum stipend is currently $4,515 per academic year.
Duration 1 year; may be renewed.
Additional information This program is administered by the North Carolina State Education Assistance Authority.

Number awarded Varies each year; recently, 614 of these grants, with a value of $1,808,032, were awarded.
Deadline Deadline not specified.

[175]
NORTH DAKOTA NATIONAL GUARD ENLISTED ASSOCIATION SCHOLARSHIPS

North Dakota National Guard Enlisted Association
c/o MSG Joe Lovelace
4900 107th Avenue S.E.
Minot, ND 58701-9207
E-mail: joseph.m.lovelace@us.army.mil
Web: www.ndngea.org/forms.html

Summary To provide financial assistance to members of the North Dakota National Guard Enlisted Association (NDNGEA) and their families who are interested in attending college in any state.
Eligibility This program is open to association members who have at least 1 year remaining on their enlistment or have completed 20 or more years in service. Also eligible are their unmarried dependent children and spouses and the unremarried spouses and unmarried dependent children of deceased NDNGEA members who were in good standing at the time of death. Applicants must be attending or planning to attend a university, college, or trade/business school in any state. Graduate students are not eligible. Selection is based on academic achievement, leadership, character, and financial need.
Financial data The stipend is $1,000. Funds are sent directly to the school in the recipient's name.
Duration 1 year.
Number awarded 1 or more each year.
Deadline November of each year.

[176]
NORTH DAKOTA NATIONAL GUARD TUITION ASSISTANCE PROGRAM

North Dakota National Guard
Attn: Education Services Office
P.O. Box 5511
Bismarck, ND 58506-5511
(701) 333-3064   E-mail: ngndj1esos@ng.army.mil
Web: www.ndguard.ngb.army.mil

Summary To provide financial assistance to members of the North Dakota National Guard who plan to attend college or graduate school in the state.
Eligibility This program is open to members of the North Dakota National Guard who have a record of satisfactory participation (no more than 9 unexcused absences in the past 12 months) and service remaining after completion of the class for which they are requesting assistance. Applicants must be seeking support for trade or vocational training or work on an associate, baccalaureate, or graduate degree. They must be attending or planning to attend a North Dakota higher education public institution or a participating private institution (currently, Jamestown College, University of Mary in Bismarck, MedCenter One College of Nursing, Rasmussen College, or Trinity Bible College). Full-time AGR personnel do not qualify for this program. This is an entitlement program, provided all requirements are met.
Financial data Participating colleges and universities waive 25% of tuition for eligible courses (undergraduate only),

up to 25% of the tuition at the University of North Dakota. Through this program, the National Guard provides reimbursement of the remaining 75% of tuition for eligible courses (undergraduate and graduate), or up to 75% of the tuition at the University of North Dakota. The program also reimburses 100% of all regular fees, not to exceed 100% of the regular fees charged by the University of North Dakota. State reimbursements are paid directly to the student in the form of a check, based upon the number of credit hours successfully completed.
Duration Benefits are available for up to 144 semester credit hours or the completion of an undergraduate or graduate degree, provided the recipient earns a grade of "C" or higher in each undergraduate course or "B" or higher in each graduate course.
Number awarded Varies each year.
Deadline Applications should be submitted at least 30 days before the semester begins.

[177]
NUCLEAR PROPULSION OFFICER CANDIDATE (NUPOC) PROGRAM

U.S. Navy
Attn: Navy Personnel Command
5722 Integrity Drive
Millington, TN 38054-5057
(901) 874-3070   Toll Free: (888) 633-9674
Fax: (901) 874-2651
E-mail: nukeprograms@cnrc.navy.mil
Web: www.navy.com

Summary To provide financial assistance to college juniors and seniors who wish to serve in the Navy's nuclear propulsion training program following graduation.
Eligibility This program is open to U.S. citizens who are entering their junior or senior year of college as a full-time student. Strong technical majors (mathematics, physics, chemistry, or an engineering field) are encouraged. Applicants must have completed at least 1 year of calculus and 1 year of physics and must have earned a grade of "C" or better in all mathematics, science, and technical courses. They must be younger than 29 years of age.
Financial data Participants become Active Reserve enlisted Navy personnel and receive a salary that ranges from $3,280 to $5,610 per month; the exact amount depends on the local cost of living and other factors.
Duration Up to 30 months, until completion of a bachelor's degree.
Additional information Following graduation, participants attend Officer Candidate School in Pensacola, Florida for 4 months and receive their commissions. They have a service obligation of 8 years (of which at least 5 years must be on active duty), beginning with 6 months at the Navy Nuclear Power Training Command in Charleston, South Carolina and 6 more months of hands-on training at a nuclear reactor facility.
Number awarded Varies each year.
Deadline Deadline not specified.

[178]

NUCLEAR (SUBMARINE AND SURFACE) OPTION OF THE SEAMAN TO ADMIRAL-21 PROGRAM

U.S. Navy
Attn: Commander, Naval Service Training Command
250 Dallas Street, Suite A
Pensacola, FL 32508-5268
(850) 452-9563   Fax: (850) 452-2486
E-mail: PNSC_STA21@navy.mil
Web: www.sta-21.navy.mil/program_options.asp

Summary   To allow outstanding enlisted Navy personnel to attend college, affiliate with an NROTC unit, complete a bachelor's degree, and receive a commission in the nuclear officer community.

Eligibility   This program is open to U.S. citizens who are currently serving on active duty in the U.S. Navy or Naval Reserve, including Full Time Support (FTS), Selected Reserves (SELRES), and Navy Reservists on active duty, except for those on active duty for training (ACDUTRA). Only personnel currently enrolled in the Naval Nuclear Power School or Naval Nuclear Power Training Unit or assigned there as staff pickup instructors or sea returnee instructors are eligible. Applicants must be high school graduates (or GED recipients) who are able to complete requirements for a baccalaureate degree in 36 months or less. When they complete their degree requirements, they must be younger than 26 years of age. Sea returnee staff instructors must finish prior to their 31st birthday. Applicants must have taken the SAT or ACT within the past 3 years and achieved a score of 1140 or higher on the SAT or 50 or higher on the ACT. Their proposed college major must be in a technical area.

Financial data   Awardees continue to receive their regular Navy pay and allowances while they attend college on a full-time basis. They also receive reimbursement for tuition, fees, and books up to $10,000 per year. If base housing is available, they are eligible to live there. Participants are not eligible to receive benefits under the Navy's Tuition Assistance Program (TA), the Montgomery GI Bill (MGIB), the Navy College Fund, or the Veterans Educational Assistance Program (VEAP).

Duration   Selectees are supported for up to 36 months of full-time, year-round study or completion of a bachelor's degree, as long as they maintain a GPA of 3.0 or higher.

Additional information   This program began in 2001 as a replacement for the Nuclear Enlisted Commissioning Program (NECP). Upon acceptance into the program, selectees attend the Naval Science Institute (NSI) in Newport, Rhode Island for an 8-week program in the fundamental core concepts of being a naval officer (navigation, engineering, weapons, military history and justice, etc.). They then enter 1 of 18 universities with an NROTC nuclear unit (University of Arizona, Auburn University, The Citadel, University of Idaho, University of Illinois, University of Kansas, University of New Mexico, North Carolina State University, Oregon State University, Pennsylvania State University, Purdue University, Southern University and A&M College, SUNY Maritime College, University of South Carolina, University of Texas, University of Utah, University of Washington, or University of Wisconsin) to work full time on a bachelor's degree. They become members of and drill with the NROTC unit. When they complete their degree, they are commissioned as ensigns in the United States Naval Reserve and assigned to initial training for their nuclear officer community. After com-

missioning, participants incur an active-duty obligation of 5 years.

Number awarded   Varies each year.

Deadline   June of each year.

[179]

NURSE CORPS OPTION OF THE SEAMAN TO ADMIRAL-21 PROGRAM

U.S. Navy
Attn: Commander, Naval Service Training Command
250 Dallas Street, Suite A
Pensacola, FL 32508-5268
(850) 452-9563   Fax: (850) 452-2486
E-mail: PNSC_STA21@navy.mil
Web: www.sta-21.navy.mil/program_options.asp

Summary   To allow outstanding enlisted Navy personnel to attend college, affiliate with an NROTC unit, complete a bachelor's degree, and receive a commission in the Nurse Corps.

Eligibility   This program is open to U.S. citizens who are currently serving on active duty in the U.S. Navy or Naval Reserve, including Full Time Support (FTS), Selected Reserves (SELRES), and Navy Reservists on active duty, except for those on active duty for training (ACDUTRA). Applicants must be high school graduates (or GED recipients) who are able to complete requirements for a baccalaureate degree in nursing in 36 months or less. They must have completed at least 30 semester units in undergraduate nursing prerequisite courses with a GPA of 2.5 or higher. They must be at least 18 years of age and able to complete degree requirements and be commissioned prior to age 42. Within the past 3 years, they must have taken the SAT (and achieved scores of at least 500 on the mathematics section and 500 on the critical reading section) or the ACT (and achieved a score of at least 21 on the mathematics portion and 20 on the English portion).

Financial data   Awardees continue to receive their regular Navy pay and allowances while they attend college on a full-time basis. They also receive reimbursement for tuition, fees, and books up to $10,000 per year. If base housing is available, they are eligible to live there. Participants are not eligible to receive benefits under the Navy's Tuition Assistance Program (TA), the Montgomery GI Bill (MGIB), the Navy College Fund, or the Veterans Educational Assistance Program (VEAP).

Duration   Selectees are supported for up to 36 months of full-time, year-round study or completion of a bachelor's degree, as long as they maintain a GPA of 2.5 or higher.

Additional information   This program began in 2001 as a replacement for the Fleet Accession to Naval Reserve Officer Training Corps (NROTC) Nurse Option. Upon acceptance into the program, selectees attend the Naval Science Institute (NSI) in Newport, Rhode Island for an 8-week program in the fundamental core concepts of being a naval officer (navigation, engineering, weapons, military history and justice, etc.). They then enter an NROTC affiliated college or university with a nursing program that confers an accredited baccalaureate degree in nursing to pursue full-time study. They become members of and drill with the NROTC unit. When they complete their bachelor's degree in nursing, they are commissioned as ensigns in the United States Naval Reserve and assigned to initial training as an officer in the Nurse Corps. After commissioning, 5 years of active service are required.

Number awarded Varies each year.
Deadline June of each year.

[180]
OCEANOGRAPHY OPTION OF THE SEAMAN TO ADMIRAL-21 PROGRAM

U.S. Navy
Attn: Commander, Naval Service Training Command
250 Dallas Street, Suite A
Pensacola, FL 32508-5268
(850) 452-9563   Fax: (850) 452-2486
E-mail: PNSC_STA21@navy.mil
Web: www.sta-21.navy.mil/program_options.asp

Summary To allow outstanding enlisted Navy personnel to attend college, affiliate with an NROTC unit, complete a bachelor's degree, and receive a commission as an oceanography officer.

Eligibility This program is open to U.S. citizens who are currently serving on active duty in the U.S. Navy or Naval Reserve, including Full Time Support (FTS), Selected Reserves (SELRES), and Navy Reservists on active duty, except for those on active duty for training (ACDUTRA). Applicants must be at least 18 years of age and high school graduates (or GED recipients) who are able to complete requirements for a baccalaureate degree in 36 months or less. They must be planning to work on a degree in physical science, meteorology, or physical oceanography; other related fields may be considered, as long as the applicant possesses strong analytical ability and good communication skills (both oral and written). When they complete their degree requirements, they must be younger than 35 years of age. Within the past 3 years, they must have taken the SAT (and achieved scores of at least 500 on the mathematics section and 500 on the critical reading section) or the ACT (and achieved a score of at least 21 on the mathematics portion and 20 on the English portion).

Financial data Awardees continue to receive their regular Navy pay and allowances while they attend college on a full-time basis. They also receive reimbursement for tuition, fees, and books up to $10,000 per year. If base housing is available, they are eligible to live there. Participants are not eligible to receive benefits under the Navy's Tuition Assistance Program (TA), the Montgomery GI Bill (MGIB), the Navy College Fund, or the Veterans Educational Assistance Program (VEAP).

Duration Selectees are supported for up to 36 months of full-time, year-round study or completion of a bachelor's degree, as long as they maintain a GPA of 2.5 or higher.

Additional information Upon acceptance into the program, selectees attend the Naval Science Institute (NSI) in Newport, Rhode Island for an 8-week program in the fundamental core concepts of being a naval officer (navigation, engineering, weapons, military history and justice, etc.). They then enter a college or university with an NROTC unit or affiliation to work full time on a bachelor's degree. They become members of and drill with the NROTC unit. When they complete their degree, they are commissioned as ensigns in the United States Naval Reserve and assigned to initial training within the oceanography community. After commissioning, 5 years of active service are required.

Number awarded Varies each year.
Deadline June of each year.

[181]
OHIO NATIONAL GUARD ASSOCIATION LEADERSHIP GRANTS

Ohio National Guard Association
Attn: Leadership Grant Committee
1299 Virginia Avenue
P.O. Box 8070
Columbus, OH 43201
Toll Free: (800) 642-6642
E-mail: ONGAKoper@prodigy.net
Web: www.ohionga.org/schlolarship.html

Summary To provide financial assistance to members of the Ohio National Guard Association (ONGA) and their families who are interested in attending college in any state.

Eligibility This program is open to active members (either officers or warrant officers) of the ONGA and the dependents of active, life, retired, or deceased members. Applicants must be enrolled or planning to enroll at a college or university in any state. Along with their application, they must submit transcripts, SAT/ACT scores, and a 2-page essay explaining why they should be selected to receive a grant. Selection is based on grades, future plans, membership and leadership, honors and awards, need, and overall impression.

Financial data A stipend is awarded (amount not specified).

Duration 1 year; nonrenewable.

Additional information This program began in 1996.

Number awarded Varies each year; recently, 5 were awarded.

Deadline November of each year.

[182]
OHIO NATIONAL GUARD SCHOLARSHIP PROGRAM

Adjutant General's Department
Attn: ONG Scholarship Program Office
2825 West Dublin Granville Road
Columbus, OH 43235-2789
(614) 336-7143   Toll Free: (888) 400-6484
Fax: (614) 336-7318   E-mail: ongsp@ongsp.org
Web: www.ongsp.org

Summary To provide financial assistance to members of the Ohio National Guard interested in working on a college degree.

Eligibility This program is open to members of the Ohio Army and Air National Guard attending a 2- or 4-year public college or university in the state. Applicants must commit to and/or complete a 6-year enlistment in the Ohio Guard. New enlistees must complete basic training and obtain a military job skill.

Financial data The program covers 100% of the tuition and general fee charges at state-assisted 2- and 4-year colleges and universities in Ohio or an equivalent sum at private and proprietary institutions.

Duration The grant is limited to 12 quarters or 8 semesters and participants must remain enrolled as a full-time undergraduate student for that time. Enrollment in the institution of higher education must begin no later than 12 months after the completion of Initial Active Duty for Training (IADT), or date of reenlistment, or date of extension of current enlistment.

Additional information This program began in 1999. Grant assistance is not available for an additional baccalaureate degree, for postgraduate courses, or for courses not applicable to a degree.

Number awarded Grants are limited to the annual average student load of 4,000 full-time equivalent students per term.

Deadline June for fall term; October for winter quarter or spring semester; January for spring quarter; or March for summer term.

[183]
OKLAHOMA NATIONAL GUARD ASSOCIATION SCHOLARSHIPS

National Guard Association of Oklahoma
Attn: Scholarship Foundation
6500 North Kelley Avenue
Oklahoma City, OK 73111
(405) 475-2152   Fax: (405) 475-2183
E-mail: ngaok@coxinet.net
Web: www.ngaok.org/scholarship

Summary To provide financial assistance to members of the National Guard Association of Oklahoma (NGAOK) and their dependents who are interested in attending college in any state.

Eligibility This program is open to NGAOK members and their dependents who are attending or planning to attend a college or university in any state. The primary next of kin of members of the Oklahoma National Guard killed in action after September 11, 2001 are considered life member of NGAOK. Applicants must submit a 2-page statement that describes their academic performance, character, demonstrated leadership and leadership ability, aspirations, and future goals or plans.

Financial data Stipends are $500 or $1,000.

Duration 1 year.

Number awarded 20 to 25 each year.

Deadline January of each year.

[184]
OKLAHOMA NATIONAL GUARD TUITION WAIVER PROGRAM

Oklahoma State Regents for Higher Education
Attn: Director of Scholarship and Grant Programs
655 Research Parkway, Suite 200
P.O. Box 108850
Oklahoma City, OK 73101-8850
(405) 225-9239   Toll Free: (800) 858-1840
Fax: (405) 225-9230   E-mail: studentinfo@osrhe.edu
Web: secure.okcollegestart.org

Summary To provide financial assistance to members of the Oklahoma National Guard who plan to attend college in the state.

Eligibility This program is open to current members in good standing of the Oklahoma National Guard who do not have any other baccalaureate or graduate degree. Applicants must be attending or planning to attend a state-supported college or university in Oklahoma to work on an associate or baccalaureate degree. They must have submitted a plan for completion of their degree to the Guard. Courses leading to a certification, continuing education courses, and career technology courses that are not counted towards a degree at another institution are not covered.

Financial data Under this program, all tuition is waived.

Duration 1 year; may be renewed as long as the Guard member remains in good standing both in the unit and in the college or university, to a maximum of 6 years from the date of first application.

Number awarded Varies each year.

Deadline Deadline not specified.

[185]
ONGEA SCHOLARSHIP PROGRAM

Ohio National Guard Enlisted Association
Attn: Scholarship Chair
1299 Virginia Avenue
Columbus, OH 43212
(740) 574-5932   Toll Free: (800) 642-6642
Fax: (614) 520-6146   E-mail: ongea@juno.com
Web: www.ongea.org/12.html

Summary To provide financial assistance to members of the Ohio National Guard Enlisted Association (ONGEA) and children of members of the ONGEA Auxiliary who are interested in attending college in any state.

Eligibility This program is open to 1) children of ONGEA and ONGEA Auxiliary members (ONGEA member spouses must be Auxiliary members in order for a child to be eligible); 2) unmarried dependent children of deceased ONGEA and ONGEA Auxiliary members who were in good standing the time of their death; and 3) ONGEA members (if married, the spouse must also be a member of the Auxiliary). Applicants must be enrolling as full-time undergraduate students at a college, university, trade school, or business school in any state. Selection is based on academic record, character, leadership, and financial need.

Financial data Stipends are $1,000 or $500. After verification of enrollment is provided, checks are sent to the recipient and made out to the recipient's school.

Duration 1 year; nonrenewable.

Additional information This program is sponsored jointly by ONGEA, the ONGEA Auxiliary, USAA Insurance Corporation, and the First Cleveland Cavalry Association.

Number awarded 5 to 10 each year, depending upon the availability of funds.

Deadline March of each year.

[186]
OREGON NATIONAL GUARD ASSOCIATION SCHOLARSHIPS

Oregon National Guard Association
Attn: Scholarship Committee
1776 Militia Way, S.E.
P.O. Box 14350
Salem, OR 97309-5047
(503) 584-3456   Fax: (503) 584-3052
E-mail: diane.r.beach.mil/mail.mil
Web: www.ornga.org/scholarships

Summary To provide financial assistance to members of the Oregon National Guard, the Oregon National Guard Association (ORNGA), and their children and spouses who are interested in attending college in any state.

Eligibility This program is open to active members of the Oregon Army and Air National Guard, members of the ORNGA, and their children and spouses. Applicants must be high school seniors, graduates, or GED recipients and interested in working on an undergraduate degree at a college, university, or trade school in any state. The parent, spouse, or applicant must have an ETS date beyond the end of the academic year for which the scholarship is used. Selection is based on demonstrated qualities of leadership, civic action, and academic achievement.

Financial data The stipend is $1,500.

Duration 1 year.

Number awarded Up to 10 each year.

Deadline March of each year.

[187]
PENNSYLVANIA NATIONAL GUARD EDUCATIONAL ASSISTANCE PROGRAM

Pennsylvania Higher Education Assistance Agency
Attn: Special Programs
1200 North Seventh Street
P.O. Box 8157
Harrisburg, PA 17105-8157
(717) 720-2800   Toll Free: (800) 692-7392
Fax: (717) 720-3786   TDD: (800) 654-5988
Web: www.pheaa.org

Summary To provide scholarship/loans for college or graduate school to Pennsylvania National Guard members.

Eligibility This program is open to active members of the Pennsylvania National Guard who are Pennsylvania residents and serving as enlisted personnel, warrant officers, or commissioned officers of any grade. Applicants must accept an obligation to serve in the Pennsylvania National Guard for a period of 6 years from the date of entry into the program. Students who do not possess a baccalaureate degree must be enrolled full or part time in an approved program of education at an approved institution of higher learning in Pennsylvania. Master's degree students are supported on a part-time basis only. Guard members receiving an ROTC scholarship of any type are not eligible.

Financial data Full-time undergraduate students receive payment of 100% of tuition at a state-owned university. Part-time students receive either actual tuition charged or two-thirds of the full-time tuition charged to a Pennsylvania resident at a state-owned university, whichever is less. Graduate students receive either half the actual tuition charged or one-third of the full-time tuition charged to a Pennsylvania resident at a state-owned university, whichever is less. Recipients who fail to fulfill the service obligation must repay all funds received within 10 years, including interest at 7%.

Duration Up to 5 years.

Additional information This program, first offered in 1997, is jointly administered by the Pennsylvania Department of Military and Veterans Affairs and the Pennsylvania Higher Education Assistance Agency. Support for summer and graduate school is available only if funding permits.

Number awarded Varies each year; recently, 1,789 members of the Pennsylvania National Guard were enrolled in this program.

Deadline April of each year for students at colleges, universities, and transferable programs at community colleges; July of each year for students at business schools, trade/technical schools, hospital schools of nursing, and non-transferable programs at community colleges.

[188]
PENNSYLVANIA NATIONAL GUARD SCHOLARSHIP FUND

Pennsylvania National Guard Associations
Attn: Pennsylvania National Guard Scholarship Fund
Biddle Hall (Building 9-109)
Fort Indiantown Gap
Annville, PA 17003-5002
(717) 865-9631   Toll Free: (800) 997-8885
Fax: (717) 861-5560   E-mail: oswalddean@aol.com
Web: www.pngas.net/news/75652

Summary To provide financial assistance to Pennsylvania National Guard members and the children of disabled or deceased members who are interested in attending college in any state.

Eligibility This program is open to active members of the Pennsylvania Army or Air National Guard. Children of members of the Guard who died or were permanently disabled while on Guard duty are also eligible. Applicants must be entering their first year of higher education as a full-time student or presently attending a college or vocational school in any state as a full-time student. Along with their application, they must submit an essay that outlines their military and civilian plans for the future. Selection is based on academic potential, military commitment, extracurricular activities, and Guard participation.

Financial data Stipends range from $400 to $1,000.

Duration 1 year.

Additional information The sponsoring organization includes the National Guard Association of Pennsylvania (NGAP) and the Pennsylvania National Guard Enlisted Association (PNGEA). This program, which began in 1977, includes the following named scholarships: the BG Richard E. Thorn Memorial Scholarship, the Murtha Memorial Scholarship, the BG Hugh S. Niles Memorial Scholarship, the PNGEA USAA Scholarship (sponsored by the USAA Insurance Corporation), and the 28th Infantry Division Scholarship.

Number awarded Varies each year; recently, 13 were awarded: 4 at $1,000, 2 at $500, and 7 at $400.

Deadline June of each year.

[189]
PHOENIX/EANGKY SCHOLARSHIP

Enlisted Association National Guard of Kentucky
Attn: Scholarship Committee
P.O. Box 4062
Frankfort, KY 40604-4062
Web: www.ngaky.org/scholarships

Summary To provide financial assistance to members of the Enlisted Association National Guard of Kentucky (EANGKY) and their families who are interested in attending college in any state.

Eligibility This program is open to EANGKY members and their dependent children and spouses; children of deceased members who were in good standing at the time of their death are also eligible. Applicants must be attending or planning to attend a college, university, or trade school in any state. Along with their application, they must submit transcripts, letters of recommendation, and a statement describing their long-range personal educational goals and explaining why they need the scholarship assistance.

Financial data The stipend is $1,000.
Duration 1 year.
Number awarded 1 or more each year.
Deadline December of each year.

[190]
PILOT OPTION OF THE SEAMAN TO ADMIRAL-21 PROGRAM

U.S. Navy
Attn: Commander, Naval Service Training Command
250 Dallas Street, Suite A
Pensacola, FL 32508-5268
(850) 452-9563   Fax: (850) 452-2486
E-mail: PNSC_STA21@navy.mil
Web: www.sta-21.navy.mil/program_options.asp

Summary To allow outstanding enlisted Navy personnel to attend college, affiliate with an ROTC unit, complete a bachelor's degree, and receive a commission as a pilot.

Eligibility This program is open to U.S. citizens who are currently serving on active duty in the U.S. Navy or Naval Reserve, including Full Time Support (FTS), Selected Reserves (SELRES), and Navy Reservists on active duty, except for those on active duty for training (ACDUTRA). Applicants must be high school graduates (or GED recipients) who are at least 19 years of age and able to complete requirements for a baccalaureate degree in 36 months or less. When they complete their degree requirements, they must be younger than 27 years of age (may be adjusted to 29 years of age for prior active-duty service). Within the past 3 years, they must have taken the SAT (and achieved scores of at least 500 on the mathematics section and 500 on the critical reading section) or the ACT (and achieved a score of at least 21 on the mathematics portion and 20 on the English portion). They must also achieve a score of at least the following: AQR (4), PFAR (5) on the Pilot Flight Aptitude Rating (PFAR) portions of the Aviation Selection Test Battery.

Financial data Awardees continue to receive their regular Navy pay and allowances while they attend college on a full-time basis. They also receive reimbursement for tuition, fees, and books up to $10,000 per year. If base housing is available, they are eligible to live there. Participants are not eligible to receive benefits under the Navy's Tuition Assistance Program (TA), the Montgomery GI Bill (MGIB), the Navy College Fund, or the Veterans Educational Assistance Program (VEAP).

Duration Selectees are supported for up to 36 months of full-time, year-round study or completion of a bachelor's degree, as long as they maintain a GPA of 2.5 or higher.

Additional information This program began in 2001 as a replacement for the Aviation Enlisted Commissioning Program (AECP). Upon acceptance into the program, selectees attend the Naval Science Institute (NSI) in Newport, Rhode Island for an 8-week program in the fundamental core concepts of being a naval officer (navigation, engineering, weapons, military history and justice, etc.). They then enter a college or university with an NROTC unit or affiliation to work full time on a bachelor's degree. They become members of and drill with the NROTC unit. When they complete their degree, they are commissioned as ensigns in the United States Naval Reserve and assigned to flight training. After commissioning, participants incur an active-duty obligation of 8 years after

designation as a Naval Aviator or 6 years from the date of disenrollment from flight training.

Number awarded Varies each year.
Deadline June of each year.

[191]
PLATOON LEADERS CLASS MARINE CORPS TUITION ASSISTANCE PROGRAM

U.S. Marine Corps
Attn: Marine Corps Recruiting Command
3280 Russell Road
Quantico, VA 22134-5103
(703) 784-9449   Fax: (703) 784-9859
E-mail: wendelrf@mcrc.usmc.mil
Web: www.marines.com

Summary To provide financial assistance to undergraduate and law students interested in participating in summer Marine Corps training programs and becoming an officer.

Eligibility This program is open to members of the Marine Corps Reserves enrolled full time in a bachelor's or law (J.D. or equivalent) degree program. Applicants must participate in the Marine Corps Platoon Leader Class (PLC) Program for 2 summers (if they enter the program as freshmen or sophomores) or for 1 summer (if they enter the program as juniors, seniors, or law students). They must agree to accept a commission in the active-duty Marine Corps and serve 5 years following completion of their degree. Undergraduates must have a score of at least 1000 on the critical reading and mathematics sections of the SAT, a combined score of at least 45 on the verbal and mathematics section of the ACT, or at least 120 on the Armed Forces Vocational Aptitude Battery. Law students must have an LSAT score of 150 or higher.

Financial data This program provides reimbursement of tuition, books, and required fees, up to a maximum of $5,200 per academic year.

Duration Up to 3 consecutive years, or completion of a bachelor's or law degree.

Additional information Participants who successfully obtain a bachelor's or law degree and complete officer candidate training are commissioned as second lieutenants in the Regular Marine Corps. This program was established in 1999.

Number awarded Up to 1,200 each year.
Deadline December of each year.

[192]
POST-9/11 GI BILL

Department of Veterans Affairs
Attn: Veterans Benefits Administration
810 Vermont Avenue, N.W.
Washington, DC 20420
(202) 418-4343   Toll Free: (888) GI-BILL1
Web: www.benefits.va.gov/gibill/post911_gibill.asp

Summary To provide financial assistance to military personnel and veterans who entered service on or after September 11, 2001.

Eligibility This program is open to current and former military personnel who 1) served on active duty for at least 90 aggregate days after September 11, 2001; or 2) were discharged with a service-connected disability after 30 days. Applicants must be planning to enroll in an educational program, including work on an undergraduate or graduate degree, vocational/technical training, on-the-job training, flight training, correspondence training, licensing and national testing programs, entrepreneurship training, and tutorial assistance.

Financial data Participants working on an undergraduate or graduate degree at public institutions in their state receive full payment of tuition and fees. For participants who attend private institutions in most states, tuition and fee reimbursement is capped at $20,235.02 per academic year. Benefits for other types of training programs depend on the amount for which the veteran qualified under prior educational programs. Veterans also receive a monthly housing allowance that is 1) based on the Department of Defense Basic Allowance for Housing (BAH) for an E-5 with dependents (which depends on the location of the school but ranges from approximately $1,000 per month to approximately $2,500 per month); 2) $1,509 per month at schools in foreign countries; or 3) $754.50 per month for online training classes. They also receive an annual book allowance of $1,000 and (for participants who live in a rural county remote from an educational institution) a rural benefit payment of $500 per year.

Duration Most participants receive up to 36 months of entitlement under this program. Benefits are payable for up to 15 years following release from active duty.

Additional information This program, referred to as Chapter 33, began in 2009 as a replacement for previous educational programs for veterans and military personnel (e.g., Montgomery GI Bill, REAP). Current participants in those programs may be able to transfer benefits from those programs to this new plan. To qualify for 100% of Post 9/11-GI Bill benefits, transferees must have at least 36 months of active-duty service. Transferees with less service are entitled to smaller percentages of benefits, ranging down to 40% for those with only 90 days of service.

Number awarded Varies each year; since the program began, it has awarded approximately $30 billion in benefits to nearly 1 million veterans.

Deadline Deadline not specified.

[193]
PROFESSIONAL OFFICER COURSE EARLY RELEASE PROGRAM

U.S. Air Force
Attn: Headquarters AFROTC/RRUE
Jeanne M. Holm Center for Officer Accession and Citizen Development
551 East Maxwell Boulevard, Building 500
Maxwell AFB, AL 36112-5917
(334) 953-2091   Toll Free: (866) 4-AFROTC
Fax: (334) 953-6167   E-mail: enlisted@afrotc.com
Web: www.au.af.mil

Summary To allow selected enlisted Air Force personnel to earn a baccalaureate degree by providing financial assistance for full-time college study as an ROTC cadet.

Eligibility Eligible to participate in this program are enlisted members of the Air Force under the age of 30 (or otherwise able to be commissioned before becoming 35 years of age) who have completed at least 1 year on continuous active duty, have served on station for at least 1 year, and have no more than 2 years remaining to complete their initial baccalaureate degree. Scholarship applicants must be younger than 31 years of age when they graduate and earn their commission.

All applicants must have been accepted at a college or university offering the AFROTC 4-year program and must have a cumulative college GPA of 2.5 or higher. Their Air Force Officer Qualifying Test (AFOQT) scores must be at least 15 on the verbal and 10 on the quantitative. Applicants who have not completed 24 units of college work must have an ACT composite score of 24 or higher or an SAT combined critical reading and mathematics score of 1100 or higher. U.S. citizenship is required. All academic majors are eligible.

Financial data Participants receive a stipend of $350 to $400 per month and an allowance of $900 per year for books. No other scholarship funding is provided.

Duration 2 years (no more and no less).

Additional information Upon completing their degree, selectees are commissioned as officers in the Air Force with a 4-year service obligation. Further information is available from base education service officers or an Air Force ROTC unit. Recipients must attend a school with annual tuition and fees less than $15,000 per year. They are not allowed to pay the difference to attend a higher cost school.

Number awarded Varies each year.

Deadline October of each year.

[194]
RALPH S. FRENCH CHARITABLE FOUNDATION SCHOLARSHIPS

AMVETS National Headquarters
Attn: Programs Department
4647 Forbes Boulevard
Lanham, MD 20706-3807
(301) 459-9600   Toll Free: (877) 7-AMVETS, ext. 4031
Fax: (301) 459-7924   E-mail: amvets@amvets.org
Web: www.amvets.org/programs/scholarships

Summary To provide financial assistance for college to 1) members of the National Guard and Reserves and 2) veterans.

Eligibility This program is open to veterans and current members of the National Guard and Reserves. Applicants must be interested in working full or part time on an undergraduate degree or certification from an accredited technical/trade school. They must have exhausted all other government aid. U.S. citizenship is required. Selection is based on financial need, academic promise, military duty and awards, volunteer activities, community services, jobs held during the past 4 years, and an essay of 50 to 100 words on "This award will help me achieve my career/vocational goal, which is..."

Financial data The stipend is $1,000 per year.

Duration Up to 4 years.

Number awarded Varies each year; recently, 18 were awarded.

Deadline April of each year.

[195]
RANGER MEMORIAL SCHOLARSHIPS

National Ranger Memorial Foundation
Attn: Executive Secretary
P.O. Box 53369
Fort Benning, GA 31995
(706) 687-0906   E-mail: rangermemorial@gmail.com
Web: www.rangermemorial.com

Summary To provide financial assistance for college to U.S. Army Rangers and their descendants.

Eligibility This program is open to Rangers from any era and their descendants; some awards (those offered by the Ranger Battalions Association of WWII) are limited to descendants of Rangers who served during the World War II era. Applicants must be graduating high school seniors or students currently enrolled at an accredited 2- or 4-year educational or technical institution. They must have a GPA of 3.0 or higher. Along with their application, they must submit information on their leadership activities, future goals and how they plan to attain those, and honors and awards received to date. Financial need is not considered in the selection process.

Financial data The stipend is $1,000.

Duration 1 year.

Additional information The National Ranger Memorial Foundation began awarding scholarships in 1999. The Ranger Battalions Association of WWII became a partner in 2007 and offered additional scholarships to descendants of World War II era Rangers.

Number awarded 49 each year: 45 offered by the National Ranger Memorial Foundation and 4 by the Ranger Battalions Association of WWII.

Deadline May of each year.

[196]
REDUCED TUITION FOR SOUTH DAKOTA NATIONAL GUARD MEMBERS

South Dakota Board of Regents
Attn: Scholarship Committee
306 East Capitol Avenue, Suite 200
Pierre, SD 57501-2545
(605) 773-3455   Fax: (605) 773-2422
E-mail: info@sdbor.edu
Web: www.sdbor.edu

Summary To provide financial assistance for college or graduate school to members of the South Dakota National Guard.

Eligibility Eligible to apply for this assistance are members of the South Dakota Army or Air National Guard who are South Dakota residents, have satisfactorily completed Initial Active Duty for Training (IADT), meet the entrance requirements at 1 of the 6 state educational institutions or 4 state vocational/technical schools, maintain sustained membership in their National Guard unit, and maintain satisfactory academic progress.

Financial data Qualifying Guard members are eligible for a 50% reduction in tuition at any state-supported postsecondary institution in South Dakota.

Duration This assistance is available for up to 128 credit hours at the undergraduate level and up to 32 credit hours at the graduate level.

Additional information Students participating in the Army Continuing Education Systems (ACES) or the Montgomery GI Bill are not authorized to use this program.

Number awarded Varies each year.

Deadline Deadline not specified.

[197]
RESERVE EDUCATIONAL ASSISTANCE PROGRAM

Department of Veterans Affairs
Attn: Veterans Benefits Administration
810 Vermont Avenue, N.W.
Washington, DC 20420
(202) 418-4343   Toll Free: (888) GI-BILL1
Web: www.benefits.va.gov/gibill/reap.asp

Summary To provide financial assistance for college or graduate school to members of the Reserves or National Guard who are called to active duty during a period of national emergency.

Eligibility This program is open to members of the Selected Reserve and Individual Ready Reserve (including Reserve elements of the Army, Navy, Air Force, Marine Corps, and Coast Guard, as well as the Army National Guard and the Air National Guard) who have served on active duty on or after September 11, 2001 for at least 90 consecutive days. Applicants must be interested in working on an undergraduate or graduate degree, vocational or technical training, on-the-job or apprenticeship training, correspondence training, tests for licenses or certificates, or flight training.

Financial data For full-time study at a college or university, the current monthly rate is $686.80 for personnel with consecutive service of 90 days but less than 1 year, $1030.20 for personnel with consecutive service of more than 1 year but less than 2 years, or $1,373.60 for those with consecutive service of 2 years or more. Reduced rates apply for part-time college or university study, apprenticeship and on-the-job training, licensing and certification training, cooperative education, correspondence courses, and flight training.

Duration Up to 36 months for full-time study. There is no fixed time for persons eligible for this program to utilize its benefits (except in the case of a member separated from the Ready Reserve for a disability, who are entitled to benefits for 10 years after the date of eligibility).

Additional information This program, established in 2005, is frequently referred to as Chapter 1607.

Number awarded Varies each year.

Deadline Applications may be submitted at any time.

[198]
RHODE ISLAND NATIONAL GUARD STATE TUITION ASSISTANCE PROGRAM

Rhode Island National Guard
Joint Force Headquarters
Attn: Education Service Office
645 New London Avenue
Cranston, RI 02920-3097
(401) 275-4039   Fax: (401) 275-4014
E-mail: dean.l.mansfield.mil@mail.mil
Web: states.ng.mil

Summary To provide financial support to members of the National Guard in Rhode Island interested in attending college or graduate school in the state.

Eligibility This program is open to active members of the Rhode Island National Guard in good standing who are currently satisfactorily participating in all unit training assemblies and annual training periods. Applicants must have at least 1 year of service remaining. They must be enrolled in or planning to enroll in an associate, bachelor's, or master's degree program at a public institution in the state.

Financial data Qualified Guard members are exempt from payment of tuition for up to 5 courses per semester.

Duration 1 semester; may be renewed.

Additional information This program began in 1999. The designated institutions are the University of Rhode Island, Rhode Island College, and the Community College of Rhode Island.

Number awarded Varies each year.

Deadline Deadline not specified.

[199]
ROBERT H. CONNAL EDUCATION AWARDS

Enlisted Association of the New York National Guard, Inc.
Attn: Educational Award Chair
330 Old Niskayuna Road
Latham, NY 12110-2224
(518) 344-2670   E-mail: awards@eanyng.org
Web: www.eanyng.org/AwardsandScholarships.html

Summary To provide financial assistance to members of the Enlisted Association of the New York National Guard (EANYNG) and their families who are interested in attending college in any state.

Eligibility This program is open to EANYNG members and their spouses, children, and grandchildren. Applicants must be high school seniors or current undergraduates at a college or university in any state. The applicant or sponsor must have belonged to EANYNG for more than 1 year. Membership in EANYNG is limited to enlisted personnel in the New York Air or Army National Guard. Selection is based on academic achievement, community service, extracurricular activities, and leadership abilities.

Financial data Stipends are $1,000, $700, or $500.

Duration 1 year; nonrenewable.

Additional information Funding for this program is provided by the production of the association's yearly journal, members' dues, and a donation from USAA Insurance Corporation.

Number awarded 5 each year: 2 at $1,000, 1 at $700, and 2 at $500.

Deadline March of each year.

[200]
ROBERT W. BRUNSMAN MEMORIAL SCHOLARSHIP

International Military Community Executives' Association
Attn: Scholarship
P.O. Box 7946
Round Rock, TX 78683-7946
(940) 463-5145   Fax: (866) 369-2435
E-mail: imcea@imcea.org
Web: www.imcea.org/awards/scholarship-info

Summary To provide financial assistance to members of the International Military Community Executives' Association (IMCEA) who are working in the field of military morale, welfare, and recreation (MWR) and currently enrolled in college or graduate school.

Eligibility This program is open to regular IMCEA members who are currently employed in the field of military MWR. Applicants must be already enrolled at a college or university, either on-campus or online, and taking undergraduate or graduate courses related to MWR. Along with their application, they must submit a 2-page essay on how all MWR ser-

vices (e.g., clubs, bowling, golf, child care, libraries) might work together to create synergy and enhance the mission of IMCEA. Selection is based on that essay, participation in IMCEA activities, and involvement in military MWR services.

Financial data The stipend is $1,000.

Duration 1 year.

Additional information Regular membership in IMCEA is open to Army, Air Force, Navy, Marine Corps, and Coast Guard personnel who provide MWR services at military installations and bases worldwide.

Number awarded 1 each year.

Deadline May of each year.

[201]
ROSAMOND P. HAEBERLE MEMORIAL SCHOLARSHIP

Daughters of the American Revolution-Michigan State Society
c/o Jacki Gonterman, Memorial Scholarship Committee
8613A Nebraska Street
Oscoda, MI 48750-2254
(989) 739-8283   E-mail: jackigopd@att.net
Web: www.michigandar.org/RPHMS.htm

Summary To provide financial assistance to military personnel and veterans in Michigan who are interested in attending college in the state.

Eligibility This program is open to residents of Michigan who have served on active duty in the U.S. armed forces (including Reserves and National Guard) for at least 6 continuous months and are either currently serving in the armed forces or have received a separation from active duty under honorable conditions. Applicants must be currently accepted to and/or enrolled at a 2- or 4-year accredited college, university, or technical/trade school in Michigan. They must be enrolled at least half time and have a cumulative high school or undergraduate GPA of 2.5 or higher. Along with their application, they must submit a 1-page essay on what serving their country has meant to them and how it has influenced their future goals and priorities. Selection is based on academic performance, extracurricular activities, community service, potential to succeed in an academic environment, financial need, and military service record.

Financial data The stipend is $1,500.

Duration 1 year.

Additional information This program began in 2007.

Number awarded 1 each year.

Deadline March of each year.

[202]
SAN FRANCISCO BAY AREA NDTA VETERANS MERIT SCHOLARSHIP

National Defense Transportation Association-San Francisco Bay Area Chapter
Attn: Scholarship Committee
600 Rock Oak Road
Walnut Creek, CA 94598
E-mail: c_madison@msn.com
Web: www.ndta-sf.com/schlrgrnt_info

Summary To provide financial assistance to military personnel and veterans in California who are majoring in a field related to transportation at a school in any state.

Eligibility This program is open to military personnel on active duty and veterans who have been on active duty within the past 5 years. Applicants must be residents of California and enrolled or planning to enroll in an undergraduate or vocational program at an accredited institution in any state with a major in transportation, logistics, business, marketing, engineering, planning, or environment. They must be preparing for a career related to transportation. Along with their application, they must submit a certified copy of their high school or college transcript, 3 letters of recommendation, and a 1-page essay detailing their career goals and ambitions (with an emphasis on transportation and related areas). Selection is based on academic ability, professional interest, potential, and character.

Financial data The stipend is $1,000.

Duration 1 year.

Number awarded 1 or more each year.

Deadline May of each year.

[203]
SCHOLARSHIPS FOR OUTSTANDING AIRMEN TO ROTC (SOAR)

U.S. Air Force
Attn: Headquarters AFROTC/RRUE
Jeanne M. Holm Center for Officer Accession and Citizen
  Development
551 East Maxwell Boulevard, Building 500
Maxwell AFB, AL 36112-5917
(334) 953-2091   Toll Free: (866) 4-AFROTC
Fax: (334) 953-6167   E-mail: enlisted@afrotc.com
Web: www.au.af.mil

Summary To allow selected enlisted Air Force personnel to earn a bachelor's degree by providing financial assistance for full-time college study.

Eligibility Eligible to participate in this program are enlisted members of the Air Force who have completed from 1 to 6 years of active duty and have at least 1 year time-on-station. Candidates must be nominated by their commanding officers and be accepted at a college or university offering the AFROTC 4-year program. Airmen with 24 semester hours or more of graded college credit must have a cumulative GPA of 2.5 or higher; airmen with less than 24 semester hours must have an ACT score of 24 or higher or an SAT combined mathematics and critical reading score of 1100 or higher. All applicants must earn Air Force Officer Qualifying Test (AFOQT) scores of 15 or more on the verbal scale and 10 or more on the quantitative scale. They must complete 24 semesters of mathematics and physical sciences or 4 semesters of a foreign language and major in an approved field; for a list of currently-approved majors, contact the program. U.S. citizenship is required. When the recipients complete the program, they may be no more than 31 years of age.

Financial data Selectees receive a tuition and fees scholarship of up to $18,000 per year, an annual textbook allowance of $900, and a monthly non-taxable stipend of $250 to $400.

Duration 2 to 4 years.

Additional information Upon completing their degree, selectees are commissioned as officers in the Air Force with a 4-year service obligation. Further information is available from base education service officers or an Air Force ROTC unit.

Number awarded 51 each year.

Deadline October of each year.

[204]
SEAMAN TO ADMIRAL-21 CORE PROGRAM

U.S. Navy
Attn: Commander, Naval Service Training Command
250 Dallas Street, Suite A
Pensacola, FL 32508-5268
(850) 452-9563   Fax: (850) 452-2486
E-mail: PNSC_STA21@navy.mil
Web: www.sta-21.navy.mil/program_options.asp

Summary To allow outstanding enlisted Navy personnel to attend college, affiliate with an NROTC unit, complete a bachelor's degree, and receive a commission.

Eligibility This program is open to U.S. citizens who are currently serving on active duty in the U.S. Navy or Naval Reserve, including Full Time Support (FTS), Selected Reserves (SELRES), and Navy Reservists on active duty, except for those on active duty for training (ACDUTRA). Applicants must be high school graduates (or GED recipients) who are able to complete requirements for a baccalaureate degree in 36 months or less. They may apply to the core program or a target group option. The core program allows participants the most flexibility in selecting a major and requesting schools to attend. When they complete their degree requirements, they must be younger than 31 years of age. Within the past 3 years, they must have taken the SAT (and achieved scores of at least 500 on the mathematics section and 500 on the critical reading section) or the ACT (and achieved a score of at least 21 on the mathematics portion and 20 on the English portion).

Financial data Awardees continue to receive their regular Navy pay and allowances while they attend college on a full-time basis. They also receive reimbursement for tuition, fees, and books up to $10,000 per year. If base housing is available, they are eligible to live there. Participants are not eligible to receive benefits under the Navy's Tuition Assistance Program (TA), the Montgomery GI Bill (MGIB), the Navy College Fund, or the Veterans Educational Assistance Program (VEAP).

Duration Selectees are supported for up to 36 months of full-time, year-round study or completion of a bachelor's degree, as long as they maintain a GPA of 2.5 or higher.

Additional information This program began in 2001 as a replacement for the Seaman to Admiral Program (established in 1994), the Enlisted Commissioning Program, and other specialized programs for sailors to earn a commission. Upon acceptance into the program, selectees attend the Naval Science Institute (NSI) in Newport, Rhode Island for an 8-week program in the fundamental core concepts of being a naval officer (navigation, engineering, weapons, military history and justice, etc.). They then enter a college or university with an NROTC unit or affiliation to work full time on a bachelor's degree. They become members of and drill with the NROTC unit. When core program participants complete their degree, they are commissioned as ensigns in the United States Naval Reserve and assigned to an Unrestricted Line (URL) Navy officer designator upon commissioning. After commissioning, 5 years of active service are required.

Number awarded Varies each year.

Deadline June of each year.

[205]
SERGEANTS HENRY AND JEANNE ROSE SCHOLARSHIPS

Marines' Memorial Association
c/o Marines Memorial Club and Hotel
609 Sutter Street
San Francisco, CA 94102
(415) 673-6672, ext. 293   Fax: (415) 441-3649
E-mail: scholarship@marineclub.com
Web: www.marineclub.com/membership/scholarship.php

Summary To provide financial assistance for college to members of the Marines' Memorial Association from all branches of the armed forces and their descendants.

Eligibility This program is open to active members of the association and their children and grandchildren. Applicants must be high school seniors or students currently enrolled full time in an undergraduate degree program at a college or university. Along with their application, they must submit an essay of 250 to 500 words on why the United States has the highest rates of poverty and income inequality of any developed nation and what we can do to reduce the prevalence of those problems in our country. Graduating high school seniors must submit a high school transcript and SAT or ACT scores; continuing college students must submit a college transcript. Selection is based on the essay, academic merit, references, and financial need.

Financial data The stipend is $10,000 per year.

Duration 1 year; recipients may reapply for up to 3 additional years.

Additional information Membership in the association is open to veterans of the Marines, Army, Navy, Air Force, or Coast Guard and to personnel currently serving in a branch of the armed forces.

Number awarded 2 each year.

Deadline April of each year.

[206]
SFC CURTIS MANCINI MEMORIAL SCHOLARSHIPS

Association of the United States Army-Rhode Island
    Chapter
c/o CSM (Ret) Anthony Ferri, Secretary
47 Spokane Street
Providence, RI 02904
(401) 861-2997   E-mail: afnf458673755@aol.com
Web: www.ausari.org/index.html

Summary To provide financial assistance to members of the Rhode Island Chapter of the Association of the United States Army (AUSA) and their families who are interested in attending college or graduate school in any state.

Eligibility This program is open to members of the AUSA Rhode Island Chapter and their family members (spouses, children, and grandchildren). Applicants must be high school seniors or graduates accepted at an accredited college, university, or vocational/technical school in any state or current undergraduate or graduate students. Along with their application, they must submit a 250-word essay on why they feel their achievements should qualify them for this award. Selection is based on academic and individual achievements; financial need is not considered. Membership in AUSA is open to current and retired Army personnel (including Reserves and National Guard), ROTC cadets, or civilian employees of the Army.

Financial data The stipend is $1,000.

Duration 1 year.

Number awarded 2 each year.

Deadline March of each year.

[207]
SIGMA CHI MILITARY SERVICE SCHOLARSHIPS

Sigma Chi Foundation
Attn: Scholarship Committee
1714 Hinman Avenue
Evanston, IL 60201
(847) 869-3655, ext. 270   Fax: (847) 869-4906
E-mail: heidi.holley@sigmachi.org
Web: foundation.sigmachi.org

Summary To provide financial assistance to undergraduate and graduate student members of Sigma Chi who are serving or have served in the military.

Eligibility This program is open to undergraduate and graduate brothers of the fraternity who are currently serving or have served in the military (Army, Navy, Air Force, Marines, Coast Guard, or National Guard). They must have earned a GPA of 2.5 or higher and have completed at least 2 semesters of undergraduate study.

Financial data The stipend is $1,000. Funds are to be used for tuition/fees only and are paid directly to the recipient's school.

Duration 1 year.

Number awarded Varies each year.

Deadline May of each year.

[208]
SIMULTANEOUS MEMBERSHIP PROGRAM (SMP)

U.S. Army
Attn: U.S. Army Cadet Command
G2 Incentives Division
1307 Third Avenue
Fort Knox, KY 40121-2725
(502) 624-7371   Toll Free: (888) 550-ARMY
Fax: (502) 624-6937   E-mail: train2lead@usacc.army.mil
Web: www.goarmy.com/rotc/enroll/enlisted.html

Summary To provide financial assistance to individuals who serve simultaneously in the Army National Guard or Army Reserve and the Army Reserve Officers' Training Corps (ROTC) while they are in college.

Eligibility Students who are members of the Army National Guard or the Army Reserve and Army ROTC at the same time are eligible for this assistance. Applicants must have completed basic training or the equivalent, have at least 4 years remaining on their current military obligation, be full-time college juniors, have a GPA of 2.0 or higher, and be U.S. citizens.

Financial data Advanced ROTC Simultaneous Membership Program (SMP) participants are paid at the rate of at least a Sergeant E-5 for their Guard or Reserve training assemblies (recently, $290 to $340 per month, depending on the number of years of service), plus an ROTC stipend for 10 months of the year at $450 per month during their junior year and $500 per month during their senior year.

Duration Up to 2 years.

Additional information Participants serve as officer trainees in their Guard or Reserve units and, under the close supervision of a commissioned officer, perform duties commensurate with those of a second lieutenant. Cadets who successfully complete the SMP program graduate with a commission as a second lieutenant. Once commissioned, they may continue to serve in their Guard or Reserve units, or they may apply for active duty in the U.S. Army.

Number awarded Varies each year.

Deadline Deadline not specified.

[209]
SOUTH CAROLINA NATIONAL GUARD COLLEGE ASSISTANCE PROGRAM

South Carolina Commission on Higher Education
Attn: Student Services
1122 Lady Street, Suite 300
Columbia, SC 29201
(803) 737-2144   Toll Free: (877) 349-7183
Fax: (803) 737-2297   E-mail: mbrown@che.sc.gov
Web: www.che.sc.gov

Summary To provide financial assistance to members of the South Carolina National Guard who are interested in attending college in the state.

Eligibility This program is open to members of the South Carolina National Guard who are in good standing and have not already received a bachelor's or graduate degree. Applicants must be admitted, enrolled, and classified as a degree-seeking full- or part-time student at an eligible institution in South Carolina. They may not be taking continuing education or graduate course work. U.S. citizenship or permanent resident status is required.

Financial data This program provides full payment of the cost of attendance, including tuition, fees, and textbooks, to a maximum of $9,000 per year for members of the Air National Guard or $4,500 for members of the Army National Guard. The cumulative total of all benefits received from this program may not exceed $18,000.

Duration Support is provided for up to 130 semester hours of study, provided the Guard member maintains satisfactory academic progress as defined by the institution.

Additional information This program is administered by the South Carolina Commission on Higher Education in consultation with the state Adjutant General. The General Assembly established this program in 2007 as a replacement for the South Carolina National Guard Student Loan Repayment Program. Enlisted personnel are required to continue their service in the National Guard during all terms of courses covered by the benefit received. Officers must continue their service with the National Guard for at least 4 years after completion of the most recent award or degree completion.

Number awarded Varies each year.

Deadline Deadline not specified.

[210]
SPECIAL DUTY OFFICER (INFORMATION WARFARE) OPTION OF THE SEAMAN TO ADMIRAL-21 PROGRAM

U.S. Navy
Attn: Commander, Naval Service Training Command
250 Dallas Street, Suite A
Pensacola, FL 32508-5268
(850) 452-9563   Fax: (850) 452-2486
E-mail: PNSC_STA21@navy.mil
Web: www.sta-21.navy.mil/program_options.asp

Summary To allow outstanding enlisted Navy personnel to attend college, affiliate with an NROTC unit, complete a bachelor's degree, and receive a commission as a special duty officer (information warfare).

Eligibility This program is open to U.S. citizens who are currently serving on active duty in the U.S. Navy or Naval Reserve, including Full Time Support (FTS), Selected Reserves (SELRES), and Navy Reservists on active duty, except for those on active duty for training (ACDUTRA). Applicants must be high school graduates (or GED recipients) who are at least 18 years of age and able to complete requirements for a baccalaureate degree in 36 months or less. Sailors in all ratings are eligible, but preference is given to cryptologic technicians, intelligence specialists, and information professionals. When they complete their degree requirements, they must be younger than 35 years of age. Within the past 3 years, they must have taken the SAT (and achieved scores of at least 500 on the mathematics section and 500 on the critical reading section) or the ACT (and achieved a score of at least 21 on the mathematics portion and 20 on the English portion). They must also meet relevant medical standards. Although technical degrees are preferred, the program does not specify required majors; instead, it seeks officers who possess strong analytical ability and communication skills (both oral and written).

Financial data Awardees continue to receive their regular Navy pay and allowances while they attend college on a full-time basis. They also receive reimbursement for tuition, fees, and books up to $10,000 per year. If base housing is available, they are eligible to live there. Participants are not eligible to receive benefits under the Navy's Tuition Assistance Program (TA), the Montgomery GI Bill (MGIB), the Navy College Fund, or the Veterans Educational Assistance Program (VEAP).

Duration Selectees are supported for up to 36 months of full-time, year-round study or completion of a bachelor's degree, as long as they maintain a GPA of 2.5 or higher.

Additional information This program began in 2001 as a replacement for the Seaman to Admiral Program (established in 1994), the Enlisted Commissioning Program, and other specialized programs for sailors to earn a commission. Upon acceptance into the program, selectees attend the Naval Science Institute (NSI) in Newport, Rhode Island for an 8-week program in the fundamental core concepts of being a naval officer (navigation, engineering, weapons, military history and justice, etc.). They then enter a college or university with an NROTC unit or affiliation to work full time on a bachelor's degree. They become members of and drill with the NROTC unit. When they complete their degree, they are commissioned as ensigns in the United States Naval Reserve and assigned to initial training as a special duty officer (information warfare); that designation was formerly special duty officer (cryptologic). After commissioning, 5 years of active service are required.

Number awarded   Varies each year.

Deadline   June of each year.

[211]
SPECIAL DUTY OFFICER (INTELLIGENCE) OPTION OF THE SEAMAN TO ADMIRAL-21 PROGRAM

U.S. Navy
Attn: Commander, Naval Service Training Command
250 Dallas Street, Suite A
Pensacola, FL 32508-5268
(850) 452-9563   Fax: (850) 452-2486
E-mail: PNSC_STA21@navy.mil
Web: www.sta-21.navy.mil/program_options.asp

Summary   To allow outstanding enlisted Navy personnel to attend college, affiliate with an NROTC unit, complete a bachelor's degree, and receive a commission as a special duty officer (intelligence).

Eligibility   This program is open to U.S. citizens who are currently serving on active duty in the U.S. Navy or Naval Reserve, including Full Time Support (FTS), Selected Reserves (SELRES), and Navy Reservists on active duty, except for those on active duty for training (ACDUTRA). Applicants must be high school graduates (or GED recipients) who are at least 18 years of age and able to complete requirements for a baccalaureate degree in 36 months or less. They may currently have any rating. When they complete their degree requirements, they must be younger than 35 years of age. Within the past 3 years, they must have taken the SAT (and achieved scores of at least 500 on the mathematics section and 500 on the critical reading section) or the ACT (and achieved a score of at least 21 on the mathematics portion and 20 on the English portion). They must also meet relevant medical standards. Although technical degrees are preferred, the program does not specify required majors; instead, it seeks officers who possess strong analytical ability and communication skills (both oral and written).

Financial data   Awardees continue to receive their regular Navy pay and allowances while they attend college on a full-time basis. They also receive reimbursement for tuition, fees, and books up to $10,000 per year. If base housing is available, they are eligible to live there. Participants are not eligible to receive benefits under the Navy's Tuition Assistance Program (TA), the Montgomery GI Bill (MGIB), the Navy College Fund, or the Veterans Educational Assistance Program (VEAP).

Duration   Selectees are supported for up to 36 months of full-time, year-round study or completion of a bachelor's degree, as long as they maintain a GPA of 2.5 or higher.

Additional information   This program began in 2001 as a replacement for the Seaman to Admiral Program (established in 1994), the Enlisted Commissioning Program, and other specialized programs for sailors to earn a commission. Upon acceptance into the program, selectees attend the Naval Science Institute (NSI) in Newport, Rhode Island for an 8-week program in the fundamental core concepts of being a naval officer (navigation, engineering, weapons, military history and justice, etc.). They then enter a college or university with an NROTC unit or affiliation to work full time on a bachelor's degree. They become members of and drill with the NROTC unit. When they complete their degree, they are commis-

sioned as ensigns in the United States Naval Reserve and assigned to initial training as a special duty officer (intelligence). After commissioning, 5 years of active service are required.

Number awarded   Varies each year.

Deadline   June of each year.

[212]
SPECIAL WARFARE OPTION OF THE SEAMAN TO ADMIRAL-21 PROGRAM

U.S. Navy
Attn: Commander, Naval Service Training Command
250 Dallas Street, Suite A
Pensacola, FL 32508-5268
(850) 452-9563   Fax: (850) 452-2486
E-mail: PNSC_STA21@navy.mil
Web: www.sta-21.navy.mil/program_options.asp

Summary   To allow outstanding enlisted Navy personnel to attend college, affiliate with an NROTC unit, complete a bachelor's degree, and receive a commission as a special warfare officer.

Eligibility   This program is open to U.S. citizens who are currently serving on active duty in the U.S. Navy or Naval Reserve, including Full Time Support (FTS), Selected Reserves (SELRES), and Navy Reservists on active duty, except for those on active duty for training (ACDUTRA). Only males are eligible for this option. They must be a member of the SEAL community. Applicants must be high school graduates (or GED recipients) who are able to complete requirements for a baccalaureate degree in 36 months or less. When they complete their degree requirements, they must be younger than 29 years of age. That age limitation may be adjusted upward for active service on a month-for-month basis up to 24 months, and waivers are considered for enlisted personnel who possess particularly exceptional qualifications if they can complete their degree prior to their 35th birthday. Within the past 3 years, they must have taken the SAT (and achieved scores of at least 500 on the mathematics section and 500 on the critical reading section) or the ACT (and achieved a score of at least 21 on the mathematics portion and 20 on the English portion). They must also meet physical regulations that include qualification for diving duty and/or combat swimmer. Preference is given to applicants who plan to major in a technical field (e.g., chemistry, computer science, engineering, mathematics, oceanography, operations analysis, physical sciences, or physics).

Financial data   Awardees continue to receive their regular Navy pay and allowances while they attend college on a full-time basis. They also receive reimbursement for tuition, fees, and books up to $10,000 per year. If base housing is available, they are eligible to live there. Participants are not eligible to receive benefits under the Navy's Tuition Assistance Program (TA), the Montgomery GI Bill (MGIB), the Navy College Fund, or the Veterans Educational Assistance Program (VEAP).

Duration   Selectees are supported for up to 36 months of full-time, year-round study or completion of a bachelor's degree, as long as they maintain a GPA of 2.5 or higher.

Additional information   This program began in 2001 as a replacement for the Seaman to Admiral Program (established in 1994), the Enlisted Commissioning Program, and other specialized programs for sailors to earn a commission. Upon acceptance into the program, selectees attend the Naval Science Institute (NSI) in Newport, Rhode Island for an 8-week program in the fundamental core concepts of being a naval officer (navigation, engineering, weapons, military history and justice, etc.). They then enter a college or university with an NROTC unit or affiliation to work full time on a bachelor's degree. They become members of and drill with the NROTC unit. When they complete their degree, they are commissioned as ensigns in the United States Naval Reserve and assigned to initial training as a special warfare officer. After commissioning, 5 years of active service are required.

Number awarded Varies each year.

Deadline June of each year.

[213]
SPORTS CLIPS HELP A HERO SCHOLARSHIPS

Veterans of Foreign Wars of the United States
Attn: National Military Services
406 West 34th Street, Suite 216
Kansas City, MO 64111
(816) 756-3390   Toll Free: (866) 789-NEED
E-mail: HelpAHero@vfw.org
Web: www.vfw.org

Summary To provide financial assistance to military personnel and veterans who are interested in attending college.

Eligibility This program is open to military personnel on active duty, retired and honorably discharged veterans, and members of the National Guard or Reserves who have completed basic training and follow-on training. Applicants must be U.S. citizens at the rank of E-5 or below and be able to demonstrated financial need. They must be enrolled or planning to enroll at a VA-approved program or institution of higher education.

Financial data The stipend is $5,000. Funds are paid directly to the recipient's institution.

Duration 1 year.

Additional information This program began in 2014 with support from Sports Clips, Inc.

Number awarded This program attempts to provide support to 115 veterans and military members each year.

Deadline April of each year for fall semester; November of each year for spring semester.

[214]
SUPPLY CORPS OPTION OF THE SEAMAN TO ADMIRAL-21 PROGRAM

U.S. Navy
Attn: Commander, Naval Service Training Command
250 Dallas Street, Suite A
Pensacola, FL 32508-5268
(850) 452-9563   Fax: (850) 452-2486
E-mail: PNSC_STA21@navy.mil
Web: www.sta-21.navy.mil/program_options.asp

Summary To allow outstanding enlisted Navy personnel to attend college, affiliate with an NROTC unit, complete a bachelor's degree in business, engineering, or mathematics, and receive a commission in the Supply Corps.

Eligibility This program is open to U.S. citizens who are currently serving on active duty in the U.S. Navy or Naval Reserve, including Full Time Support (FTS), Selected Reserves (SELRES), and Navy Reservists on active duty, except for those on active duty for training (ACDUTRA). Appli-

cants must be high school graduates (or GED recipients) who are able to complete requirements for a baccalaureate degree in a business, engineering, or mathematics related field in 36 months or less. When they complete their degree requirements, they must be younger than 31 years of age. Within the past 3 years, they must have taken the SAT (and achieved scores of at least 500 on the mathematics section and 500 on the critical reading section) or the ACT (and achieved a score of at least 21 on the mathematics portion and 20 on the English portion).

Financial data Awardees continue to receive their regular Navy pay and allowances while they attend college on a full-time basis. They also receive reimbursement for tuition, fees, and books up to $10,000 per year. If base housing is available, they are eligible to live there. Participants are not eligible to receive benefits under the Navy's Tuition Assistance Program (TA), the Montgomery GI Bill (MGIB), the Navy College Fund, or the Veterans Educational Assistance Program (VEAP).

Duration Selectees are supported for up to 36 months of full-time, year-round study or completion of a bachelor's degree, as long as they maintain a GPA of 2.5 or higher.

Additional information This program began in 2001 as a replacement for the Seaman to Admiral Program (established in 1994), the Enlisted Commissioning Program, and other specialized programs for sailors to earn a commission. Upon acceptance into the program, selectees attend the Naval Science Institute (NSI) in Newport, Rhode Island for an 8-week program in the fundamental core concepts of being a naval officer (navigation, engineering, weapons, military history and justice, etc.). They then enter a college or university with an NROTC unit or affiliation to work full time on a bachelor's degree. They become members of and drill with the NROTC unit. When they complete their degree, they are commissioned as ensigns in the United States Naval Reserve and assigned to initial training as an officer in the Supply Corps. After commissioning, 5 years of active service are required.

Number awarded Varies each year.

Deadline June of each year.

[215]
SURFACE WARFARE OFFICER/ENGINEER OPTION OF THE SEAMAN TO ADMIRAL-21 PROGRAM

U.S. Navy
Attn: Commander, Naval Service Training Command
250 Dallas Street, Suite A
Pensacola, FL 32508-5268
(850) 452-9563   Fax: (850) 452-2486
E-mail: PNSC_STA21@navy.mil
Web: www.sta-21.navy.mil/program_options.asp

Summary To allow outstanding enlisted Navy personnel to attend college, affiliate with an NROTC unit, complete a bachelor's degree, and receive a commission as a surface warfare officer/engineer.

Eligibility This program is open to U.S. citizens who are currently serving on active duty in the U.S. Navy or Naval Reserve, including Full Time Support (FTS), Selected Reserves (SELRES), and Navy Reservists on active duty, except for those on active duty for training (ACDUTRA). Applicants must be high school graduates (or GED recipients) who are able to complete requirements for a baccalaureate degree in 36 months or less. When they complete their degree requirements, they must be younger than 35 years of age. Within the past 3 years, they must have taken the SAT (and achieved scores of at least 500 on the mathematics section and 500 on the critical reading section) or the ACT (and achieved a score of at least 21 on the mathematics portion and 20 on the English portion). They must also pass relevant medical standards. No specific academic major is required, but applicants are encouraged to work on a technical degree in engineering or physical science.

Financial data Awardees continue to receive their regular Navy pay and allowances while they attend college on a full-time basis. They also receive reimbursement for tuition, fees, and books up to $10,000 per year. If base housing is available, they are eligible to live there. Participants are not eligible to receive benefits under the Navy's Tuition Assistance Program (TA), the Montgomery GI Bill (MGIB), the Navy College Fund, or the Veterans Educational Assistance Program (VEAP).

Duration Selectees are supported for up to 36 months of full-time, year-round study or completion of a bachelor's degree, as long as they maintain a GPA of 2.5 or higher.

Additional information Upon acceptance into the program, selectees attend the Naval Science Institute (NSI) in Newport, Rhode Island for an 8-week program in the fundamental core concepts of being a naval officer (navigation, engineering, weapons, military history and justice, etc.). They then enter a college or university with an NROTC unit or affiliation to work full time on a bachelor's degree. They become members of and drill with the NROTC unit. When they complete their degree, they are commissioned as ensigns in the United States Naval Reserve and assigned to initial training as a special duty officer (engineering duty). After commissioning, 5 years of active service are required.

Number awarded Varies each year.

Deadline June of each year.

[216]
SURFACE WARFARE OFFICER/INFORMATION PROFESSIONAL OPTION OF THE SEAMAN TO ADMIRAL-21 PROGRAM

U.S. Navy
Attn: Commander, Naval Service Training Command
250 Dallas Street, Suite A
Pensacola, FL 32508-5268
(850) 452-9563   Fax: (850) 452-2486
E-mail: PNSC_STA21@navy.mil
Web: www.sta-21.navy.mil/program_options.asp

Summary To allow outstanding enlisted Navy personnel to attend college, affiliate with an ROTC unit, complete a bachelor's degree, and receive a commission as a surface warfare officer/information professional (SWO/IP).

Eligibility This program is open to U.S. citizens who are currently serving on active duty in the U.S. Navy or Naval Reserve, including Full Time Support (FTS), Selected Reserves (SELRES), and Navy Reservists on active duty, except for those on active duty for training (ACDUTRA). Applicants must be high school graduates (or GED recipients) who are able to complete requirements for a baccalaureate degree in 36 months or less. When they complete their degree requirements, they must be younger than 28 years of age. Within the past 3 years, they must have taken the SAT (and achieved scores of at least 500 on the mathematics sec-

tion and 500 on the critical reading section) or the ACT (and achieved a score of at least 21 on the mathematics portion and 20 on the English portion). They must also pass relevant medical standards. No specific academic major is required, but applicants are encouraged to work on a technical degree in computer science, computer or electrical engineering, mathematics, physics, information systems, or operations.

Financial data Awardees continue to receive their regular Navy pay and allowances while they attend college on a full-time basis. They also receive reimbursement for tuition, fees, and books up to $10,000 per year. If base housing is available, they are eligible to live there. Participants are not eligible to receive benefits under the Navy's Tuition Assistance Program (TA), the Montgomery GI Bill (MGIB), the Navy College Fund, or the Veterans Educational Assistance Program (VEAP).

Duration Selectees are supported for up to 36 months of full-time, year-round study or completion of a bachelor's degree, as long as they maintain a GPA of 2.5 or higher.

Additional information Upon acceptance into the program, selectees attend the Naval Science Institute (NSI) in Newport, Rhode Island for an 8-week program in the fundamental core concepts of being a naval officer (navigation, engineering, weapons, military history and justice, etc.). They then enter a college or university with an NROTC unit or affiliation to work full time on a bachelor's degree. They become members of and drill with the NROTC unit. When they complete their degree, they are commissioned as ensigns in the United States Naval Reserve and assigned to initial training as a special duty officer (information professional). After commissioning, 5 years of active service are required.

Number awarded Varies each year.

Deadline June of each year.

[217]
SURFACE WARFARE OFFICER/OCEANOGRAPHY OPTION OF THE SEAMAN TO ADMIRAL-21 PROGRAM

U.S. Navy
Attn: Commander, Naval Service Training Command
250 Dallas Street, Suite A
Pensacola, FL 32508-5268
(850) 452-9563   Fax: (850) 452-2486
E-mail: PNSC_STA21@navy.mil
Web: www.sta-21.navy.mil/program_options.asp

Summary To allow outstanding enlisted Navy personnel to attend college, affiliate with an NROTC unit, complete a bachelor's degree, and receive a commission as a surface warfare officer/oceanography.

Eligibility This program is open to U.S. citizens who are currently serving on active duty in the U.S. Navy or Naval Reserve, including Full Time Support (FTS), Selected Reserves (SELRES), and Navy Reservists on active duty, except for those on active duty for training (ACDUTRA). Applicants must be high school graduates (or GED recipients) who are able to complete requirements for a baccalaureate degree in 36 months or less. They must be planning to work on a technical degree in chemistry, computer science, engineering, geospatial information systems, hydrography, marine science, mathematics, meteorology, oceanography, operational analysis, physical sciences, or physics. When they complete their degree requirements, they must be younger than 31 years of age. Within the past 3 years, they must have taken the SAT (and achieved scores of at least 500 on the mathematics section and 500 on the critical reading section) or the ACT (and achieved a score of at least 21 on the mathematics portion and 20 on the English portion). They must also pass relevant medical standards.

Financial data Awardees continue to receive their regular Navy pay and allowances while they attend college on a full-time basis. They also receive reimbursement for tuition, fees, and books up to $10,000 per year. If base housing is available, they are eligible to live there. Participants are not eligible to receive benefits under the Navy's Tuition Assistance Program (TA), the Montgomery GI Bill (MGIB), the Navy College Fund, or the Veterans Educational Assistance Program (VEAP).

Duration Selectees are supported for up to 36 months of full-time, year-round study or completion of a bachelor's degree, as long as they maintain a GPA of 2.5 or higher.

Additional information Upon acceptance into the program, selectees attend the Naval Science Institute (NSI) in Newport, Rhode Island for an 8-week program in the fundamental core concepts of being a naval officer (navigation, engineering, weapons, military history and justice, etc.). They then enter a college or university with an NROTC unit or affiliation to work full time on a bachelor's degree. They become members of and drill with the NROTC unit. When they complete their degree, they are commissioned as ensigns in the United States Naval Reserve and assigned to initial training as a special duty officer (oceanography). After commissioning, 5 years of active service are required.

Number awarded Varies each year.

Deadline June of each year.

[218]
SURFACE WARFARE OFFICER OPTION OF THE SEAMAN TO ADMIRAL-21 PROGRAM

U.S. Navy
Attn: Commander, Naval Service Training Command
250 Dallas Street, Suite A
Pensacola, FL 32508-5268
(850) 452-9563   Fax: (850) 452-2486
E-mail: PNSC_STA21@navy.mil
Web: www.sta-21.navy.mil/program_options.asp

Summary To allow outstanding enlisted Navy personnel to attend college, affiliate with an NROTC unit, complete a bachelor's degree, and receive a commission as a surface warfare officer (SWO).

Eligibility This program is open to U.S. citizens who are currently serving on active duty in the U.S. Navy or Naval Reserve, including Full Time Support (FTS), Selected Reserves (SELRES), and Navy Reservists on active duty, except for those on active duty for training (ACDUTRA). Applicants must be high school graduates (or GED recipients) who are able to complete requirements for a baccalaureate degree in 36 months or less. When they complete their degree requirements, they must be younger than 31 years of age. Within the past 3 years, they must have taken the SAT (and achieved scores of at least 500 on the mathematics section and 500 on the critical reading section) or the ACT (and achieved a score of at least 21 on the mathematics portion and 20 on the English portion). They must also meet relevant medical standards. Preference is given to applicants who

plan to major in a technical field (e.g., chemistry, computer science, engineering, mathematics, oceanography, operations analysis, physical sciences, or physics).

Financial data Awardees continue to receive their regular Navy pay and allowances while they attend college on a full-time basis. They also receive reimbursement for tuition, fees, and books up to $10,000 per year. If base housing is available, they are eligible to live there. Participants are not eligible to receive benefits under the Navy's Tuition Assistance Program (TA), the Montgomery GI Bill (MGIB), the Navy College Fund, or the Veterans Educational Assistance Program (VEAP).

Duration Selectees are supported for up to 36 months of full-time, year-round study or completion of a bachelor's degree, as long as they maintain a GPA of 2.5 or higher.

Additional information This program began in 2001 as a replacement for the Seaman to Admiral Program (established in 1994), the Enlisted Commissioning Program, and other specialized programs for sailors to earn a commission. Upon acceptance into the program, selectees attend the Naval Science Institute (NSI) in Newport, Rhode Island for an 8-week program in the fundamental core concepts of being a naval officer (navigation, engineering, weapons, military history and justice, etc.). They then enter a college or university with an NROTC unit or affiliation to work full time on a bachelor's degree. They become members of and drill with the NROTC unit. When they complete their degree, they are commissioned as ensigns in the United States Naval Reserve and assigned to initial training as a surface warfare officer. After commissioning, 5 years of active service are required.

Number awarded Varies each year.

Deadline June of each year.

[219]
TAILHOOK EDUCATIONAL FOUNDATION SCHOLARSHIPS

Tailhook Educational Foundation
9696 Businesspark Avenue
P.O. Box 26626
San Diego, CA 92196-0626
(858) 689-9223   Toll Free: (800) 322-4665
E-mail: tag@tailhook.net
Web: www.tailhook.net/A_Foundation_Index.html

Summary To provide financial assistance for college to personnel associated with naval aviation and their children.

Eligibility This program is open to 1) the children (natural, step, and adopted) and grandchildren of current or former U.S. Navy, Coast Guard, or Marine Corps personnel who served as an aviator, flight officer, or air crewman; or 2) personnel and children and grandchildren of personnel who are serving or have served on board a U.S. Navy aircraft carrier as a member of the ship's company or air wing. Applicants must be enrolled or accepted for enrollment at an accredited college or university. Selection is based on educational and extracurricular achievements, merit, and citizenship.

Financial data The stipend ranges from $1,500 to $23,000.

Duration 1 to 2 years.

Number awarded Varies each year; recently, 80 were awarded.

Deadline March of each year.

[220]
TENNESSEE HELPING HEROES GRANTS

Tennessee Student Assistance Corporation
Parkway Towers
404 James Robertson Parkway, Suite 1510
Nashville, TN 37243-0820
(615) 741-1346   Toll Free: (800) 342-1663
Fax: (615) 741-6101   E-mail: TSAC.Aidinfo@tn.gov
Web: www.tn.gov/collegepays/mon_college/hh_grant.htm

Summary To provide financial assistance to 1) current Reservists or National Guard members and 2) veterans who are residents of Tennessee and enrolled at a college or university in the state.

Eligibility This program is open to residents of Tennessee who are veterans honorably discharged from the U.S. armed forces and former or current members of a Reserve or Tennessee National Guard unit who were called into active military service. Applicants must have been awarded, on or after September 11, 2001, the Iraq Campaign Medal, the Afghanistan Campaign Medal, or the Global War on Terrorism Expeditionary Medal. They must be enrolled at least half time at an eligible college or university in Tennessee and receive no final failing grade in any course. No academic standard or financial need requirements apply.

Financial data Grants are $1,000 per semester for full-time study or $500 per semester for part-time study. Funds are awarded after completion of each semester of work.

Duration Grants are awarded until completion of the equivalent of 8 full semesters of work, completion of a baccalaureate degree, or the eighth anniversary of honorable discharge from military service, whichever comes first.

Additional information This program was added as a component of the Tennessee Education Lottery Scholarship Program in 2005.

Number awarded Varies each year; recently, 486 students received $765,855 in scholarships through this program.

Deadline August of each year for fall enrollment, January of each year for spring, or April of each year for summer.

[221]
TEXAS NATIONAL GUARD TUITION ASSISTANCE PROGRAM

Texas Higher Education Coordinating Board
Attn: Grants and Special Programs
1200 East Anderson Lane
P.O. Box 12788
Austin, TX 78711-2788
(512) 427-6340   Toll Free: (800) 242-3062
Fax: (512) 427-6420   E-mail: grantinfo@thecb.state.tx.us
Web: www.collegeforalltexans.com

Summary To provide financial assistance for college or graduate school to members of the Texas National Guard.

Eligibility This program is open to Texas residents who are active, drilling members of the Texas National Guard, the Texas Air Guard, or the State Guard. Applicants may be undergraduate or graduate students attending or planning to attend a public or private college or university in Texas; attendance at career colleges or universities is not supported.

Financial data Eligible Guard members receive exemption from tuition at Texas public colleges and universities. For students who attend a private, nonprofit institution, the award is based on public university tuition charges for 12 semester credit hours at the resident rate.

Duration Tuition assistance is available for up to 12 semester credit hours per semester for up to 10 semesters or 5 academic years, whichever occurs first.

Number awarded Varies each year; recently, 864 Guard members participated in this program.

Deadline June of each year for the fall semester; November of each year for the spring semester.

[222]
TILLMAN MILITARY SCHOLARS PROGRAM

Pat Tillman Foundation
217 North Jefferson Street, Suite 602
Chicago, IL 60661
(773) 360-5277
E-mail: scholarships@pattillmanfoundation.org
Web: www.pattillmanfoundation.org/apply-to-be-a-scholar

Summary To provide financial assistance to active servicemembers, veterans, and their spouses who are interested in working on an undergraduate or graduate degree.

Eligibility This program is open to veterans and active servicemembers of all branches of the armed forces from both the pre- and post-September 11 era and their spouses; children are not eligible. Applicants must be enrolled or planning to enroll full time at a 4-year public or private college or university to work on an undergraduate, graduate, or postgraduate degree. Current and former servicemembers must submit 400-word essays on 1) their motivation and decision to serve in the U.S. military and how that decision and experience has changed their life and ambitions; and 2) their educational and career goals, how they will incorporate their military service experience into those goals, and how they intend to continue their service to others and the community. Spouses must submit 400-word essays on 1) their previous service to others and the community; and 2) their educational and career goals, how they will incorporate their service experiences and the impact of their spouse's military service into those goals, and how they intend to continue their service to others and the community. Selection is based on those essays, educational and career ambitions, record of military service, record of personal achievement, demonstration of service to others in the community, desire to continue such service, and leadership potential.

Financial data The stipend depends on the need of the recipient and the availability of funds; recently, stipends averaged approximately $15,000.

Duration 1 year; may be renewed, provided the recipient maintains a GPA of 3.0 or higher, remains enrolled full time, and documents participation in civic action or community service.

Additional information This program began in 2009.

Number awarded 60 each year. Since the program began, it has awarded more than $6 million to 348 scholars.

Deadline March of each year.

[223]
TONY LOPEZ SCHOLARSHIP PROGRAM

Louisiana National Guard Enlisted Association
c/o CMSgt John Harris
694 South Rue Marcel
Gretna, LA 70056
(504) 388-5423   E-mail: john.harris1@bellsouth.net
Web: www.langea.org

Summary To provide financial assistance to members of the Louisiana National Guard Enlisted Association (LANGEA) and their dependents who plan to attend college in any state.

Eligibility This program is open to members of the association, their spouses and unmarried dependent children, and the unremarried spouses and unmarried dependent children of deceased members who were in good standing at the time of their death. The qualifying LANGEA members must have at least 1 year remaining on their enlistment following completion of the school year for which the application is submitted or have served 20 years of more in the Louisiana National Guard. Applicants must be enrolled or planning to enroll full time at an accredited college, university, trade school, or business school in any state. Graduate students are not eligible. Selection is based on academic achievement, character, leadership, and financial need.

Financial data The stipend is $2,000.

Duration 1 year; nonrenewable.

Number awarded 2 each year.

Deadline April of each year.

[224]
TROOPS-TO-TEACHERS PROGRAM

Defense Activity for Non-Traditional Education Support
Attn: Troops to Teachers
6490 Saufley Field Road
Pensacola, FL 32509-5243
Toll Free: (800) 231-6242   Fax: (850) 452-1096
E-mail: ttt@navy.mil
Web: www.troopstoteachers.net/Home.aspx

Summary To provide funding 1) to earn a teaching certificate or 2) for a bonus to military personnel and veterans interested in a second career as a public school teacher.

Eligibility This program is open to 1) active-duty military personnel who are retired or currently serving and have an approved date of retirement within 1 year; 2) members of a Reserve component who are retired or currently serving in the Selected Reserve with 10 or more years of credible service and commit to serving an additional 3 years or until eligible for retirement; 3) military personnel with at least 6 years on continuous active duty, will transfer to the Selected Reserve within 4 years, and are willing to commit to at least 3 years in the Selected Reserve or until eligible for retirement; and 4) active-duty or Selected Reserve personnel who separated on or after January 8, 2002 for a service-connected physical disability and who register for this program within 4 years of separation. Applicants must have a baccalaureate or advanced degree, the equivalent of 1 year of college with 6 years of work experience in a vocational or technical field, or meet state requirements for vocational/technical teacher referral. A bonus is available to applicants who are willing to accept employment as a teacher in 1) a school district that has at least 10% of the students from families living below the poverty level; and 2) at a specific school within the district where at least 50% of the students are eligible for the free or reduced cost lunch program or where at least 13.5% of the students have disabilities. A stipend is available to applicants who are willing to accept employment as a teacher at 1) any school within a "high need" district that has at least 20% of the students from families living below the poverty level; or 2) at a specific school where at least 50% of the students are eligible for the free or reduced cost lunch program or at least 13.5% of the students have disabilities, as long as that school is in a district that has between 10% and 20% of students who come from poverty-level families. Preference is given to applicants interested in teaching mathematics, science, or special education.

Financial data A bonus of $10,000 is awarded to recipients who agree to teach for 3 years in a school that serves a high percentage of students from low-income families. A stipend of $5,000 is awarded to recipients who agree to teach for 3 years in a school located in a "high-need" district; stipend funds are also intended to help pay for teacher certification costs.

Duration The bonuses are intended as 1-time grants.

Additional information This program began in 1994 by the Department of Defense (DoD). In 2000, program oversight and funding were transferred to the U.S. Department of Education, but DoD continues to operate the program. The No Child Left Behind Act of 2001 provided for continuation of the program.

Number awarded Varies each year.

Deadline Deadline not specified.

[225]
UNITED STATES FIELD ARTILLERY ASSOCIATION SCHOLARSHIPS

United States Field Artillery Association
Attn: Scholarship Committee
Building 758, McNair Avenue
P.O. Box 33027
Fort Sill, OK 73503-0027
(580) 355-4677   Toll Free: (866) 355-4677
Fax: (580) 355-8745   E-mail: suzette@fieldartillery.org
Web: www.fieldartillery.org/#!membership/c1ghi

Summary To provide financial assistance for college to members of the United States Field Artillery Association (USFAA) and their immediate family.

Eligibility This program is open to 3 categories of students: USFAA members (officer or enlisted), immediate family of enlisted members, and immediate family of officer members. Applicants must have been accepted for admission as an undergraduate at an accredited college, university, or vocational program. Along with their application, they must submit an essay explaining their educational goals and how this scholarship will help meet those goals. Financial need is also considered in the selection process. The highest-ranked applicant receives the GEN Donald R. Keith Scholarship.

Financial data Stipends range from $1,000 to $2,500.

Duration 1 year.

Additional information The USFAA services the field artillery branch of the military.

Number awarded Varies each year; recently, 11 were awarded: 1 at $2,500 (the GEN Donald R. Keith Scholarship), 4 at $1,500, and 6 at $1,000.

Deadline March of each year.

[226]
U.S. ARMY WOMEN'S FOUNDATION LEGACY SCHOLARSHIPS

U.S. Army Women's Foundation
Attn: Scholarship Committee
P.O. Box 5030
Fort Lee, VA 23801-0030
(804) 734-3078   E-mail: info@awfdn.org
Web: www.awfdn.org/programs/legacyscholarships.shtml

Summary To provide financial assistance for college or graduate school to women who are serving or have served in the Army and their children.

Eligibility This program is open to 1) women who have served or are serving honorably in the U.S. Army, U.S. Army Reserve, or Army National Guard; and 2) children of women who served honorably in the U.S. Army, U.S. Army Reserve, or Army National Guard. Applicants must be 1) high school graduates or GED recipients enrolled at a community college or technical certificate program who have a GPA of 2.5 or higher; 2) sophomores or higher at an accredited college or university who have a GPA of 3.0 or higher; or 3) students enrolled in or accepted to a graduate program who have a GPA of 3.0 or higher. Along with their application, they must submit a 2-page essay on why they should be considered for this scholarship, their future plans as related to their program of study, and information about their community service, activities, and work experience. Selection is based on merit, academic potential, community service, and financial need.

Financial data The stipend is $2,500 for college and graduate students or $1,000 for community college and certificate students.

Duration 1 year.

Number awarded 5 to 10 each year.

Deadline January of each year.

[227]
USMCCCA SCHOLARSHIPS

United States Marine Corps Combat Correspondents
  Association
Attn: Executive Director
110 Fox Court
Wildwood, FL 34785
(352) 748-4698   E-mail: usmccca@cfl.rr.com
Web: www.usmccca.org/archives/4941

Summary To provide financial assistance to members of the U.S. Marine Corps Combat Correspondents Association (USMCCCA) or their dependents and Marines in designated occupational fields who are interested in studying communications in college.

Eligibility This program is open to 1) members of USMCCCA, their dependents, and their spouses; and 2) active-duty Marines in Occupational Fields 4300 and 4600 and their dependents who are USMCCCA members or will agree to become members if awarded a scholarship. Applicants must be enrolled or planning to enroll in an undergraduate program in communications. Along with their application, they must submit 500-word essays on 1) their noteworthy

achievements and long-range goals; and 2) "the United States I want to see in 15 years and my role in the transformation." Financial need is not considered in the selection process.

Financial data Stipends range up to $3,000; funds are disbursed directly to the recipient's institution to be used exclusively for tuition, books, and/or fees.

Duration 1 year.

Number awarded 1 or more each year.

Deadline May of each year.

[228]
USS LITTLE ROCK ASSOCIATION NROTC SCHOLARSHIP PROGRAM

USS Little Rock Association
c/o LCDR Robert M. Baker, USN (Retired), Scholarship
  Committee Chair
18426 Mount Lock Hill Road
Sharpsburg, MD 21782-2029
(301) 799-9089   E-mail: rmbusnret@gmail.com
Web: www.usslittlerock.org/scholarship.html

Summary To provide financial assistance to Naval ROTC midshipmen in college who have a personal or family connection to the sea services or are members of the USS Little Rock Association.

Eligibility This program is open to students entering their third academic year of an NROTC program (scholarship, college program, Marine Enlisted Commissioning Program, or Seaman to Admiral). Applicants must 1) be the children or direct descendants of active, retired, or honorably discharged members of the sea services (U.S. Navy, U.S. Marine Corps, or U.S. Coast Guard) or their Reserve components; 2) themselves be serving or have served in any of the regular or Reserve sea services; or 3) have been Junior Associate members of the USS Little Rock Association for at least 2 years. They must have a GPA of 3.0 or higher and have demonstrated superior leadership qualities and aptitude for service in all of their NROTC activities. Along with their application, they must submit a 500-word letter describing why they consider themselves worthy of the award.

Financial data The stipend is $1,000 per year.

Duration 1 year; may be renewed 1 additional year.

Additional information This program began in 2001.

Number awarded 1 or 2 each year.

Deadline May of each year.

[229]
USS PITTSBURGH FUND

Pittsburgh Foundation
Attn: Scholarship Coordinator
Five PPG Place, Suite 250
Pittsburgh, PA 15222-5414
(412) 391-5122   Fax: (412) 391-7259
E-mail: turnerd@pghfdn.org
Web: www.pittsburghfoundation.org/node/1725

Summary To provide financial assistance for college to students with ties to the USS Pittsburgh.

Eligibility This program is open to past and present crewmembers and dependents of crewmembers of the USS Pittsburgh. Applicants must be attending or planning to attend an institution of higher education to major in engineering or other "hard" science. Along with their application, they must submit a resume, a statement of why the scholarship is desired, 2 letters of reference, and transcripts.

Financial data The stipend is $2,500.

Duration 1 year.

Additional information This program was established by the Pittsburgh Council of the Navy League of the United States.

Number awarded 3 each year.

Deadline April of each year.

[230]
UTAH ASMC CHAPTER SCHOLARSHIPS

American Society of Military Comptrollers-Utah Chapter
c/o Donna Parada, Scholarship Chair
AFLCMC/LZPED
6020 Gum Lane, Building 1218
Hill AFB, UT 84056
(801) 586-4908   E-mail: Donna.Parada@us.af.mil
Web: chapters.asmconline.org/utah/category/scholarships

Summary To provide financial assistance to members of the Utah Chapter of the American Society of Military Comptrollers (ASMC) and their families who are interested in studying any field at a college in any state.

Eligibility This program is open to members of the ASMC Utah Chapter, their spouses, and their dependents. Applicants must be attending or planning to attend a college or university in any state and work on a degree in any field. Along with their application, they must submit 3 essays, up to 150 words each, on 1) their extracurricular activities; 2) their leadership skills, abilities, opportunities, and experiences; and 3) their involvement in and service to their neighborhood, community, church, or other organizations. Selection is based on the information in those essays (10 points each), GPA (30 points), ACT/SAT scores (10 points), difficulty of classes (20 points), a personal letter on their educational and career goals (5 points), and reference letters (5 points).

Financial data The stipend is $1,000.

Duration 1 year.

Additional information The ASMC is open to all financial management professionals employed by the U.S. Department of Defense and Coast Guard, both civilian and military.

Number awarded Varies each year; recently, 4 were awarded.

Deadline April of each year.

[231]
UTAH NATIONAL GUARD STATE TUITION ASSISTANCE PROGRAM

Utah Army National Guard
Attn: UT-G1-ESO
12953 South Minuteman Drive
P.O. Box 1776
Draper, UT 84020-1776
(801) 432-4354
E-mail: ng.ut.utarng.list.education-office@mail.mil
Web: www.ut.ngb.army.mil/education2/statetuition.htm

Summary To provide tuition assistance to currently-enrolled members of the Utah National Guard interested in working on an undergraduate or graduate degree.

Eligibility This program is open to Utah residents who are MOS/AFSC qualified members of the Utah National Guard.

Applicants must be seeking funding to obtain a 1) high school diploma or GED certification; 2) undergraduate, graduate, vocational, technical, or licensure certificate; 3) associate degree; 4) baccalaureate degree; or 5) master's degree. Support is not provided for doctoral or first professional degrees, such as architecture, certified public accountant, podiatry (D.P.M.), dentistry (D.D.S. or D.M.D.), medicine (M.D.), optometry (O.D.), osteopathic medicine (D.O.), pharmacy (Pharm.D.), law (J.D.), or theology (M.Div. or M.H.L.). Enlisted personnel must have remaining obligation on their existing enlistment contract that will extend to or beyond the last date of course enrollment for these funds. Officers must have at least 4 years of Selected Reserve service remaining from the date of completion of the course for which this funding is provided.

Financial data Support is provided for 100% of the cost of tuition, to a maximum of $250 per hour or a maximum of $4,500 per year.

Duration 1 semester; recipients may renew.

Additional information Recipients of this funding may continue to receive any GI Bill funding to which they are entitled, but they may not simultaneously apply for this and federal Tuition Assistance benefits.

Number awarded Varies each year; recently, a total of $750,000 was available for this program.

Deadline Applications must be received at least 3 weeks prior to the course start date. They are processed on a first-come, first-served basis.

[232]
UTAH NATIONAL GUARD STATE TUITION WAIVER

Utah Army National Guard
Attn: UT-G1-ESO
12953 South Minuteman Drive
P.O. Box 1776
Draper, UT 84020-1776
(801) 432-4354
E-mail: ng.ut.utarng.list.education-office@mail.mil
Web: www.ut.ngb.army.mil/education2/statetuition.htm

Summary To waive tuition for members of the Utah National Guard at public institutions in the state.

Eligibility This program is open to Utah residents who are MOS/AFSC qualified members of the Utah National Guard. Applicants must have been accepted as a full-time student at a public college or university in the state. They may not currently be on active duty and may not already have a 4-year degree. Along with their application, they must submit a short essay on their military goals and how their civilian education will assist them in achieving those goals.

Financial data This program provides waiver of tuition at Utah public colleges and universities.

Duration 1 semester; recipients may renew.

Additional information Recipients of these waivers may continue to receive any GI Bill funding to which they are entitled and they may utilize state Tuition Assistance or federal Tuition Assistance to pay for fees or credits not covered by this program.

Number awarded Varies each year. Each Utah public college and university is required to set aside 2.5% of its scholarship funds for members of the National Guard.

Deadline May of each year.

[233]
VADM SAMUEL L. GRAVELY, JR., USN (RET.)
MEMORIAL SCHOLARSHIPS

Armed Forces Communications and Electronics
    Association
Attn: AFCEA Educational Foundation
4400 Fair Lakes Court
Fairfax, VA 22033-3899
(703) 631-6138   Toll Free: (800) 336-4583, ext. 6138
Fax: (703) 631-4693   E-mail: scholarship@afcea.org
Web: www.afcea.org

Summary   To provide funding to students (especially those who are military enlisted personnel or veterans) majoring in specified scientific fields at an Historically Black College or University (HBCU).

Eligibility   This program is open to sophomores and juniors enrolled full or part time at an accredited 2- or 4-year HBCU or in a distance learning or online degree program affiliated with those institutions. They must be working toward a bachelor's degree in engineering (aerospace, computer, electrical, or systems), computer science, computer engineering technology, computer information systems, mathematics, physics, information systems management, or other field directly related to the support of U.S. intelligence or homeland security enterprises. Special consideration is given to military enlisted personnel and veterans.

Financial data   The stipend is $5,000.

Duration   1 year; may be renewed.

Additional information   This program began in 2009 with support from American Systems.

Number awarded   Varies each year; recently, 3 were awarded.

Deadline   May of each year.

[234]
VETERANS APPRECIATION SCHOLARSHIP
PROGRAM

Northwest Career Colleges Federation
4200 Sixth Avenue S.E., Suite 313
Lacey, WA 98503
(425) 376-0369
E-mail: scholarships@nwcareercolleges.org
Web: www.nwcareercolleges.org/scholarships

Summary   To provide financial assistance to military personnel and veterans in Idaho, Oregon, and Washington who are interested in attending a career college in those states.

Eligibility   This program is open to residents of Idaho, Oregon, or Washington who are discharged veterans and served after September 11, 2001. Applicants must be interested in attending 1 of 43 private career colleges in those state. They may not be currently attending the college.

Financial data   Stipends are $1,000 or $500. Funds must be used to pay for tuition at a participating career college.

Duration   1 year.

Number awarded   Varies each year; recently, 51 were awarded.

Deadline   Deadline not specified.

[235]
VETERANS UNITED FOUNDATION SCHOLARSHIPS

Veterans United Home Loans
Attn: Veterans United Foundation
1400 Veterans United Drive
Columbia, MO 65203
(573) 445-7999   Toll Free: (800) 884-5560
E-mail: customer_service@vu.com
Web: www.enhancelives.com/scholarships

Summary   To provide financial assistance for college or graduate school to students who have a tie to the military.

Eligibility   This program is open to 1) active-duty military personnel with plans to attend college; 2) honorably-discharged veterans of the U.S. military; 3) spouses of military members or veterans; 4) surviving spouses and children of fallen servicemembers; and 5) children of veterans or active-duty military. Applicants must be attending or planning to attend college as a full-time undergraduate or graduate student. They must have a GPA of 2.5 or higher. Selection is based primarily on an essay.

Financial data   The stipend is $2,000.

Duration   1 year.

Additional information   This program began in 2007.

Number awarded   Up to 20 each year: 10 each term.

Deadline   April or October of each year.

[236]
VIRGINIA NATIONAL GUARD ASSOCIATION
SCHOLARSHIP

Virginia National Guard Association
Attn: Scholarship Committee
11518 Hardwood Drive
Midlothian, VA 23114
(804) 350-0175
Web: www.vnga.org/scholarship.shtml

Summary   To provide financial assistance to members of the Virginia National Guard Association (VNGA) and their families who are interested in attending college in any state.

Eligibility   Applicants must have been enrolled at a college or university in any state for 1 year and qualify under 1 of the following conditions: 1) an officer or warrant officer in the Virginia National Guard and a VNGA member; 2) the dependent child or spouse of an officer or warrant officer in the Virginia National Guard who is a VNGA member; 3) the dependent child or spouse of a retired officer or warrant officer who is a VNGA member; 4) the dependent child or spouse of a deceased retired officer or warrant officer; or 5) the dependent child or spouse of a Virginia National Guard officer or warrant officer who died while in the Virginia National Guard. Along with their application, they must submit a brief description of their educational and/or military objectives, a list of their leadership positions and honors, and a brief statement of their financial need.

Financial data   A stipend is awarded; the amount is determined annually.

Duration   1 year; may be renewed for 2 additional years.

Additional information   The association also offers a special scholarship in memory of CW4 William C. Singletary who, in rescuing 2 elderly women from drowning, gave his own life.

Number awarded   Varies each year.

Deadline   September of each year.

[237]
VIRGINIA NATIONAL GUARD TUITION ASSISTANCE PROGRAM

Virginia National Guard
Attn: Educational Services Officer
Fort Pickett, Building 316
Blackstone, VA 23824-6316
(434) 298-3020 Toll Free: (888) 483-2682
Fax: (434) 298-6296
E-mail: ng.va.vaarng.mbx.ngva-education@mail.mil
Web: vko.va.ngb.army.mil

Summary To provide financial assistance to members of the Virginia National Guard who are interested in attending college or graduate school in the state.

Eligibility This program is open to active members of the Virginia National Guard who are residents of Virginia and interested in attending college or graduate school in the state. Awards are presented in the following priority order: 1) enlisted personnel who have previously received assistance through this program; 2) officers who need to complete a bachelor's degree in order to be eligible for promotion to captain; 3) warrant officers working on an associate or bachelor's degree; 4) any member working on an undergraduate degree; and 4) any member working on a graduate degree.

Financial data The program provides reimbursement of tuition at approved colleges, universities, and vocational/technical schools in Virginia, to a maximum of $2,000 per semester or $6,000 per year. Bookstore grants up to $350 per semester are also provided.

Duration 1 semester; may be renewed.

Additional information This program began in 1983. Recipients must remain in the Guard for at least 2 years after being funded.

Number awarded Varies each year.

Deadline June of each year for fall semester; October of each year for spring semester; March of each year for summer session.

[238]
VIRGINIA PENINSULA POST SAME SCHOLARSHIPS

Society of American Military Engineers-Virginia Peninsula Post
c/o James H. King, Jr., Scholarship Chair
129 Andrews Street, Suite 217
Hampton, VA 23665
(757) 764-7570 Fax: (757) 764-3439
E-mail: james.king.45@us.af.mil

Summary To provide financial assistance to high school seniors, undergraduates, and graduate students entering or enrolled at universities in Virginia who have a tie to the Virginia Peninsula Post of the Society of American Military Engineers (SAME) and are majoring in engineering or architecture.

Eligibility This program is open to 1) high school seniors planning to enroll in an engineering or architecture program at an accredited college or university in Virginia; 2) students enrolled as freshmen through graduate students at an accredited college or university in Virginia and working on a bachelor's or higher degree in engineering or architecture; and 3) members and dependents of members of the SAME Virginia Peninsula Post. Applicants must have demonstrated commitment to future military service by enrolling in an ROTC

program, a commissioning program, or an extended enlistment. Selection is based on academic standing and accomplishments (50%), involvement in university and community programs, including those with military involvement (30%), and financial need (20%).

Financial data The stipend is $1,500.

Duration 1 year.

Number awarded 4 each year: 1 to a high school senior, 1 to a college freshman or sophomore, 1 to a college junior or senior, and 1 to a graduate student.

Deadline February of each year.

[239]
WALTER BEALL SCHOLARSHIP

Walter Beall Scholarship Foundation
c/o W. Ralph Holcombe, Secretary/Treasurer
4911 Fennell Court
Suffolk, VA 23435
(757) 484-7403 Fax: (757) 686-5952
E-mail: info@walterbeallscholarship.org
Web: www.walterbeallscholarship.org

Summary To provide financial assistance to members of the Fleet Reserve Association (FRA) and their families who are interested in studying engineering, aeronautical engineering, or aviation in college.

Eligibility This program is open to FRA members who have been in good standing for at least the past 2 consecutive years and their spouses, children, and grandchildren. Students in a Reserve officer candidate program receiving aid or attending a military academy are not eligible. Applicants must be enrolled at an accredited college, university, or technical institution in the United States in a program related to general engineering, aviation, or aeronautical engineering. Selection is based on GPA, scholastic aptitude test scores, curriculum goals, interests, community activities, awards, and financial need. U.S. citizenship is required.

Financial data The amounts of the awards depend on the availability of funds and the need of the recipients; they range from $2,000 to $5,000.

Duration 1 year; recipients may reapply.

Additional information The Walter Beall Scholarship Foundation is sponsored by the Past Regional Presidents Club of the Fleet Reserve Association. Membership in the FRA is restricted to active-duty, retired, and Reserve members of the Navy, Marine Corps, and Coast Guard.

Number awarded 1 or more each year.

Deadline April of each year.

[240]
WASHINGTON NATIONAL GUARD SCHOLARSHIP PROGRAM

Washington National Guard
Attn: Education Services Office
41st Division Drive, Building 15
Camp Murray, WA 98430
(253) 512-8435 Toll Free: (800) 606-9843 (within WA)
Fax: (253) 512-8941
E-mail: education@washingtonguard.org
Web: washingtonguard.org/edu

Summary To provide forgivable loans to members of the Washington National Guard who wish to attend college or graduate school in the state.

Eligibility This program is open to members of the Washington National Guard who have already served for at least 1 year and have at least 2 years remaining on their current contract. Applicants must have a rank between E1 and O3. They must be attending an accredited college as a resident of Washington state and must already have utilized all available federal educational benefits. Army Guard members must have completed BCT/AIT and awarded initial MOS; Air Guard members must have completed BMT/initial tech school and been awarded "3-Level" AFSC. Graduate students are eligible, but undergraduates receive preference as long as they are making satisfactory progress toward a baccalaureate degree. The minimum GPA requirement is 2.5 for undergraduates or 3.0 for graduate students.

Financial data This program provides a stipend that is based on the number of credits completed but does not exceed the amount required for tuition, books, and fees at the University of Washington. Recipients incur a service obligation of 1 additional year in the Guard for the initial scholarship award and 1 additional year for each full year of academic credit completed with this assistance. The grant serves as a loan which is forgiven if the recipient completes the contracted service time in the Washington National Guard. Failure to meet the service obligation requires the recipient to repay the loan plus 8% interest.

Duration 1 year; may be renewed.

Number awarded Varies each year. A total of $100,000 is available for this program annually; scholarships are awarded on a first-come, first-served basis as long as funds are available.

Deadline June of each year.

[241]
WEST VIRGINIA NATIONAL GUARD EDUCATIONAL ENCOURAGEMENT PROGRAM

Office of the Adjutant General
Attn: Education Officer
1703 Coonskin Drive
Charleston, WV 25311-1085
(304) 561-6306   Toll Free: (866) 986-4326
Fax: (304) 561-6307   E-mail: kathy.kidd@us.army.mil
Web: www.wv.ngb.army.mil/education/benefits/default.aspx

Summary To provide financial assistance to members of the National Guard in West Virginia who are interested in attending college or graduate school in the state.

Eligibility This program is open to active members of the West Virginia National Guard who are residents of West Virginia and interested in attending a public or private college in the state. Applicants must have maintained satisfactory participation (90% attendance) in the Guard. They must be interested in working on a vocational, associate, bachelor's, or master's degree. In some instances, support may also be available to Guard members who are interested in working on an M.D., D.O., P.A., or J.D. degree.

Financial data The program provides payment of 100% of the tuition and fees at participating colleges and universities in West Virginia, to a maximum of $6,500 per year.

Duration 1 academic year; may be renewed.

Number awarded Varies each year.

Deadline Deadline not specified.

[242]
WISCONSIN NATIONAL GUARD ENLISTED ASSOCIATION COLLEGE GRANT PROGRAM

Wisconsin National Guard Enlisted Association
Attn: Executive Director
2400 Wright Street
Madison, WI 53704-2572
(608) 242-3112   E-mail: WNGEA@yahoo.com
Web: www.wngea.org/extrasforyou/exfy-scho.htm

Summary To provide financial assistance to members of the Wisconsin National Guard Enlisted Association (WNGEA) and their spouses and children who are interested in attending college or graduate school in any state.

Eligibility This program is open to WNGEA members, the unmarried children and spouses of WNGEA members, and the unmarried children and spouses of deceased WNGEA members. WNGEA member applicants, as well as the parents or guardians of unmarried children who are applicants, must have at least 1 year remaining on their enlistment following completion of the school year for which application is submitted (or they must have 20 or more years of service). Applicants must be enrolled full or part time at a college, university, graduate school, trade school, or business school in any state. Selection is based on financial need, leadership, and moral character.

Financial data Stipends are $1,000 or $500 per year.

Duration 1 year; recipients may not reapply for 2 years.

Additional information This program includes 1 scholarship sponsored by the USAA Insurance Corporation.

Number awarded Varies each year; recently, 5 were awarded: the Raymond A. Matera Scholarship at $1,000 and 4 others (1 reserved for a graduate student) at $500 each.

Deadline April of each year.

[243]
WISCONSIN NATIONAL GUARD TUITION GRANT

Wisconsin Department of Military Affairs
Attn: Education Services Office
WIAR-PA-ED
P.O. Box 8111
Madison, WI 53708-8111
(608) 242-3159   Toll Free: (800) 335-5147
Fax: (608) 242-3154
E-mail: karen.behling@wisconsin.gov
Web: dma.wi.gov/dma/dma/education.asp

Summary To provide financial assistance for college to members of the Wisconsin National Guard.

Eligibility Eligible to apply for these grants are enlisted members and warrant officers in good standing in the Wisconsin National Guard who wish to work on an undergraduate degree. Applicants may not have been flagged for unexcused absences or failing to meet Guard standards. They must be attending or planning to attend an extension division or campus of the University of Wisconsin system, a public institution of higher education under the Minnesota-Wisconsin student reciprocity agreement, a campus of the Wisconsin Technical College System, or an accredited institution of higher education located within Wisconsin.

Financial data This program offers assistance based on the undergraduate tuition rate of the University of Wisconsin at Madison (recently, that was $10,402 per year for full-time study).

Duration 8 semesters of full-time study or completion of a bachelor's degree.

Number awarded Varies each year.

Deadline Applications may be submitted at any time, but they must be received at least 30 days prior to the beginning of the course.

[244]
WOMEN MARINES ASSOCIATION SCHOLARSHIP PROGRAM

Women Marines Association
P.O. Box 377
Oaks, PA 19456-0377
Toll Free: (888) 525-1943
E-mail: scholarship@womenmarines.org
Web: www.womenmarines.org

Summary To provide financial assistance for college or graduate school to students with ties to the military who are sponsored by members of the Women Marines Association (WMA).

Eligibility Applicants must be sponsored by a WMA member and fall into 1 of the following categories: 1) have served or are serving in the U.S. Marine Corps, regular or Reserve; 2) are a direct descendant by blood or legal adoption or a stepchild of a Marine on active duty or who has served honorably in the U.S. Marine Corps, regular or Reserve; 3) are a sibling or a descendant of a sibling by blood or legal adoption or a stepchild of a Marine on active duty or who has served honorably in the U.S. Marine Corps, regular or Reserve; or 4) have completed 2 years in a Marine Corps JROTC program. WMA members may sponsor an unlimited number of applicants per year. High school seniors must submit transcripts (GPA of 3.0 or higher) and SAT or ACT scores. Undergraduate and graduate students must have a GPA of 3.0 or higher.

Financial data Stipends are $1,500 or $3,000 per year.

Duration 1 year; may be renewed 1 additional year.

Additional information This program includes the following named scholarships: the WMA Memorial Scholarships, the Lily H. Gridley Memorial Scholarship, the Ethyl and Armin Wiebke Memorial Scholarship, the Maj. Megan Malia McClung Memorial Scholarship, the Agnes Sopcak Memorial Scholarship, the Virginia Guveyan Memorial Scholarship, and the LaRue A. Ditmore Music Scholarships. Applicants must know a WMA member to serve as their sponsor; the WMA will not supply listings of the names or addresses of chapters or individual members.

Number awarded Varies each year.

Deadline January of each year.

[245]
WOMEN'S OVERSEAS SERVICE LEAGUE SCHOLARSHIPS FOR WOMEN

Women's Overseas Service League
Attn: Scholarship Committee
P.O. Box 124
Cedar Knolls, NJ 07927-0124
E-mail: kelsey@openix.com
Web: www.wosl.org/scholarships.htm

Summary To provide financial assistance for college to women who are committed to a military or other public service career.

Eligibility This program is open to women who are committed to a military or other public service career. Applicants must have completed at least 12 semester hours of postsecondary study with a GPA of 2.5 or higher. They must be working on an academic degree (the program may be professional or technical in nature) and must agree to enroll for at least 6 semester hours of study each academic period. Along with their application, they must submit a 250-word essay on their career goals. Financial need is considered in the selection process.

Financial data Stipends range from $500 to $1,000 per year.

Duration 1 year; may be renewed 1 additional year.

Additional information The Women's Overseas Service League is a national organization of women who have served overseas in or with the armed forces.

Number awarded Varies each year.

Deadline February of each year.

[246]
WYOMING NATIONAL GUARD ASSOCIATION SCHOLARSHIPS

Wyoming National Guard Association
c/o Laura Jeffrey
P.O. Box 2615
Cheyenne, WY 82003-2615
(307) 214-3114   E-mail: buckinhorses@gmail.com
Web: www.wynga.org/scholarships

Summary To provide financial assistance to members of the Wyoming National Guard Association (WYNGA) and their families who are interested in attending college in any state.

Eligibility This program is open to enlisted and officer members of the WYNGA and their spouses and unmarried children. Applicants must be attending or planning to attend an accredited institution of higher education in any state. Along with their application, they must submit a cover letter that includes information on their educational career goals, their need for this scholarship, their family involvement in WYNGA, and a list of awards, honors, extracurricular activities, and organizations in which they have participated.

Financial data A stipend is awarded (amount not specified).

Duration 1 year.

Additional information This program includes the following named scholarships: the MG Charles J. Wing Family Program Scholarship, the Mrs. Beverly Holmes Scholarship, the Wyoming Army National Guard Combined Club Scholarship, and the USAA Insurance Corporation Scholarship.

Number awarded Varies each year; recently, 7 were awarded.

Deadline February of each year.

[247]
WYOMING NATIONAL GUARD EDUCATIONAL ASSISTANCE PLAN

Wyoming National Guard
Attn: Education Services Officer
5410 Bishop Boulevard
Cheyenne, WY 82009
(307) 777-8160   Fax: (307) 777-8105
E-mail: philip.oconnor@wyo.gov
Web: wyomilitary.wyo.gov

Summary To provide financial assistance to members of the Wyoming National Guard who are interested in attending college or graduate school in the state.

Eligibility This program is open to members of the Wyoming Army National Guard and the Wyoming Air National Guard who have spent at least 6 years in the Guard or are currently serving under their initial 6-year enlistment period. New enlistees who commit to serving 6 years are also eligible. Applicants may be pursuing, or planning to pursue, a degree at any level at the University of Wyoming, a Wyoming community college, or an approved technical institution in Wyoming.

Financial data The program provides full payment of tuition at eligible institutions.

Duration Guard members may continue to receive these benefits as long as they maintain a GPA of 2.0 or higher, keep up with Guard standards for drill attendance, and remain in good standing with the Guard.

Additional information The Wyoming legislature created this program in 2001. Recipients must agree to serve in the Guard for at least 2 years after they graduate or stop using the plan.

Number awarded Varies each year.

Deadline Deadline not specified.

ROTC Students

[248]
AFCEA ROTC SCHOLARSHIPS
Armed Forces Communications and Electronics
    Association
Attn: AFCEA Educational Foundation
4400 Fair Lakes Court
Fairfax, VA 22033-3899
(703) 631-6138   Toll Free: (800) 336-4583, ext. 6138
Fax: (703) 631-4693   E-mail: scholarship@afcea.org
Web: www.afcea.org/education/scholarships/rotc/rotc1.asp

Summary To provide financial assistance to ROTC cadets who are majoring in fields related to communications and electronics.

Eligibility This program is open to ROTC cadets majoring in electronics, engineering (aerospace, chemical, computer, electrical, or systems), mathematics, computer science, physics, science or mathematics education, technology management, foreign languages, global security and intelligence studies, security and intelligence, international studies, or other fields directly related to the support of U.S. national security enterprises. Applicants must be nominated by their ROTC professor, be entering their junior or senior year, be U.S. citizens, be of good moral character, have demonstrated academic excellence, be motivated to complete a college education and serve as officers in the U.S. armed forces, and be able to demonstrate financial need.

Financial data The stipend is $2,000.

Duration 1 year; may be renewed.

Number awarded 18 each year, divided equally among Army, Navy/Marine Corps, and Air Force ROTC programs; for each service, 3 are awarded to rising juniors and 3 to rising seniors.

Deadline February of each year.

[249]
AIR FORCE ROTC HIGH SCHOOL SCHOLARSHIPS
U.S. Air Force
Attn: Headquarters AFROTC/RRUC
551 East Maxwell Boulevard
Maxwell AFB, AL 36112-6106
(334) 953-2091   Toll Free: (866) 4-AFROTC
Fax: (334) 953-6167   E-mail: afrotc1@maxwell.af.mil
Web: www.afrotc.com/scholarships

Summary To provide financial assistance to high school seniors or graduates who are interested in joining Air Force ROTC in college and are willing to serve as Air Force officers following completion of their bachelor's degree.

Eligibility This program is open to high school seniors who are U.S. citizens at least 17 years of age and have been accepted at a college or university with an Air Force ROTC unit on campus or a college with a cross-enrollment agreement with such a college. Applicants must have a cumulative GPA of 3.0 or higher and an ACT composite score of 26 or higher or an SAT score of 1180 or higher (mathematics and critical reading portion only). They must agree to serve for at least 4 years as active-duty Air Force officers following graduation from college. Recently, scholarships were offered to students planning to major (in order or priority) in 1) the science and technical fields of architecture, chemistry, computer science, engineering (aeronautical, aerospace, astronautical, architectural, civil, computer, electrical, environmental, mechanical, or nuclear), mathematics, meteorology and atmospheric sciences, nuclear physics, operations research, or physics; 2) foreign languages (Arabic, Baluchi, Chinese (Amoy, Cantonese, Mandarin, and Wu), Hindi, Indonesian, Japanese, Javanese, Korean, Pashto-Afghan, Persian-Afghan, Persian-Iranian, Punjabi, Russian, Somali, Turkish, Turkmen, or Urdu); 3) all other fields.

Financial data Type 1 scholarships provide payment of full tuition and most laboratory fees, as well as $900 per year for books. Type 2 scholarships pay the same benefits except tuition is capped at $18,000 per year; students who attend an institution where tuition exceeds $18,000 must pay the difference. Type 7 scholarships pay full tuition and most laboratory fees, but students must attend a public college or university where they qualify for the in-state tuition rate or a college or university where the tuition is less than the in-state rate; they may not attend an institution with higher tuition and pay the difference. Approximately 5% of scholarship offers are for Type 1, approximately 15% are for Type 2, and approximately 80% are for Type 7. All recipients are also awarded a tax-free subsistence allowance for 10 months of each year that is $250 per month as a freshman, $300 per month as a sophomore, $350 per month as a junior, and $400 per month as a senior.

Duration 4 years.

Additional information While scholarship recipients can major in any subject, they must enroll in 4 years of aerospace studies courses at 1 of the 143 colleges and universities that have an Air Force ROTC unit on campus; students may also attend 850 other colleges that have cross-enrollment agreements with the institutions that have an Air Force ROTC unit on campus. Recipients must attend a 4-week summer training camp at an Air Force base, usually between their sophomore and junior years. Most cadets incur a 4-year active-duty commitment.

Number awarded   Approximately 2,000 each year.

Deadline   November of each year.

[250]
AIR FORCE ROTC NURSING SCHOLARSHIPS

U.S. Air Force
Attn: Headquarters AFROTC/RRUC
551 East Maxwell Boulevard
Maxwell AFB, AL 36112-5917
(334) 953-2091   Toll Free: (866) 4-AFROTC
Fax: (334) 953-6167   E-mail: afrotc1@maxwell.af.mil
Web: www.afrotc.com/careers/programs

Summary   To provide financial assistance to college students who are interested in a career as a nurse, are interested in joining Air Force ROTC, and are willing to serve as Air Force officers following completion of their bachelor's degree.

Eligibility   This program is open to U.S. citizens who are freshmen or sophomores in college and interested in a career as a nurse. Applicants must have a cumulative GPA of 2.5 or higher at the end of their freshman year and meet all other academic and physical requirements for participation in AFROTC. They must be interested in working on a nursing degree from an accredited program. At the time of Air Force commissioning, they may be no more than 31 years of age. They must be able to pass the Air Force Officer Qualifying Test (AFOQT) and the Air Force ROTC Physical Fitness Test.

Financial data   Awards are type 2 AFROTC scholarships that provide for payment of tuition and fees up to $18,000 per year; students who attend an institution where tuition exceeds $18,000 must pay the difference. All recipients are also awarded an annual book allowance of $900 and a tax-free subsistence allowance for 10 months of each year that is $300 per month during their sophomore year, $350 during their junior year, and $400 during their senior year.

Duration   2 or 3 years, provided the recipient maintains a GPA of 2.5 or higher.

Additional information   Recipients must also complete 4 years of aerospace studies courses at 1 of the 143 colleges and universities that have an Air Force ROTC unit on campus or 1 of the 850 colleges that have cross-enrollment agreements with those institutions. They must also attend a 4-week summer training camp at an Air Force base, usually between their sophomore and junior years. Following completion of their bachelor's degree, scholarship recipients earn a commission as a second lieutenant in the Air Force and serve at least 4 years.

Number awarded   Varies each year.

Deadline   June of each year.

[251]
AIR FORCE ROTC PROFESSIONAL OFFICER CORPS INCENTIVE

U.S. Air Force
Attn: Headquarters AFROTC/RRUC
551 East Maxwell Boulevard
Maxwell AFB, AL 36112-5917
(334) 953-2091   Toll Free: (866) 4-AFROTC
Fax: (334) 953-6167   E-mail: afrotc1@maxwell.af.mil
Web: www.afrotc.com/scholarships

Summary   To provide financial assistance for undergraduate and graduate studies to individuals who have completed 2 years of college and who are willing to join Air Force ROTC and serve as Air Force officers following completion of their degree.

Eligibility   Applicants must be U.S. citizens who have completed 2 years of the general military course at a college or university with an Air Force ROTC unit on campus or a college with a cross-enrollment agreement with such a college. They must be full-time students, have a GPA of 2.0 or higher both cumulatively and for the prior term, be enrolled in both Aerospace Studies class and Leadership Laboratory, pass the Air Force Officer Qualifying Test, meet Air Force physical fitness and weight requirements, and be able to be commissioned before they become 31 years of age. They must agree to serve for at least 4 years as active-duty Air Force officers following graduation from college with either a bachelor's or graduate degree.

Financial data   This scholarship provides a monthly subsistence allowance of $350 as a junior or $400 as a senior.

Duration   Until completion of a graduate degree.

Additional information   Scholarship recipients must complete 4 years of aerospace studies courses at 1 of the 143 colleges and universities that have an Air Force ROTC unit on campus; students may also attend 850 other colleges that have cross-enrollment agreements with the institutions that have an Air Force ROTC unit on campus. Recipients must also attend a 4-week summer training camp at an Air Force base between their junior and senior year.

Number awarded   Varies each year.

Deadline   Deadline not specified.

[252]
AIRLIFT AND TANKER ASSOCIATION SCHOLARSHIPS

Arnold Air Society-Silver Wings
c/o Executive Management Center
1501 Lee Highway, Suite 400
Arlington, VA 22209
E-mail: mgmt.center@arnold-air.org
Web: www.aas-sw.org/?nd=scholarships

Summary   To provide financial assistance for continuing college education to ROTC students and other members of Arnold Air Society and Silver Wings.

Eligibility   This program is open to 1) members of Arnold Air Society enrolled as cadets in Air Force ROTC; and 2) non-cadet members of Silver Wings enrolled as sophomores or juniors. Each AFROTC Detachment Commander may nominate 1 Arnold Air Society member and 1 Silver Wings member. Selection is based primarily on a 3-page essay on an individual, event, campaign, innovative equipment, organization, or other subject involved in air mobility.

Financial data　The stipend is $1,000.

Duration　1 year.

Additional information　This program is supported by the Airlift and Tanker Association (ATA). The scholarships provided by the Arnold Air Society-Silver Wing Board of Trustees are named the BGen Ed Brya Scholarship and the Lt Col Bill Morley Scholarship.

Number awarded　7 each year: 5 sponsored by ATA and 2 by the Arnold Air Society-Silver Wing Board of Trustees.

Deadline　February of each year.

[253]
ARMY ROTC 4-YEAR SCHOLARSHIPS

U.S. Army
Attn: U.S. Army Cadet Command
G2 Incentives Division
1307 Third Avenue
Fort Knox, KY 40121-2725
(502) 624-7371　　　　　　　Toll Free: (888) 550-ARMY
Fax: (502) 624-1120
E-mail: usarmy.knox.usacc.mbx.train2lead@mail.mil
Web: www.goarmy.com/rotc/high-school-students.html

Summary　To provide financial assistance to high school seniors or graduates who are interested in enrolling in Army ROTC in college.

Eligibility　Applicants for this program must 1) be U.S. citizens; 2) be between 17 and 26 years of age; 3) score at least 920 on the combined mathematics and critical reading SAT or 19 on the ACT; 4) have a high school GPA of 2.5 or higher; and 5) meet medical and other regulatory requirements. Current college or university students may apply if their school considers them beginning freshmen with 4 academic years remaining for a bachelor's degree.

Financial data　This scholarship provides financial assistance of up to $20,000 per year for college tuition and educational fees or for room and board, whichever the student selects. In addition, a flat rate of $1,200 per year is provided for the purchase of textbooks, classroom supplies, and equipment. Recipients are also awarded a stipend for up to 10 months of each year that is $300 per month during their freshman year, $350 per month during their sophomore year, $450 per month during their junior year, and $500 per month during their senior year.

Duration　4 years, until completion of a baccalaureate degree.

Additional information　Scholarship recipients participate in the Army ROTC program as part of their college curriculum by enrolling in 4 years of military science classes and attending a 6-week summer camp between the junior and senior years. Following graduation, they receive a commission as a Regular Army, Army Reserve, or Army National Guard officer. Scholarship winners must serve in the Army for 8 years, including 4 years of full-time service and 4 years in the Individual Ready Reserve (IRR). They may elect to serve part time in the Army Reserve or Army National Guard while pursuing a civilian career.

Number awarded　Approximately 1,500 each year.

Deadline　January of each year.

[254]
ARMY ROTC COLLEGE SCHOLARSHIP PROGRAM

U.S. Army
Attn: U.S. Army Cadet Command
G2 Incentives Division
1307 Third Avenue
Fort Knox, KY 40121-2725
(502) 624-7371　　　　　　　Toll Free: (888) 550-ARMY
Fax: (502) 624-6937
E-mail: usarmy.knox.usacc.mbx.train2lead@mail.mil
Web: www.goarmy.com/rotc/college-students.html

Summary　To provide financial assistance to students who are or will be enrolled in Army ROTC.

Eligibility　This program is open to U.S. citizens between 17 and 26 years of age who have already completed 1 or 2 years in a college or university with an Army ROTC unit on campus or in a college with a cross-enrollment agreement with a college with an Army ROTC unit on campus. Applicants must have 2 or 3 years remaining for their bachelor's degree (or 4 years of a 5-year bachelor's program) and must be able to complete that degree before their 31st birthday. They must have a high school GPA of 2.5 or higher and scores of at least 920 on the combined mathematics and critical reading SAT or 19 on the ACT.

Financial data　These scholarships provide financial assistance for college tuition and educational fees, up to an annual amount of $20,000. In addition, a flat rate of $1,200 is provided for the purchase of textbooks, classroom supplies, and equipment. Recipients are also awarded a stipend for up to 10 months of each year that is $350 per month during their sophomore year, $450 per month during their junior year, and $500 per month during their senior year.

Duration　2 or 3 years, until the recipient completes the bachelor's degree.

Additional information　Applications must be made through professors of military science at 1 of the schools hosting the Army ROTC program. Preference is given to students who have already enrolled as non-scholarship students in military science classes at 1 of the more than 270 institutions with an Army ROTC unit on campus, at 1 of the 75 college extension centers, or at 1 of the more than 1,000 colleges with cross-enrollment or extension agreements with 1 of the colleges with an Army ROTC unit. Scholarship winners must serve full time in the Army for 4 years. They may elect to serve part time in the Army Reserve or Army National Guard while pursuing a civilian career.

Number awarded　Varies each year; a recent allocation provided for 700 4-year scholarships, 1,800 3-year scholarships, and 2,800 2-year scholarships.

Deadline　December of each year.

[255]
ARMY ROTC NURSE PROGRAM

U.S. Army
Attn: U.S. Army Cadet Command
G2 Incentives Division
1307 Third Avenue
Fort Knox, KY 40121-2725
(502) 624-6298　　　　　　　Toll Free: (888) 550-ARMY
Fax: (502) 624-6937
E-mail: usarmy.knox.usacc.mbx.train2lead@mail.mil
Web: www.goarmy.com

Summary To provide financial assistance to high school seniors or graduates who are interested in enrolling in Army ROTC and majoring in nursing in college.

Eligibility Applicants for the Army Reserve Officers' Training Corps (ROTC) Nurse program must 1) be U.S. citizens; 2) be at least 17 years of age by October of the year in which they are seeking a scholarship; 3) be no more than 27 years of age when they graduate from college after 4 years; 4) score at least 920 on the combined mathematics and critical reading SAT or 19 on the ACT; 5) have a high school GPA of 2.5 or higher; and 6) meet medical and other regulatory requirements. This program is open to ROTC scholarship applicants who wish to enroll in a nursing program at 1 of approximately 100 designated partner colleges and universities and become Army nurses after graduation.

Financial data This scholarship provides financial assistance toward college tuition and educational fees up to an annual amount of $20,000. In addition, a flat rate of $1,200 is provided for the purchase of textbooks, classroom supplies, and equipment. Recipients are also awarded a stipend for up to 10 months of each year that is $300 per month during their freshman year, $350 per month during their sophomore year, $450 per month during their junior year, and $500 per month during their senior year.

Duration 4 years, until completion of a baccalaureate degree. A limited number of 2-year and 3-year scholarships are also available to students who are already attending an accredited B.S.N. program on a campus affiliated with ROTC.

Additional information This program began in 1996 to ensure that ROTC cadets seeking nursing careers would be admitted to the upper-level division of a baccalaureate program. The 56 partnership nursing schools affiliated with Army ROTC have agreed to guarantee upper-level admission to students who maintain an established GPA during their first 2 years. During the summer, recipients have the opportunity to participate in the Nurse Summer Training Program, a paid 3- to 4-week clinical elective at an Army hospital in the United States, Germany, or Korea. Following completion of their baccalaureate degree, participants become commissioned officers in the Army Nurse Corps. Scholarship winners must serve in the military for 8 years. That service obligation may be fulfilled 1) by serving on active duty for 4 years followed by service in the Army National Guard (ARNG), the United States Army Reserve (USAR), or the Inactive Ready Reserve (IRR) for the remainder of the 8 years; or 2) by serving 8 years in an ARNG or USAR troop program unit that includes a 3- to 6-month active-duty period for initial training.

Number awarded A limited number each year.

Deadline November of each year.

[256]
BOSTON POST SAME SCHOLARSHIPS

Society of American Military Engineers-Boston Post
c/o Cristen M. Sardano, Scholarship Committee Chair
CB&I Federal Services
150 Royall Street
Canton, MA 02021
(617) 589-5111   Fax: (617) 589-2156
E-mail: Christen.sardano@cbifederalservices.com
Web: www.sameboston.org

Summary To provide financial assistance to residents of New England (particularly current military personnel, veter-ans, and students enrolled in ROTC) who are majoring in a program related to construction at a college in any state.

Eligibility This program is open to residents of New England who are currently enrolled in an accepted engineering or architecture program, preferably in civil engineering, environmental engineering, architecture, or other construction-related program, at a college or university in any state. Applicants must have completed at least 1 academic year and have at least 1 year remaining. They must be nominated by their institution. Along with their application, they must submit a resume describing their academic and career objectives, extracurricular and community activities, work experience, and special interests or hobbies; transcripts; documentation of financial need; and a personal letter describing their qualifications and needs. An interview is required. Selection is based on academic achievement, financial need, extracurricular and community activities, the letter, and the interview. Preference is given to applicants who are enrolled in ROTC (preferably not a recipient of an ROTC scholarship), have current or prior service in the U.S. armed forces, are interested in the U.S. Public Health Service, and/or are interested in other public service with federal, state, or local government. U.S. citizenship is required.

Financial data The stipend is approximately $2,000 per year.

Duration 1 year.

Number awarded Approximately 25 each year.

Deadline February of each year.

[257]
BRAXTON BRAGG CHAPTER AUSA
SCHOLARSHIPS

Association of the United States Army-Braxton Bragg Chapter
Attn: Vice President for Scholarships
P.O. Box 70036
Fort Bragg, NC 28307
(910) 396-3755   E-mail: hbraxtonbraggc@nc.rr.com
Web: www.braggausa.org/?page_id=1425

Summary To provide financial assistance to members of the Braxton Bragg Chapter of the Association of the United States Army (AUSA) in North Carolina and their dependents who are interested in attending college or graduate school in any state.

Eligibility This program is open to chapter members and their families in North Carolina who are working on or planning to work on an undergraduate, graduate, or technical degree at a college or technical school in any state. Applicants must submit a 500-word essay on how the Army and Army values have influenced their life; letters of recommendation; a list of personal accomplishments; and a transcript that includes their ACT or SAT score. Selection is based on academic achievement, participation in extracurricular activities at school, and participation in community service activities. Membership in AUSA is open to current and retired Army personnel (including Reserves and National Guard), ROTC cadets, or civilian employees of the Army. Active-duty soldiers are especially encouraged to apply.

Financial data The stipend is $1,000.

Duration 1 year; recipients may reapply.

Additional information Membership in the Braxton Bragg Chapter is open to all Army active, National Guard, and

Reserve members in North Carolina, along with Department of the Army civilians, retirees, concerned citizens, and family members.

Number awarded Varies each year; recently, 26 were awarded.

Deadline April of each year.

[258]
BRIGADIER GENERAL JOHN F. KINNEY FELLOWSHIP

Alpha Tau Omega Foundation
32 East Washington Street, Suite 1350
Indianapolis, IN 46204
(317) 472-0935   Toll Free: (800) 508-5131
Fax: (317) 472-0945
E-mail: jplummer@atofoundation.org
Web: www.ato.org/atofoundation/Scholarships.aspx

Summary To provide financial assistance to members of Alpha Tau Omega fraternity who are serving in the military or an ROTC unit while they attend college.

Eligibility This program is open to members of the fraternity who have a GPA of 3.5 or higher. Applicants must be serving in a National Guard or Reserve component of the military or enrolled in an ROTC training program. They must be planning to serve on active duty in the National Guard, the Reserves, or the active armed forces following graduation. Selection is based on academic achievement (40%), demonstrated leadership in the fraternity (30%), and demonstrated initiative on campus and in the community (30%).

Financial data A stipend is awarded (amount not specified).

Duration 1 year.

Number awarded 1 each year.

Deadline March of each year.

[259]
BRIGADIER GENERAL ROSCOE C. CARTWRIGHT AWARDS

The ROCKS, Inc.
c/o WSC Associates, LLP
P.O. Box 47435
Forestville, MD 20753
(301) 856-9319   Toll Free: (888) 762-5747
Fax: (301) 856-5220   E-mail: therocks@aol.com
Web: www.rocksinc.org

Summary To provide financial assistance to students enrolled in ROTC programs at Historically Black Colleges and Universities (HBCUs).

Eligibility This program is open to Army and Air Force Cadets and Navy Midshipmen at HBCUs. Applicants must be planning to enter military service as officers following graduation from college. They must submit a letter of recommendation from their professor of military science evaluating their appearance, attitude, character, dedication, initiative, integrity, judgment, leadership potential, and written and oral communication ability. Financial need is not considered in the selection process.

Financial data The stipend is $1,500.

Duration 1 year.

Additional information This program began in 1974.

Number awarded Varies each year; recently, 12 were awarded.

Deadline February of each year.

[260]
BRYCE ROWEN MEMORIAL SCHOLARSHIP

New Mexico Engineering Foundation
Attn: Scholarship Chair
P.O. Box 3828
Albuquerque, NM 87190-3828
(505) 615-1800   E-mail: info@nmef.net
Web: www.nmef.net/?section=scholarship

Summary To provide financial assistance to residents of any state working on a degree in engineering at specified universities in New Mexico (preference given to ROTC students).

Eligibility This program is open to juniors and seniors working on a degree in engineering at the University of New Mexico, New Mexico State University, or New Mexico Institute of Mining and Technology. Preference is given to non-scholarship ROTC students. Financial need is considered in the selection process.

Financial data The stipend is $1,000.

Duration 1 year; nonrenewable.

Additional information This program is offered by the Albuquerque Post of the Society of American Military Engineers.

Number awarded 1 each year.

Deadline February of each year.

[261]
CAPE FEAR CHAPTER MOAA SENIOR ROTC SCHOLARSHIPS

Military Officers Association of America-Cape Fear
  Chapter
P.O. Box 53621
Fayetteville, NC 28305
E-mail: info@cfmoaa.org
Web: cfmoaa.org/_outgoing.php

Summary To provide financial assistance to students from any state who are enrolled in ROTC programs at colleges in the service area of the Cape Fear Chapter of the Military Officers Association of America (MOAA) in North Carolina.

Eligibility This program is open to students from any state currently enrolled at colleges and universities within the MOAA's Cape Fear Chapter service area (the North Carolina counties of Bladen, Cumberland, Harnett, Hoke, Robeson, and Sampson). Applicants must have signed a contract to participate in advanced course ROTC. Along with their application, they must submit a 500-word essay on why they have selected their area of study, their future plans in that field, and why the scholarship would be important to them.

Financial data The stipend is $1,000.

Duration 1 year.

Additional information The chapter supports ROTC programs at 5 colleges in its service area. For a list, contact the chapter.

Number awarded Normally 4 each year.

Deadline May of each year.

[262]
CIVIL ENGINEER CORPS OPTION OF THE SEAMAN TO ADMIRAL-21 PROGRAM

U.S. Navy
Attn: Commander, Naval Service Training Command
250 Dallas Street, Suite A
Pensacola, FL 32508-5268
(850) 452-9563   Fax: (850) 452-2486
E-mail: PNSC_STA21@navy.mil
Web: www.sta-21.navy.mil/program_options.asp

Summary To allow outstanding enlisted Navy personnel to attend a college or university, affiliate with an NROTC unit, complete a bachelor's degree, and receive a commission in the Civil Engineer Corps (CEC).

Eligibility This program is open to U.S. citizens who are currently serving on active duty in the Navy as enlisted personnel in any rating. Applicants must have completed at least 4 years of active duty, of which at least 3 years were in an other than formal training environment. They must be high school graduates (or GED recipients) who are able to complete requirements for a professional Accreditation Board for Engineering and Technology (ABET) engineering degree or National Architectural Accrediting Board (NAAB) architectural degree within 36 months or less. Preferred specialties are civil, electrical, mechanical, or ocean engineering. When applicants complete their degree requirements, they must be younger than 42 years of age. Within the past 3 years, they must have taken the SAT (and achieved scores of at least 500 on the mathematics section and 500 on the critical reading section) or the ACT (and achieved a score of at least 21 on the mathematics portion and 20 on the English portion).

Financial data Awardees continue to receive their regular Navy pay and allowances while they attend college on a full-time basis. They also receive reimbursement for tuition, fees, and books up to $10,000 per year. If base housing is available, they are eligible to live there. Participants are not eligible to receive benefits under the Navy's Tuition Assistance Program (TA), the Montgomery GI Bill (MGIB), the Navy College Fund, or the Veterans Educational Assistance Program (VEAP).

Duration Selectees are supported for up to 36 months of full-time, year-round study or completion of a bachelor's degree, as long as they maintain a GPA of 3.0 or higher.

Additional information This program began in 2001 as a replacement for the Civil Engineer Corps Enlisted Commissioning Program (CECECP). Upon acceptance into the program, selectees attend the Naval Science Institute (NSI) in Newport, Rhode Island for an 8-week program in the fundamental core concepts of being a naval officer (navigation, engineering, weapons, military history and justice, etc.). They then enter a college or university with an NROTC unit that is designated for the CEC to work full time on a bachelor's degree. They become members of and drill with the NROTC unit. When they complete their degree, they are commissioned as ensigns in the United States Naval Reserve and assigned to initial training as an officer in the CEC. After commissioning, 5 years of active service are required.

Number awarded Varies each year.

Deadline June of each year.

[263]
CONGRESSIONAL MEDAL OF HONOR SCHOLARSHIPS

Congressional Medal of Honor Foundation
1501 Lee Highway, Suite 300
Arlington, VA 22209
(703) 469-1861   E-mail: rrand@cmohfoundation.org
Web: www.cmohfoundation.org/?page_id=2139

Summary To provide financial assistance to students currently enrolled in an ROTC program.

Eligibility This program is open to students currently enrolled in an ROTC program of the Air Force, Army, Marine Corps, or Navy at a 4-year college or university. Applicants must be enrolled full time as either a sophomore or junior and have a GPA of 3.0 or higher. They must be U.S. citizens. Selection is based on academic excellence, moral character, potential to serve as an officer in the U.S. armed forces, and financial need.

Financial data The stipend is $5,000.

Duration 1 year.

Number awarded 8 each year: 2 for a student in each ROTC branch.

Deadline February of each year.

[264]
DAEDALIAN ACADEMIC MATCHING SCHOLARSHIP PROGRAM

Daedalian Foundation
Attn: Scholarship Committee
55 Main Circle, Building 676
P.O. Box 249
Randolph AFB, TX 78148-0249
(210) 945-2113   Fax: (210) 945-2112
E-mail: daedalus@daedalians.org
Web: www.daedalians.org/scholarships.htm

Summary To provide financial assistance to ROTC and other college students who wish to become military pilots.

Eligibility Eligible are students who are attending or have been accepted at an accredited 4-year college or university and have demonstrated the desire and potential to become a commissioned military pilot. Usually, students in ROTC units of all services apply to local chapters (Flights) of Daedalian; if the Flight awards a scholarship, the application is forwarded to the Daedalian Foundation for 1 of these matching scholarships. College students not part of a ROTC program are eligible to apply directly to the Foundation if their undergraduate goals and performance are consistent with Daedalian criteria. Selection is based on intention to pursue a career as a military pilot, demonstrated moral character and patriotism, scholastic and military standing and aptitude, and physical condition and aptitude for flight. Financial need may also be considered. Additional eligibility criteria may be set by a Flight Scholarship Selection Board.

Financial data The amount awarded varies but is intended to serve as matching funds for the Flight scholarship. Generally, the maximum awarded is $2,000.

Duration 1 year.

Number awarded Up to 99 each year.

Deadline Students who are members of Daedalian Flights must submit their applications by November of each year; students who apply directly to the Daedalian Foundation must submit their applications by July of each year.

[265]
DEDICATED ARMY NATIONAL GUARD (DEDARNG) SCHOLARSHIPS

U.S. Army National Guard
Education Support Center
Camp J.T. Robinson
Box 46
North Little Rock, AR 72199-9600
Toll Free: (866) 628-5999   E-mail: esc@ng.army.mil
Web: www.nationalguard.com/tools/guard-scholarships

Summary To provide financial assistance to college and graduate students who are interested in enrolling in Army ROTC and serving in the Army National Guard following graduation.

Eligibility This program is open to full-time students entering their sophomore or junior year of college with a GPA of 2.5 or higher. Applicants must have a GPA of 2.5 or higher and scores of at least 19 on the ACT or 920 on the combined mathematics and critical reading SAT. Graduate students may also be eligible if they have only 2 years remaining for completion of their degree. Students who have been awarded an ROTC campus-based scholarship may apply to convert to this program during their freshman year. Applicants must meet all medical and moral character requirements for enrollment in Army ROTC. They must be willing to enroll in the Simultaneous Membership Program (SMP) of an ROTC unit on their campus; the SMP requires simultaneous membership in Army ROTC and the Army National Guard.

Financial data Participants receive full reimbursement of tuition, a grant of $1,200 per year for books, plus an ROTC stipend for 10 months of the year at $350 per month during their sophomore year, $450 per month during their junior year, and $500 per month during their senior year. As a member of the Army National Guard, they also receive weekend drill pay at the pay grade of a sergeant (approximately $225 per month) while participating in the SMP.

Duration 2 or 3 years.

Additional information After graduation, participants serve 3 to 6 months on active duty in the Officer Basic Course (OBC). Following completion of OBC, they are released from active duty and are obligated to serve 8 years in the Army National Guard.

Number awarded Approximately 600 each year.

Deadline Deadline not specified.

[266]
DIVISION COMMANDER'S HIP POCKET SCHOLARSHIPS

U.S. Army
Attn: U.S. Army Cadet Command
G2 Incentives Division
1307 Third Avenue
Fort Knox, KY 40121-2725
(502) 624-7371   Toll Free: (888) 550-ARMY
Fax: (502) 624-6937
E-mail: usarmy.knox.usacc.mbx.train2lead@mail.mil
Web: www.goarmy.com

Summary To enable soldiers who are nominated by their Division Commanding General to obtain an early discharge from the Army and return to college to participate in the Army Reserve Officers' Training Corps (ROTC).

Eligibility Enlisted soldiers who have served at least 2 but less than 10 years on active duty are eligible for this program. They must be nominated by their Division Commanding General to obtain an early discharge in order to enroll in a baccalaureate degree program. Nominees must have a cumulative high school or college GPA of 2.5 or higher, a score of at least 21 on the ACT or 1100 on the combined mathematics and critical reading SAT, a General Technical (GT) score of 110 or higher, and a recent (within the past 6 months) Army Physical Fitness Test (APFT) score of 180 or higher (including 60 points in each event). They may not have a spouse who is also in the military or dependent children under 18 years of age (those requirements may be waived). At the time they graduate and are commissioned, they must be under 31 years of age. Selection is made by the Division Commanding General; no additional review is made by Cadet Command Headquarters.

Financial data Scholarship winners receive full payment of tuition, a grant of $1,200 per year for books and supplies, a monthly stipend of up to $500 per month (depending on academic status) for 10 months per year, and pay for attending the 6-week Leader Development and Assessment Course (LDAC) during the summer between the junior and senior year of college.

Duration 2, 3, or 4 years.

Additional information Recipients who had previously qualified for benefits from the Army College Fund and/or the Montgomery GI Bill are still entitled to receive those in addition to any benefits from this program. Upon graduation from college, scholarship winners are commissioned as second lieutenants and are required to serve in the military for 8 years. That obligation may be fulfilled by serving 4 years on active duty followed by 4 years in the Inactive Ready Reserve (IRR).

Number awarded Varies each year; recently, 117 were awarded.

Deadline March of each year.

[267]
DONALDSON D. FRIZZELL MEMORIAL SCHOLARSHIPS

First Command Educational Foundation
Attn: Scholarship Programs Manager
1 FirstComm Plaza
Fort Worth, TX 76109-4999
(817) 569-2634   Toll Free: (877) 872-8289
Fax: (817) 569-2970   E-mail: Scholarships@fcef.com
Web: www.fcef.com

Summary To provide financial assistance to students, especially those with ties to the military (including ROTC), who are entering or attending college or graduate school.

Eligibility This program is open to 1) members of a U.S. uniformed service and their spouses and dependents; 2) clients of First Command Financial Services and their family members; 3) dependent family members of First Command Advisors or field office staff members; or 4) non-contractual ROTC students. Applicants may be traditional students (high school seniors and students already enrolled at a college, university, or accredited trade school) or nontraditional students (those defined by their institution as nontraditional and adult students planning to return to a college, university, or accredited trade school. They must have a GPA of 3.0 or higher and be working on a trade school certification or associate, undergraduate, or graduate degree. Applicants must submit 1-page essays on 1) their active involvement in community service programs; 2) the impact of financial literacy on their future; and 3) why they need this scholarship. Selection is based primarily on the essays, academic merit, and financial need.

Financial data Stipends are $5,000 or $2,500. Funds are disbursed directly to the recipient's college, university, or trade school.

Duration 1 year.

Additional information The sponsoring organization was formerly known as the USPA & IRA Educational Foundation, founded in 1983 to provide scholarships to the children of active, retired, or deceased military personnel. In addition to these scholarships, for which students may apply directly, it supports scholarships offered by a number of partner organizations. Since its establishment, it has awarded scholarships worth nearly $4 million.

Number awarded 6 each year: 2 at $5,000 and 4 at $2,500. Awards are split evenly between the 2 categories.

Deadline The online application process begins in February of each year and continues until 200 applications have been received in each category.

[268]
DR. JON L. BOYES, VICE ADMIRAL, USN (RET.) MEMORIAL SCHOLARSHIP

Armed Forces Communications and Electronics
  Association
Attn: AFCEA Educational Foundation
4400 Fair Lakes Court
Fairfax, VA 22033-3899
(703) 631-6138   Toll Free: (800) 336-4583, ext. 6138
Fax: (703) 631-4693 E-mail: ScholarshipsInfo@afcea.org
Web: www.afcea.org

Summary To provide financial assistance to Navy ROTC midshipmen who are majoring in electrical engineering.

Eligibility This program is open to Navy ROTC midshipmen enrolled full time at an accredited degree-granting 4-year college or university in the United States. Applicants must be sophomores or juniors at the time of application and have a GPA of 3.0 or higher with a major in electrical engineering. Their application must be endorsed by the professor of naval science at their institution. Selection is based on demonstrated dedication, superior performance, and potential to serve as an officer in the United States Navy. Financial need is not considered in the selection process.

Financial data The stipend is $3,000.

Duration 1 year.

Number awarded 1 each year.

Deadline February of each year.

[269]
EXPLOSIVE ORDNANCE DISPOSAL OPTION OF THE SEAMAN TO ADMIRAL-21 PROGRAM

U.S. Navy
Attn: Commander, Naval Service Training Command
250 Dallas Street, Suite A
Pensacola, FL 32508-5268
(850) 452-9563   Fax: (850) 452-2486
E-mail: PNSC_STA21@navy.mil
Web: www.sta-21.navy.mil/program_options.asp

Summary To allow outstanding enlisted Navy personnel to attend college, affiliate with an NROTC unit, complete a bachelor's degree, and receive a commission as an explosive ordnance disposal (EOD) officer.

Eligibility This program is open to U.S. citizens who are currently serving on active duty in the U.S. Navy or Naval Reserve, including Full Time Support (FTS), Selected Reserves (SELRES), and Navy Reservists on active duty, except for those on active duty for training (ACDUTRA). Applicants must have 1 of the following NECs: 5332, 5333, 5334, 5335, 5336, 5337, 5342, 5343 and 8493 or 8494. They must be high school graduates (or GED recipients) who are able to complete requirements for a baccalaureate degree in 36 months or less. When they complete their degree requirements, they must be younger than 29 years of age. That age limitation may be adjusted upward for active service on a month-for-month basis up to 24 months, and waivers are considered for enlisted personnel who possess particularly exceptional qualifications if they can complete their degree prior to their 35th birthday. Within the past 3 years, they must have taken the SAT (and achieved scores of at least 500 on the mathematics section and 500 on the critical reading section) or the ACT (and achieved a score of at least 21 on the mathematics portion and 20 on the English portion). They must also meet physical regulations that include qualification for diving duty and/or combat swimmer. Preference is given to applicants who plan to major in a technical field (e.g., chemistry, computer science, engineering, mathematics, oceanography, operations analysis, physical sciences, or physics).

Financial data Awardees continue to receive their regular Navy pay and allowances while they attend college on a full-time basis. They also receive reimbursement for tuition, fees, and books up to $10,000 per year. If base housing is available, they are eligible to live there. Participants are not eligible to receive benefits under the Navy's Tuition Assistance Program (TA), the Montgomery GI Bill (MGIB), the Navy College Fund, or the Veterans Educational Assistance Program (VEAP).

Duration Selectees are supported for up to 36 months of full-time, year-round study or completion of a bachelor's degree, as long as they maintain a GPA of 2.5 or higher.

Additional information This program began in 2001 as a replacement for the Seaman to Admiral Program (established in 1994), the Enlisted Commissioning Program, and other specialized programs for sailors to earn a commission. Upon acceptance into the program, selectees attend the Naval Science Institute (NSI) in Newport, Rhode Island for an 8-week program in the fundamental core concepts of being a naval officer (navigation, engineering, weapons, military history and justice, etc.). They then enter a college or university with an NROTC unit or affiliation to work full time on a bachelor's degree. They become members of and drill with the NROTC unit. When they complete their degree, they are commissioned as ensigns in the United States Naval Reserve and assigned to initial training as an EOD officer. After commissioning, 5 years of active service are required.

Number awarded   Varies each year.

Deadline   June of each year.

[270]
FAIRFAX-LEE AUSA SCHOLARSHIPS

Association of the United States Army-Fairfax-Lee
  Chapter
Attn: Scholarship Committee Chair
7542 Laurel Creek Lane
Springfield, VA 22150
E-mail: scholars@ausafairfaxlee.org
Web: www.ausafairfaxlee.org

Summary   To provide financial assistance to residents of the National Capital Region who have an affiliation with the Fairfax-Lee Chapter of the Association of the United States Army (AUSA) and are interested in attending college in any state.

Eligibility   This program is open to graduating high school seniors and current full- and part-time undergraduates who fall into 1 of the following categories: 1) National Capital Region active-duty, Army Reserve, and Army National Guard soldiers and their family members; 2) Warrior Transition Battalion soldiers and family members; 3) students enrolled in a senior ROTC or JROTC program; 4) National Capital Region Department of the Army civilian employees; 5) current Fairfax-Lee Chapter members and their families; or 6) students who fall into any of those categories and are majoring in a field of science, technology, engineering, or mathematics (STEM). Applicants must submit a 500-word essay on why they believe they are deserving of this scholarship, including any special family considerations.

Financial data   Stipends range from $750 to $1,500.

Duration   1 year.

Additional information   This program receives support from GEICO, Lockheed Martin, Peduzzi Associates, and other corporate sponsors. The National Capital Region is defined to include Washington, D.C.; the Maryland counties of Charles, Frederick, Montgomery, and Prince George's; the Virginia counties of Arlington, Fairfax, Loudoun, and Prince William; and the Virginia cities of Alexandria, Fairfax, Falls Church, Manassas, and Manassas Park.

Number awarded   Varies each year; recently, 24 of these scholarships, with a total value of $20,000, were awarded.

Deadline   April of each year.

[271]
FREDERICK C. BRANCH MARINE CORPS LEADERSHIP SCHOLARSHIPS

U.S. Navy
Attn: Naval Service Training Command Officer
  Development
NAS Pensacola
250 Dallas Street
Pensacola, FL 32508-5220
(850) 452-4941, ext. 29395
Toll Free: (800) NAV-ROTC, ext. 29395
Fax: (850) 452-2486
E-mail: pnsc_nrotc.scholarship@navy.mil
Web: www.nrotc.navy.mil/fcb.aspx

Summary   To provide financial assistance to students who are entering or enrolled at specified Historically Black Colleges or Universities (HBCUs) and interested in joining Navy ROTC to prepare for service as an officer in the U.S. Marine Corps.

Eligibility   This program is open to students attending or planning to attend 1 of 17 specified HBCUs with a Navy ROTC unit on campus. Applicants may either apply through their local Marine recruiter for a 4-year scholarship or be nominated by the professor of naval science at their institution and meet academic requirements set by each school for 2- or 3-year scholarships. They must be U.S. citizens between 17 and 23 years of age who are willing to serve for 4 years as active-duty Marine Corps officers following graduation from college. They must not have reached their 27th birthday by the time of college graduation and commissioning; applicants who have prior active-duty military service may be eligible for age adjustments for the amount of time equal to their prior service, up to a maximum of 36 months. The qualifying scores are 1000 composite on the SAT or 22 composite on the ACT. Current enlisted and former military personnel are also eligible if they will complete the program by the age of 30.

Financial data   These scholarships provide payment of full tuition and required educational fees, as well as a specified amount for textbooks, supplies, and equipment. The program also provides a stipend for 10 months of the year that is $250 per month as a freshman, $300 per month as a sophomore, $350 per month as a junior, and $400 per month as a senior.

Duration   Scholarships are available for 2-, 3-, or 4-year terms.

Additional information   Recipients must complete 4 years of study in naval science classes as students at 1 of the following HBCUs: Allen University, Clark Atlanta University, Dillard University, Florida A&M University, Hampton University, Howard University, Huston-Tillotson University, Morehouse College, Norfolk State University, Prairie View A&M University, Savannah State University, Southern University and A&M College, Spelman College, Tennessee State University, Texas Southern University, Tuskegee University, or Xavier University. After completing the program, all participants are commissioned as second lieutenants in the Marine Corps Reserve with an 8-year service obligation, including 4 years of active duty. Current military personnel who are accepted into this program are released from active duty and are not eligible for active-duty pay and allowances, medical benefits, or other active-duty entitlements.

Number awarded   Varies each year.

Deadline   January of each year for students applying for a 4-year scholarship through their local Marine recruiter; July of each year if applying for a 2- or 3-year scholarship through the Navy ROTC unit at their institution.

[272]
GENERAL JAMES M. ROCKWELL, JR. SCHOLARSHIP

Armed Forces Communications and Electronics
  Association
Attn: AFCEA Educational Foundation
4400 Fair Lakes Court
Fairfax, VA 22033-3899
(703) 631-6138   Toll Free: (800) 336-4583, ext. 6138
Fax: (703) 631-4693   E-mail: scholarship@afcea.org
Web: www.afcea.org/education/scholarships/rotc

Summary To provide financial assistance to outstanding Army ROTC students who are working on a degree in fields related to the work of the Armed Forces Communications and Electronics Association (AFCEA).

Eligibility This program is open to U.S. citizens who are members of an Army ROTC detachment at an accredited college or university in any state. Applicants must be enrolled as sophomores or juniors at the time of application with a major in an AFCEA-related field (e.g., aerospace engineering, communications engineering, communications technology, computer engineering, computer science or technology, electrical engineering, electronics, information technology, mathematics, physics, systems engineering). They must exhibit dedication and superior performance based upon demonstrate academic excellence and the potential to serve as an officer of the U.S. Army. Financial need is considered in the selection process.

Financial data The stipend is $3,000. Funds are paid directly to the recipient.

Duration 1 year.

Additional information This program began in 2012.

Number awarded 1 each year.

Deadline February of each year.

[273]
GEORGE AND VICKI MUELLNER FOUNDATION SCHOLARSHIPS

Air Force Association
Attn: Manager, Awards and Scholarships
1501 Lee Highway
Arlington, VA 22209-1198
(703) 247-5800, ext. 4807
Toll Free: (800) 727-3337, ext. 4807
Fax: (703) 247-5853   E-mail: awards@afa.org
Web: www.afa.org

Summary To provide financial assistance to members of Arnold Air Society and Silver Wings (including ROTC students).

Eligibility This program is open to members of Arnold Air Society and Silver Wings. Arnold Air Society is an honorary organization of cadets preparing for careers in the U.S. Air Force, including those in ROTC units at universities throughout the country and those at the Air Force Academy in Colorado Springs. Silver Wings is a partner co-educational organization of civilians interested in personal development, leadership, service, and support of our military personnel. Applicants must have a GPA of 2.5 or higher and be able to demonstrate financial need.

Financial data The stipend is $5,000.

Duration 1 year; nonrenewable.

Number awarded 2 each year.

Deadline Deadline not specified.

[274]
GETCHELL AND ROTC SCHOLARSHIPS

Daedalian Foundation
Attn: Scholarship Committee
55 Main Circle (Building 676)
P.O. Box 249
Randolph AFB, TX 78148-0249
(210) 945-2113   Fax: (210) 945-2112
E-mail: daedalus@daedalians.org
Web: www.daedalians.org/scholarships.htm

Summary To provide financial assistance to ROTC students who wish to become military pilots.

Eligibility This program is open to students who are currently enrolled in an ROTC program at their college or university. Applicants must be interested in preparing for a career as a military pilot. They must apply through their ROTC detachment. Selection is based on intention to pursue a career as a military pilot, demonstrated moral character and patriotism, scholastic and military standing and aptitude, and physical condition and aptitude for flight. Financial need may also be considered.

Financial data The stipend is $2,000.

Duration 1 year.

Number awarded 19 each year: 5 designated as Getchell Scholarships, 8 for Air Force ROTC cadets, 3 for Army ROTC cadets, and 3 for Navy/Marine ROTC midshipmen.

Deadline November of each year.

[275]
GREATER OMAHA CHAPTER AFCEA AFROTC SCHOLARSHIP

Armed Forces Communications and Electronics
  Association-Greater Omaha Chapter
Attn: Vice President for Academic Affairs
P.O. Box 1673
Bellevue, NE 68005
(402) 312-6295   E-mail: academic@afcea-omaha.org
Web: www.afcea-omaha.org

Summary To provide financial assistance to Air Force ROTC cadets attending college in specified sections of Nebraska and Iowa who are majoring in designated science and engineering fields.

Eligibility This program is open to professional officer candidates in Air Force ROTC units at universities in eastern Nebraska and western Iowa. Applicants must be working full time on a bachelor's degree in a field related to a career in communications and electronics (e.g., mathematics, computer science, telecommunications, physics, computer engineering, electrical engineering). Selection is based on academic performance, recommendations, community or organizational involvement, and financial need.

Financial data The stipend is $1,000.

Duration 1 year.

Number awarded 1 each year.

Deadline March of each year.

[276]
GREEN TO GOLD NON-SCHOLARSHIP PROGRAM

U.S. Army
Attn: U.S. Army Cadet Command
G2 Incentives Division
1307 Third Avenue
Fort Knox, KY 40121-2725
(502) 624-7371   Toll Free: (888) 550-ARMY
Fax: (502) 624-6937
E-mail: usarmy.knox.usacc.mbx.train2lead@mail.mil
Web: www.goarmy.com

Summary   To provide financial assistance to soldiers who wish to obtain an early discharge from the Army and return to college to participate in the Army Reserve Officers' Training Corps (ROTC).

Eligibility   This program is open to enlisted soldiers who have served at least 2 years on active duty and have also completed at least 2 years of college with a GPA of 2.0 or higher. Applicants must be under 30 years of age when they graduate (waivers up to 32 years of age are available). They apply for this program to obtain an early discharge from active duty in order to enroll in a baccalaureate degree program.

Financial data   Cadets receive a stipend for 10 months of the year that is $450 per month during their junior year and $500 per month during their senior year, as well as pay for attending the 6-week Leader Development and Assessment Course (LDAC) during the summer between the junior and senior year of college.

Duration   2 years.

Additional information   Cadets who had previously qualified for benefits from the Army College Fund and/or the Montgomery GI Bill are still entitled to receive those in addition to any benefits from this program. Cadets are also entitled to participate in the Simultaneous Membership Program and serve with pay in a drilling unit of the Army Reserve or Army National Guard. Upon graduation from college, cadets are commissioned as second lieutenants and are required to serve in the military for 8 years. That obligation may be fulfilled by serving 3 years on active duty and 5 years in the Inactive Ready Reserve (IRR).

Number awarded   Varies each year.

Deadline   March or September of each year.

[277]
GREEN TO GOLD SCHOLARSHIP PROGRAM

U.S. Army
Attn: U.S. Army Cadet Command
G2 Incentives Division
1307 Third Avenue
Fort Knox, KY 40121-2725
(502) 624-7371   Toll Free: (888) 550-ARMY
Fax: (502) 624-6937
E-mail: usarmy.knox.usacc.mbx.train2lead@mail.mil
Web: www.goarmy.com

Summary   To provide scholarships and other payments to soldiers who wish to obtain an early discharge from the Army and return to college to participate in the Army Reserve Officers' Training Corps (ROTC).

Eligibility   This program is open to enlisted soldiers who have served at least 2 years on active duty plus 3 months of active duty for each month of specialized training. Applicants must have a cumulative high school or college GPA of 2.5 or higher, a General Technical (GT) score of 110 or higher, and a recent (within the past 6 months) Army Physical Fitness Test (APFT) score of 180 or higher (including 60 points in each event). They may have no more than 3 dependents including a spouse (that requirement may be waived) and must be under 31 years of age when they graduate and are commissioned. They must have been accepted at a college or university offering Army ROTC. U.S. citizenship is required.

Financial data   Scholarship winners receive up to $20,000 per year as support for tuition and fees or for room and board, whichever the recipient selects; additional support up to $1,200 per year for textbooks, supplies, and equipment; a stipend for 10 months of the year that is $350 per month during their sophomore year, $450 per month during their junior year, and $500 per month during their senior year; and pay for attending the 6-week Leader Development and Assessment Course (LDAC) during the summer between the junior and senior year of college.

Duration   Scholarships are for 2, 3, or 4 years; soldiers without prior college credit or whose colleges accept them as academic freshmen are eligible for 4-year scholarships; soldiers with 1 year of college completed are eligible for 3-year scholarships; soldiers with 2 years of college completed are eligible for 2-year scholarships.

Additional information   Recipients who had previously qualified for benefits from the Army College Fund and/or the Montgomery GI Bill are still entitled to receive those in addition to any benefits from this program. Upon graduation from college, scholarship winners are commissioned as second lieutenants and are required to serve in the military for 8 years. That obligation may be fulfilled by serving 4 years on active duty followed by 4 years in the Inactive Ready Reserve (IRR).

Number awarded   Varies each year.

Deadline   March or September of each year.

[278]
GUARANTEED RESERVE FORCES DUTY (GRFD) SCHOLARSHIPS

U.S. Army National Guard
Education Support Center
Camp J.T. Robinson
Box 46
North Little Rock, AR 72199-9600
Toll Free: (866) 628-5999   E-mail: esc@ng.army.mil
Web: www.nationalguard.com/tools/guard-scholarships

Summary   To provide financial assistance to upper-division students who are willing to 1) enroll simultaneously in Army ROTC and either the Army National Guard or Army Reserve and then 2) serve in a Reserve component of the Army following graduation.

Eligibility   This program is open to full-time students entering their junior year of college who have a GPA of 2.5 or higher and scores of 920 on the SAT or 19 on the ACT. Applicants must meet all other medical and moral character requirements for enrollment in Army ROTC and be able to complete the basic course requirements or basic training. They must be willing to enroll in the Simultaneous Membership Program (SMP) of an ROTC unit on their campus; the SMP requires simultaneous membership in Army ROTC and either the Army National Guard or Army Reserve.

Financial data Participants receive full reimbursement of tuition, a grant of $1,200 per year for books, plus an ROTC stipend for 10 months of the year at $450 per month during their junior year and $500 per month during their senior year. As a member of the Army National Guard or Army Reserve, they also receive weekend drill pay at the pay grade of a sergeant (approximately $225 per month) while participating in the SMP.

Duration 2 years.

Additional information After graduation, participants serve 3 to 6 months on active duty in the Officer Basic Course (OBC). Following completion of OBC, they are released from active duty and are obligated to serve 8 years in the Army National Guard or Army Reserve.

Number awarded Approximately 400 each year.

Deadline Deadline not specified.

[279]
HONOLULU POST SAME SCHOLARSHIPS

Society of American Military Engineers-Honolulu Post
P.O. Box 201445
Honolulu, HI 96820
Web: www.samehonolulu.org

Summary To provide financial assistance to residents of Hawaii (particularly military servicemembers, military dependents, and ROTC students) who are interested in attending college or graduate school in any state to work on a degree in engineering or architecture.

Eligibility This program is open to residents of Hawaii who are graduating high school seniors or current undergraduates enrolled or planning to enroll full time at an accredited college or university in any state. Applicants must be planning to work on an undergraduate or graduate degree in engineering or architecture. They must be U.S. citizens and have a GPA of 3.0 or higher. Military affiliation or experience (i.e., ROTC, member or dependent of a member of the Society of Military Engineers (SAME), military dependent, Junior ROTC) is not required but is given preference. Along with their application, they must submit a transcript; a resume of work experience, academic activities, and extracurricular accomplishments; and a 1-page essay on how their engineering or architecture degree will impact our nation.

Financial data The stipend is $2,000 or $1,500 per year.

Duration 1 year for the $2,000 scholarships; 4 years for the $1,500 scholarships.

Number awarded Varies each year; recently, 6 were awarded: 2 at $2,000 for 1 year and 4 at $1,500 per year for 4 years.

Deadline March of each year.

[280]
HUMAN RESOURCES OPTION OF THE SEAMAN TO ADMIRAL-21 PROGRAM

U.S. Navy
Attn: Commander, Naval Service Training Command
250 Dallas Street, Suite A
Pensacola, FL 32508-5268
(850) 452-9563   Fax: (850) 452-2486
E-mail: PNSC_STA21@navy.mil
Web: www.sta-21.navy.mil/program_options.asp

Summary To allow outstanding enlisted Navy personnel to attend a college or university, affiliate with an NROTC unit, complete a bachelor's degree, and receive a commission as a human resources officer.

Eligibility This program is open to U.S. citizens who are currently serving on active duty in the U.S. Navy or Naval Reserve, including Full Time Support (FTS), Selected Reserves (SELRES), and Navy Reservists on active duty, except for those on active duty for training (ACDUTRA). Applicants must be high school graduates (or GED recipients) who are able to complete requirements for a baccalaureate degree in 36 months or less. They must be planning to work on a degree in human resources/personnel, financial management, manpower systems analysis, operations analysis, business administration, education/training management, or a related field. When they complete their degree requirements, they must be younger than 29 years of age. Within the past 3 years, they must have taken the SAT (and achieved scores of at least 500 on the mathematics section and 500 on the critical reading section) or the ACT (and achieved a score of at least 21 on the mathematics portion and 20 on the English portion).

Financial data Awardees continue to receive their regular Navy pay and allowances while they attend college on a full-time basis. They also receive reimbursement for tuition, fees, and books up to $10,000 per year. If base housing is available, they are eligible to live there. Participants are not eligible to receive benefits under the Navy's Tuition Assistance Program (TA), the Montgomery GI Bill (MGIB), the Navy College Fund, or the Veterans Educational Assistance Program (VEAP).

Duration Selectees are supported for up to 36 months of full-time, year-round study or completion of a bachelor's degree, as long as they maintain a GPA of 2.5 or higher.

Additional information Upon acceptance into the program, selectees attend the Naval Science Institute (NSI) in Newport, Rhode Island for an 8-week program in the fundamental core concepts of being a naval officer (navigation, engineering, weapons, military history and justice, etc.). They then enter a college or university with an NROTC unit or affiliation to work full time on a bachelor's degree. They become members of and drill with the NROTC unit. When they complete their degree, they are commissioned as ensigns in the United States Naval Reserve and assigned to initial training as a human resources officer. After commissioning, 5 years of active service are required.

Number awarded Varies each year.

Deadline June of each year.

[281]
JOAN BOWDEN SCHOLARSHIP

Armed Forces Communications and Electronics Association
Attn: AFCEA Educational Foundation
4400 Fair Lakes Court
Fairfax, VA 22033-3899
(703) 631-6138   Toll Free: (800) 336-4583, ext. 6138
Fax: (703) 631-4693   E-mail: scholarship@afcea.org
Web: www.afcea.org/education/scholarships/rotc

Summary To provide financial assistance to outstanding ROTC students at colleges in Alabama, Georgia, and Mississippi.

Eligibility This program is open to U.S. citizens who are members of an ROTC detachment at an accredited college or university in Alabama, Georgia, or Mississippi. Applicants must be enrolled in a degree-granting major as sophomores or juniors at the time of application. They must exhibit dedication and superior performance based upon demonstrate academic excellence and the potential to serve as an officer of the U.S. armed forces. Financial need is considered in the selection process.

Financial data The stipend is $3,000. Funds are paid directly to the recipient.

Duration 1 year.

Additional information This program began in 1987 with support from the Montgomery Chapter of the Armed Forces Communications and Electronics Association (AFCEA).

Number awarded 1 each year.

Deadline February of each year.

[282]
JOHN AND ALICE EGAN MULTI-YEAR SCHOLARSHIPS

Daedalian Foundation
Attn: Scholarship Committee
55 Main Circle (Building 676)
P.O. Box 249
Randolph AFB, TX 78148-0249
(210) 945-2113   Fax: (210) 945-2112
E-mail: daedalus@daedalians.org
Web: www.daedalians.org/scholarships.htm

Summary To provide financial assistance to college students who are participating in a ROTC program and wish to become military pilots.

Eligibility This program is open to students who have completed at least the freshman year at an accredited 4-year college or university and have a GPA of 3.0 or higher. Applicants must be participating in an ROTC program and be medically qualified for flight training. They must plan to apply for and be awarded a military pilot training allocation at the appropriate juncture in their ROTC program. Selection is based on intention to prepare for a career as a military pilot, demonstrated moral character and patriotism, scholastic and military standing and aptitude, and physical condition and aptitude for flight. Financial need may also be considered.

Financial data The stipend is $2,500 per year, including $500 provided by a local Flight of the organization and $2,000 as a matching award provided by the foundation.

Duration 1 year; may be renewed up to 2 or 3 additional years, provided the recipient maintains a GPA of 3.0 or higher and is enrolled in an undergraduate program.

Additional information This program began in 2003. It includes a mentoring component.

Number awarded Up to 11 each year.

Deadline July of each year.

[283]
KENTUCKIANA POST SAME SCHOLARSHIP

Society of American Military Engineers-Kentuckiana Post
c/o Kristen Crumpton, Scholarship Committee Co-Chair
URS Corporation
325 West Main Street, Suite 1200
Louisville, KY 40202
(502) 569-2301   Fax: (502) 569-2304
E-mail: kristen.crumpton@urs.com
Web: posts.same.org/kentuckiana

Summary To provide financial assistance to residents of Indiana and Kentucky who are majoring in engineering in college (especially those who are 1) currently serving in the military, 2) the family members of current service personnel, or ROTC students).

Eligibility This program is open to students who fall into 1 of the following categories: a dependent of a current Society of American Military Engineers (SAME) Kentuckiana Post member; an employee or dependent of an employee of a Kentuckiana Post sustaining member firm; an employee or dependent of an employee of the Louisville District Corps of Engineers; a current student member of the Kentuckiana Post; a student whose permanent home address is within the Kentuckiana Post's geographic boundary (Kentucky and Indiana) and who is enrolled in an ROTC program or military academy; or an individual on active duty or the dependent of an individual on active duty who is assigned to an installation within the Kentuckiana Post's geographic boundary. Applicants must be U.S. citizens accepted at an undergraduate ABET-accredited engineering program; undergraduates enrolled in engineering technology programs are not eligible. Along with their application, they must submit an essay of 300 to 500 words on a topic that changes annually; recently, applicants were invited to write on how winning this scholarship would promote a promising future for their engineering career and how they might envision that career supporting the mission of SAME. Financial need is not considered in the selection process.

Financial data The stipend is $4,000 per year.

Duration 1 year; may be renewed 1 additional year.

Additional information Recipients are required to attend the scholarship luncheon ceremony in Louisville in May.

Number awarded Varies each year; recently, 6 were awarded.

Deadline March of each year.

[284]
LEXINGTON-CONCORD CHAPTER AFCEA ROTC SCHOLARSHIPS

Armed Forces Communications and Electronics
  Association-Lexington-Concord Chapter
Attn: Claire Goulet
Oasis Systems, Inc.
24 Hartwell Avenue
Lexington, MA 02421
(781) 676-7344   Fax: (781) 676-7353
E-mail: cgoulet@oasissystems.com
Web: www.afceaboston.com/aboutlexcon.asp

Summary To recognize and reward ROTC students at universities in New England.

Eligibility This program is open to students who are enrolled in ROTC programs at universities in Maine, Massachusetts, New Hampshire, and Vermont. They must be nominated by their ROTC unit. The nominee selected as the most qualified student receives an additional award.

Financial data Each nominee receives a $1,000 award. The nominee selected as the most qualified student receives an additional $1,000.

Duration The awards are presented annually.

Number awarded 15 ROTC students receive these awards each year, of whom 1 receives the additional award.

Deadline Nominations must be submitted in February or March of each year.

[285]
LGS INNOVATIONS LT. GENERAL RONALD IVERSON ROTC SCHOLARSHIP

Armed Forces Communications and Electronics
  Association
Attn: AFCEA Educational Foundation
4400 Fair Lakes Court
Fairfax, VA 22033-3899
(703) 631-6138   Toll Free: (800) 336-4583, ext. 6138
Fax: (703) 631-4693 E-mail: ScholarshipsInfo@afcea.org
Web: www.afcea.org/education/scholarships/rotc

Summary To provide financial assistance to Air Force ROTC midshipmen who are majoring in a field of science, technology, engineering, or mathematics (STEM).

Eligibility This program is open to Air Force ROTC cadets enrolled full time at an accredited degree-granting 4-year college or university in the United States. Applicants must be sophomores or juniors at the time of application and have a GPA of 3.0 or higher with a major in a field of STEM. Their application must be endorsed by the professor of aviation science at their institution. Selection is based on demonstrated dedication, superior performance, and potential to serve as an officer in the United States Air Force. Financial need is not considered in the selection process.

Financial data The stipend is $2,500.

Duration 1 year.

Additional information This program, sponsored by LGS Innovations, began in 2012.

Number awarded 4 each year.

Deadline February of each year.

[286]
LIEUTENANT COLONEL MARVIN T. STEWART

Military Officers Association of America-Louisiana Council
  of Chapters
c/o LTC Lessie A. Griffith, Scholarship Chair
1786 Glendale Road
DeRidder, LA 70634-3065
(337) 462-0143   E-mail: griffithgrp@hotmail.com
Web: lcoc-moaa.org/scholarships

Summary To provide financial assistance to high school seniors in Louisiana who plan to attend college in any state and enroll in ROTC.

Eligibility This program is open to seniors graduating from high schools in Louisiana and planning to enroll full time at a college or university in any state. Preference is given to applicants planning to enroll in the ROTC program of any service at their institution. Selection is based on academic achievement, demonstrated leadership qualities, school and community service, and personal initiative.

Financial data The stipend is $1,500.

Duration 1 year.

Number awarded 1 each year.

Deadline April of each year.

[287]
LIEUTENANT GENERAL WILLIAM T. LORD SCHOLARSHIP

Armed Forces Communications and Electronics
  Association
Attn: AFCEA Educational Foundation
4400 Fair Lakes Court
Fairfax, VA 22033-3899
(703) 631-6138   Toll Free: (800) 336-4583, ext. 6138
Fax: (703) 631-4693   E-mail: scholarship@afcea.org
Web: www.afcea.org/education/scholarships/rotc

Summary To provide financial assistance to outstanding Air Force ROTC students in Alabama who are working on a degree in fields related to the work of the Armed Forces Communications and Electronics Association (AFCEA).

Eligibility This program is open to U.S. citizens who are members of an Air Force ROTC detachment at an accredited college or university in Alabama. Applicants must be enrolled as sophomores or juniors at the time of application with a major in an AFCEA-related field (e.g., engineering, computer science, information technology, or other cyber-related curriculum). They must exhibit dedication and superior performance based upon demonstrate academic excellence and the potential to serve as an officer of the U.S. Air Force. Financial need is considered in the selection process.

Financial data The stipend is $3,000. Funds are paid directly to the recipient.

Duration 1 year.

Additional information This program began in 2012 with support from the Montgomery Chapter of the Armed Forces Communications and Electronics Association (AFCEA).

Number awarded 1 each year.

Deadline February of each year.

[288]
LOS ANGELES CHAPTER AFCEA SCHOLARSHIPS

Armed Forces Communications and Electronics
  Association-Los Angeles Chapter
c/o Eli Cohen, Scholarships Vice President
Electronic Systems Innovation, Inc.
5777 West Century Boulevard, Suite 1225
Los Angeles, CA 90045-5698
(310) 645-8400, ext. 210   Fax: (310) 645-9600
E-mail: afceala@esinv.com
Web: www.afcea-la.org/content/scholarships

Summary To provide financial assistance to ROTC students from any state who are enrolled at colleges and universities in the greater Los Angeles area.

Eligibility This program is open to ROTC cadets and midshipmen enrolled at colleges and universities in the greater Los Angeles area. Preference is given to applicants majoring in science, mathematics, engineering, computer science, or natural sciences.

Financial data A stipend is awarded (amount not specified).

Duration 1 year.

Number awarded Varies each year; a total of $8,000 is available for this program annually.

Deadline March of each year.

[289]
LOUIS J. SCHOBER MEMORIAL SCHOLARSHIP

Society of American Military Engineers-Louisiana Post
c/o Chris Dunn, Young Members Committee Chair
U.S. Army Corps of Engineers, New Orleans District
7400 Leake Avenue
P.O. Box 60267
New Orleans, LA 70160
(504) 862-1799
E-mail: Christopher.L.Dunn@usace.army.mil
Web: posts.same.org/louisiana/YoungMembers.htm

Summary To provide financial assistance to students from Louisiana majoring in engineering, particularly those who are enrolled in ROTC, are serving or have served in the armed forces, or are children of members of the Society of American Military Engineers (SAME) Louisiana Post.

Eligibility This program is open to students currently working on an undergraduate degree in engineering. Applicants must be either 1) enrolled at a college or university in Louisiana; or 2) the children of a member of the SAME Louisiana Post (who may be studying at a college or university in any state). Graduate students are not eligible; high school seniors may be considered if no suitable college students apply. Selection is based primarily on academic record and demonstration of leadership characteristics; other factors considered are participation in SAME posts and activities, enrollment in an ROTC program, former or current military service, and participation in school and community activities.

Financial data The stipend is $2,000.

Duration 1 year; nonrenewable.

Number awarded 1 or more each year.

Deadline May of each year.

[290]
LT. PAUL (JAY) SMITH MEMORIAL ENDOWMENT SCHOLARSHIP

First Command Educational Foundation
Attn: Scholarship Programs Manager
1 FirstComm Plaza
Fort Worth, TX 76109-4999
(817) 569-2634   Toll Free: (877) 872-8289
Fax: (817) 569-2970   E-mail: Scholarships@fcef.com
Web: www.fcef.com

Summary To provide financial assistance to outstanding Air Force ROTC cadets.

Eligibility This program is open to students enrolled as cadets in the Air Force ROTC unit at their college or university. Selection is based on "leadership and dedicated service to community and country."

Financial data The stipend is $2,000.

Duration 1 year.

Additional information This program began in 1996 and was transferred to First Command Educational Foundation in 2007.

Number awarded 1 each year.

Deadline Applications must be submitted to the Air Force ROTC unit, each of which sets its own deadline.

[291]
LTG EDWARD HONOR SCHOLARSHIP AWARD

The ROCKS, Inc.
c/o WSC Associates, LLP
P.O. Box 47435
Forestville, MD 20753
(301) 856-9319   Toll Free: (888) 762-5747
Fax: (301) 856-5220   E-mail: therocks@aol.com
Web: www.rocksinc.org

Summary To recognize and reward college seniors who have participated in ROTC programs at Historically Black Colleges and Universities (HBCUs).

Eligibility This award is available to graduating seniors who are Army or Air Force Cadets or Navy Midshipmen at HBCUs. Applicants must submit 1) a 1-page paper on a topic related to leadership or mentorship; 2) information on their participation in ROTC and other extracurricular activities; and 3) a letter of recommendation from their professor of military science evaluating their appearance, attitude, character, dedication, initiative, integrity, judgment, leadership potential, and written and oral communication ability.

Financial data The award is $2,000.

Duration The award is presented annually.

Number awarded 1 each year.

Deadline February of each year.

[292]
MARK YAMANE MILITARY SCHOLARSHIP

Nisei Veterans Committee
Attn: Military Scholarship
1212 South King Street
Seattle, WA 98144-2025
(206) 322-1122   E-mail: scholarship@nvcfoundation.org
Web: www.seattlenvc.org/education/scholarship

Summary To provide financial assistance for college to military personnel or ROTC students, especially those with ties to Washington, who are of Japanese ancestry.

Eligibility This program is open to individuals of Japanese ancestry who are regular military stationed at Fort Lewis, McChord Air Force Base, Whidbey Island Naval Air Station, Naval Station Everett, Naval Station Bangor, or Naval Station Bremerton; members of the U.S. Coast Guard under the command of the 13th District; residents of Washington who are members of the National Guard or Reserves and have served on active duty for a total of at least 2 years or are current on active duty; ROTC students at universities in the state of Washington; Washington state residents who are ROTC students at universities in any state; Washington state residents who are attending 1 of the military academies; or relatives of members of the Nisei Veterans Committee who are serving on active duty at any military base worldwide. Applicants must submit an essay on how the legacy of Japanese American soldiers who served during World War II has affected them and their military service to their country.

Financial data The stipend is $1,500. Funds may be used to buy a computer and software, pay off existing student loans, pay for books and tuition not covered by the military, or any combination of those.

Duration 1 year.

Number awarded 1 or more each year.

Deadline January of each year.

[293]
MEDAL OF HONOR AFCEA ROTC SCHOLARSHIPS

Armed Forces Communications and Electronics
Association
Attn: AFCEA Educational Foundation
4400 Fair Lakes Court
Fairfax, VA 22033-3899
(703) 631-6138   Toll Free: (800) 336-4583, ext. 6138
Fax: (703) 631-4693   E-mail: scholarship@afcea.org
Web: www.afcea.org

Summary   To provide financial assistance to ROTC cadets who demonstrate outstanding leadership performance and potential.

Eligibility   This program is open to ROTC cadets enrolled full time at an accredited degree-granting 4-year college or university in the United States. Applicants must be sophomores or juniors at the time of application and have a GPA of 3.0 or higher with a major in an academic discipline. They must be U.S. citizens. Selection is based on demonstrated leadership performance and potential and strong commitment to serve in the U.S. armed forces.

Financial data   The stipend is $5,000.

Duration   1 year.

Additional information   This program, established in 2005, is sponsored by the Congressional Medal of Honor Foundation in partnership with the Armed Forces Communications and Electronics Association (AFCEA) Educational Foundation.

Number awarded   4 each year: 1 each for Army, Navy, Marine Corps, and Air Force ROTC students.

Deadline   February of each year.

[294]
MEDICAL CORPS OPTION OF THE SEAMAN TO ADMIRAL-21 PROGRAM

U.S. Navy
Attn: Commander, Naval Service Training Command
250 Dallas Street, Suite A
Pensacola, FL 32508-5268
(850) 452-9563   Fax: (850) 452-2486
E-mail: PNSC_STA21@navy.mil
Web: www.sta-21.navy.mil/program_options.asp

Summary   To allow outstanding enlisted Navy personnel to work on a bachelor's degree, affiliate with an ROTC unit, be accepted to medical school, earn an M.D. or D.O. degree, and be commissioned in the Navy Medical Corps.

Eligibility   This program is open to U.S. citizens who are currently serving on active duty in the U.S. Navy or Naval Reserve, including Full Time Support (FTS), Selected Reserves (SELRES), and Navy Reservists on active duty, except for those on active duty for training (ACDUTRA). Applicants must be high school graduates (or GED recipients) who are able to 1) complete requirements for a baccalaureate degree within 36 months; 2) complete a medical degree through the Uniformed Services University of Health Services (USUHS) or the Health Professions Scholarship Program (HPSP); and 3) complete 20 years of active commissioned service as a physician by age 62. Within the past 3 years, they must have taken the SAT (and achieved scores of at least 500 on the mathematics section and 500 on the critical reading section) or the ACT (and achieved a score of at least 21 on the mathematics portion and 20 on the English portion).

Financial data   Awardees continue to receive their regular Navy pay and allowances while they attend college on a full-time basis. They also receive reimbursement for tuition, fees, and books up to $10,000 per year. If base housing is available, they are eligible to live there. Participants are not eligible to receive benefits under the Navy's Tuition Assistance Program (TA), the Montgomery GI Bill (MGIB), the Navy College Fund, or the Veterans Educational Assistance Program (VEAP).

Duration   Selectees are supported for up to 36 months of full-time, year-round study or completion of a bachelor's degree, as long as they maintain a GPA of 3.0 or higher. They are then supported until completion of a medical degree.

Additional information   Upon acceptance into the program, selectees attend the Naval Science Institute (NSI) in Newport, Rhode Island for an 8-week program in the fundamental core concepts of being a naval officer (navigation, engineering, weapons, military history and justice, etc.). They then enter an NROTC affiliated college or university with a pre-medical program that confers an accredited B.S. degree to pursue full-time study. They become members of and drill with the NROTC unit. After they complete their bachelor's degree, they are commissioned as an ensign in the Naval Reserve. They must apply to and be accepted at medical school, either the USUSH or a civilian medical school through the HPSP. Following completion of medical school, they are promoted to lieutenant and assigned to active duty in the Medical Corps. Selectees incur a service obligation of 5 years for their baccalaureate degree support plus whatever obligation they incur for medical degree support (usually 7 years if they attend USUSH or 4 years if they attend a civilian institution through HPSP).

Number awarded   Varies each year.

Deadline   June of each year.

[295]
MG EUGENE C. RENZI, USA (RET.) ROTC LEADERSHIP SCHOLARSHIP

Armed Forces Communications and Electronics
Association
Attn: AFCEA Educational Foundation
4400 Fair Lakes Court
Fairfax, VA 22033-3899
(703) 631-6138   Toll Free: (800) 336-4583, ext. 6138
Fax: (703) 631-4693   E-mail: scholarship@afcea.org
Web: www.afcea.org/education/scholarships/rotc

Summary   To provide financial assistance to students participating in ROTC programs at universities in designated northeastern states.

Eligibility   This program is open to ROTC students at universities in Connecticut, Maine, Massachusetts, New York, and Rhode Island. Selection is based on demonstrated leadership in ROTC, in universities activities, and in extracurricular activities.

Financial data   A stipend is awarded (amount not specified).

Duration   1 year.

Additional information   This program began in 2012 with support from Value Enterprise Solutions, Inc.

Number awarded 1 each year.
Deadline February of each year.

[296]
MICHAEL WILSON SCHOLARSHIPS

Air Force Association
Attn: Manager, Awards and Scholarships
1501 Lee Highway
Arlington, VA 22209-1198
(703) 247-5800, ext. 4807
Toll Free: (800) 727-3337, ext. 4807
Fax: (703) 247-5853   E-mail: awards@afa.org
Web: www.afa.org

Summary To provide financial assistance to Air Force ROTC cadets who are entering their junior or senior year of college.

Eligibility This program is open to Air Force ROTC cadets entering their junior or senior year as full-time students with a GPA of 2.8 or higher. Applicants must be enrolled in the Professional Air Force ROTC Officer Course program and attending both the Aerospace Studies class and the Leadership Laboratory each semester. Along with their application, they must submit essays of 500 words each on the following topics: 1) how their choice of a major or career will support the mission of the Air Force; 2) what single issue affecting the military would they bring to the attention of the President if they had the opportunity to speak with him; and 3) who or what inspired them to make the choice to become a leader in the Air Force and why.

Financial data The stipend is $15,000.
Duration 1 year.
Number awarded 2 each year.
Deadline Deadline not specified.

[297]
MINORITY SERVING INSTITUTION SCHOLARSHIP PROGRAM

U.S. Navy
Attn: Naval Service Training Command Officer
  Development
NAS Pensacola
250 Dallas Street
Pensacola, FL 32508-5220
(850) 452-4941, ext. 29395
Toll Free: (800) NAV-ROTC, ext. 29395
Fax: (850) 452-2486
E-mail: pnsc_nrotc.scholarship@navy.mil
Web: www.nrotc.navy.mil/MSI.aspx

Summary To provide financial assistance to students at specified minority institutions who are interested in joining Navy ROTC to prepare for service as an officer in the U.S. Navy.

Eligibility This program is open to students attending or planning to attend 1 of 17 specified Historically Black Colleges or Universities (HBCUs), 1 of 3 High Hispanic Enrollment (HHE) schools, or 1 other minority institution, all of which have a Navy ROTC unit on campus. Applicants must be nominated by the professor of naval science at their institution and meet academic requirements set by each school. They must be U.S. citizens between 17 and 23 years of age who are willing to serve for 4 years as active-duty Navy officers following graduation from college. They must not have

reached their 27th birthday by the time of college graduation and commissioning; applicants who have prior active-duty military service may be eligible for age adjustments for the amount of time equal to their prior service, up to a maximum of 36 months. The qualifying scores are 530 critical reading and 520 mathematics on the SAT or 22 on English and 21 on mathematics on the ACT. Current enlisted and former military personnel are also eligible if they will complete the program by the age of 30.

Financial data These scholarships provide payment of full tuition and required educational fees, as well as a specified amount for textbooks, supplies, and equipment. The program also provides a stipend for 10 months of the year that is $250 per month as a freshman, $300 per month as a sophomore, $350 per month as a junior, and $400 per month as a senior.

Duration Up to 4 years.

Additional information The eligible HBCUs are Allen University, Clark Atlanta University, Dillard University, Florida A&M University, Hampton University, Howard University, Huston-Tillotson University, Morehouse College, Norfolk State University, Prairie View A&M University, Savannah State University, Southern University and A&M College, Spelman College, Tennessee State University, Texas Southern University, Tuskegee University, and Xavier University. The eligible HHEs are Central New Mexico Community College, Pima Community College, and the University of New Mexico. The other minority institution is Kennedy King College. After completing the program, all participants are commissioned as ensigns in the Naval Reserve with an 8-year service obligation, including 4 years of active duty. Current military personnel who are accepted into this program are released from active duty and are not eligible for active-duty pay and allowances, medical benefits, or other active-duty entitlements.

Number awarded Varies each year.
Deadline June of each year.

[298]
MR. MORT MARKS MEMORIAL SCHOLARSHIP

Armed Forces Communications and Electronics
  Association
Attn: AFCEA Educational Foundation
4400 Fair Lakes Court
Fairfax, VA 22033-3899
(703) 631-6138   Toll Free: (800) 336-4583, ext. 6138
Fax: (703) 631-4693   E-mail: scholarship@afcea.org
Web: www.afcea.org/education/scholarships/rotc

Summary To provide financial assistance for college to outstanding Air Force ROTC cadets.

Eligibility This program is open to U.S. citizens who are enrolled in the Air Force ROTC detachment at an accredited college or university in the United States. Applicants must be enrolled in a degree-granting major as sophomores or juniors at the time of application. They must exhibit dedication and superior performance based upon demonstrate academic excellence and the potential to serve as an officer of the U.S. Air Force. Financial need is considered in the selection process.

Financial data The stipend is $3,000. Funds are paid directly to the recipient.
Duration 1 year.

Additional information This program began in 2010 with support from the Montgomery Chapter of the Armed Forces Communications and Electronics Association (AFCEA).
Number awarded 1 each year.
Deadline May of each year.

[299]
NARRAGANSETT BAY POST SAME SCHOLARSHIP

Society of American Military Engineers-Narragansett Bay Post
Attn: Scholarship Committee
15 Mohegan Avenue
New London, CT 06320
(860) 444-8312 Fax: (860) 444-8219
E-mail: Gregory.j.carabine@uscg.mil
Web: posts.same.org/Narragansett/scholarship.htm

Summary To provide financial assistance to residents of New England (particularly ROTC students and military family members) who are interested in working on a bachelor's degree in construction-related fields at colleges in any state.
Eligibility This program is open to residents of New England (preferably Connecticut, Massachusetts, and Rhode Island) who are graduating high school seniors or students currently enrolled at a college or university in any state. Applicants must be interested in working on a bachelor's degree in an accredited engineering or architectural program, preferably in civil engineering, environmental engineering, architecture, or other construction-related program. Preference is given to students who 1) are dependents of or sponsored by a member of the Narragansett Bay Post of the Society of American Military Engineers (SAME); 2) are enrolled in ROTC (preferably not a recipient of an ROTC scholarship); or 3) have prior U.S. military service and/or public service. Along with their application, they must submit a 500-word essay about themselves, their achievements, or their situation. Selection is based on that essay, grades and class rank, school or community honors, extracurricular activities, leadership, volunteer activities, and completeness and quality of the application. U.S. citizenship is required.
Financial data The stipend is $1,000.
Duration 1 year.
Number awarded 1 each year.
Deadline May of each year.

[300]
NAVAL FLIGHT OFFICER OPTION OF THE SEAMAN TO ADMIRAL-21 PROGRAM

U.S. Navy
Attn: Commander, Naval Service Training Command
250 Dallas Street, Suite A
Pensacola, FL 32508-5268
(850) 452-9563 Fax: (850) 452-2486
E-mail: PNSC_STA21@navy.mil
Web: www.sta-21.navy.mil/program_options.asp

Summary To allow outstanding enlisted Navy personnel to attend college, affiliate with an NROTC unit, complete a bachelor's degree, and receive a commission as a naval flight officer (NFO).
Eligibility This program is open to U.S. citizens who are currently serving on active duty in the U.S. Navy or Naval Reserve, including Full Time Support (FTS), Selected Reserves (SELRES), and Navy Reservists on active duty,

except for those on active duty for training (ACDUTRA). Applicants must be high school graduates (or GED recipients) who are able to complete requirements for a baccalaureate degree in 36 months or less. When they complete their degree requirements, they must be younger than 27 years of age (may be adjusted to 31 years of age for prior active-duty service). Within the past 3 years, they must have taken the SAT (and achieved scores of at least 500 on the mathematics section and 500 on the critical reading section) or the ACT (and achieved a score of at least 21 on the mathematics portion and 20 on the English portion). They must also achieve a score of at least the following: AQR (4), FOFAR (5) on the Aviation Selection Test Battery.
Financial data Awardees continue to receive their regular Navy pay and allowances while they attend college on a full-time basis. They also receive reimbursement for tuition, fees, and books up to $10,000 per year. If base housing is available, they are eligible to live there. Participants are not eligible to receive benefits under the Navy's Tuition Assistance Program (TA), the Montgomery GI Bill (MGIB), the Navy College Fund, or the Veterans Educational Assistance Program (VEAP).
Duration Selectees are supported for up to 36 months of full-time, year-round study or completion of a bachelor's degree, as long as they maintain a GPA of 2.5 or higher.
Additional information This program began in 2001 as a replacement for the Aviation Enlisted Commissioning Program (AECP). Upon acceptance into the program, selectees attend the Naval Science Institute (NSI) in Newport, Rhode Island for an 8-week program in the fundamental core concepts of being a naval officer (navigation, engineering, weapons, military history and justice, etc.). They then enter a college or university with an NROTC unit or affiliation to work full time on a bachelor's degree. They become members of and drill with the NROTC unit. When they complete their degree, they are commissioned as ensigns in the United States Naval Reserve and assigned to flight training. After commissioning, participants incur an active-duty obligation of 6 years after designation as a Naval Flight Officer or 6 years from the date of disenrollment from flight training.
Number awarded Varies each year.
Deadline June of each year.

[301]
NAVY NURSE CORPS NROTC SCHOLARSHIP PROGRAM

U.S. Navy
Attn: Naval Service Training Command Officer Development
NAS Pensacola
250 Dallas Street
Pensacola, FL 32508-5220
(850) 452-4941, ext. 29395
Toll Free: (800) NAV-ROTC, ext. 29395
Fax: (850) 452-2486
E-mail: pnsc_nrotc.scholarship@navy.mil
Web: www.nrotc.navy.mil/nurse.aspx

Summary To provide financial assistance to graduating high school seniors who are interested in joining Navy ROTC and majoring in nursing in college.
Eligibility Eligible to apply for these scholarships are graduating high school seniors who have been accepted at a col-

lege with a Navy ROTC unit on campus or a college with a cross-enrollment agreement with such a college. Applicants must be U.S. citizens between the ages of 17 and 23 who plan to study nursing in college and are willing to serve for 4 years as active-duty Navy officers in the Navy Nurse Corps following graduation from college. They must not have reached their 27th birthday by the time of college graduation and commissioning; applicants who have prior active-duty military service may be eligible for age adjustments for the amount of time equal to their prior service, up to a maximum of 36 months. They must have minimum SAT scores of 530 in critical reading and 520 in mathematics or minimum ACT scores of 22 in English and 21 in mathematics.

Financial data   This scholarship provides payment of full tuition and required educational fees, as well as $375 per semester for textbooks, supplies, and equipment. The program also provides a stipend for 10 months of the year that is $250 per month as a freshman, $300 per month as a sophomore, $350 per month as a junior, and $400 per month as a senior.

Duration   4 years.

Number awarded   Varies each year.

Deadline   January of each year.

[302]
NAVY-MARINE CORPS ROTC 2- AND 3-YEAR SCHOLARSHIPS

U.S. Navy
Attn: Naval Service Training Command Officer
   Development
NAS Pensacola
250 Dallas Street
Pensacola, FL 32508-5220
(850) 452-4941, ext. 29395
Toll Free: (800) NAV-ROTC, ext. 29395
Fax: (850) 452-2486
E-mail: pnsc_nrotc.scholarship@navy.mil
Web: www.nrotc.navy.mil/scholarships.aspx

Summary   To provide financial assistance to students currently enrolled in college who are interested in joining Navy ROTC.

Eligibility   This program is open to students who have completed at least 30 semester hours of college and have a GPA of 2.5 or higher overall. Preference is given to students at colleges with a Navy ROTC unit on campus or at colleges with a cross-enrollment agreement with a college with an NROTC unit. Applicants must be U.S. citizens between the ages of 17 and 21 who plan to pursue an approved course of study in college and complete their degree before they reach the age of 27. Former and current enlisted military personnel are also eligible if they will complete the program by the age of 30.

Financial data   These scholarships provide payment of full tuition and required educational fees, as well as $750 per year for textbooks, supplies, and equipment. The program also provides a stipend for 10 months of the year that is 300 per month as a sophomore, $350 per month as a junior, and $400 per month as a senior.

Duration   2 or 3 years, until the recipient completes the bachelor's degree.

Additional information   Applications must be made through professors of naval science at 1 of the schools hosting the Navy ROTC program. Prior to final selection, appli-

cants must attend, at Navy expense, a 6-week summer training course at the Naval Science Institute at Newport, Rhode Island. Recipients must also complete 4 years of study in naval science classes as students either at 1 of the 74 colleges with NROTC units or at 1 of the more than 100 institutions with cross-enrollment agreements (in which case they attend their home college for their regular academic courses but attend naval science classes at a nearby school with an NROTC unit). After completing the program, all participants are commissioned as ensigns in the Naval Reserve with an 8-year service obligation, including 4 years of active duty.

Number awarded   Approximately 800 each year.

Deadline   March of each year.

[303]
NAVY-MARINE CORPS ROTC 4-YEAR SCHOLARSHIPS

U.S. Navy
Attn: Naval Service Training Command Officer
   Development
NAS Pensacola
250 Dallas Street
Pensacola, FL 32508-5220
(850) 452-4941, ext. 29395
Toll Free: (800) NAV-ROTC, ext. 29395
Fax: (850) 452-2486
E-mail: pnsc_nrotc.scholarship@navy.mil
Web: www.nrotc.navy.mil/scholarships.aspx

Summary   To provide financial assistance to graduating high school seniors who are interested in joining Navy ROTC in college.

Eligibility   This program is open to graduating high school seniors who have been accepted at a college with a Navy ROTC unit on campus or a college with a cross-enrollment agreement with such a college. Applicants must be U.S. citizens between 17 and 23 years of age who are willing to serve for 4 years as active-duty Navy officers following graduation from college. They must not have reached their 27th birthday by the time of college graduation and commissioning; applicants who have prior active-duty military service may be eligible for age adjustments for the amount of time equal to their prior service, up to a maximum of 36 months. The qualifying scores for the Navy option are 530 critical reading and 520 mathematics on the SAT or 22 on English and 21 on mathematics on the ACT; for the Marine Corps option they are 1000 composite on the SAT or 22 composite on the ACT. Eligible academic majors are classified as Tier 1 for engineering programs of Navy interest (aerospace, aeronautical, astronautical, chemical, electrical, mechanical, naval, nuclear, ocean, and systems); Tier 2 for other engineering, mathematics, and science programs (e.g., general engineering and other engineering specialties; biochemistry and other specialties within biology; chemistry; mathematics; oceanography; pharmacology and toxicology; physics; quantitative economics; physics); or Tier 3 for selected regional and cultural area studies, designated foreign languages, or other academic majors.

Financial data   These scholarships provide payment of full tuition and required educational fees, as well as $750 per year for textbooks, supplies, and equipment. The program also provides a stipend for 10 months of the year that is $250 per month as a freshman, $300 per month as a sophomore, $350 per month as a junior, and $400 per month as a senior.

Duration 4 years.

Additional information Students may apply for either a Navy or Marine Corps option scholarship but not for both. Navy option applicants apply through Navy recruiting offices; Marine Corps applicants apply through Marine Corps recruiting offices. Recipients must also complete 4 years of study in naval science classes as students either at 1 of the 74 colleges, universities, and maritime institutes with NROTC units or at 1 of the approximately 100 institutions with cross-enrollment agreements (in which case they attend their home college for their regular academic courses but attend naval science classes at a nearby school with an NROTC unit). After completing the program, all participants are commissioned as ensigns in the Naval Reserve or second lieutenants in the Marine Corps Reserve with an 8-year service obligation, including 4 years of active duty. Current military personnel who are accepted into this program are released from active duty and are not eligible for active-duty pay and allowances, medical benefits, or other active-duty entitlements.

Number awarded Approximately 2,200 each year; approximately 85% of the scholarships are awarded to students with Tier 1 or 2 majors.

Deadline January of each year.

[304]
NAVY-MARINE CORPS ROTC COLLEGE PROGRAM

U.S. Navy
Attn: Naval Service Training Command Officer
  Development
NAS Pensacola
250 Dallas Street
Pensacola, FL 32508-5220
(850) 452-4941, ext. 29395
Toll Free: (800) NAV-ROTC, ext. 29395
Fax: (850) 452-2486
E-mail: PNSC_NROTC.scholarship@navy.mil
Web: www.nrotc.navy.mil/scholarships.aspx

Summary To provide financial assistance to lower-division students who are interested in joining Navy ROTC in college.

Eligibility Applicants must be U.S. citizens between the ages of 17 and 21 who are already enrolled as non-scholarship students in naval science courses at a college or university with a Navy ROTC program on campus. They must apply before the spring of their sophomore year. All applications must be submitted through the professors of naval science at the college or university attended.

Financial data Participants in this program receive free naval science textbooks, all required uniforms, and a stipend for 10 months of the year that is $350 per month as a junior and $400 per month as a senior.

Duration 2 or 4 years.

Additional information Following acceptance into the program, participants attend the Naval Science Institute in Newport, Rhode Island for 6 and a half weeks during the summer between their sophomore and junior year. During the summer between their junior and senior year, they participate in an additional training program, usually at sea for Navy midshipmen or at Quantico, Virginia for Marine Corps midshipmen. After graduation from college, they are commissioned ensigns in the Naval Reserve or second lieutenants in the Marine Corps Reserve with an 8-year service obligation, including 3 years of active duty.

Number awarded Varies each year.

Deadline March of each year.

[305]
NORTHERN NEW JERSEY CHAPTER ROTC SCHOLARSHIPS

Military Officers Association of America-Northern New
  Jersey Chapter
Attn: LTC Michael J. Renahan, Scholarships
US Army ARDEC
Building 121
Picatinny Arsenal, NJ 07806-5000
(973) 822-1539   E-mail: renahanconsult@aol.com
Web: nnj-moaa.org/activities

Summary To provide financial assistance to residents of New Jersey who are enrolled in an ROTC program at a college in any state.

Eligibility This program is open to residents of New Jersey who are attending a college or university in any state. Applicants must be preparing for a military career through the ROTC program at their institution.

Financial data The stipend is $1,000.

Duration 1 year.

Number awarded 3 each year.

Deadline Deadline not specified.

[306]
NUCLEAR (SUBMARINE AND SURFACE) OPTION OF THE SEAMAN TO ADMIRAL-21 PROGRAM

U.S. Navy
Attn: Commander, Naval Service Training Command
250 Dallas Street, Suite A
Pensacola, FL 32508-5268
(850) 452-9563   Fax: (850) 452-2486
E-mail: PNSC_STA21@navy.mil
Web: www.sta-21.navy.mil/program_options.asp

Summary To allow outstanding enlisted Navy personnel to attend college, affiliate with an NROTC unit, complete a bachelor's degree, and receive a commission in the nuclear officer community.

Eligibility This program is open to U.S. citizens who are currently serving on active duty in the U.S. Navy or Naval Reserve, including Full Time Support (FTS), Selected Reserves (SELRES), and Navy Reservists on active duty, except for those on active duty for training (ACDUTRA). Only personnel currently enrolled in the Naval Nuclear Power School or Naval Nuclear Power Training Unit or assigned there as staff pickup instructors or sea returnee instructors are eligible. Applicants must be high school graduates (or GED recipients) who are able to complete requirements for a baccalaureate degree in 36 months or less. When they complete their degree requirements, they must be younger than 26 years of age. Sea returnee staff instructors must finish prior to their 31st birthday. Applicants must have taken the SAT or ACT within the past 3 years and achieved a score of 1140 or higher on the SAT or 50 or higher on the ACT. Their proposed college major must be in a technical area.

Financial data Awardees continue to receive their regular Navy pay and allowances while they attend college on a full-time basis. They also receive reimbursement for tuition, fees, and books up to $10,000 per year. If base housing is available, they are eligible to live there. Participants are not eligible to receive benefits under the Navy's Tuition Assistance Program (TA), the Montgomery GI Bill (MGIB), the Navy College Fund, or the Veterans Educational Assistance Program (VEAP).

Duration   Selectees are supported for up to 36 months of full-time, year-round study or completion of a bachelor's degree, as long as they maintain a GPA of 3.0 or higher.

Additional information   This program began in 2001 as a replacement for the Nuclear Enlisted Commissioning Program (NECP). Upon acceptance into the program, selectees attend the Naval Science Institute (NSI) in Newport, Rhode Island for an 8-week program in the fundamental core concepts of being a naval officer (navigation, engineering, weapons, military history and justice, etc.). They then enter 1 of 18 universities with an NROTC nuclear unit (University of Arizona, Auburn University, The Citadel, University of Idaho, University of Illinois, University of Kansas, University of New Mexico, North Carolina State University, Oregon State University, Pennsylvania State University, Purdue University, Southern University and A&M College, SUNY Maritime College, University of South Carolina, University of Texas, University of Utah, University of Washington, or University of Wisconsin) to work full time on a bachelor's degree. They become members of and drill with the NROTC unit. When they complete their degree, they are commissioned as ensigns in the United States Naval Reserve and assigned to initial training for their nuclear officer community. After commissioning, participants incur an active-duty obligation of 5 years.

Number awarded   Varies each year.

Deadline   June of each year.

[307]
NURSE CORPS OPTION OF THE SEAMAN TO ADMIRAL-21 PROGRAM

U.S. Navy
Attn: Commander, Naval Service Training Command
250 Dallas Street, Suite A
Pensacola, FL 32508-5268
(850) 452-9563   Fax: (850) 452-2486
E-mail: PNSC_STA21@navy.mil
Web: www.sta-21.navy.mil/program_options.asp

Summary   To allow outstanding enlisted Navy personnel to attend college, affiliate with an NROTC unit, complete a bachelor's degree, and receive a commission in the Nurse Corps.

Eligibility   This program is open to U.S. citizens who are currently serving on active duty in the U.S. Navy or Naval Reserve, including Full Time Support (FTS), Selected Reserves (SELRES), and Navy Reservists on active duty, except for those on active duty for training (ACDUTRA). Applicants must be high school graduates (or GED recipients) who are able to complete requirements for a baccalaureate degree in nursing in 36 months or less. They must have completed at least 30 semester units in undergraduate nursing prerequisite courses with a GPA of 2.5 or higher. They must be at least 18 years of age and able to complete degree requirements and be commissioned prior to age 42. Within the past 3 years, they must have taken the SAT (and achieved scores of at least 500 on the mathematics section and 500 on the critical reading section) or the ACT (and achieved a score of at least 21 on the mathematics portion and 20 on the English portion).

Financial data   Awardees continue to receive their regular Navy pay and allowances while they attend college on a full-time basis. They also receive reimbursement for tuition, fees, and books up to $10,000 per year. If base housing is available, they are eligible to live there. Participants are not eligible to receive benefits under the Navy's Tuition Assistance Program (TA), the Montgomery GI Bill (MGIB), the Navy College Fund, or the Veterans Educational Assistance Program (VEAP).

Duration   Selectees are supported for up to 36 months of full-time, year-round study or completion of a bachelor's degree, as long as they maintain a GPA of 2.5 or higher.

Additional information   This program began in 2001 as a replacement for the Fleet Accession to Naval Reserve Officer Training Corps (NROTC) Nurse Option. Upon acceptance into the program, selectees attend the Naval Science Institute (NSI) in Newport, Rhode Island for an 8-week program in the fundamental core concepts of being a naval officer (navigation, engineering, weapons, military history and justice, etc.). They then enter an NROTC affiliated college or university with a nursing program that confers an accredited baccalaureate degree in nursing to pursue full-time study. They become members of and drill with the NROTC unit. When they complete their bachelor's degree in nursing, they are commissioned as ensigns in the United States Naval Reserve and assigned to initial training as an officer in the Nurse Corps. After commissioning, 5 years of active service are required.

Number awarded   Varies each year.

Deadline   June of each year.

[308]
OCEANOGRAPHY OPTION OF THE SEAMAN TO ADMIRAL-21 PROGRAM

U.S. Navy
Attn: Commander, Naval Service Training Command
250 Dallas Street, Suite A
Pensacola, FL 32508-5268
(850) 452-9563   Fax: (850) 452-2486
E-mail: PNSC_STA21@navy.mil
Web: www.sta-21.navy.mil/program_options.asp

Summary   To allow outstanding enlisted Navy personnel to attend college, affiliate with an NROTC unit, complete a bachelor's degree, and receive a commission as an oceanography officer.

Eligibility   This program is open to U.S. citizens who are currently serving on active duty in the U.S. Navy or Naval Reserve, including Full Time Support (FTS), Selected Reserves (SELRES), and Navy Reservists on active duty, except for those on active duty for training (ACDUTRA). Applicants must be at least 18 years of age and high school graduates (or GED recipients) who are able to complete requirements for a baccalaureate degree in 36 months or less. They must be planning to work on a degree in physical science, meteorology, or physical oceanography; other related fields may be considered, as long as the applicant possesses strong analytical ability and good communication skills (both oral and written). When they complete their degree requirements, they must be younger than 35 years of age. Within the past 3 years, they must have taken the SAT (and achieved scores of at least 500 on the mathematics section and 500 on the critical reading section) or the ACT (and achieved a score of at least 21 on the mathematics portion and 20 on the English portion).

Financial data Awardees continue to receive their regular Navy pay and allowances while they attend college on a full-time basis. They also receive reimbursement for tuition, fees, and books up to $10,000 per year. If base housing is available, they are eligible to live there. Participants are not eligible to receive benefits under the Navy's Tuition Assistance Program (TA), the Montgomery GI Bill (MGIB), the Navy College Fund, or the Veterans Educational Assistance Program (VEAP).

Duration Selectees are supported for up to 36 months of full-time, year-round study or completion of a bachelor's degree, as long as they maintain a GPA of 2.5 or higher.

Additional information Upon acceptance into the program, selectees attend the Naval Science Institute (NSI) in Newport, Rhode Island for an 8-week program in the fundamental core concepts of being a naval officer (navigation, engineering, weapons, military history and justice, etc.). They then enter a college or university with an NROTC unit or affiliation to work full time on a bachelor's degree. They become members of and drill with the NROTC unit. When they complete their degree, they are commissioned as ensigns in the United States Naval Reserve and assigned to initial training within the oceanography community. After commissioning, 5 years of active service are required.

Number awarded Varies each year.

Deadline June of each year.

[309]
PILOT OPTION OF THE SEAMAN TO ADMIRAL-21 PROGRAM

U.S. Navy
Attn: Commander, Naval Service Training Command
250 Dallas Street, Suite A
Pensacola, FL 32508-5268
(850) 452-9563　　　　　　Fax: (850) 452-2486
E-mail: PNSC_STA21@navy.mil
Web: www.sta-21.navy.mil/program_options.asp

Summary To allow outstanding enlisted Navy personnel to attend college, affiliate with an ROTC unit, complete a bachelor's degree, and receive a commission as a pilot.

Eligibility This program is open to U.S. citizens who are currently serving on active duty in the U.S. Navy or Naval Reserve, including Full Time Support (FTS), Selected Reserves (SELRES), and Navy Reservists on active duty, except for those on active duty for training (ACDUTRA). Applicants must be high school graduates (or GED recipients) who are at least 19 years of age and able to complete requirements for a baccalaureate degree in 36 months or less. When they complete their degree requirements, they must be younger than 27 years of age (may be adjusted to 29 years of age for prior active-duty service). Within the past 3 years, they must have taken the SAT (and achieved scores of at least 500 on the mathematics section and 500 on the critical reading section) or the ACT (and achieved a score of at least 21 on the mathematics portion and 20 on the English portion). They must also achieve a score of at least the following: AQR (4), PFAR (5) on the Pilot Flight Aptitude Rating (PFAR) portions of the Aviation Selection Test Battery.

Financial data Awardees continue to receive their regular Navy pay and allowances while they attend college on a full-time basis. They also receive reimbursement for tuition, fees, and books up to $10,000 per year. If base housing is available, they are eligible to live there. Participants are not eligible to receive benefits under the Navy's Tuition Assistance Program (TA), the Montgomery GI Bill (MGIB), the Navy College Fund, or the Veterans Educational Assistance Program (VEAP).

Duration Selectees are supported for up to 36 months of full-time, year-round study or completion of a bachelor's degree, as long as they maintain a GPA of 2.5 or higher.

Additional information This program began in 2001 as a replacement for the Aviation Enlisted Commissioning Program (AECP). Upon acceptance into the program, selectees attend the Naval Science Institute (NSI) in Newport, Rhode Island for an 8-week program in the fundamental core concepts of being a naval officer (navigation, engineering, weapons, military history and justice, etc.). They then enter a college or university with an NROTC unit or affiliation to work full time on a bachelor's degree. They become members of and drill with the NROTC unit. When they complete their degree, they are commissioned as ensigns in the United States Naval Reserve and assigned to flight training. After commissioning, participants incur an active-duty obligation of 8 years after designation as a Naval Aviator or 6 years from the date of disenrollment from flight training.

Number awarded Varies each year.

Deadline June of each year.

[310]
PISCATAQUA POST SAME SCHOLARSHIPS

Society of American Military Engineers-Piscataqua Post
c/o David Abrahamson, Post Secretary
Weston Solutions
45 Constitution Avenue, Suite 100
Concord, NH 03301
(603) 656-5400　　　　　　Fax: (603) 656-5401
E-mail: samepiscataquapost@gmail.com
Web: same-piscataqua.org/index.php

Summary To provide financial assistance to high school seniors in Maine, Massachusetts, and New Hampshire (especially those interested in joining ROTC or with ties to the military) who are planning to attend college in any state to major in engineering or the physical sciences.

Eligibility This program is open to seniors graduating from high schools in Maine, Massachusetts, or New Hampshire and planning to attend a college or university in any state. Applicants must be interested in majoring in engineering or the physical sciences and enrolling in ROTC, especially if they do not receive an ROTC scholarship. They should be willing to attend meetings of the Society of American Military Engineers (SAME) to share their learning experiences. Preference is given to students who are related to members of the Piscataqua Post of SAME and those whose relatives have prior or current U.S. military service.

Financial data The stipend is $1,500.

Duration 1 year.

Number awarded Up to 2 each year.

Deadline March or June of each year.

[311]
REAR ADMIRAL BENJAMIN T. HACKER, USN MEMORIAL SCHOLARSHIP

National Naval Officers Association-Washington, D.C. Chapter
c/o LCDR Stephen Williams
P.O. Box 30784
Alexandria, VA 22310
(703) 566-3840   Fax: (703) 566-3813
E-mail: Stephen.Williams@navy.mil
Web: dcnnoa.memberlodge.com/page-309002

Summary To provide financial assistance to minority high school seniors from the Washington, D.C. area who are interested in attending an Historically Black College or University (HBCU) in any state and enrolling in the Navy Reserve Officers Training Corps (NROTC) program.

Eligibility This program is open to minority seniors graduating from high schools in the Washington, D.C. metropolitan area who plan to enroll full time at an HBCU in any state that has an NROTC program; they may enroll at another college or university that shares the NROTC unit located at an HBCU. Applicants must have a GPA of 2.5 or higher and be U.S. citizens or permanent residents. Selection is based on academic achievement, community involvement, and financial need.

Financial data The stipend is $1,000.

Duration 1 year; nonrenewable.

Additional information If the recipient fails to enroll in the NROTC unit, all scholarship funds must be returned.

Number awarded 1 each year.

Deadline March of each year.

[312]
ROTC DISTINGUISHED ACHIEVEMENT SCHOLARSHIPS

Armed Forces Communications and Electronics Association
Attn: AFCEA Educational Foundation
4400 Fair Lakes Court
Fairfax, VA 22033-3899
(703) 631-6138   Toll Free: (800) 336-4583, ext. 6138
Fax: (703) 631-4693   E-mail: scholarship@afcea.org
Web: www.afcea.org/education/scholarships/rotc

Summary To provide financial assistance for college to ROTC cadets who demonstrate outstanding leadership performance and academic achievement.

Eligibility This program is open to ROTC cadets enrolled full time at an accredited degree-granting 4-year college or university in the United States. Applicants must be sophomores or juniors at the time of application and have a GPA of 3.0 or higher with a major in an academic discipline. They must be U.S. citizens. Selection is based on demonstrated leadership performance and academic achievement, along with a strong commitment to serve in the U.S. armed forces.

Financial data The stipend is $4,000.

Duration 1 year.

Additional information This program is sponsored by the Congressional Medal of Honor Foundation in partnership with the Armed Forces Communications and Electronics Association (AFCEA) Educational Foundation.

Number awarded 4 each year: 1 each for Army, Navy, Marine Corps, and Air Force ROTC students.

Deadline February of each year.

[313]
SAN ANTONIO POST SAME SCHOLARSHIPS

Society of American Military Engineers-San Antonio Post
Attn: Scholarship Awards Committee
20770 U.S. Highway 281 N, Suite 108
PMB 451
San Antonio, TX 78258-7500
(210) 671-2977   E-mail: david.dentino@us.af.mil
Web: www.same-satx.org

Summary To provide financial assistance to students (especially those participating in ROTC) who are majoring in designated fields at colleges and universities in Texas.

Eligibility This program is open to full-time students majoring in architecture, community planning, construction science or management, engineering, physical science, or a related program at a college or university in Texas. Preference is given to students participating in an ROTC program and planning a career in the U.S. Army, Navy, Marine Corps, Coast Guard, or Air Force. Selection is based on academic achievement, leadership, professionalism, participation in extracurricular activities, and service to university and/or local community. Financial need is not considered, but students receiving a full scholarship from another source are not eligible.

Financial data Stipends range from $2,000 to $5,000.

Duration 1 year; nonrenewable.

Additional information This program includes the following named awards: the General Edwin Jadwin Scholarship, the Brigadier General Hubert O. "Hub" Johnson Scholarship, the Colonel William "Bill" Myers Scholarship, the John Hill Carruth Scholarship, the Larry Martin Small Business Scholarship, and the Thomas Russell Scholarship. Recipients are asked to join the Society of American Military Engineers (SAME) as a student member.

Number awarded Varies each year; recently, this program awarded the 6 named scholarships at $5,000 each and 8 other scholarships at $2,000 to $3,000.

Deadline October of each year.

[314]
SEAMAN TO ADMIRAL-21 CORE PROGRAM

U.S. Navy
Attn: Commander, Naval Service Training Command
250 Dallas Street, Suite A
Pensacola, FL 32508-5268
(850) 452-9563   Fax: (850) 452-2486
E-mail: PNSC_STA21@navy.mil
Web: www.sta-21.navy.mil/program_options.asp

Summary To allow outstanding enlisted Navy personnel to attend college, affiliate with an NROTC unit, complete a bachelor's degree, and receive a commission.

Eligibility This program is open to U.S. citizens who are currently serving on active duty in the U.S. Navy or Naval Reserve, including Full Time Support (FTS), Selected Reserves (SELRES), and Navy Reservists on active duty, except for those on active duty for training (ACDUTRA). Applicants must be high school graduates (or GED recipients) who are able to complete requirements for a baccalaureate degree in 36 months or less. They may apply to the core program or a target group option. The core program allows participants the most flexibility in selecting a major and requesting schools to attend. When they complete their degree requirements, they must be younger than 31 years of age. Within the past 3 years, they must have taken the SAT (and achieved scores of at least 500 on the mathematics section and 500 on the critical reading section) or the ACT (and achieved a score of at least 21 on the mathematics portion and 20 on the English portion).

Financial data Awardees continue to receive their regular Navy pay and allowances while they attend college on a full-time basis. They also receive reimbursement for tuition, fees, and books up to $10,000 per year. If base housing is available, they are eligible to live there. Participants are not eligible to receive benefits under the Navy's Tuition Assistance Program (TA), the Montgomery GI Bill (MGIB), the Navy College Fund, or the Veterans Educational Assistance Program (VEAP).

Duration Selectees are supported for up to 36 months of full-time, year-round study or completion of a bachelor's degree, as long as they maintain a GPA of 2.5 or higher.

Additional information This program began in 2001 as a replacement for the Seaman to Admiral Program (established in 1994), the Enlisted Commissioning Program, and other specialized programs for sailors to earn a commission. Upon acceptance into the program, selectees attend the Naval Science Institute (NSI) in Newport, Rhode Island for an 8-week program in the fundamental core concepts of being a naval officer (navigation, engineering, weapons, military history and justice, etc.). They then enter a college or university with an NROTC unit or affiliation to work full time on a bachelor's degree. They become members of and drill with the NROTC unit. When core program participants complete their degree, they are commissioned as ensigns in the United States Naval Reserve and assigned to an Unrestricted Line (URL) Navy officer designator upon commissioning. After commissioning, 5 years of active service are required.

Number awarded Varies each year.

Deadline June of each year.

[315]
SFC CURTIS MANCINI MEMORIAL SCHOLARSHIPS

Association of the United States Army-Rhode Island
  Chapter
c/o CSM (Ret) Anthony Ferri, Secretary
47 Spokane Street
Providence, RI 02904
(401) 861-2997   E-mail: afnf458673755@aol.com
Web: www.ausari.org/index.html

Summary To provide financial assistance to members of the Rhode Island Chapter of the Association of the United States Army (AUSA) and their families who are interested in attending college or graduate school in any state.

Eligibility This program is open to members of the AUSA Rhode Island Chapter and their family members (spouses, children, and grandchildren). Applicants must be high school seniors or graduates accepted at an accredited college, university, or vocational/technical school in any state or current undergraduate or graduate students. Along with their application, they must submit a 250-word essay on why they feel their achievements should qualify them for this award. Selection is based on academic and individual achievements;

financial need is not considered. Membership in AUSA is open to current and retired Army personnel (including Reserves and National Guard), ROTC cadets, or civilian employees of the Army.

Financial data The stipend is $1,000.

Duration 1 year.

Number awarded 2 each year.

Deadline March of each year.

[316]
SIMULTANEOUS MEMBERSHIP PROGRAM (SMP)

U.S. Army
Attn: U.S. Army Cadet Command
G2 Incentives Division
1307 Third Avenue
Fort Knox, KY 40121-2725
(502) 624-7371   Toll Free: (888) 550-ARMY
Fax: (502) 624-6937   E-mail: train2lead@usacc.army.mil
Web: www.goarmy.com/rotc/enroll/enlisted.html

Summary To provide financial assistance to individuals who serve simultaneously in the Army National Guard or Army Reserve and the Army Reserve Officers' Training Corps (ROTC) while they are in college.

Eligibility Students who are members of the Army National Guard or the Army Reserve and Army ROTC at the same time are eligible for this assistance. Applicants must have completed basic training or the equivalent, have at least 4 years remaining on their current military obligation, be full-time college juniors, have a GPA of 2.0 or higher, and be U.S. citizens.

Financial data Advanced ROTC Simultaneous Membership Program (SMP) participants are paid at the rate of at least a Sergeant E-5 for their Guard or Reserve training assemblies (recently, $290 to $340 per month, depending on the number of years of service), plus an ROTC stipend for 10 months of the year at $450 per month during their junior year and $500 per month during their senior year.

Duration Up to 2 years.

Additional information Participants serve as officer trainees in their Guard or Reserve units and, under the close supervision of a commissioned officer, perform duties commensurate with those of a second lieutenant. Cadets who successfully complete the SMP program graduate with a commission as a second lieutenant. Once commissioned, they may continue to serve in their Guard or Reserve units, or they may apply for active duty in the U.S. Army.

Number awarded Varies each year.

Deadline Deadline not specified.

[317]
SPECIAL DUTY OFFICER (INFORMATION WARFARE) OPTION OF THE SEAMAN TO ADMIRAL-21 PROGRAM

U.S. Navy
Attn: Commander, Naval Service Training Command
250 Dallas Street, Suite A
Pensacola, FL 32508-5268
(850) 452-9563   Fax: (850) 452-2486
E-mail: PNSC_STA21@navy.mil
Web: www.sta-21.navy.mil/program_options.asp

Summary To allow outstanding enlisted Navy personnel to attend college, affiliate with an NROTC unit, complete a bachelor's degree, and receive a commission as a special duty officer (information warfare).

Eligibility   This program is open to U.S. citizens who are currently serving on active duty in the U.S. Navy or Naval Reserve, including Full Time Support (FTS), Selected Reserves (SELRES), and Navy Reservists on active duty, except for those on active duty for training (ACDUTRA). Applicants must be high school graduates (or GED recipients) who are at least 18 years of age and able to complete requirements for a baccalaureate degree in 36 months or less. Sailors in all ratings are eligible, but preference is given to cryptologic technicians, intelligence specialists, and information professionals. When they complete their degree requirements, they must be younger than 35 years of age. Within the past 3 years, they must have taken the SAT (and achieved scores of at least 500 on the mathematics section and 500 on the critical reading section) or the ACT (and achieved a score of at least 21 on the mathematics portion and 20 on the English portion). They must also meet relevant medical standards. Although technical degrees are preferred, the program does not specify required majors; instead, it seeks officers who possess strong analytical ability and communication skills (both oral and written).

Financial data   Awardees continue to receive their regular Navy pay and allowances while they attend college on a full-time basis. They also receive reimbursement for tuition, fees, and books up to $10,000 per year. If base housing is available, they are eligible to live there. Participants are not eligible to receive benefits under the Navy's Tuition Assistance Program (TA), the Montgomery GI Bill (MGIB), the Navy College Fund, or the Veterans Educational Assistance Program (VEAP).

Duration   Selectees are supported for up to 36 months of full-time, year-round study or completion of a bachelor's degree, as long as they maintain a GPA of 2.5 or higher.

Additional information   This program began in 2001 as a replacement for the Seaman to Admiral Program (established in 1994), the Enlisted Commissioning Program, and other specialized programs for sailors to earn a commission. Upon acceptance into the program, selectees attend the Naval Science Institute (NSI) in Newport, Rhode Island for an 8-week program in the fundamental core concepts of being a naval officer (navigation, engineering, weapons, military history and justice, etc.). They then enter a college or university with an NROTC unit or affiliation to work full time on a bachelor's degree. They become members of and drill with the NROTC unit. When they complete their degree, they are commissioned as ensigns in the United States Naval Reserve and assigned to initial training as a special duty officer (information warfare); that designation was formerly special duty officer (cryptologic). After commissioning, 5 years of active service are required.

Number awarded   Varies each year.
Deadline   June of each year.

[318]
SPECIAL DUTY OFFICER (INTELLIGENCE) OPTION OF THE SEAMAN TO ADMIRAL-21 PROGRAM
U.S. Navy
Attn: Commander, Naval Service Training Command
250 Dallas Street, Suite A
Pensacola, FL 32508-5268
(850) 452-9563   Fax: (850) 452-2486
E-mail: PNSC_STA21@navy.mil
Web: www.sta-21.navy.mil/program_options.asp

Summary   To allow outstanding enlisted Navy personnel to attend college, affiliate with an NROTC unit, complete a bachelor's degree, and receive a commission as a special duty officer (intelligence).

Eligibility   This program is open to U.S. citizens who are currently serving on active duty in the U.S. Navy or Naval Reserve, including Full Time Support (FTS), Selected Reserves (SELRES), and Navy Reservists on active duty, except for those on active duty for training (ACDUTRA). Applicants must be high school graduates (or GED recipients) who are at least 18 years of age and able to complete requirements for a baccalaureate degree in 36 months or less. They may currently have any rating. When they complete their degree requirements, they must be younger than 35 years of age. Within the past 3 years, they must have taken the SAT (and achieved scores of at least 500 on the mathematics section and 500 on the critical reading section) or the ACT (and achieved a score of at least 21 on the mathematics portion and 20 on the English portion). They must also meet relevant medical standards. Although technical degrees are preferred, the program does not specify required majors; instead, it seeks officers who possess strong analytical ability and communication skills (both oral and written).

Financial data   Awardees continue to receive their regular Navy pay and allowances while they attend college on a full-time basis. They also receive reimbursement for tuition, fees, and books up to $10,000 per year. If base housing is available, they are eligible to live there. Participants are not eligible to receive benefits under the Navy's Tuition Assistance Program (TA), the Montgomery GI Bill (MGIB), the Navy College Fund, or the Veterans Educational Assistance Program (VEAP).

Duration   Selectees are supported for up to 36 months of full-time, year-round study or completion of a bachelor's degree, as long as they maintain a GPA of 2.5 or higher.

Additional information   This program began in 2001 as a replacement for the Seaman to Admiral Program (established in 1994), the Enlisted Commissioning Program, and other specialized programs for sailors to earn a commission. Upon acceptance into the program, selectees attend the Naval Science Institute (NSI) in Newport, Rhode Island for an 8-week program in the fundamental core concepts of being a naval officer (navigation, engineering, weapons, military history and justice, etc.). They then enter a college or university with an NROTC unit or affiliation to work full time on a bachelor's degree. They become members of and drill with the NROTC unit. When they complete their degree, they are commissioned as ensigns in the United States Naval Reserve and assigned to initial training as a special duty officer (intelligence). After commissioning, 5 years of active service are required.

Number awarded   Varies each year.

Deadline   June of each year.

[319]
SPECIAL WARFARE OPTION OF THE SEAMAN TO ADMIRAL-21 PROGRAM

U.S. Navy
Attn: Commander, Naval Service Training Command
250 Dallas Street, Suite A
Pensacola, FL 32508-5268
(850) 452-9563   Fax: (850) 452-2486
E-mail: PNSC_STA21@navy.mil
Web: www.sta-21.navy.mil/program_options.asp

Summary   To allow outstanding enlisted Navy personnel to attend college, affiliate with an NROTC unit, complete a bachelor's degree, and receive a commission as a special warfare officer.

Eligibility   This program is open to U.S. citizens who are currently serving on active duty in the U.S. Navy or Naval Reserve, including Full Time Support (FTS), Selected Reserves (SELRES), and Navy Reservists on active duty, except for those on active duty for training (ACDUTRA). Only males are eligible for this option. They must be a member of the SEAL community. Applicants must be high school graduates (or GED recipients) who are able to complete requirements for a baccalaureate degree in 36 months or less. When they complete their degree requirements, they must be younger than 29 years of age. That age limitation may be adjusted upward for active service on a month-for-month basis up to 24 months, and waivers are considered for enlisted personnel who possess particularly exceptional qualifications if they can complete their degree prior to their 35th birthday. Within the past 3 years, they must have taken the SAT (and achieved scores of at least 500 on the mathematics section and 500 on the critical reading section) or the ACT (and achieved a score of at least 21 on the mathematics portion and 20 on the English portion). They must also meet physical regulations that include qualification for diving duty and/or combat swimmer. Preference is given to applicants who plan to major in a technical field (e.g., chemistry, computer science, engineering, mathematics, oceanography, operations analysis, physical sciences, or physics).

Financial data   Awardees continue to receive their regular Navy pay and allowances while they attend college on a full-time basis. They also receive reimbursement for tuition, fees, and books up to $10,000 per year. If base housing is available, they are eligible to live there. Participants are not eligible to receive benefits under the Navy's Tuition Assistance Program (TA), the Montgomery GI Bill (MGIB), the Navy College Fund, or the Veterans Educational Assistance Program (VEAP).

Duration   Selectees are supported for up to 36 months of full-time, year-round study or completion of a bachelor's degree, as long as they maintain a GPA of 2.5 or higher.

Additional information   This program began in 2001 as a replacement for the Seaman to Admiral Program (established in 1994), the Enlisted Commissioning Program, and other specialized programs for sailors to earn a commission. Upon acceptance into the program, selectees attend the Naval Science Institute (NSI) in Newport, Rhode Island for an 8-week program in the fundamental core concepts of being a naval officer (navigation, engineering, weapons, military history and justice, etc.). They then enter a college or university with an NROTC unit or affiliation to work full time on a bachelor's degree. They become members of and drill with the NROTC unit. When they complete their degree, they are commissioned as ensigns in the United States Naval Reserve and assigned to initial training as a special warfare officer. After commissioning, 5 years of active service are required.

Number awarded   Varies each year.

Deadline   June of each year.

[320]
SUPPLY CORPS OPTION OF THE SEAMAN TO ADMIRAL-21 PROGRAM

U.S. Navy
Attn: Commander, Naval Service Training Command
250 Dallas Street, Suite A
Pensacola, FL 32508-5268
(850) 452-9563   Fax: (850) 452-2486
E-mail: PNSC_STA21@navy.mil
Web: www.sta-21.navy.mil/program_options.asp

Summary   To allow outstanding enlisted Navy personnel to attend college, affiliate with an NROTC unit, complete a bachelor's degree in business, engineering, or mathematics, and receive a commission in the Supply Corps.

Eligibility   This program is open to U.S. citizens who are currently serving on active duty in the U.S. Navy or Naval Reserve, including Full Time Support (FTS), Selected Reserves (SELRES), and Navy Reservists on active duty, except for those on active duty for training (ACDUTRA). Applicants must be high school graduates (or GED recipients) who are able to complete requirements for a baccalaureate degree in a business, engineering, or mathematics related field in 36 months or less. When they complete their degree requirements, they must be younger than 31 years of age. Within the past 3 years, they must have taken the SAT (and achieved scores of at least 500 on the mathematics section and 500 on the critical reading section) or the ACT (and achieved a score of at least 21 on the mathematics portion and 20 on the English portion).

Financial data   Awardees continue to receive their regular Navy pay and allowances while they attend college on a full-time basis. They also receive reimbursement for tuition, fees, and books up to $10,000 per year. If base housing is available, they are eligible to live there. Participants are not eligible to receive benefits under the Navy's Tuition Assistance Program (TA), the Montgomery GI Bill (MGIB), the Navy College Fund, or the Veterans Educational Assistance Program (VEAP).

Duration   Selectees are supported for up to 36 months of full-time, year-round study or completion of a bachelor's degree, as long as they maintain a GPA of 2.5 or higher.

Additional information   This program began in 2001 as a replacement for the Seaman to Admiral Program (established in 1994), the Enlisted Commissioning Program, and other specialized programs for sailors to earn a commission. Upon acceptance into the program, selectees attend the Naval Science Institute (NSI) in Newport, Rhode Island for an 8-week program in the fundamental core concepts of being a naval officer (navigation, engineering, weapons, military history and justice, etc.). They then enter a college or university with an NROTC unit or affiliation to work full time on a bachelor's degree. They become members of and drill with the NROTC unit. When they complete their degree, they are commissioned as ensigns in the United States Naval Reserve and assigned to initial training as an officer in the Supply Corps. After commissioning, 5 years of active service are required.

Number awarded Varies each year.

Deadline June of each year.

[321]
SURFACE WARFARE OFFICER/ENGINEER OPTION OF THE SEAMAN TO ADMIRAL-21 PROGRAM

U.S. Navy
Attn: Commander, Naval Service Training Command
250 Dallas Street, Suite A
Pensacola, FL 32508-5268
(850) 452-9563   Fax: (850) 452-2486
E-mail: PNSC_STA21@navy.mil
Web: www.sta-21.navy.mil/program_options.asp

Summary To allow outstanding enlisted Navy personnel to attend college, affiliate with an NROTC unit, complete a bachelor's degree, and receive a commission as a surface warfare officer/engineer.

Eligibility This program is open to U.S. citizens who are currently serving on active duty in the U.S. Navy or Naval Reserve, including Full Time Support (FTS), Selected Reserves (SELRES), and Navy Reservists on active duty, except for those on active duty for training (ACDUTRA). Applicants must be high school graduates (or GED recipients) who are able to complete requirements for a baccalaureate degree in 36 months or less. When they complete their degree requirements, they must be younger than 35 years of age. Within the past 3 years, they must have taken the SAT (and achieved scores of at least 500 on the mathematics section and 500 on the critical reading section) or the ACT (and achieved a score of at least 21 on the mathematics portion and 20 on the English portion). They must also pass relevant medical standards. No specific academic major is required, but applicants are encouraged to work on a technical degree in engineering or physical science.

Financial data Awardees continue to receive their regular Navy pay and allowances while they attend college on a full-time basis. They also receive reimbursement for tuition, fees, and books up to $10,000 per year. If base housing is available, they are eligible to live there. Participants are not eligible to receive benefits under the Navy's Tuition Assistance Program (TA), the Montgomery GI Bill (MGIB), the Navy College Fund, or the Veterans Educational Assistance Program (VEAP).

Duration Selectees are supported for up to 36 months of full-time, year-round study or completion of a bachelor's degree, as long as they maintain a GPA of 2.5 or higher.

Additional information Upon acceptance into the program, selectees attend the Naval Science Institute (NSI) in Newport, Rhode Island for an 8-week program in the fundamental core concepts of being a naval officer (navigation, engineering, weapons, military history and justice, etc.). They then enter a college or university with an NROTC unit or affiliation to work full time on a bachelor's degree. They become members of and drill with the NROTC unit. When they complete their degree, they are commissioned as ensigns in the United States Naval Reserve and assigned to initial training as a special duty officer (engineering duty). After commissioning, 5 years of active service are required.

Number awarded Varies each year.

Deadline June of each year.

[322]
SURFACE WARFARE OFFICER/INFORMATION PROFESSIONAL OPTION OF THE SEAMAN TO ADMIRAL-21 PROGRAM

U.S. Navy
Attn: Commander, Naval Service Training Command
250 Dallas Street, Suite A
Pensacola, FL 32508-5268
(850) 452-9563   Fax: (850) 452-2486
E-mail: PNSC_STA21@navy.mil
Web: www.sta-21.navy.mil/program_options.asp

Summary To allow outstanding enlisted Navy personnel to attend college, affiliate with an ROTC unit, complete a bachelor's degree, and receive a commission as a surface warfare officer/information professional (SWO/IP).

Eligibility This program is open to U.S. citizens who are currently serving on active duty in the U.S. Navy or Naval Reserve, including Full Time Support (FTS), Selected Reserves (SELRES), and Navy Reservists on active duty, except for those on active duty for training (ACDUTRA). Applicants must be high school graduates (or GED recipients) who are able to complete requirements for a baccalaureate degree in 36 months or less. When they complete their degree requirements, they must be younger than 28 years of age. Within the past 3 years, they must have taken the SAT (and achieved scores of at least 500 on the mathematics section and 500 on the critical reading section) or the ACT (and achieved a score of at least 21 on the mathematics portion and 20 on the English portion). They must also pass relevant medical standards. No specific academic major is required, but applicants are encouraged to work on a technical degree in computer science, computer or electrical engineering, mathematics, physics, information systems, or operations.

Financial data Awardees continue to receive their regular Navy pay and allowances while they attend college on a full-time basis. They also receive reimbursement for tuition, fees, and books up to $10,000 per year. If base housing is available, they are eligible to live there. Participants are not eligible to receive benefits under the Navy's Tuition Assistance Program (TA), the Montgomery GI Bill (MGIB), the Navy College Fund, or the Veterans Educational Assistance Program (VEAP).

Duration Selectees are supported for up to 36 months of full-time, year-round study or completion of a bachelor's degree, as long as they maintain a GPA of 2.5 or higher.

Additional information Upon acceptance into the program, selectees attend the Naval Science Institute (NSI) in Newport, Rhode Island for an 8-week program in the fundamental core concepts of being a naval officer (navigation, engineering, weapons, military history and justice, etc.). They then enter a college or university with an NROTC unit or affiliation to work full time on a bachelor's degree. They become members of and drill with the NROTC unit. When they complete their degree, they are commissioned as ensigns in the United States Naval Reserve and assigned to initial training as a special duty officer (information professional). After commissioning, 5 years of active service are required.

Number awarded Varies each year.

Deadline June of each year.

[323]
SURFACE WARFARE OFFICER/OCEANOGRAPHY OPTION OF THE SEAMAN TO ADMIRAL-21 PROGRAM

U.S. Navy
Attn: Commander, Naval Service Training Command
250 Dallas Street, Suite A
Pensacola, FL 32508-5268
(850) 452-9563   Fax: (850) 452-2486
E-mail: PNSC_STA21@navy.mil
Web: www.sta-21.navy.mil/program_options.asp

Summary To allow outstanding enlisted Navy personnel to attend college, affiliate with an NROTC unit, complete a bachelor's degree, and receive a commission as a surface warfare officer/oceanography.

Eligibility This program is open to U.S. citizens who are currently serving on active duty in the U.S. Navy or Naval Reserve, including Full Time Support (FTS), Selected Reserves (SELRES), and Navy Reservists on active duty, except for those on active duty for training (ACDUTRA). Applicants must be high school graduates (or GED recipients) who are able to complete requirements for a baccalaureate degree in 36 months or less. They must be planning to work on a technical degree in chemistry, computer science, engineering, geospatial information systems, hydrography, marine science, mathematics, meteorology, oceanography, operational analysis, physical sciences, or physics. When they complete their degree requirements, they must be younger than 31 years of age. Within the past 3 years, they must have taken the SAT (and achieved scores of at least 500 on the mathematics section and 500 on the critical reading section) or the ACT (and achieved a score of at least 21 on the mathematics portion and 20 on the English portion). They must also pass relevant medical standards.

Financial data Awardees continue to receive their regular Navy pay and allowances while they attend college on a full-time basis. They also receive reimbursement for tuition, fees, and books up to $10,000 per year. If base housing is available, they are eligible to live there. Participants are not eligible to receive benefits under the Navy's Tuition Assistance Program (TA), the Montgomery GI Bill (MGIB), the Navy College Fund, or the Veterans Educational Assistance Program (VEAP).

Duration Selectees are supported for up to 36 months of full-time, year-round study or completion of a bachelor's degree, as long as they maintain a GPA of 2.5 or higher.

Additional information Upon acceptance into the program, selectees attend the Naval Science Institute (NSI) in Newport, Rhode Island for an 8-week program in the fundamental core concepts of being a naval officer (navigation, engineering, weapons, military history and justice, etc.). They then enter a college or university with an NROTC unit or affiliation to work full time on a bachelor's degree. They become members of and drill with the NROTC unit. When they complete their degree, they are commissioned as ensigns in the United States Naval Reserve and assigned to initial training as a special duty officer (oceanography). After commissioning, 5 years of active service are required.

Number awarded Varies each year.

Deadline June of each year.

[324]
SURFACE WARFARE OFFICER OPTION OF THE SEAMAN TO ADMIRAL-21 PROGRAM

U.S. Navy
Attn: Commander, Naval Service Training Command
250 Dallas Street, Suite A
Pensacola, FL 32508-5268
(850) 452-9563   Fax: (850) 452-2486
E-mail: PNSC_STA21@navy.mil
Web: www.sta-21.navy.mil/program_options.asp

Summary To allow outstanding enlisted Navy personnel to attend college, affiliate with an NROTC unit, complete a bachelor's degree, and receive a commission as a surface warfare officer (SWO).

Eligibility This program is open to U.S. citizens who are currently serving on active duty in the U.S. Navy or Naval Reserve, including Full Time Support (FTS), Selected Reserves (SELRES), and Navy Reservists on active duty, except for those on active duty for training (ACDUTRA). Applicants must be high school graduates (or GED recipients) who are able to complete requirements for a baccalaureate degree in 36 months or less. When they complete their degree requirements, they must be younger than 31 years of age. Within the past 3 years, they must have taken the SAT (and achieved scores of at least 500 on the mathematics section and 500 on the critical reading section) or the ACT (and achieved a score of at least 21 on the mathematics portion and 20 on the English portion). They must also meet relevant medical standards. Preference is given to applicants who plan to major in a technical field (e.g., chemistry, computer science, engineering, mathematics, oceanography, operations analysis, physical sciences, or physics).

Financial data Awardees continue to receive their regular Navy pay and allowances while they attend college on a full-time basis. They also receive reimbursement for tuition, fees, and books up to $10,000 per year. If base housing is available, they are eligible to live there. Participants are not eligible to receive benefits under the Navy's Tuition Assistance Program (TA), the Montgomery GI Bill (MGIB), the Navy College Fund, or the Veterans Educational Assistance Program (VEAP).

Duration Selectees are supported for up to 36 months of full-time, year-round study or completion of a bachelor's degree, as long as they maintain a GPA of 2.5 or higher.

Additional information This program began in 2001 as a replacement for the Seaman to Admiral Program (established in 1994), the Enlisted Commissioning Program, and other specialized programs for sailors to earn a commission. Upon acceptance into the program, selectees attend the Naval Science Institute (NSI) in Newport, Rhode Island for an 8-week program in the fundamental core concepts of being a naval officer (navigation, engineering, weapons, military history and justice, etc.). They then enter a college or university with an NROTC unit or affiliation to work full time on a bachelor's degree. They become members of and drill with the NROTC unit. When they complete their degree, they are commissioned as ensigns in the United States Naval Reserve and assigned to initial training as a surface warfare officer. After commissioning, 5 years of active service are required.

Number awarded Varies each year.

Deadline June of each year.

[325]
TEXAS ARMED SERVICES SCHOLARSHIP PROGRAM

Texas Higher Education Coordinating Board
Attn: Grants and Special Programs
1200 East Anderson Lane
P.O. Box 12788
Austin, TX 78711-2788
(512) 427-6340   Toll Free: (800) 242-3062
Fax: (512) 427-6420   E-mail: grantinfo@thecb.state.tx.us
Web: www.collegeforalltexans.com

Summary To provide scholarship/loans to high school seniors in Texas who plan to participate in an ROTC program at a college in the state and then serve in the U.S. armed forces, the Texas National Guard, or the Texas Air National Guard.

Eligibility This program is open to seniors graduating from high schools in Texas who can meet any 2 of the following requirements: 1) are on track to graduate with the Distinguished Achievement Program (DAP) or International Baccalaureate (IB) Program; 2) have a high school GPA of 3.0 or higher; 3) have an SAT score of 1590 or higher or an ACT score of 23 or higher; or 4) rank in the top third of their class. Applicants must plan to attend a public or private college or university in Texas and enter into a written agreement to complete 4 years of ROTC training, graduate within 5 years, and serve 4 years as a member of the Texas Army or Air Force National Guard or as a commissioned officer in the U.S. armed services. They must apply through their state senator or representative.

Financial data The current stipend is $10,000 per year. If recipients fail to fulfill their service agreement, they must repay all funds received.

Duration 1 year; may be renewed up to 3 additional years.

Additional information This program began in 2010.

Number awarded Up to 185 each year.

Deadline Legislators must submit nominations by August of each year.

[326]
USS LITTLE ROCK ASSOCIATION NROTC SCHOLARSHIP PROGRAM

USS Little Rock Association
c/o LCDR Robert M. Baker, USN (Retired), Scholarship
  Committee Chair
18426 Mount Lock Hill Road
Sharpsburg, MD 21782-2029
(301) 799-9089   E-mail: rmbusnret@gmail.com
Web: www.usslittlerock.org/scholarship.html

Summary To provide financial assistance to Naval ROTC midshipmen in college who have a personal or family connection to the sea services or are members of the USS Little Rock Association.

Eligibility This program is open to students entering their third academic year of an NROTC program (scholarship, college program, Marine Enlisted Commissioning Program, or Seaman to Admiral). Applicants must 1) be the children or direct descendants of active, retired, or honorably discharged members of the sea services (U.S. Navy, U.S. Marine Corps, or U.S. Coast Guard) or their Reserve components; 2) themselves be serving or have served in any of the regular or Reserve sea services; or 3) have been Junior Associate members of the USS Little Rock Association for at least 2 years. They must have a GPA of 3.0 or higher and have demonstrated superior leadership qualities and aptitude for service in all of their NROTC activities. Along with their application, they must submit a 500-word letter describing why they consider themselves worthy of the award.

Financial data The stipend is $1,000 per year.

Duration 1 year; may be renewed 1 additional year.

Additional information This program began in 2001.

Number awarded 1 or 2 each year.

Deadline May of each year.

[327]
VIRGINIA PENINSULA POST SAME SCHOLARSHIPS

Society of American Military Engineers-Virginia Peninsula
  Post
c/o James H. King, Jr., Scholarship Chair
129 Andrews Street, Suite 217
Hampton, VA 23665
(757) 764-7570   Fax: (757) 764-3439
E-mail: james.king.45@us.af.mil

Summary To provide financial assistance to high school seniors, undergraduates, and graduate students entering or enrolled at universities in Virginia who have a tie to the Virginia Peninsula Post of the Society of American Military Engineers (SAME) and are majoring in engineering or architecture.

Eligibility This program is open to 1) high school seniors planning to enroll in an engineering or architecture program at an accredited college or university in Virginia; 2) students enrolled as freshmen through graduate students at an accredited college or university in Virginia and working on a bachelor's or higher degree in engineering or architecture; and 3) members and dependents of members of the SAME Virginia Peninsula Post. Applicants must have demonstrated commitment to future military service by enrolling in an ROTC program, a commissioning program, or an extended enlistment. Selection is based on academic standing and accomplishments (50%), involvement in university and community programs, including those with military involvement (30%), and financial need (20%).

Financial data The stipend is $1,500.

Duration 1 year.

Number awarded 4 each year: 1 to a high school senior, 1 to a college freshman or sophomore, 1 to a college junior or senior, and 1 to a graduate student.

Deadline February of each year.

[328]
WASHINGTON ADMIRAL'S FUND SCHOLARSHIP

National Naval Officers Association-Washington, D.C.
  Chapter
c/o LCDR Stephen Williams
P.O. Box 30784
Alexandria, VA 22310
(703) 566-3840   Fax: (703) 566-3813
E-mail: Stephen.Williams@navy.mil
Web: dcnnoa.memberlodge.com/page-309002

Summary To provide financial assistance to minority high school seniors from the Washington, D.C. area who are interested in attending a college or university in any state and enrolling in the Navy Reserve Officers Training Corps (NROTC) program.

Eligibility This program is open to minority seniors graduating from high schools in the Washington, D.C. metropolitan area who plan to enroll full time at an accredited 2- or 4-year college or university in any state. Applicants must be planning to enroll in the NROTC program. They must have a GPA of 2.5 or higher and be U.S. citizens or permanent residents. Selection is based on academic achievement, community involvement, and financial need.

Financial data The stipend is $1,000.

Duration 1 year; nonrenewable.

Additional information If the recipient fails to enroll in the NROTC unit, all scholarship funds must be returned.

Number awarded 1 each year.

Deadline March of each year.

Military Family Members

[329]
100TH INFANTRY BATTALION MEMORIAL SCHOLARSHIP FUND

Hawai'i Community Foundation
Attn: Scholarship Department
827 Fort Street Mall
Honolulu, HI 96813
(808) 566-5570   Toll Free: (888) 731-3863
Fax: (808) 521-6286
E-mail: scholarships@hcf-hawaii.org
Web: www.hawaiicommunityfoundation.org/scholarships

Summary To provide financial assistance for college or graduate school to descendants of 100th Infantry Battalion World War II veterans.

Eligibility This program is open to entering and continuing full-time undergraduate and graduate students at 2- and 4-year colleges and universities. Applicants must be a direct descendant of a World War II veteran of the 100th Infantry Battalion (which was comprised of Americans of Japanese descent). They must be able to demonstrate academic achievement (GPA of 3.5 or higher), an active record of extracurricular activities and community service, a willingness to promote the legacy of the 100th Infantry Battalion of World War II, and financial need. Along with their application, they must submit a short statement indicating their reasons for attending college, their planned course of study, their career goals, and what community service means to them. They must also submit a separate essay on the legacy of the 100th Infantry Battalion and how they will contribute to forwarding that legacy. Current residency in Hawaii is not required.

Financial data The amounts of the awards depend on the availability of funds and the need of the recipient. Recently, the average value of each of the scholarships awarded by the foundation was $2,200.

Duration 1 year.

Number awarded Varies each year; recently, 2 were awarded.

Deadline February of each year.

[330]
10TH MOUNTAIN DIVISION DESCENDANT MERIT SCHOLARSHIP

10th Mountain Division Descendants, Inc.
c/o Patricia Ann Thornton
112 Maple Avenue
Bala Cynwyd, PA 19004
E-mail: pthornton@gmail.com
Web: www.10thmtndivdesc.org/scholarship.html

Summary To provide financial assistance for college to descendants of former members of the 10th Mountain Division.

Eligibility This program is open to the descendants of veterans who served in the 10th Mountain Division during World War II. Applicants must be entering their first year of college. Selection is based on service to the World War II 10th Mountain Division by completing a project dedicated to or for the division. Financial need is not considered.

Financial data The stipend is $1,000.

Duration 1 year.

Number awarded 1 each year.

Deadline April each year.

[331]
10TH MOUNTAIN DIVISION (LIGHT INFANTRY) SCHOLARSHIPS

Northern New York Community Foundation, Inc.
120 Washington Street, Suite 400
Watertown, NY 13601
(315) 782-7110   Fax: (315) 782-0047
E-mail: info@nnycf.org
Web: www.nnycf.org/scholarships.asp?mm=6

Summary To provide financial assistance for college to current and former members of the 10th Mountain Division and their dependents.

Eligibility This program is open to current and former members of the 10th Mountain Division and their dependents (children and spouses). Applicants must be high school seniors applying for the freshmen year or traditional or nontraditional students enrolled as full-time undergraduates in any year of college or technical school. Along with their application, they must submit a 150-word essay on the character traits that have contributed the most to their success, how they have contributed to their success, and how each will contribute to their vision of a successful life. High school juniors who will graduate early because they are in an advanced placement program may also apply. Interviews are required. Selection is based on academic achievement, personal data, and financial need.

Financial data The stipend is $5,000.

Duration 1 year.

Number awarded Varies each year; recently, 8 were awarded.

Deadline March of each year.

[332]
11TH ARMORED CAVALRY VETERANS OF VIETNAM AND CAMBODIA SCHOLARSHIP

11th Armored Cavalry Veterans of Vietnam and
Cambodia
Attn: National Headquarters
P.O. Box 956
Coffeyville, TX 76034-0956
Web: www.11thcavnam.com/scholarship/scholar.html

Summary To provide financial assistance for college or graduate school to members of the 11th Armored Cavalry Veterans of Vietnam and Cambodia (11ACVVC) and to their children.

Eligibility This program is open to 1) current members of the 11ACVVC; 2) children and stepchildren of current members of the 11ACVVC; 3) children whose legal guardian is a current member of the 11ACVVC; 4) children of 11th Armored Cavalry troopers who were killed in action, died of wounds, or died as a result of service in Vietnam or Cambodia; and 5) children and stepchildren of 11th Armored Cavalry Regiment veterans who served in Vietnam or Cambodia but are not members of the 11ACVVC. There is no age limit. Applicants must be enrolled or planning to enroll as an undergraduate or graduate student. Along with their application, they must submit brief essays on 1) the field of study they plan to enter and why; and 2) why they would be a worthy recipient of this scholarship. Selection is based on those essays (15 points), completeness and legibility of the application (7 points), and grades (8 points); financial need is not considered.

Financial data The stipend is $4,000; funds are paid directly to the recipient's school, in 2 equal installments.

Duration 1 year; nonrenewable.

Additional information This program began in 1997. Recipients must use the awarded money within 44 months of being notified.

Number awarded Up to 24 each year. Since the program was established, it has awarded more than $1 million in scholarships.

Deadline May of each year.

[333]
25TH INFANTRY DIVISION ASSOCIATION EDUCATIONAL MEMORIAL SCHOLARSHIP AWARD

25th Infantry Division Association
P.O. Box 7
Flourtown, PA 19031-0007
E-mail: TropicLtn@aol.com
Web: www.25thida.org/association/scholarships

Summary To provide financial assistance for college to descendants of members of the 25th Infantry Division Association and of deceased members of the 25th Infantry Division.

Eligibility This program is open to 1) children and grandchildren of active members of the association; and 2) children of former members of the division deceased during active combat with the division or as a result of it. Applicants must be enrolling in the freshman year of an accredited 4-year college or university, junior college, or trade school and intending to work toward a baccalaureate degree by enrolling in at least 12 semester hours of study each semester. They must submit 1) a personal letter describing the reasons for their request,

future plans, school interests and activities, and financial situation; 2) a transcript of high school credits; 3) their most recent ACT or SAT scores; 4) 3 letters of recommendation; 5) a letter of acceptance from the institution they plan to attend; and 6) a photograph.

Financial data Stipends up to $1,500 are available.

Duration Each grant is a 1-time award, which may be spent over any period of time.

Additional information This program includes the George and Rosemary Murray Scholarship Award.

Number awarded Varies each year.

Deadline February of each year.

[334]
37TH DIVISION VETERANS SCHOLARSHIP GRANT

37th Division Veterans Association
35 East Chestnut Street, Suite 512
Columbus, OH 43215
(614) 228-3788   Fax: (614) 228-3793
E-mail: mandy@37thdva.org
Web: www.37thdva.org/scholarship_grants

Summary To provide financial assistance for college to members of the 37th Division Veterans Association and their descendants.

Eligibility This program is open to veterans and descendants of veterans who served honorably with a unit of the 37th Infantry Division until its deactivation in 1968. The veteran must be an active or life member of the association or, if deceased, must have been a member at the time of his death. Applicants may be seniors in high school or already enrolled in a college program. They must have a GPA of 2.25 or higher. Along with their application, they must submit transcripts that include ACT and/or SAT scores, a statement of future educational and career goals, and a 2-page essay on why they should be selected to receive this grant. Financial need is not considered in the selection process.

Financial data The stipend is $1,000.

Duration 1 year.

Number awarded Varies each year.

Deadline April of each year.

[335]
43D INFANTRY DIVISION VETERANS ASSOCIATION SCHOLARSHIPS

43d Infantry Division Veterans Association
c/o David Thiede, Secretary/Treasurer
P.O. Box 7281
Berlin, CT 06037
E-mail: dutch2001@aol.com
Web: www.winged-victory.org/scholarship.html

Summary To provide financial assistance for college to members of the 43d Infantry Division Veterans Association and their families.

Eligibility This program is open to members of the association; the wives, children, grandchildren, and great-grandchildren of members; and the widows, children, grandchildren, and great-grandchildren of deceased members who were in good standing at the time of their death. Descendants of members of the 43d Infantry Division who died on active duty with the division during World War II are also eligible. Financial need is considered in the selection process.

Financial data The stipend is $1,000.
Duration 1 year.
Number awarded At least 1 each year.
Deadline March of each year.

[336]
506TH AIRBORNE INFANTRY REGIMENT ASSOCIATION SCHOLARSHIP

506th Airborne Infantry Regiment Association
c/o Alfred May, Scholarship Committee
30 Sweetman Lane
West Milford, NJ 07480-2933
(973) 728-1458   E-mail: alfredmay@aol.com
Web: www.506infantry.org

Summary To provide financial assistance for college or graduate school to former members of the 506th Airborne Infantry Regiment and their families.

Eligibility This program is open to veterans who served with the 506th Airborne Infantry Regiment and their children, grandchildren, spouses, and siblings. Applicants must be entering or attending an undergraduate or graduate program at a college or university in the United States. They must submit a statement describing their personal achievements and career objectives. Selection is based on academic excellence, quality of the institution the applicant has chosen to attend, and financial need.

Financial data The stipend is $1,000.
Duration 1 year; nonrenewable.
Additional information This program includes the Marilyn and Eugene Overton Scholarship Award.
Number awarded 4 each year.
Deadline April of each year.

[337]
531 GRAY GHOST SQUADRON ASSOCIATION SCHOLARSHIP

531 Gray Ghost Squadron Association
c/o Marine Corps Scholarship Foundation
Attn: Scholarship Office
909 North Washington Street, Suite 400
Alexandria, VA 22314
(703) 549-0060   Toll Free: (866) 496-5462
Fax: (703) 549-9474   E-mail: students@mcsf.org
Web: www.mcsf.org/apply/eligibility

Summary To provide financial assistance for college to the grandchildren of veterans who served with the 531 Gray Ghost Squadron of Marines.

Eligibility This program is open to grandchildren of veterans who served with the 531 Gray Ghost Squadron and are or were members of its association. Applicants must be high school seniors, high school graduates, or current college students. Along with their application, they must submit academic transcripts, a copy of their grandparent's honorable discharge, and a 500-word essay on a topic that changes periodically. Only undergraduate study is supported. The family income of applicants must be less than $93,000 per year.

Financial data Stipends depend on the need of the recipient and the availability of funds, but generally range from $500 to $2,500 per year.

Duration 1 year; may be renewed for up to 3 additional years.

Additional information tudents pursuing their second bachelor's degree, graduate school of any kind, or Federal Service Academies are not eligible.

Number awarded Varies each year; recently, 2 were awarded.

Deadline February of each year.

[338]
82ND AIRBORNE DIVISION ASSOCIATION AWARDS

82nd Airborne Division Association
Attn: Educational Fund Treasurer
P.O. Box 65089
Fayetteville, NC 28306-5089
(281) 341-5264   E-mail: 82dassnedfund@earthlink.net
Web: www.82ndairborneassociation.org

Summary To provide financial assistance for college to members of the 82d Airborne Division Association and their dependent children.

Eligibility Eligible to apply for this award are 1) dependent children of 82nd Airborne Division Association voting members; 2) dependent children of 82nd Airborne servicemen killed in combat; 3) dependent children of deceased Life or All American members of the 82nd Airborne Division Association; and 4) former active-duty 82nd Airborne Division troopers who are association members, are within 2 years of honorable discharge, and served no more than 2 enlistments. Applicants must be enrolled in an accredited university or college. Selection is based on academic achievement and financial need.

Financial data The stipend is $2,000 per year. Funds are paid to the recipient's college or university.

Duration 1 semester (the second in a school year); recipients may reapply for up to 3 additional annual awards.

Additional information In years when a suitable candidate applies, 1 of these awards is designated the General Mathew B. Ridgeway Scholarship and another as the Past President Herb Altman Memorial Scholarship. Membership in the association is open to anyone who ever served in the 82nd Airborne Division, anyone who is currently serving on active duty in jump status, and anyone who has ever served in any of the uniformed services on either jump or glider status and was honorably discharged.

Number awarded Varies each year; in the past 10 years, this program has awarded $1,637,000 in scholarships.

Deadline October of each year.

[339]
AAFES RETIRED EMPLOYEES ASSOCIATION SCHOLARSHIPS

AAFES Retired Employees Association
Attn: Scholarship Committee
7045 Rembrandt Drive
Plano, TX 75093
(972) 862-8099   E-mail: gall.tom@verizon.net
Web: www.aafes.com

Summary To provide financial assistance for college to high school seniors who have a tie to the Army and Air Force Exchange Service (AAFES).

Eligibility This program is open to high school seniors who are 1) the child of an active, retired, or deceased AAFES employee; 2) the child of assigned military personnel; or 3) an AAFES employee. Military retirees must have retired while on assignment with AAFES. Deceased parents must have died while an active or retired AAFES employee or military assignee. All retired parents must be members of the AAFES Retired Employees Association. Students who qualify as an AAFES employee must have been employed for at least 1 year. At least 1 qualifying parent must have been an AAFES employee or military assignee for at least 1 year. Applicants must be planning to attend an accredited college or university or a U.S. military academy. They must have scores of at least 1750 on the SAT or 25 on the ACT. Along with their application, they must submit an essay on why they should be awarded this scholarship. Selection is based on that essay; academic honors and other recognition received; school activity participation; outside activities, hobbies, and special talents; and letters of recommendation.

Financial data Stipends range up to $5,000.

Duration 1 year.

Additional information These scholarships were first awarded in 1985.

Number awarded Varies each year; recently, 13 were awarded: 2 at $5,000 and 11 at $3,000. Since the program began, it has awarded 286 scholarships, worth $565,795.

Deadline March of each year.

[340]
ACADEMY SPOUSES CLUB MERIT SCHOLARSHIPS FOR SPOUSES

Academy Spouses Club
Attn: Sally Mueh, Scholarship Chair
P.O. Box 78
USAF Academy, CO 80840-0078
(719) 599-0694   E-mail: usafascholarships@live.com
Web: www.usafasc.org/scholarships.html

Summary To provide financial assistance to spouses of personnel affiliated with the Air Force Academy who are working on an undergraduate or graduate degree at a school in any state.

Eligibility This program is open to non-military spouses who are entering or continuing work on a degree at an accredited vocational school, junior college, 4-year college or university, or graduate school in any state. Military spouses at the rank of O-3 or below are also eligible. Applicants must be the spouse of 1) an active-duty military member stationed at the Air Force Academy; 2) a retiree who is eligible for membership in the sponsoring organization and resides in the Colorado Springs area; 3) an active-duty military member whose last assignment was the Air Force Academy and is on a remote tour and whose dependents remain in the area for the purpose of completing a high school education; 4) a POW/MIA or a deceased military member (applicant must reside in the area and have a military ID); 5) an Air Force National Guard or Reserve member currently assigned to the Air Force Academy; 6) a Department of Defense civilian employed at the Air Force Academy; or 7) an AFAAA employee. Selection is based on a statement of academic and personal goals, academic achievement, and community activities.

Financial data Stipends range from $500 to $1,000. Funds are sent directly to the recipient's school.

Duration 1 year; nonrenewable.

Number awarded Varies each year.

Deadline March of each year.

[341]
ADA MUCKLESTONE MEMORIAL SCHOLARSHIPS

American Legion Auxiliary
Department of Illinois
2720 East Lincoln Street
P.O. Box 1426
Bloomington, IL 61702-1426
(309) 663-9366   Fax: (309) 663-5827
E-mail: karen.boughan@ilala.org
Web: www.ilala.org/education.html

Summary To provide financial assistance to high school seniors in Illinois who are the descendants of veterans and planning to attend college in any state.

Eligibility This program is open to the children, grandchildren, or great-grandchildren of veterans who served during eligibility dates for membership in the American Legion. Applicants must be high school seniors or graduates who have not yet attended an institution of higher learning and are planning to attend college in any state. They must be residents of Illinois or members of the American Legion Family, Department of Illinois. Along with their application, they must submit a 1,000-word essay on "What My Education Will Do for Me." Selection is based on that essay (25%), character and leadership (25%), scholarship (25%), and financial need (25%).

Financial data The stipend is $1,000.

Duration 1 year.

Number awarded Varies each year.

Deadline March of each year.

[342]
ADELAIDE KOOP ADAMS PRIZE

Daughters of the Cincinnati
Attn: Scholarship Administrator
20 West 44th Street, Suite 508
New York, NY 10036
(212) 991-9945
E-mail: scholarships@daughters1894.org
Web: www.daughters1894.org/scholarship.htm

Summary To provide financial assistance to high school seniors who are the daughters of active-duty, deceased, or retired military officers and plan to study history in college.

Eligibility This program is open to high school seniors who are the daughters of career commissioned officers of the regular Army, Navy, Air Force, Coast Guard, or Marine Corps on active duty, deceased, or retired. Applicants must be planning to enroll at a college or university in any state and major in history. Along with their application, they must submit an official school transcript, SAT or ACT scores, a letter of recommendation, an essay on their choice of 3 assigned topics, and documentation of financial need.

Financial data Scholarship amounts have recently averaged $4,000 per year. Funds are paid directly to the college of the student's choice.

Duration 1 year; may be renewed up to 3 additional years, provided the recipient remains in good academic standing.

Number awarded 1 each year.

Deadline March of each year.

[343]
ADRIAN AND CORENA SWANIER EDUCATION SCHOLARSHIPS

Ketia4Kidz Foundation
3012 Gold Creek Drive
Villa Rica, GA 30180
(706) 577-1731   Fax: (770) 456-9766
E-mail: ketia4kidz@yahoo.com
Web: www.ketia4kidz.org/programs.html

Summary To provide financial assistance for college to children of active-duty, retired, and deceased military personnel.

Eligibility This program is open to unmarried children younger than 23 years of age of active-duty personnel, retired military members, and deceased members. Applicants must be enrolled or planning to enroll full time at an accredited college or university to work on a 4-year degree and have a GPA of 3.0 or higher. They may attend a community, vocational, technical, or junior college if they are enrolled in a program of studies designed to allow them to transfer directly into a 4-year program. Along with their application, they must submit a 2-page essay about their experience as a military brat.

Financial data The stipend is $1,000.

Duration 1 year.

Additional information This program began in 2010.

Number awarded 5 each year.

Deadline Deadline not specified.

[344]
ADRIENNE ALIX SCHOLARSHIP

American Legion Auxiliary
Department of New Hampshire
State House Annex
25 Capitol Street, Room 432
Concord, NH 03301-6312
(603) 271-2212   Toll Free: (800) 778-3816
Fax: (603) 271-5352
E-mail: nhalasec@amlegion.state.nh.us
Web: www.nhlegion.com/page241.html

Summary To provide financial assistance to New Hampshire residents, including those recently discharged from the military, who wish to refresh or upgrade their skills at a school in any state.

Eligibility This program is open to New Hampshire residents and to members of a unit of the American Legion Auxiliary, Department of New Hampshire, who have been members for at least 3 consecutive years. Applicants must be 1) reentering the workforce or upgrading skills; 2) displaced from the workforce; or 3) recently discharged honorably from the military. They must be interested in taking a refresher course or advancing their knowledge or techniques needed in today's workforce at a school in any state. Along with their application, they must submit a 500-word essay explaining their career goals and objectives.

Financial data The stipend is $1,000.

Duration 1 year.

Number awarded 1 each year.

Deadline April of each year.

[345]
AFCEA NOVA SCHOLARSHIPS

Armed Forces Communications and Electronics
   Association-Northern Virginia Chapter
Attn: Scholarship Chair
400 North Washington Street, Suite 300
Alexandria, VA 22314
(703) 778-4645   Fax: (703) 683-5480
E-mail: scholarships@afceanova.org
Web: www.afceanova.org/scholarships

Summary To provide financial assistance for undergraduate and graduate study in fields of science, technology, engineering, or mathematics (STEM) to military and civilian personnel affiliated with the Northern Virginia chapter of the Armed Forces Communications and Electronics Association (AFCEA NOVA).

Eligibility This program is open to residents of the greater Washington, D.C. area and to members of AFCEA NOVA and their children who live elsewhere. Applicants must be U.S. government service employees or military personnel (enlisted or junior grade officers) or their offspring; veterans are also given consideration. Applicants must be working on an undergraduate or graduate degree in a field of STEM (including information technology, computer science, and other technology fields supportive of national security). Selection is based on merit, although financial need and past and current military and government service may also be considered. U.S. citizenship is required.

Financial data The stipend is $2,000 for full-time students or $1,000 for part-time students.

Duration 1 year.

Additional information The greater Washington area is defined to include the District of Columbia; the Maryland counties of Calvert, Charles, Frederick, Montgomery, and Prince George's; the Virginia cities of Alexandria, Fairfax, Falls Church, Fredericksburg, Manassas, and Manassas Park; the Virginia counties of Arlington, Clarke, Culpeper, Fairfax, Fauquier, King George, Loudoun, Prince William, Spotsylvania, Stafford, and Warren; and the West Virginia counties of Berkeley and Jefferson.

Number awarded More than 30 each year.

Deadline February of each year.

[346]
AGGIE PARKS SCHOLARSHIP

American Legion Auxiliary
Department of Alaska
Attn: Secretary/Treasurer
P.O. Box 670750
Chugiak, AK 99567
(907) 688-0241   Fax: (907) 688-0241
E-mail: aladepak@gci.net
Web: www.alaskalegionauxiliary.org

Summary To provide financial assistance to the descendants of war veterans in Alaska who plan to attend college in any state.

Eligibility This program is open to children, stepchildren, grandchildren, and great-grandchildren of veterans who served during wartime. Applicants must be high school seniors who have completed at least 50 hours of volunteer service within their community and plan to attend a college or university in any state. Nominees must submit a 1,000-word essay on a topic that changes annually; recently, students were asked to write on "Pass It On-How Can I Be a Leader in My Community." Selection is based on the essay (25%), character and leadership (25%), scholarship, (25%), and financial need (25%).

Financial data The stipend is $1,000.

Duration 1 year.

Number awarded 1 each year.

Deadline February of each year.

[347]
AIR FORCE AID SOCIETY EDUCATION LOAN PROGRAM

Air Force Aid Society
Attn: Education Assistance Department
241 18th Street South, Suite 202
Arlington, VA 22202-3409
(703) 972-2647   Toll Free: (866) 896-5637
Fax: (703) 972-2646   E-mail: ed@afas-hq.org
Web: www.afas.org/ed-loans

Summary To provide educational loans to dependents of active-duty and retired Air Force personnel.

Eligibility This program is open to dependent children of Air Force personnel who are active duty, Reservists on extended active duty, or retired with at least 20 years of creditable service. Applicants must be enrolled or planning to enroll as full-time undergraduate students at an accredited college, university, or vocational/trade school. They must be able to demonstrate need for additional funding to help pay for college.

Financial data The maximum loan is $1,000. No interest is charged, but repayment by allotment must begin immediately and be completed within 10 months.

Duration 1 year.

Number awarded Varies each year.

Deadline September of each year.

[348]
AIR FORCE AID SOCIETY MERIT SCHOLARSHIPS

Air Force Aid Society
Attn: Education Assistance Department
241 18th Street South, Suite 202
Arlington, VA 22202-3409
(703) 972-2647   Toll Free: (866) 896-5637
Fax: (703) 972-2646   E-mail: ed@afas-hq.org
Web: www.afas.org/merit

Summary To provide merit-based financial assistance for college to dependents of active-duty, retired, disabled, or deceased Air Force personnel.

Eligibility This program is open to dependent children of Air Force personnel who are active duty, Reservists on extended active duty, retired due to length of active-duty service or disability, or deceased while on active duty or in retired status. Applicants must be entering their freshman year as full-time undergraduate students at an accredited college, university, or vocational/trade school. Selection is based on cumulative GPA, SAT/ACT scores, transcripts, extracurricular activities, volunteer and/or work experience, a resume, and an essay on a specified topic.

Financial data The stipend is $5,000.

Duration 1 year.

Number awarded Varies each year; recently, 15 were awarded.

Deadline March of each year.

[349]
AIR FORCE OFFICERS' WIVES' CLUB OF WASHINGTON, D.C. CURRENT COLLEGE STUDENT SCHOLARSHIPS

Air Force Officers' Wives' Club of Washington, D.C.
Attn: Scholarship Committee
P.O. Box 8490
Washington, DC 20032
(202) 239-1932   E-mail: scholarships@afowc.com
Web: www.afoscdc.com/Scholarship_Application.html

Summary To provide financial assistance for undergraduate education in any state to the dependent children of Air Force members in the Washington, D.C. area.

Eligibility This program is open to the dependent children of Air Force enlisted or commissioned personnel residing in the Washington, D.C. metropolitan area in the following categories: active duty, Reserve, Guard, retired, or deceased. Applicants must be between 17 and 22 years of age and currently enrolled at an accredited college or university in any state. They must have a GPA of 3.0 or higher. Along with their application, they must submit an essay of 500 to 1,000 words on a topic that changes annually; recently, students were asked to write on the advice they would give to new military parents to help their child be successful in overcoming the challenges military families face. Selection is based on their essay, academic achievement, standardized test scores, extracurricular activities, work history, citizenship, leadership roles, awards and honors, and character references.

Financial data The stipend recently was $2,000. Funds may be used only for payment of tuition or academic fees.

Duration 1 year; nonrenewable.

Number awarded Varies each year; recently, 3 were awarded.

Deadline February of each year.

[350]
AIR FORCE OFFICERS' WIVES' CLUB OF WASHINGTON, D.C. HIGH SCHOOL SCHOLARSHIPS

Air Force Officers' Wives' Club of Washington, D.C.
Attn: Scholarship Committee
P.O. Box 8490
Washington, DC 20032
(202) 239-1932   E-mail: scholarships@afowc.com
Web: www.afoscdc.com/Scholarship_Application.html

Summary To provide financial assistance for college to high school seniors who are dependents of Air Force members in the Washington, D.C. area.

Eligibility This program is open to high school seniors residing in the Washington, D.C. metropolitan area who are dependents of Air Force enlisted or commissioned personnel in the following categories: active duty, retired, Reserve, Guard, or deceased. Applicants must be planning to work on an accredited undergraduate degree at a college or university in any state. They must have a GPA of 3.25 or higher. Along with their application, they must submit an essay of 500 to 1,000 words on a topic that changes annually; recently, students were asked to write on the advice the would give to new military parents to help their child be successful in overcoming the challenges military families face. Selection is based on their essay, academic achievement, standardized test scores, extracurricular activities, work history, citizenship, leadership roles, awards and honors, and reference letters.

Financial data The stipend recently was $2,000. Funds may be used only for payment of tuition or academic fees.

Duration 1 year; nonrenewable.

Number awarded Varies each year; recently, 3 were awarded.

Deadline February of each year.

[351]
AIR FORCE OFFICERS' WIVES' CLUB OF WASHINGTON, D.C. STEM SCHOLARSHIPS

Air Force Officers' Wives' Club of Washington, D.C.
Attn: Scholarship Committee
P.O. Box 8490
Washington, DC 20032
(202) 239-1932   E-mail: scholarships@afowc.com
Web: www.afoscdc.com/Scholarship_Application.html

Summary To provide financial assistance to children and spouses of Air Force members in the Washington, D.C. area who are interested in studying a field of science, technology, engineering, or mathematics (STEM) at a college in any state.

Eligibility This program is open to residents of the Washington, D.C. metropolitan area who are children or spouses of Air Force enlisted or commissioned personnel in the following categories: active duty, retired, Reserve, Guard, or deceased. Applicants must be enrolled or planning to enroll at an accredited college or university in any state to work on a degree in a field of STEM. High school seniors must have a GPA of 3.25 or higher; current college students and spouses must have a GPA of 3.0 or higher. Along with their application, they must submit an essay of 500 to 1,000 words on a topic that changes annually; recently, applicants were asked to write on the advice the would give to military families to help them cope with the challenges military families face. Selection is based on their essay, academic achievement, standardized test scores, extracurricular activities, work history, citizenship, leadership roles, awards and honors, and reference letters.

Financial data The stipend recently was $3,000. Funds may be used only for payment of tuition or academic fees.

Duration 1 year; nonrenewable.

Additional information This program is sponsored by Lockheed Martin.

Number awarded 5 each year.

Deadline February of each year.

[352]
AIR FORCE SERGEANTS ASSOCIATION INTERNATIONAL AUXILIARY EDUCATION GRANTS

Air Force Sergeants Association
Attn: Membership and Field Relations
5211 Auth Road
Suitland, MD 20746
(301) 899-3500   Toll Free: (800) 638-0594
Fax: (301) 899-8136   E-mail: balsobrooks@hqafsa.org
Web: www.hqafsa.org/scholarships.html

Summary To provide financial assistance for college to members of the Air Force Sergeants Association (AFSA) Auxiliary.

Eligibility This program is open to AFSA Auxiliary members who need assistance to enhance their income potential through formal education and/or training. Applicants must be seeking to obtain effective education and/or training to acquire improved marketable skills. They must be 19 years of age or older and have been members for at least 1 year.

Financial data Stipends range up to $2,000 per year. Funds are sent directly to the recipient's school to be used for tuition, room and board, fees, books, supplies, child care, meals, and transportation.

Duration 1 year; may be renewed if the student maintains full-time enrollment.

Additional information This program began in 1990.

Number awarded Varies each year; recently, 5 were awarded. Since the program began, it has awarded grants worth more than $149,000.

Deadline March of each year.

[353]
AIR FORCE SERGEANTS ASSOCIATION SCHOLARSHIPS

Air Force Sergeants Association
Attn: Membership and Field Relations
5211 Auth Road
Suitland, MD 20746
(301) 899-3500   Toll Free: (800) 638-0594
Fax: (301) 899-8136   E-mail: balsobrooks@hqafsa.org
Web: www.hqafsa.org/scholarships.html

Summary To provide financial assistance for undergraduate education to the dependent children of Air Force enlisted personnel.

Eligibility This program is open to the unmarried children (including stepchildren and legally adopted children) of active-duty, retired, or veteran members of the U.S. Air Force, Air National Guard, or Air Force Reserves. Applicants must be attending or planning to attend an accredited academic institution. They must have an unweighted GPA of 3.5 or higher. Their parent must be a member of the Air Force Sergeants Association or its auxiliary. Along with their application, they must submit 1) a paragraph on their life objectives and what they plan to do with the education they receive; and 2) an essay on the most urgent problem facing society today. High school seniors must also submit a transcript of all high school grades and a record of their SAT or ACT scores. Selection is based on academic record, character, leadership skills, writing ability, versatility, and potential for success. Financial need is not a consideration.

Financial data Stipends range from $1,500 to $2,500 per year. Funds may be used for tuition, room and board, fees, books, supplies, and transportation.

Duration 1 year; may be renewed if the student maintains full-time enrollment.

Additional information This program began in 1968.

Number awarded Varies each year; recently, 12 were awarded: 4 at $2,500, 3 at $2,000, and 5 at $1,500. Since the program began, it has awarded nearly 560 scholarships worth more than $800,000.

Deadline March of each year.

[354]
AIR FORCE SERVICES CLUB MEMBERSHIP SCHOLARSHIP PROGRAM

Air Force Services Agency
Attn: HQ AFPC/SVOFT
10100 Reunion Place, Suite 501
San Antonio, TX 78216-4138
(210) 395-7351   E-mail: clubs@myairforcelife.com
Web: www.myairforcelife.com/Clubs/Scholarship.aspx

Summary To recognize and reward, with funding for undergraduate or graduate studies, Air Force Club members and their families who submit outstanding essays.

Eligibility This program is open to Air Force Club members and their spouses, children, and stepchildren who have been accepted by or are enrolled at an accredited college or university. Grandchildren are eligible if they are the dependent of a club member. Applicants may be undergraduate or graduate students enrolled full or part time. They must submit an essay of up to 500 words on a topic that changes annually; a recent topic was "My Contribution to the Air Force." Applicants must also include a 1-page summary of their long-term career and life goals and previous accomplishments, including civic, athletic, and academic awards.

Financial data Awards are $1,000 scholarships. Each winner also receives a laptop computer.

Duration The competition is held annually.

Additional information This competition, first held in 1997, is sponsored by Chase Military Credit Card Services.

Number awarded 25 each year.

Deadline April of each year.

[355]
AIRMEN MEMORIAL FOUNDATION SCHOLARSHIP PROGRAM

Air Force Sergeants Association
Attn: Membership and Field Relations
5211 Auth Road
Suitland, MD 20746
(301) 899-3500   Toll Free: (800) 638-0594
Fax: (301) 899-8136   E-mail: balsobrooks@hqafsa.org
Web: www.hqafsa.org/scholarships.html

Summary To provide financial assistance for college to the dependent children of enlisted Air Force personnel.

Eligibility This program is open to the unmarried children (including stepchildren and legally adopted children) of active-duty, retired, or veteran members of the U.S. Air Force, Air National Guard, or Air Force Reserves. Applicants must be attending or planning to attend an accredited academic institution. They must have an unweighted GPA of 3.5 or higher. Along with their application, they must submit 1) a paragraph on their life objectives and what they plan to do with the education they receive; and 2) an essay on the most urgent problem facing society today. High school seniors must also submit a transcript of all high school grades and a record of their SAT or ACT scores. Selection is based on academic record, character, leadership skills, writing ability, versatility, and potential for success. Financial need is not a consideration.

Financial data Stipends are $2,000, $1,500, or $1,000; funds may be used for tuition, room and board, fees, books, supplies, and transportation.

Duration 1 year; may be renewed if the recipient maintains full-time enrollment.

Additional information The Air Force Sergeants Association administers this program, which began in 1987, on behalf of the Airmen Memorial Foundation.

Number awarded Varies each year; recently, 20 were awarded: 5 at $2,000, 9 at $1,500, and 6 at $1,000, including 5 sponsored by the United Services Automobile Association (USAA) Insurance Corporation. Since this program began, it has awarded more than 500 scholarships worth nearly $600,000.

Deadline March of each year.

[356]
AL AND WILLAMARY VISTE SCHOLARSHIP PROGRAM

101st Airborne Division Association
32 Screaming Eagle Boulevard
P.O. Box 929
Fort Campbell, KY 42223-0929
(931) 431-0199   Fax: (931) 431-0195
E-mail: 101stairbornedivisionassociation@comcast.net
Web: www.screamingeaglefoundation.org

Summary To provide financial assistance to the spouses, children, and grandchildren of members of the 101st Airborne Division Association who are upper-division or graduate students working on a degree in science.

Eligibility This program is open to college juniors, seniors, and graduate students who maintained a GPA of 3.75 or higher during the preceding school year and whose parent, grandparent, or spouse is (or, if deceased, was) a regular or life (not associate) member of the 101st Airborne Division. Preference is given to students working on a degree in a physical science, medical science, or other scientific research field. Applicants must submit a 500-word essay on what it means to be an American and a letter on their course of study, community service, hobbies, interests, personal achievements, and how a higher education for them in their chosen field can benefit our nation. Selection is based on the letter, career objectives, academic record, and letters of recommendation.

Financial data A stipend is awarded (amount not specified).

Duration 1 year; may be renewed.

Number awarded At least 1 each year.

Deadline May of each year.

[357]
ALABAMA G.I. DEPENDENTS' SCHOLARSHIP PROGRAM

Alabama Department of Veterans Affairs
770 Washington Avenue, Suite 470
Montgomery, AL 36102-1509
(334) 242-5077   Fax: (334) 242-5102
Web: www.va.state.al.us/gi_dep_scholarship.aspx

Summary To provide educational benefits to the dependents of disabled, deceased, and other Alabama veterans.

Eligibility This program is open to children, spouses, and unremarried widow(er)s of veterans who are currently rated as 20% or more service-connected disabled or were so rated at time of death, were a former prisoner of war, have been declared missing in action, died as the result of a service-connected disability, or died while on active military duty in the line of duty. The veteran must have been a permanent civilian resident of Alabama for at least 1 year prior to entering active military service and served honorably for at least 90 days during wartime (or less, in case of death or service-connected disability). Veterans who were not Alabama residents at the time of entering active military service may also qualify if they have a 100% disability and were permanent residents of Alabama for at least 5 years prior to filing the application for this program or prior to death, if deceased. Children and step-children must be under the age of 26, but spouses and widow(er)s may be of any age. Spouses cease to be eligible if they become divorced from the qualifying veteran. Widow(er)s cease to be eligible if they remarry.

Financial data Eligible dependents may attend any state-supported Alabama institution of higher learning or enroll in a prescribed course of study at any Alabama state-supported trade school without payment of any tuition, book fees, or laboratory charges.

Duration This is an entitlement program for 5 years of full-time undergraduate or graduate study or part-time equivalent for all qualifying children and for spouses and unremarried widow(er)s who veteran spouse is or was rated 100% disabled or meets other qualifying requirements. Spouses and unremarried widow(er)s whose veteran spouse is or was rated between 20% and 90% disabled may attend only 3 standard academic years.

Additional information Benefits for children, spouses, and unremarried widow(er)s are available in addition to federal government benefits. Assistance is not provided for non-credit courses, placement testing, GED preparation, continuing educational courses, pre-technical courses, or state board examinations.

Number awarded Varies each year.

Deadline Applications may be submitted at any time.

[358]
ALASKA FREE TUITION FOR SPOUSE OR DEPENDENT OF ARMED SERVICES MEMBER

Department of Military and Veterans Affairs
Attn: Office of Veterans Affairs
4600 DeBarr Road, Suite 180
Anchorage, AK 99508
(907) 334-0874   Toll Free: (888) 248-3682
Fax: (907) 334-0869 E-mail: alaska.veterans@alaska.gov
Web: veterans.alaska.gov/education-benefits.html

Summary To provide financial assistance for college to dependents and spouses in Alaska of servicemembers who died or were declared prisoners of war or missing in action.

Eligibility Eligible for this benefit are the spouses and dependent children of Alaska residents who died in the line of duty, died of injuries sustained in the line of duty, or were listed by the Department of Defense as a prisoner of war or missing in action. Applicants must be in good standing at a state-supported educational institution in Alaska.

Financial data Those eligible may attend any state-supported educational institution in Alaska without payment of tuition or fees.

Duration 1 year; may be renewed.

Additional information Information is available from the financial aid office of state-supported universities in Alaska.

Number awarded Varies each year.

Deadline Deadline not specified.

[359]
ALASKA SEA SERVICES SCHOLARSHIPS

Navy League of the United States
Attn: Scholarships
2300 Wilson Boulevard, Suite 200
Arlington, VA 22201-5424
(703) 528-1775   Toll Free: (800) 356-5760
Fax: (703) 528-2333
E-mail: scholarships@navyleague.org
Web: www.navyleague.org/aboutus/scholarship.html

Summary To provide financial assistance to spouses and dependent children of naval personnel in Alaska who are interested in attending college in any state.

Eligibility This program is open to U.S. citizens who are 1) dependents or direct descendants of an active, Reserve, retired, or honorably discharged member of the U.S. sea service (including the Navy, Marine Corps, Coast Guard, or Merchant Marine); or 2) currently an active member of the Naval Sea Cadet Corps. Applicants must be high school seniors in Alaska entering their freshman year at an accredited college or university. They must have a GPA of 3.0 or higher. Along with their application, they must submit transcripts, 2 letters of recommendation, SAT/ACT scores, documentation of financial need, proof of qualifying sea service duty, and a 1-page personal statement on why they should be considered for this scholarship.

Financial data The stipend is $1,000; funds are paid directly to the academic institution for tuition, books, and fees.

Duration 1 year.

Additional information This program began in 1986 with funds originally raised as a War Bond during World War II to honor the sailors of USS Juneau.

Number awarded 6 each year.

Deadline February of each year.

[360]
ALBERT M. LAPPIN SCHOLARSHIP

American Legion
Department of Kansas
1314 S.W. Topeka Boulevard
Topeka, KS 66612-1886
(785) 232-9315   Fax: (785) 232-1399
Web: www.ksamlegion.org

Summary To provide financial assistance to the children of members of the Kansas American Legion or American Legion Auxiliary who plan to attend college in the state.

Eligibility This program is open to high school seniors and college freshmen and sophomores who are attending or planning to attend an approved Kansas college, university, or trade school. At least 1 of their parents must be a veteran and have been a member of an American Legion post or Auxiliary in Kansas for the past 3 consecutive years. Along with their application, they must submit an essay of 250 to 500 words on "Why I Want to Go to College." Financial need is also considered in the selection process.

Financial data The stipend is $1,000.

Duration 1 year.

Number awarded 1 each year.
Deadline February of each year.

[361]
ALBERT T. MARCOUX MEMORIAL SCHOLARSHIP

American Legion
Department of New Hampshire
121 South Fruit Street
Concord, NH 03301
(603) 856-8951   Fax: (603) 856-8943
E-mail: adjutantnh@nhlegion.com
Web: www.nhlegion.com/page216.html

Summary To provide financial assistance to the children of members of the New Hampshire Department of the American Legion or American Legion Auxiliary who are interested in studying any field at a college in any state.

Eligibility This program is open to residents of New Hampshire who are entering their first year at an accredited 4-year college or university in any state to work on a bachelor's degree in any field. Applicant's parent must be a member of the American Legion or its Auxiliary (or if deceased have been a member at time of death). They must have a GPA of 3.0 or higher in their junior and senior high school years. Financial need is considered in the selection process.

Financial data The stipend is $2,000.

Duration 1 year.

Number awarded 1 each year.

Deadline April of each year.

[362]
ALBUQUERQUE POST SOCIETY OF AMERICAN MILITARY ENGINEERS HIGH SCHOOL SCHOLARSHIPS

New Mexico Engineering Foundation
Attn: Scholarship Chair
P.O. Box 3828
Albuquerque, NM 87190-3828
(505) 615-1800   E-mail: info@nmef.net
Web: www.nmef.net/?section=scholarship

Summary To provide financial assistance to high school seniors in New Mexico interested in studying engineering, mathematics, or science at a college in the state.

Eligibility This program is open to seniors graduating from high schools in New Mexico who plan to work on an undergraduate degree in engineering, mathematics, or science at a college or university in the state. Applicants must have a GPA of 3.0 or higher and minimum scores of at least 29 on the ACT mathematics, 25 on the ACT English, 600 on the SAT mathematics, and 500 on the SAT critical reading. Along with their application, they must submit 12 brief statements related to their past activities and future plans. Selection is based on academic record, demonstrated school leadership positions, community involvement, and ability to earn partial tuition costs and fulfill financial needs. Preference is given to children of a parent killed in military action.

Financial data The stipend is $1,500.

Duration 1 year; nonrenewable.

Additional information This program is offered by the Albuquerque Post of the Society of American Military Engineers.

Number awarded 2 each year.
Deadline February of each year.

[363]
ALEXANDER KREIGLOWA NAVY AND MARINE CORPS DEPENDENTS EDUCATION FOUNDATION SCHOLARSHIP

Navy League of the United States-San Diego Council
Attn: Scholarship Committee
2115 Park Boulevard
San Diego, CA 92101
(619) 230-0301   Fax: (619) 230-0302
Web: www.navyleague-sd.com/Scholarship.htm

Summary To provide financial assistance to high school seniors in California who are children of Naval Service personnel and interested in attending college in any state.

Eligibility This program is open to seniors graduating from high schools in California in the top 10% of their class. Applicants must be the dependent child of an active-duty, retired, or deceased member of the Naval Service (U.S. Navy or U.S. Marine Corps). They must be planning to enroll at an accredited 4-year college or university in any state. Along with their application, they must submit an essay of 1 to 2 pages describing their high school experience and accomplishments and how those will help them as they pursue a college education. Financial need is considered in the selection process.

Financial data The stipend ranges up to $15,000 per year.

Duration 1 year; may be renewed up to 3 additional years.

Number awarded 1 each year.

Deadline March of each year.

[364]
ALLIE MAE ODEN MEMORIAL SCHOLARSHIP

Ladies Auxiliary of the Fleet Reserve Association
c/o Sandra Robbins, National Scholarship Chair
2712 Holly Ridge Road
Orange Park, FL 32073
(904) 269-2136   E-mail: slgr@bellsouth.net
Web: www.la-fra.org/scholarship.html

Summary To provide financial assistance for college to the children and grandchildren of members of the Fleet Reserve Association (FRA).

Eligibility This program is open to the children and grandchildren of living or deceased FRA members or of persons who were eligible to be FRA members at the time of their death. Applicants must submit an essay on their life experiences, career objectives, and what motivated them to select those objectives. Selection is based on academic record, financial need, extracurricular activities, leadership skills, and participation in community activities. U.S. citizenship is required.

Financial data The stipend is $2,500.

Duration 1 year; may be renewed.

Additional information Membership in the FRA is open to active-duty, retired, and Reserve members of the Navy, Marine Corps, and Coast Guard.

Number awarded 1 each year.

Deadline April of each year.

[365]
AMERICAL DIVISION VETERANS ASSOCIATION SCHOLARSHIP

Americal Division Veterans Association
c/o William Bruinsma, Scholar Fund Chair
5425 Parmalee Road
Middleville, MI 49333
E-mail: wb3379@gmail.com
Web: www.americal.org/programs/scholor.html

Summary To provide financial assistance for college to the dependents of members of the Americal Division Veterans Association.

Eligibility This program is open to the children and grand-children of members of the Americal Division Veterans Association and to the children of Americal Division veterans who were killed in action or died while on active duty with the Division. Applicants must be attending or planning to attend a college or vocational school. Along with their application, they must submit an essay of 200 to 300 words on subjects pertaining to loyalty to the nation. Financial need is considered in the selection process.

Financial data Recently, stipends ranged from $1,000 to $3,000 per year.

Duration 1 year; recipients may reapply.

Number awarded Varies each year; approximately $20,000 in scholarships are awarded annually.

Deadline March of each year.

[366]
AMERICAN LEGION AUXILIARY EMERGENCY FUND

American Legion Auxiliary
Attn: AEF Program Case Manager
8945 North Meridian Street
Indianapolis, IN 46260
(317) 569-4544   Fax: (317) 569-4502
E-mail: aef@alaforveterans.org
Web: www.alaforveterans.org

Summary To provide funding to members of the American Legion Auxiliary who are facing temporary emergency needs.

Eligibility This program is open to members of the American Legion Auxiliary who have maintained their membership for the immediate past 2 consecutive years and have paid their dues for the current year. Applicants must need emergency assistance for the following purposes: 1) food, shelter, and utilities during a time of financial crisis; 2) food and shelter because of weather-related emergencies and natural disasters; or 3) educational training for eligible members who lack the necessary skills for employment or to upgrade competitive workforce skills. They must have exhausted all other sources of financial assistance, including funds and/or services available through the local Post and/or Unit, appropriate community welfare agencies, or state and federal financial aid for education. Grants are not available to settle already existing or accumulated debts, handle catastrophic illness, resettle disaster victims, or other similar problems.

Financial data The maximum grant is $2,400. Payments may be made directly to the member or to the mortgage company or utility. Educational grants may be paid directly to the educational institution.

Duration Grants are expended over no more than 3 months.

Additional information This program began in 1969. In 1981, it was expanded to include the Displaced Homemaker Fund (although that title is no longer used).

Number awarded Varies each year.

Deadline Applications may be submitted at any time.

[367]
AMERICAN LEGION AUXILIARY SCHOLARSHIP FOR NON-TRADITIONAL STUDENTS

American Legion Auxiliary
8945 North Meridian Street
Indianapolis, IN 46260
(317) 569-4500   Fax: (317) 569-4502
E-mail: alahq@alaforveterans.org
Web: www.alaforveterans.org

Summary To provide financial assistance for college to nontraditional students affiliated with the American Legion.

Eligibility This program is open to members of the American Legion, American Legion Auxiliary, or Sons of the American Legion who have paid dues for the 2 preceding years and the calendar year in which application is being made. Applicants must be nontraditional students who are either 1) returning to school after some period of time during which their formal education was interrupted; or 2) just beginning their education at a later point in life. Selection is based on scholastic standing and academic achievement (25%), character and leadership (25%), initiative and goals (25%), and financial need (25%).

Financial data The stipend is $2,000, paid directly to the school.

Duration 1 year.

Additional information Applications are available from the president of the candidate's own unit or from the secretary or education chair of the department.

Number awarded 5 each year: 1 in each division of the American Legion Auxiliary.

Deadline Applications must be submitted to the unit president by February of each year.

[368]
AMERICAN LEGION LEGACY SCHOLARSHIPS

American Legion
Attn: Americanism and Children & Youth Division
700 North Pennsylvania Street
P.O. Box 1055
Indianapolis, IN 46206-1055
(317) 630-1212   Fax: (317) 630-1223
E-mail: scholarships@legion.org
Web: www.legion.org/scholarships/legacy

Summary To provide financial assistance for college to children of U.S. military personnel killed on active duty on or after September 11, 2001.

Eligibility This program is open to the children (including adopted children and stepchildren) of active-duty U.S. military personnel (including federalized National Guard and Reserve members) who died on active duty on or after September 11, 2001. Applicants must be high school seniors or graduates planning to enroll full time at an accredited institution of higher education in the United States. Selection is based on academic achievement, school and community activities, leadership skills, and financial need.

Financial data The stipend depends on the availability of funds.

Duration 1 year; may be renewed.

Additional information This program began in 2003.

Number awarded Varies each year; a total of $50,000 is available for this program annually.

Deadline April of each year.

[369]
AMERICAN LEGION NATIONAL EAGLE SCOUT OF THE YEAR

American Legion
Attn: Americanism and Children & Youth Division
700 North Pennsylvania Street
P.O. Box 1055
Indianapolis, IN 46206-1055
(317) 630-1202   Fax: (317) 630-1223
E-mail: scouting@legion.org
Web: www.legion.org/scholarships/eaglescout

Summary To recognize and reward, with college scholarships, Eagle Scouts who are members of a troop associated with the American Legion or are the son or grandson of a member of the Legion.

Eligibility Applicants for this award must be either 1) a registered, active member of a Boy Scout Troop, Varsity Scout Team, or Venturing Crew chartered to an American Legion Post, Auxiliary Unit, or Sons of the American Legion Squadron; or 2) a registered active member of a Boy Scout Troop, Varsity Scout Team, or Venturing Crew and also the son or grandson of a member of the American Legion or American Legion Auxiliary. They must also 1) have received the Eagle Scout Award; 2) be active members of their religious institution and have received the appropriate religious emblem; 3) have demonstrated practical citizenship in church, school, Scouting, and community; 4) be at least 15 years of age and enrolled in high school; and 5) submit at least 4 letters of recommendation, including 1 each from leaders of their religious institution, school, community, and Scouting.

Financial data The Scout of the Year receives $10,000; each runner-up receives $2,500.

Duration The awards are presented annually; recipients are eligible to receive their scholarships immediately upon graduation from an accredited high school and must utilize the award within 4 years of their graduation date.

Additional information The recipients may use the scholarships at any school of their choice, provided it is accredited for education above the high school level and located within the United States or its possessions.

Number awarded 1 Scout of the Year and 3 runners-up are selected each year.

Deadline Nominations must be received by the respective department headquarters by the end of February of each year and by the national headquarters before the end of March.

[370]
AMERICAN PATRIOT FREEDOM SCHOLARSHIP AWARD

Homefront America
27375 Paseo La Serna
San Juan Capistrano, CA 92675
(949) 248-9468   E-mail: info@homefrontamerica.org
Web: www.homefrontamerica.org

Summary To provide financial assistance to children of active, Reserve, disabled, deceased, or retired military personnel.

Eligibility This program is open to students between 18 and 21 years of age who are children of 1) full-time active duty or Reserve servicemembers; 2) servicemembers disabled as a direct result of injuries sustained during a military operation; 3) deceased servicemembers killed in action during a military operation; or 4) servicemembers who are retired with an honorable discharge. Applicants must be enrolled or planning to enroll at an accredited college, university, or vocational/technical institute to work on an undergraduate degree. Selection is based primarily on a 500-word essay on significant contributions of America's greatest generation to our country.

Financial data The stipend is $1,000.

Duration 1 year.

Number awarded 5 each year.

Deadline Applications may be submitted at any time, but they must be received in time for the announcement of recipients at the end of May of each year.

[371]
AMERICAN PATRIOT SCHOLARSHIPS

Military Officers Association of America
Attn: Educational Assistance Program
201 North Washington Street
Alexandria, VA 22314-2539
(703) 549-2311   Toll Free: (800) 234-MOAA
Fax: (703) 838-5819   E-mail: edassist@moaa.org
Web: www.moaa.org/main_simplelist.aspx?id=1172

Summary To provide financial assistance for undergraduate education to children of members of the uniformed services who have died.

Eligibility This program is open to children under 24 years of age of active, Reserve, and National Guard uniformed service personnel (Army, Navy, Air Force, Marines, Coast Guard, Public Health Service, or National Oceanographic and Atmospheric Administration) whose parent has died on active service. Applicants must be working on an undergraduate degree. They must have a GPA of 3.0 or higher. Selection is based on academic ability, activities, and financial need.

Financial data The stipend is currently $2,500 per year.

Duration 1 year; may be renewed up to 4 additional years.

Additional information The MOAA was formerly named The Retired Officers Association (TROA). It established this program in 2002 in response to the tragic events of September 11, 2001.

Number awarded Varies each year; recently, 57 were awarded. Since the program was established, it has awarded $1,770,000 to 225 children of deceased military personnel.

Deadline February of each year.

[372]
AMERICA'S CHILD HIGHER EDUCATIONAL ASSISTANCE PROGRAM

America's Child
c/o Children's Fund of America
10010 Rosedale Highway, Suite 3
Bakersfield, CA 93312
(661) 633-9076   E-mail: info@ttof.org
Web: www.americaschild.org

Summary To provide funding for higher education, in the form of a Section 529 savings account, to children of military personnel who lost their lives in the war against terrorism.

Eligibility This program is open to natural-born and legally-adopted children of military personnel who lost their lives in our nation's war against terrorism. Applicants must be under 18 years of age or, if already enrolled in college, under 23. They must be attending or planning to attend an accredited 2- or 4-year college, university, or trade school. Enrollment in college must begin before they become 21 years of age.

Financial data Funds are placed in an individual Section 529 tax-deferred higher educational savings account in the recipient's name. When their attendance in college is verified, funds are released to their institution of higher education. The amount depends on the need of the recipient.

Duration Funds are intended to cover 1 year of attendance.

Number awarded Varies each year.

Deadline Deadline not specified.

[373]
AMVETS JROTC SCHOLARSHIPS

AMVETS National Headquarters
Attn: Programs Department
4647 Forbes Boulevard
Lanham, MD 20706-3807
(301) 459-9600   Toll Free: (877) 7-AMVETS, ext. 4031
Fax: (301) 459-7924   E-mail: amvets@amvets.org
Web: www.amvets.org/programs/scholarships

Summary To provide financial assistance for college to the children and grandchildren of veterans or active military servicemembers who have participated in Junior Reserve Officers' Training Corps (JROTC) in high school.

Eligibility This program is open to graduating high school seniors who are JROTC cadets and the children or grandchildren of a veteran (living or deceased) or an active military servicemember. Applicants must be interested in working full time on an undergraduate degree at an accredited college, university, or technical/trade school. They must be U.S. citizens and have a GPA of 3.0 or higher. Selection is based on financial need, academic promise, and merit.

Financial data The stipend is $1,000.

Duration 1 year; nonrenewable.

Number awarded 1 each year.

Deadline April of each year.

[374]
AMVETS NATIONAL LADIES AUXILIARY SCHOLARSHIPS

AMVETS National Ladies Auxiliary
Attn: Scholarship Officer
4647 Forbes Boulevard
Lanham, MD 20706-4380
(301) 459-6255   Fax: (301) 459-5403
E-mail: auxhdqs@amvets.org
Web: www.amvetsaux.org/scholarships.html

Summary To provide financial assistance to members and certain dependents of members of AMVETS National Ladies Auxiliary who are already enrolled in college.

Eligibility Applicants must belong to AMVETS Auxiliary or be the child or grandchild of a member. They must be in at least the second year of undergraduate study at an accredited college or university. Applications must include 3 letters of recommendation and an essay (from 200 to 500 words) about their past accomplishments, career and educational goals, and objectives for the future. Selection is based on the letters of reference (15%), academic record (15%), the essay (25%), and financial need (45%).

Financial data Scholarships are $1,000 or $750 each.

Duration 1 year.

Number awarded Up to 7 each year: 2 at $1,000 and 5 at $750.

Deadline June of each year.

[375]
AMVETS NATIONAL SCHOLARSHIPS FOR HIGH SCHOOL SENIORS

AMVETS National Headquarters
Attn: Programs Department
4647 Forbes Boulevard
Lanham, MD 20706-3807
(301) 459-9600   Toll Free: (877) 7-AMVETS, ext. 4031
Fax: (301) 459-7924   E-mail: amvets@amvets.org
Web: www.amvets.org/programs/scholarships

Summary To provide financial assistance to the children and grandchildren of members of veterans and active military servicemembers who are entering college.

Eligibility This program is open to graduating high school seniors who are the children or grandchildren of veterans (living or deceased) or active military servicemembers. Applicants must be planning to enroll full time at a college, university, or accredited technical/trade school. They must be U.S. citizens and have a GPA of 3.0 or higher. Selection is based on financial need, academic promise, and merit.

Financial data The stipend is $1,000 per year.

Duration 4 years (provided the recipient maintains a GPA of 2.0 or higher).

Number awarded 6 each year: 1 in each AMVETS national district.

Deadline April of each year.

[376]
ANCHOR SCHOLARSHIP FOUNDATION AWARD

Anchor Scholarship Foundation
4966 Euclid Road, Suite 109
Virginia Beach, VA 23462
(757) 671-3200, ext. 116   Fax: (757) 671-3300
E-mail: scholarshipadmin@anchorscholarship.com
Web: www.anchorscholarship.com

Summary To provide financial assistance for college to dependents of active-duty or retired personnel serving in the Naval Surface Forces.

Eligibility This program is open to dependents of active-duty or retired personnel who have served at least 6 years (need not be consecutive) in a unit under the administrative control of Commander, Naval Surface Forces, U.S. Atlantic Fleet or U.S. Pacific Fleet. Applicants must be high school seniors or students already attending an accredited 4-year college or university and working on a bachelor's degree as a full-time student. Spouses are eligible if they are working full time on a first bachelor's degree. Selection is based on academic proficiency, extracurricular activities, character, all-around ability, and financial need.

Financial data Stipends range up to $2,000.

Duration 1 year; may be renewed.

Additional information This foundation was established in 1980 and limited to personnel who had served in the Atlantic Fleet. Its program was originally known as the SURFLANT Scholarship Foundation Award. In 2004, the program was expanded to include those who served in the Pacific Fleet and the current name was adopted.

Number awarded Varies each year; recently, 39 students received new or renewal scholarships.

Deadline February of each year.

[377]
ANDREWS SPOUSES' CLUB SCHOLARSHIPS

Andrews Spouses' Club
Attn: Mandy Huckins, Scholarship Committee Chair
1188 Columbus Circle
Joint Base Andrews, MD 20762
Web: www.andrewsspousesclub.org/#!scholarships/c1qj6

Summary To provide financial assistance for college study in any state to children and spouses of military and civilian personnel living in the National Capital Region or assigned to Joint Base Andrews.

Eligibility This program is open to dependents of active-duty, Department of Defense civilian, National Guard, and Reserve personnel assigned to or living on Joint Base Andrews or the National Capital Region, including all tenant units and branches of service; dependents of retired or deceased military members; and current members of the Andrews Spouses' Club. Applicants may be 1) graduating high school seniors planning to attend a 2- or 4-year accredited college, university, or vocational/technical school in any state; 2) undergraduates under 23 years of age continuing at a 2- or 4-year accredited college, university, or vocational/technical school in any state; or 3) military spouses planning to enroll at least half time at a 2- or 4-year accredited college, university, or vocational/technical school in any state. Selection is based on an essay of 450 to 500 words on a choice of assigned topics related to military service, academic achieve-

ment, leadership, honors, athletics, community service, and work experience.

Financial data Stipends recently ranged from $1,500 to $3,500.

Duration 1 year.

Additional information The National Capital Region is defined to include Washington, D.C.; the Maryland counties of Charles, Frederick, Montgomery, and Prince George's; the Virginia counties of Arlington, Fairfax, Loudoun, and Prince William; and the Virginia cities of Alexandria, Fairfax, Falls Church, Manassas, and Manassas Park.

Number awarded Varies each year; recently, 8 were awarded: 1 at $3,500, 2 at $2,500, and 5 at $1,500. Joint Base Andrews was created in 2009 by the merger of the former Andrews Air Force Base in Prince George's County, Maryland and Naval Air Facility Washington.

Deadline March of each year.

[378]
A-OK STUDENT REWARD PROGRAM

U.S. Navy
Attn: Navy Exchange Service Command
3280 Virginia Beach Boulevard
Virginia Beach, VA 23452-5724
Toll Free: (800) NAV-EXCH
Web: www.mynavyexchange.com

Summary To provide financial assistance for college to children of active and retired military personnel who shop at Navy Exchange (NEX) stores.

Eligibility This program is open to dependent children of active-duty military members, Reservists, and military retirees who are enrolled in grades 1-12 and have a GPA of 3.0 or higher. Applicants submit an entry at the service desk of their NEX store. Winners are selected in a drawing.

Financial data Winners receive savings bonds for $2,500, $1,500, $1,000, or $500. Funds are intended to help pay expenses of college.

Duration Drawings are held 4 times a year (in February, May, August, and November).

Additional information This program began in 1997.

Number awarded 16 each year: at each drawing, 1 savings bond for each of the 4 denominations is awarded.

Deadline Deadline not specified.

[379]
AOWCGWA SCHOLARSHIP PROGRAM

Army Officers' Wives' Club of the Greater Washington
  Area
c/o Fort Myer Thrift Shop
Attn: Scholarship Committee Chair
P.O. Box 1112
Fort Myer, VA 22211
(703) 764-9656   E-mail: collegeaowcgwa@gmail.com
Web: www.aowcgwa.org/index.cfm?action=page&page=33

Summary To provide financial assistance for college to the children and spouses of U.S. Army personnel and veterans in the Washington, D.C. metropolitan area.

Eligibility This program is open to 1) high school seniors who are children of Army personnel; 2) college students under 22 years of age who are children of Army personnel; and 3) spouses of Army personnel. High school seniors and spouses must reside with their sponsor in the Washington metropolitan area; the sponsor of college students must reside in that area. Sponsors may be active-duty, retired, or deceased, and officer or enlisted. High school seniors and college students must have a GPA of 3.0 or higher. Applicants must submit a 2-page essay on a topic that changes annually but relates to their experience as the member of an Army family; a list of extracurricular activities, honors, church activities, community service, and employment; an official transcript that includes (for high school seniors) their SAT or ACT scores; and a letter of recommendation. Students who plan to attend a service academy or receive another full scholarship are not eligible. Selection is based on academic merit, community involvement, and/or leadership potential; financial need is not considered.

Financial data The maximum stipend is $2,000.

Duration 1 year.

Additional information The Washington metropolitan area is defined to include the Virginia cities of Alexandria, Fairfax, Falls Church, Manassas, and Manassas Park; the Virginia counties of Arlington, Fairfax, Fauquier, Loudoun, Prince William, and Stafford; the Maryland counties of Calvert, Charles, Frederick, Montgomery, and Prince George's; and the District of Columbia. This program is supported in part by the First Command Educational Foundation.

Number awarded Varies each year; recently, this sponsor awarded more than $255,000 in scholarships and community grants.

Deadline March of each year.

[380]
AREA SCHOLARSHIPS

Army and Air Force Exchange Service
Attn: Retired Employees Association
Scholarship Committee
7045 Rembrandt Drive
Plano, TX 75093
(972) 862-8099   Toll Free: (800) 527-2345
E-mail: gall.tom@verizon.net
Web: www.shopmyexchange.com

Summary To provide financial assistance for college to children of employees (civilian and military) of Army and Air Force Exchange Service (AAFES) personnel.

Eligibility This program is open to college-bound high school seniors who 1) are the natural, adopted, or custodial children of active, retired, or deceased AAFES U.S. payroll employees or assigned military personnel; or 2) work for AAFES themselves and have been paid on its regular U.S. payroll for at least 12 months. Applicants must be planning to attend an accredited college, university, or military academy. They must have a score of at least 1750 on the SAT or 25 on the ACT. If their sponsor is a military retiree, the parent must have retired while on assignment with AAFES and must be an active member of the AAFES Retired Employees Association (AREA). If their sponsor is deceased, the parent must have died while an active or retired employee. All parents must have had at least 12 consecutive months of employment or military assignment. Selection is based on an essay on why they feel they should be awarded this scholarship, academic honors and other recognition, school activity participation, outside activities and hobbies, and letters of recommendation.

Financial data The stipend averages approximately $2,500.

Duration 1 year.

Additional information This program began in 1985.

Number awarded Varies each year; recently, 21 scholarships worth $53,500 were awarded. Since the program began, it has awarded more than $624,000 in scholarships.

Deadline March of each year.

[381]
ARIZONA VFW AUXILIARY SCHOLARSHIP

Ladies Auxiliary to the Veterans of Foreign Wars-
   Department of Arizona
c/o Mary Stray-Salisbury, Scholarship Chair
3350 Yaqui Drive
Lake Havasu City, AZ 86406
(928) 706-4044   Fax: (866) 543-5819
E-mail: mcsalisbury@npgcable.com
Web: www.lavfwaz.org/scholarships.html

Summary To provide financial assistance to high school seniors in Arizona who are related to a member of the Veterans of Foreign Wars (VFW) or its Ladies Auxiliary and planning to attend college in any state.

Eligibility This program is open to seniors graduating from high schools in Arizona who are the sibling, child, or grandchild of a member of the VFW or its Ladies Auxiliary. Applicants must be planning to attend a college, university, or vocational school in any state. Along with their application, they must submit an essay that includes their goals and aspirations in life, why they should receive this scholarship, and how their relationship to a VFW or Auxiliary member has had a positive effect on their life.

Financial data A stipend is awarded (amount not specified).

Duration 1 year.

Number awarded Varies each year.

Deadline March of each year.

[382]
ARKANSAS AMERICAN LEGION AUXILIARY
ACADEMIC SCHOLARSHIP

American Legion Auxiliary
Department of Arkansas
Attn: Department Secretary
1415 West Seventh Street
Little Rock, AR 72201-2903
(501) 374-5836   Fax: (501) 372-0855
E-mail: arkaux@att.net
Web: www.auxiliary.arlegion.org/scholarships.html

Summary To provide financial assistance to descendants of veterans who are high school seniors in Arkansas and planning to attend college in any state.

Eligibility This program is open to the descendants of veterans in Arkansas who served during eligibility dates for membership in the American Legion. Both the student and the parent must be residents of Arkansas. Their total family income must be less than $55,000. The student must be a high school senior planning to attend college in any state. Along with their application, they must submit an essay of 800 to 1,000 words on what their country's flag means to them. Selection is based on character (15%), Americanism (15%), leadership (15%), financial need (15%), and scholarship (40%).

Financial data   The stipend is $1,000; funds are paid in 2 equal installments.

Duration   1 year.

Number awarded   1 each year.

Deadline   February of each year.

[383]
ARKANSAS MILITARY DEPENDENTS SCHOLARSHIP PROGRAM

Arkansas Department of Higher Education
Attn: Financial Aid Division
423 Main Street, Suite 400
Little Rock, AR 72201-3801
(501) 371-2050   Toll Free: (800) 54-STUDY
Fax: (501) 371-2001   E-mail: finaid@adhe.edu
Web: www.adhe.edu

Summary   To provide financial assistance for educational purposes to dependents of certain categories of Arkansas veterans.

Eligibility   This program is open to the natural children, adopted children, stepchildren, and spouses of Arkansas residents who have been declared to be a prisoner of war, killed in action, missing in action, killed on ordnance delivery, or 100% totally and permanently disabled during, or as a result of, active military service. Applicants and their parent or spouse must be residents of Arkansas. They must be working on, or planning to work on, a bachelor's degree or certificate of completion at a public college, university, or technical school in Arkansas.

Financial data   The program pays for tuition, general registration fees, special course fees, activity fees, room and board (if provided in campus facilities), and other charges associated with earning a degree or certificate.

Duration   1 year; undergraduates may obtain renewal as long as they make satisfactory progress toward a baccalaureate degree; graduate students may obtain renewal as long as they maintain a minimum GPA of 2.0 and make satisfactory progress toward a degree.

Additional information   This program began in 1973 as the Arkansas Missing in Action/Killed in Action Dependents Scholarship Program to provide assistance to the dependents of veterans killed in action, missing in action, or declared a prisoner of war. In 2005, it was amended to include dependents of disabled veterans and given its current name. Applications must be submitted to the financial aid director at an Arkansas state-supported institution of higher education or state-supported technical/vocational school.

Number awarded   Varies each year; recently, 4 were awarded.

Deadline   May of each year.

[384]
ARKANSAS SERVICE MEMORIAL SCHOLARSHIPS

Arkansas Community Foundation
1400 West Markham, Suite 206
Little Rock, AR 72201
(501) 372-1116   Toll Free: (800) 220-ARCF
Fax: (501) 372-1166   E-mail: arcf@arcf.org
Web: www.arcf.org

Summary   To provide financial assistance to children of deceased veterans or other government officials in Arkansas who plan to attend college in the state.

Eligibility   This program is open to seniors graduating from high schools in Arkansas whose parent died in service to the community, state, or nation. Applicants must be planning to attend an accredited 2- or 4-year college in Arkansas on a full-time basis. Selection is based on academics, leadership, and financial need.

Financial data   The stipend is $2,500 per year.

Duration   1 year; may be renewed for up to 3 additional years, provided the recipient maintains a GPA of 2.5 or higher.

Additional information   This program began in 1984.

Number awarded   Varies each year; since this program was established, it has awarded 127 scholarships worth more than $15,000.

Deadline   March of each year.

[385]
ARK-LA-TEX CHAPTER MOAA SCHOLARSHIPS

Military Officers Association of America-Ark-La-Tex
   Chapter
Attn: George Finck, Scholarship Chair
P.O. Box 134
Barksdale AFB, LA 71110-0134
(318) 965-4124   Toll Free: (866) 544-2412
E-mail: gfincksr@gmail.com
Web: www.arklatexmoaa.org/scholarships-before

Summary   To provide financial assistance to descendants of members of the Ark-La-Tex Chapter of the Military Officers Association of America (MOAA) who are high school seniors planning to attend college in any state.

Eligibility   This program is open to graduating high school seniors who are the children, grandchildren, or great-grandchildren of a member of the Ark-La-Tex Chapter of MOAA. Applicants may be attending high school in any state, as long as they are sponsored by a chapter member who is their parent, grandparent, or great-grandparent. They must be planning to attend a college or university in any state. Selection is based on academic performance, earned honors, involvement in school and community activities, and leadership.

Financial data   Stipends are at least $1,000.

Duration   1 year.

Number awarded   At least 16 each year; a total of $20,000 is available for this program annually.

Deadline   April of each year.

[386]
ARMY AVIATION ASSOCIATION OF AMERICA LOAN PROGRAM

Army Aviation Association of America
Attn: AAAA Scholarship Foundation
593 Main Street
Monroe, CT 06468-2806
(203) 268-2450   Fax: (203) 268-5870
E-mail: aaaa@quad-a.org
Web: www.quad-a.org

Summary   To provide educational loans to members of the Army Aviation Association of America (AAAA) and their relatives.

Eligibility This program is open to AAAA members and their spouses, unmarried siblings, and unmarried children and grandchildren. Applicants must be enrolled or accepted for enrollment as an undergraduate or graduate student at an accredited college or university.

Financial data The maximum loan is $1,000 per year. All loans are interest free.

Duration Up to 4 years.

Number awarded Varies each year; recently, 1 of these loans was granted.

Deadline April of each year.

[387]
ARMY AVIATION ASSOCIATION OF AMERICA SCHOLARSHIPS

Army Aviation Association of America Scholarship
  Foundation
Attn: AAAA Scholarship Foundation
593 Main Street
Monroe, CT 06468-2806
(203) 268-2450   Fax: (203) 268-5870
E-mail: aaaa@quad-a.org
Web: www.quad-a.org

Summary To provide financial aid for undergraduate or graduate study to members of the Army Aviation Association of America (AAAA) and their relatives.

Eligibility This program is open to AAAA members (or deceased members) and their spouses, unmarried siblings, unmarried children, and unmarried grandchildren. Applicants must be enrolled or accepted for enrollment as an undergraduate or graduate student at an accredited college or university. Graduate students must include a 250-word essay on their life experiences, work history, and aspirations. Some scholarships are specifically reserved for enlisted, warrant officer, company grade, and Department of the Army civilian members. Selection is based on academic merit and personal achievement.

Financial data Stipends range from $1,000 to $2,500 per year.

Duration Scholarships may be for 1 year, 2 years, or 4 years.

Number awarded Varies each year; recently, $363,500 in scholarships was awarded to 236 students. Since the program began in 1963, the foundation has awarded more than $4.5 million to nearly 2,700 qualified applicants.

Deadline April of each year.

[388]
ARMY EMERGENCY RELIEF SPOUSE EDUCATION ASSISTANCE PROGRAM

Army Emergency Relief
200 Stovall Street
Alexandria, VA 22332-0600
(703) 428-0000   Toll Free: (866) 878-6378
Fax: (703) 325-7183   E-mail: Spouse@aerhq.org
Web: www.aerhq.org/dnn563/Scholarships/Spouses.aspx

Summary To provide financial assistance for college to the dependent spouses of Army personnel.

Eligibility This program is open to spouses of Army soldiers on active duty, widow(er)s of soldiers who died while on active duty, spouses of retired soldiers, and widow(er)s of soldiers who died while in a retired status. Applicants may not be

members of the National Guard, Reserves, or other military branch. They must be working full or part time on a 4-year college degree and have a GPA of 2.0 or higher. Study for a second undergraduate or graduate degree is not supported. Selection is based primarily on financial need.

Financial data The average stipend recently was $2,559 per academic year.

Duration 1 year; may be renewed up to 3 additional years of full-time study or up to 7 additional years of part-time study.

Additional information Army Emergency Relief is a private nonprofit organization dedicated to "helping the Army take care of its own." It previously operated separate educational assistance programs for stateside and overseas spouses, but combined those effective in December, 2011.

Number awarded Varies each year; recently, 1,230 spouses received support.

Deadline April of each year.

[389]
ARMY ENGINEER MEMORIAL AWARDS

Army Engineer Spouses' Club
c/o Laura Putnam, Chair
P.O. Box 6332
Alexandria, VA 22306-6332
E-mail: scholarships@armyengineerspouses.com
Web: www.armyengineerspouses.com

Summary To provide financial assistance for college to the children of officers who served in the Army Corps of Engineers.

Eligibility This program is open to children of 1) U.S. Army Corps of Engineers officers and warrant officers who are currently on active duty, retired, or deceased while on active duty or after retiring from active duty; or 2) current Department of the Army employees of the U.S. Army Corps of Engineers. Applicants must be high school seniors planning to attend a college, university, or technical/vocational school. Along with their application, they must submit an essay of 300 to 400 words on the event that has had the greatest impact on their life so far and how they think it will affect them in the future. Selection is based on academic and extracurricular achievement during high school. U.S. citizenship is required.

Financial data The stipend is $1,000.

Duration 1 year.

Additional information This program began in 1973.

Number awarded Varies each year; recently, 9 were awarded.

Deadline February of each year.

[390]
ARMY NURSE CORPS ASSOCIATION SCHOLARSHIPS

Army Nurse Corps Association
Attn: Education Committee
P.O. Box 39235
San Antonio, TX 78218-1235
(210) 650-3534   Fax: (210) 650-3494
E-mail: education@e-anca.org
Web: e-anca.org/ANCAEduc.htm

Summary To provide financial assistance to students who have a connection to the Army and are interested in working on an undergraduate or graduate degree in nursing.

Eligibility This program is open to U.S. citizens attending colleges or universities that have accredited programs offering associate, bachelor's, master's, or doctoral degrees in nursing. Applicants must be 1) students currently enrolled in an accredited baccalaureate or advanced nursing or nurse anesthesia program who are serving or have served (and received an honorable discharge) in any branch and at any rank of a component of the U.S. Army; or 2) nursing or anesthesia students whose parent(s) or spouse are serving or have served in a component of the U.S. Army. Along with their application, they must submit a personal statement on their professional career objectives, reasons for applying for this scholarship, financial need, special considerations, personal and academic interests, and why they are preparing for a nursing career. Students who are receiving any support from any branch of the military, including ROTC scholarships, are not eligible.

Financial data The stipend is $3,000. Funds are sent directly to the recipient's school.

Duration 1 year.

Additional information Although the sponsoring organization is made up of current, retired, and honorably discharged officers of the Army Nurse Corps, it does not have an official affiliation with the Army. Therefore, students who receive these scholarships do not incur any military service obligation.

Number awarded 1 or more each year.

Deadline April of each year.

[391]
ARMY SCHOLARSHIP FOUNDATION SCHOLARSHIPS

Army Scholarship Foundation
11700 Preston Road, Suite 660-301
Dallas, TX 75230
E-mail: ContactUs@armyscholarshipfoundation.org
Web: www.armyscholarshipfoundation.org

Summary To provide financial assistance for undergraduate study to the children and spouses of Army personnel.

Eligibility This program is open to 1) children of regular active-duty, active-duty Reserve, and active-duty Army National Guard members in good standing; 2) spouses of serving enlisted regular active-duty, active-duty Reserve, and active-duty Army National Guard members in good standing; and 3) children of former U.S. Army members who received an honorable or medical discharge or were killed while serving in the U.S. Army. Applicants must be high school seniors, high school graduates, or undergraduates enrolled at an accredited college, university, or vocational/technical institute. They must be U.S. citizens and have a GPA of 2.0 or higher; children must be younger than 24 years of age. Financial need is considered in the selection process.

Financial data Stipends range from $500 to $2,000 per year.

Duration 1 year; recipients may reapply.

Additional information The Army Scholarship Foundation was established in 2001. Among the general scholarships offered by the foundation are those designated the Captain Jennifer Shafer Odom Memorial Scholarship, the Colonel Urey Woodson Alexander Memorial Scholarship, the Perot Family Scholarship, and the Lieutenant General Jack Costello Memorial Scholarship. The program also includes

programs sponsored by Hamilton Sundstrand, KBR, Fluor Corporation, General Dynamics, and BAE Systems.

Number awarded Varies each year; recently, 36 were awarded.

Deadline April of each year.

[392]
ASSOCIATION OF AVIATION ORDNANCEMEN EDUCATIONAL FOUNDATION SCHOLARSHIPS

Association of Aviation Ordnancemen
Attn: Robert L. Crow Scholarship Foundation
c/o Rick Garza, Committee Chair
10213 Rolling Green Way
Fort Washington, MD 20744
Web: www.aaoweb.org/AAO/Scholar/

Summary To provide financial assistance to members of the Association of Aviation Ordnancemen, their family, and dependents of deceased aviation ordnancemen of the Navy or Marine Corps.

Eligibility This program is open to 1) regular and associate members of the Association of Aviation Ordnancemen; 2) dependents and immediate relatives (siblings, grandchildren) of regular and associate members; and 3) dependents of deceased aviation ordnancemen of the U.S. Navy or Marine Corps. Applicants must be enrolled or planning to enroll at a college, university, technical/trade school, or postsecondary specialty school in any state. Selection is based on academic record, goals, eligibility for and award of other scholarships and educational grants, and financial need.

Financial data Stipends range from $1,250 to $4,000 per year.

Duration 1 year; recipients may reapply.

Additional information This program began in 1979. It consists primarily of scholarships designated as Robert L. Crow Awards and other scholarships named after other corporate or military sponsors (recently, those included the NAVAIRSYSCOM Weapons Program, Huntington Ingalls Shipbuilding, and the San Diego Padres.

Number awarded Varies each year; recently, 10 were awarded: 5 at $4,000, 2 at $2,100, 2 at $2,000, and 1 at $1,250.

Deadline June of each year.

[393]
ASSOCIATION OF THE UNITED STATES NAVY EDUCATIONAL ASSISTANCE PROGRAM

Association of the United States Navy
Attn: Educational Assistance Program
1619 King Street
Alexandria, VA 22314-2793
(703) 548-5800   Toll Free: (866) NAVY-411
Fax: (866) 683-3647   E-mail: linda.bautista@ausn.org
Web: www.ausn.org

Summary To provide financial assistance for college to dependents of members of the Association of the United States Navy (formerly the Naval Reserve Association).

Eligibility This program is open to dependent children, under 24 years of age, and surviving spouses of association members. Applicants must be enrolled or planning to enroll full time at a college, university, or technical school. They must be U.S. citizens. Selection is based on academic and leadership ability, potential, character, personal qualities, and financial need.

Financial data The amounts of the stipends vary but recently averaged more than $4,000 per year.

Duration 1 year; may be renewed 1 additional year.

Additional information The Association of the United States Navy was formed in 2009 as a successor to the Naval Reserve Association.

Number awarded Varies each year.

Deadline April of each year.

[394]
BART LONGO MEMORIAL SCHOLARSHIPS

National Chief Petty Officers' Association
c/o Marjorie Hays, Treasurer
1014 Ronald Drive
Corpus Christi, TX 78412-3548
Web: www.goatlocker.org/ncpoa/scholarship.htm

Summary To provide financial assistance for college or graduate school to members of the National Chief Petty Officers' Association (NCPOA) and their families.

Eligibility This program is open to members of the NCPOA and the children, stepchildren, and grandchildren of living or deceased members. Applicants may be high school seniors or graduates entering a college or university or students currently enrolled full time as undergraduate or graduate students. Selection is based on academic achievement and participation in extracurricular activities; financial need is not considered.

Financial data The stipend is $1,000.

Duration 1 year.

Additional information Membership in the NCPOA is limited to men and women who served or are serving as Chief Petty Officers in the U.S. Navy, U.S. Coast Guard, or their Reserve components for at least 30 days.

Number awarded 2 each year: 1 to a high school senior or graduate and 1 to an undergraduate or graduate student.

Deadline May of each year.

[395]
BECHTEL ENGINEERING AND SCIENCE SCHOLARSHIPS

Marines' Memorial Association
c/o Marines Memorial Club and Hotel
609 Sutter Street
San Francisco, CA 94102
(415) 673-6672, ext. 293   Fax: (415) 441-3649
E-mail: scholarship@marineclub.com
Web: www.marineclub.com/membership/scholarship.php

Summary To provide financial assistance to members of the Marines' Memorial Association from all branches of the armed forces and their descendants who are interested in studying a field of science, technology, engineering, or mathematics (STEM) in college.

Eligibility This program is open to active members of the association and their children and grandchildren. Applicants must be high school seniors or students currently enrolled full time in an undergraduate degree program in a field of STEM. Engineering programs must be ABET-accredited. Along with their application, they must submit an essay of 250 to 500 words on an ethical dilemma in relation to their field of study.

Graduating high school seniors must submit a high school transcript and SAT or ACT scores; continuing college students must submit a college transcript. Selection is based on the essay, academic merit, references, and financial need.

Financial data The stipend is $5,000 per year.

Duration 1 year; recipients may reapply for up to 3 additional years.

Additional information Membership in the association is open to veterans of the Marines, Army, Navy, Air Force, or Coast Guard and to personnel currently serving in a branch of the armed forces. This program is funded by the S.D. Bechtel, Jr. Foundation.

Number awarded 5 each year.

Deadline April of each year.

[396]
BELVOIR OFFICERS' SPOUSES' CLUB SCHOLARSHIPS

Belvoir Officers' Spouses' Club
Attn: Scholarship Committee Chair
P.O. Box 322
Fort Belvoir, VA 22060
(703) 799-1400   E-mail: boscscholarship@yahoo.com
Web: www.belvoirosc.org/scholarships.html

Summary To provide financial assistance to children and spouses of military personnel in the greater Washington, D.C. area.

Eligibility This program is open to children and spouses of active-duty, retired, or deceased members of any branch of the armed forces (including Guard and Reserves) who reside in the greater Washington, D.C. area. Applicants must be high school seniors, current college students under 22 years of age, or spouses of any age who are attending or planning to attend a 2- or 4-year college or university in any state. Along with their application, they must submit a 250-word essay on 1) for high school seniors, how being a member of a military family has influenced their education choices; 2) for current college students, the experiences they have had since high school that have influenced their career goals; or 3) for souses, how their volunteer or professional experience has influenced their course of study. Selection is based on that essay, academic honors, extracurricular and community activities, paid or volunteer employment, and other honors and recognition.

Financial data Stipends range from $1,000 to $3,000.

Duration 1 year.

Number awarded Varies each year; recently, 10 of these scholarships, with a total value of $17,000 were awarded.

Deadline March of each year.

[397]
BENTLEY-FAUCETTE-MILES SCHOLARSHIP

United Daughters of the Confederacy
Attn: Second Vice President General
328 North Boulevard
Richmond, VA 23220-4008
(804) 355-1636   Fax: (804) 353-1396
E-mail: jamieretired@sbcglobal.net
Web: www.hqudc.org/Scholarships/index.htm

Summary To provide financial assistance for college to lineal descendants of Confederate veterans, especially those from New York.

Eligibility Eligible to apply for these scholarships are lineal descendants of worthy Confederates or collateral descendants who are current or former members of the Children of the Confederacy or current members of the United Daughters of the Confederacy. Preference is given to members from New York. Applicants must submit a family financial report and certified proof of the Confederate record of 1 ancestor, with the company and regiment in which he served. They must have at least a 3.0 GPA in high school.

Financial data The amount of this scholarship depends on the availability of funds.

Duration 1 year; may be renewed.

Number awarded 1 each year.

Deadline April of each year.

[398]
BERNARD E. DILLON VOCATIONAL SKILLS SCHOLARSHIPS

American Military Retirees Association, Inc.
Attn: Scholarship Committee
5436 Peru Street, Suite 1
Plattsburgh, NY 12901
(518) 563-9479   Toll Free: (800) 424-2969
Fax: (518) 324-5204   E-mail: info@amra1973.org
Web: www.amra1973.org/Scholarship

Summary To provide financial assistance for vocational training to members of the American Military Retirees Association (AMRA) and their dependents.

Eligibility This program is open to current members of AMRA and their spouses and dependent children and grandchildren. Applicants must be attending or planning to attend a vocational/technical school. Along with their application, they must submit a 750-word essay on why they deserve this scholarship. Selection is based on academic achievement, leadership abilities, character, citizenship, and community service.

Financial data The stipend is $1,000.

Duration 1 year.

Additional information Membership in AMRA is open to all retired members of the armed forces, regardless of rank. This program began in 2014.

Number awarded 5 each year.

Deadline February of each year.

[399]
BESSIE A. CAPRON PRIZE

Daughters of the Cincinnati
Attn: Scholarship Administrator
20 West 44th Street, Suite 508
New York, NY 10036
(212) 991-9945
E-mail: scholarships@daughters1894.org
Web: www.daughters1894.org/scholarship.htm

Summary To provide financial assistance to high school seniors who are the daughters of active-duty, deceased, or retired military officers and plan to attend college to prepare for a career in education.

Eligibility This program is open to high school seniors who are the daughters of career commissioned officers of the regular Army, Navy, Air Force, Coast Guard, or Marine Corps on active duty, deceased, or retired. Applicants must be planning to enroll at a college or university in any state to prepare for a

career in education. Along with their application, they must submit an official school transcript, SAT or ACT scores, a letter of recommendation, an essay on their choice of 3 assigned topics, and documentation of financial need.

Financial data Scholarship amounts have recently averaged $4,000 per year. Funds are paid directly to the college of the student's choice.

Duration 1 year; may be renewed up to 3 additional years, provided the recipient remains in good academic standing.

Number awarded 1 each year.

Deadline March of each year.

[400]
BG BENJAMIN B. TALLEY SCHOLARSHIP

Society of American Military Engineers-Anchorage Post
Attn: BG B.B. Talley Scholarship Endowment Fund
P.O. Box 6409
Anchorage, AK 99506-6409
(907) 244-8063   E-mail: cturletes@gci.net
Web: www.sameanchorage.org/h_about/scholinfo.html

Summary To provide financial assistance to student members of the Society of American Military Engineers (SAME) from Alaska who are working on a bachelor's or master's degree in designated fields of engineering or the natural sciences.

Eligibility This program is open to members of the Anchorage Post of SAME who are residents of Alaska, attending college in Alaska, an active-duty military member stationed in Alaska, or a dependent of an active-duty military member stationed in Alaska. Applicants must be 1) sophomores, juniors, or seniors majoring in engineering, architecture, construction or project management, natural sciences, physical sciences, applied sciences, or mathematics at an accredited college or university; or 2) students working on a master's degree in those fields. They must have a GPA of 2.5 or higher. U.S. citizenship is required. Along with their application, they must submit an essay of 250 to 500 words on their career goals. Selection is based on that essay, academic achievement, participation in school and community activities, and work/family activities; financial need is not considered.

Financial data Stipends range up to $3,000.

Duration 1 year.

Additional information This program began in 1997.

Number awarded Several each year; at least 1 scholarship is reserved for a master's degree students.

Deadline December of each year.

[401]
BILL CREECH SCHOLARSHIP

Second Indianhead Division Association
P.O. Box 218
Fox Lake, IL 60020-0218
(224) 225-1202   E-mail: 2idahq@comcast.net
Web: www.2ida.org/Scholarship.htm

Summary To provide financial assistance for college to children and grandchildren of members of the Second Indianhead Division Association.

Eligibility This program is open to 1) children and grandchildren of veterans who have been members of the association for the past 3 years and have a current membership; and 2) children and grandchildren of men or women killed in action while serving with the Second Division. Applicants may be high school seniors or currently-enrolled college students. They must submit a personal letter giving reasons for the request and plans for the future; a high school and, if appropriate, college transcript; ACT or SAT test scores; a statement from their school principal attesting to their character and involvement in extracurricular activities; 2 letters of recommendation from current teachers or professors; a 200- to 300-word essay on such subjects as "What Being an American Means to Me," "Why I Should Receive This Scholarship," or "What Significant Part of U.S. Army History Has the Second Infantry Division Contributed;" and a statement from their parents or guardians on the financial support they will be able to provide the applicant.

Financial data The stipend is usually $1,000 per year.

Duration 1 year; may be renewed.

Number awarded 1 or more each year.

Deadline May of each year.

[402]
BLACKHORSE SCHOLARSHIP

Blackhorse Association
P.O. Box 223
Hemphill, TX 75948-0223
E-mail: info@blackhorse.org
Web: www.blackhorse.org/scholarships.cfm

Summary To provide financial assistance for college to children of members of the Blackhorse Association who are currently serving or have served with the 11th Armored Cavalry Regiment (ACR).

Eligibility This program is open to the natural and adopted children of current or former 11th ACR solders who are also members of the association. Applicants must be attending or planning to attend college. In the selection process, first priority is given to children who lost a parent in service of the regiment; second priority is given to children of those incapacitated by wounds or injury while serving the regiment; third priority is given based on financial need of the applicant and family.

Financial data The stipend is $3,000 per year.

Duration 1 year; may be renewed up to 3 additional years.

Additional information The Blackhorse Association was founded in 1970 by veterans of the 11th ACR who had served in Vietnam.

Number awarded Varies each year; recently, 20 were awarded. Since this program was established, it has awarded more than $600,000 in scholarships.

Deadline March of each year.

[403]
BOOZ ALLEN HAWAII SCHOLARSHIP FUND

Hawai'i Community Foundation
Attn: Scholarship Department
827 Fort Street Mall
Honolulu, HI 96813
(808) 566-5570   Toll Free: (888) 731-3863
Fax: (808) 521-6286
E-mail: scholarships@hcf-hawaii.org
Web: www.hawaiicommunityfoundation.org/scholarships

Summary To provide financial assistance to residents of Hawaii and dependents of military personnel stationed in the state who are attending college in any state.

Eligibility This program is open to residents of Hawaii and dependents of military personnel stationed in the state. Applicants must be attending a 4-year accredited college or university in any state as a full-time undergraduate student. They must be able to demonstrate academic achievement (GPA of 3.0 or higher), good moral character, and financial need. Along with their application, they must submit a short statement indicating their reasons for attending college, their planned course of study, their career goals, and what community service means to them.

Financial data The amounts of the awards depend on the availability of funds and the need of the recipient. Recently, the average value of each of the scholarships awarded by the foundation was $2,200.

Duration 1 year.

Number awarded Varies each year.

Deadline February of each year.

[404]
BOWFIN MEMORIAL ACADEMIC SCHOLARSHIPS

Pacific Fleet Submarine Memorial Association
c/o Sarah Santala, Chair
Bowfin Memorial Scholarship Committee
1568 Kupau Street
Kailua, HI 96734
(808) 423-1341   Fax: (808) 422-5201
E-mail: scholarship@pearlharborsosa.org
Web: www.bowfin.org/education

Summary To provide financial assistance to the children of submarine force personnel who live in Hawaii and plan to attend college in any state.

Eligibility This program is open to the children of submarine force personnel (active duty, retired, or deceased) who are under 23 years of age. Applicants may attend school anywhere in the United States, but their submarine sponsor or surviving parent must live in Hawaii. Selection is based on academic performance, demonstrated potential, extracurricular activities, and financial need.

Financial data Stipends range from $250 to $5,000 per year.

Duration 1 year; may be renewed upon annual reapplication.

Additional information This program began in 1985 to honor the 3,505 submariners and 52 submarines lost during World War II. It is offered in conjunction with the Pearl Harbor Submarine Officers' Spouses' Association.

Number awarded Varies each year; recently, 11 were awarded.

Deadline March of each year.

[405]
BOWFIN MEMORIAL CONTINUING EDUCATION SCHOLARSHIPS

Pacific Fleet Submarine Memorial Association
c/o Sarah Santala, Chair
Bowfin Memorial Scholarship Committee
1568 Kupau Street
Kailua, HI 96734
(808) 423-1341   Fax: (808) 422-5201
E-mail: scholarship@pearlharborsosa.org
Web: www.bowfin.org/education

Summary To provide financial assistance to the submarine force personnel and their spouses who live in Hawaii and wish to attend college in the state.

Eligibility This program is open to submarine force personnel (active duty or retired), their spouses, and the spouses of deceased submarine force personnel. Applicants must live in Hawaii and be interested in attending school in the state. Selection is based on academic performance, community involvement, motivation, goals, and financial need.

Financial data A stipend is awarded (amount not specified).

Duration 1 year; may be renewed upon annual reapplication.

Additional information This program began in 1985 to honor the 3,505 submariners and 52 submarines lost during World War II. It is offered in conjunction with the Pearl Harbor Submarine Officers' Spouses' Association.

Number awarded Varies each year.

Deadline March of each year.

[406]
BRANSTAD-REYNOLDS SCHOLARSHIP FUND

Iowa Department of Veterans Affairs
Attn: Grants/Bonus Coordinator
Camp Dodge, Building 3465
7105 N.W. 70th Avenue
Johnston, IA 50131-1824
(515) 727-3443   Toll Free: (800) VET-IOWA
Fax: (515) 727-3713   E-mail: missy.miller@iowa.gov
Web: va.iowa.gov/benefits/index.html

Summary To provide financial assistance for college in Iowa to the relatives of members of the armed forces from that state who died in active service after September 11, 2001.

Eligibility This program is open to natural children, unremarried spouses, and siblings of military personnel who died in active service or as a result of such service after September 11, 2001. The deceased servicemember must have been 1) a resident of Iowa at the time of entering into active military service; 2) assigned to a unit based in Iowa at the time of death; or 3) a resident of Iowa at the time of death. The death does not have to be combat-related. Active military status includes federal service in the armed forces, National Guard, or Reserves. Students must be attending or planning to attend a postsecondary institution located within Iowa. They must be able to demonstrate financial need.

Financial data Stipends are awarded (amount not specified); funds are to be used to subsidize the costs of tuition, books, fees, housing, special tools and equipment required for course work, school-approved tutoring, and any other required educational expenses. Once all educational expenses are met, any remaining funds will be released to the student to cover other expenses as needed.

Duration 1 year.

Number awarded Varies each year.

Deadline December of each year.

[407]
BRAXTON BRAGG CHAPTER AUSA SCHOLARSHIPS

Association of the United States Army-Braxton Bragg Chapter
Attn: Vice President for Scholarships
P.O. Box 70036
Fort Bragg, NC 28307
(910) 396-3755   E-mail: hbraxtonbraggc@nc.rr.com
Web: www.braggausa.org/?page_id=1425

Summary To provide financial assistance to members of the Braxton Bragg Chapter of the Association of the United States Army (AUSA) in North Carolina and their dependents who are interested in attending college or graduate school in any state.

Eligibility This program is open to chapter members and their families in North Carolina who are working on or planning to work on an undergraduate, graduate, or technical degree at a college or technical school in any state. Applicants must submit a 500-word essay on how the Army and Army values have influenced their life; letters of recommendation; a list of personal accomplishments; and a transcript that includes their ACT or SAT score. Selection is based on academic achievement, participation in extracurricular activities at school, and participation in community service activities. Membership in AUSA is open to current and retired Army personnel (including Reserves and National Guard), ROTC cadets, or civilian employees of the Army. Active-duty soldiers are especially encouraged to apply.

Financial data The stipend is $1,000.

Duration 1 year; recipients may reapply.

Additional information Membership in the Braxton Bragg Chapter is open to all Army active, National Guard, and Reserve members in North Carolina, along with Department of the Army civilians, retirees, concerned citizens, and family members.

Number awarded Varies each year; recently, 26 were awarded.

Deadline April of each year.

[408]
BRIAN SWEENEY MEMORIAL AWARD

Hanscom Spouses' Club
Attn: Scholarship Committee Chair
General Delivery
75 Grenier Street, Unit 888
Hanscom AFB, MA 01731
(781) 538-5811   E-mail: scholarships@hanscomsc.org
Web: www.hanscomsc.org/scholarships.html

Summary To provide financial assistance to high school seniors who are children of military personnel or veterans in the Hanscom Air Force Base area of New England and interested in studying fields related to aviation at a college in any state.

Eligibility This program is open to dependents of active-duty, retired, and deceased members of any branch of the armed forces, including Reservists and National Guard members who were activated during the school year. Applicants must be graduating high school seniors who have a valid military identification card and reside within a 60-mile radius of Hanscom Air Force Base (includes eastern Massachusetts, Rhode Island, and southern New Hampshire) or be a dependent whose military sponsor is stationed at Hanscom Air Force Base. They must be planning to attend a 2- or 4-year college or university in any state to work on a degree in a field related to aviation, including engineering (aeronautical, civil, environmental), maintenance, meteorology, airport management, and aviation safety and security. Along with their application, they must submit a 2-page essay on their educational goals, how their educational experience will help prepare them to pursue future goals, and how they intend to apply their education to better their community. Selection is based on merit.

Financial data Recently, the stipend was $3,000.

Duration 1 year; nonrenewable.

Additional information This program was established to honor a victim of an airplane crash on September 11, 2001. It is sponsored by the Paul Revere Chapter of the Air Force Association.

Number awarded 1 each year.

Deadline March of each year.

[409]
BUCKINGHAM MEMORIAL SCHOLARSHIPS

Air Traffic Control Association
Attn: Scholarship Fund
1101 King Street, Suite 300
Alexandria, VA 22314
(703) 299-2430   Fax: (703) 299-2437
E-mail: info@atca.org
Web: www.atca.org/ATCA-Scholarship

Summary To provide financial assistance for college or graduate school to children of current or former air traffic control specialists.

Eligibility This program is open to U.S. citizens who are the children, natural or adopted, of a person currently or formerly serving as an air traffic control specialist with the U.S. government, with the U.S. military, or in a private facility in the United States. Applicants must be enrolled or planning to enroll at least half time in a baccalaureate or graduate program at an accredited college or university and have at least 30 semester hours to be completed before graduation. Along with their application, they must submit a 500-word essay on how they will blend their career with community service in their adult life. Financial need is considered in the selection process.

Financial data A stipend is awarded; recently, scholarships awarded by this sponsor averaged more than $5,000.

Duration 1 year; may be renewed.

Additional information This program was formerly known as the Children of Air Traffic Control Specialists Scholarship Program.

Number awarded Varies each year; recently, 4 were awarded.

Deadline April of each year.

[410]
BUICK ACHIEVERS SCHOLARSHIP PROGRAM

Scholarship America
Attn: Scholarship Management Services
One Scholarship Way
P.O. Box 297
St. Peter, MN 56082
(507) 931-1682   Toll Free: (866) 243-4644
Fax: (507) 931-9168
E-mail: buickachievers@scholarshipamerica.org
Web: www.buickachievers.com

Summary To provide financial assistance to entering and continuing college students planning to major in specified fields related to engineering, design, or business.

Eligibility This program is open to high school seniors and graduates who are enrolled or planning to enroll full time at an accredited 4-year college or university as first-time freshmen or continuing undergraduates. Applicants must be interested in majoring in fields of engineering (chemical, computer, controls, electrical, energy, environmental, industrial, manufacturing, materials, mechanical, plastic/polymers, or software); technology (automotive technology, computer information systems, computer science, engineering technology, information technology, mechatronics); design (automotive, fine arts, graphic, industrial, product, transportation); or business (accounting, business administration, economics, ergonomics, finance, human resources, industrial hygiene, international business, labor and industrial relations, management information systems, marketing, mathematics, occupational health and safety, production management, statistics, or supply chain/logistics). U.S. citizenship or permanent resident status is required. Selection is based on academic achievement, financial need, participation and leadership in community and school activities, work experience, and interest in preparing for a career in the automotive or related industry. Special consideration is given to first-generation college students, women, minorities, military veterans, and dependents of military personnel.

Financial data Stipends are $25,000 per year.

Duration 1 year; may be renewed up to 3 additional years (and 1 additional year for students in a 5-year engineering program), provided the recipient remains enrolled full time, maintains a GPA of 3.0 or higher, and continues to major in an eligible field.

Additional information This program, which began in 2011, is funded by the General Motors Foundation.

Number awarded 100 each year.

Deadline February of each year.

[411]
CALIFORNIA FEE WAIVER PROGRAM FOR CHILDREN OF VETERANS

California Department of Veterans Affairs
Attn: Division of Veterans Services
1227 O Street, Room 105
P.O. Box 942895
Sacramento, CA 94295
(916) 653-2573   Toll Free: (877) 741-8532
Fax: (916) 653-2563   TDD: (800) 324-5966
Web: www.calvet.ca.gov

Summary To provide financial assistance for college to the children of disabled or deceased veterans in California.

Eligibility Eligible for this program are the children of veterans who 1) died of a service-connected disability; 2) had a service-connected disability at the time of death; or 3) currently have a service-connected disability of any level of severity. Applicants must plan to attend a community college in California, branch of the California State University system, or campus of the University of California. Their income, including the value of support received from parents, cannot exceed $11,945. The veteran is not required to have a connection to California for this program. Dependents in college who are eligible to receive federal education benefits from the U.S. Department of Veterans Affairs are not eligible for these fee waivers.

Financial data This program provides for waiver of registration fees to students attending any publicly-supported community or state college or university in California.

Duration 1 year; may be renewed.

Number awarded Varies each year.

Deadline Deadline not specified.

[412]
CALIFORNIA FEE WAIVER PROGRAM FOR DEPENDENTS OF DECEASED OR DISABLED NATIONAL GUARD MEMBERS

California Department of Veterans Affairs
Attn: Division of Veterans Services
1227 O Street, Room 105
P.O. Box 942895
Sacramento, CA 94295
(916) 653-2573　　　　Toll Free: (877) 741-8532
Fax: (916) 653-2563　　　TDD: (800) 324-5966
Web: www.calvet.ca.gov

Summary To provide financial assistance for college to dependents of disabled and deceased members of the California National Guard.

Eligibility Eligible for this program are dependents, unremarried surviving spouses, and current registered domestic partners (RDPs) of members of the California National Guard who, in the line of duty and in the active service of the state, were killed, died of a disability, or became permanently disabled. Applicants must be attending or planning to attend a community college, branch of the California State University system, or campus of the University of California.

Financial data Full-time college students receive a waiver of tuition and registration fees at any publicly-supported community or state college or university in California.

Duration 1 year; may be renewed.

Number awarded Varies each year.

Deadline Deadline not specified.

[413]
CALIFORNIA FEE WAIVER PROGRAM FOR DEPENDENTS OF TOTALLY DISABLED VETERANS

California Department of Veterans Affairs
Attn: Division of Veterans Services
1227 O Street, Room 105
P.O. Box 942895
Sacramento, CA 94295
(916) 653-2573　　　　Toll Free: (877) 741-8532
Fax: (916) 653-2563　　　TDD: (800) 324-5966
Web: www.calvet.ca.gov

Summary To provide financial assistance for college to dependents of disabled and other California veterans.

Eligibility Eligible for this program are spouses, children, and unremarried spouses or registered domestic partners (RDPs) of veterans who are currently totally service-connected disabled (or are being compensated for a service-connected disability at a rate of 100%) or who died of a service-connected cause or disability. The veteran parent must have served during a qualifying war period and must have been discharged or released from military service under honorable conditions. Children must be younger than 27 years of age (extended to 30 if the child is a veteran); there are no age restrictions for spouses, surviving spouses, or RDPs. This program does not have an income limit. Dependents in college are not eligible if they are qualified to receive educational benefits from the U.S. Department of Veterans Affairs. Applicants must be attending or planning to attend a community college, branch of the California State University system, or campus of the University of California.

Financial data Full-time college students receive a waiver of tuition and registration fees at any publicly-supported community or state college or university in California.

Duration Children of eligible veterans may receive postsecondary benefits until the needed training is completed or until the dependent reaches 27 years of age (extended to 30 if the dependent serves in the armed forces). Spouses and surviving spouses are limited to a maximum of 48 months' full-time training or the equivalent in part-time training.

Number awarded Varies each year.

Deadline Deadline not specified.

[414]
CALIFORNIA FEE WAIVER PROGRAM FOR RECIPIENTS OF THE MEDAL OF HONOR AND THEIR CHILDREN

California Department of Veterans Affairs
Attn: Division of Veterans Services
1227 O Street, Room 101
P.O. Box 942895
Sacramento, CA 94295
(916) 653-2573　　　　Toll Free: (877) 741-8532
Fax: (916) 653-2563　　　TDD: (800) 324-5966
Web: www.calvet.ca.gov

Summary To provide financial assistance for college to veterans in California who received the Medal of Honor and their children.

Eligibility This program is open to recipients of the Medal of Honor and their children younger than 27 years of age who are residents of California. Applicants must be attending or planning to attend a community college, branch of the California State University system, or campus of the University of California.

Financial data Full-time college students receive a waiver of tuition and registration fees at any publicly-supported community or state college or university in California.

Duration 1 year; may be renewed.

Number awarded Varies each year.

Deadline Deadline not specified.

[415]
CALIFORNIA LEGION AUXILIARY EDUCATIONAL ASSISTANCE

American Legion Auxiliary
Department of California
205 13th Street, Suite 3300
San Francisco, CA 94103-2461
(415) 861-5092   Fax: (415) 861-8365
E-mail: calegionaux@calegionaux.org
Web: www.calegionaux.org/scholarships.htm

Summary To provide financial assistance to high school seniors in California who are the children of veterans or military personnel and require assistance to continue their education.

Eligibility This program is open to seniors graduating from high schools in California who are the children of active-duty military personnel or veterans who served during wartime. Applicants must be planning to continue their education at a college, university, or business/trade school in California. Each high school in California may nominate only 1 student for these scholarships; the faculty selects the nominee if more than 1 student wishes to apply. Selection is based on the application (25%), scholarship (25%), character and leadership (25%), and financial need (25%).

Financial data Stipends are $1,000 or $500 per year.

Duration 1 year; 1 of the scholarships may be renewed 1 additional year.

Number awarded 8 each year: 1 at $1,000 per year that may be renewed 1 additional year, 4 at $1,000 that are nonrenewable, and 3 at $500 that are nonrenewable.

Deadline March of each year.

[416]
CALIFORNIA LEGION AUXILIARY PAST DEPARTMENT PRESIDENT'S JUNIOR SCHOLARSHIP

American Legion Auxiliary
Department of California
205 13th Street, Suite 3300
San Francisco, CA 94103-2461
(415) 861-5092   Fax: (415) 861-8365
E-mail: calegionaux@calegionaux.org
Web: www.calegionaux.org/scholarships.htm

Summary To provide financial assistance for college to the daughters and other female descendants of California veterans who are active in the American Legion Junior Auxiliary.

Eligibility This program is open to the daughters, granddaughters, and great- granddaughters of veterans who served during wartime. Applicants must be in their senior year at an accredited high school, must have been members of the Junior Auxiliary for at least 3 consecutive years, and must be residents of California (if eligibility for Junior Auxiliary membership is by a current member of the American Legion or Auxiliary in California, the applicant may reside elsewhere). They must be planning to attend college in California. Selection is based on scholastic merit (20%); active participation in Junior Auxiliary (15%); record of service or volunteerism within the applicant's community, school, and/or unit (35%); a brief description of the applicant's desire to pursue a higher education (15%); and 3 letters of reference (15%).

Financial data The stipend depends on the availability of funds but ranges from $300 to $1,000.

Duration 1 year.

Number awarded 1 each year.

Deadline April of each year.

[417]
CALIFORNIA LEGION AUXILIARY PAST PRESIDENTS' PARLEY NURSING SCHOLARSHIPS

American Legion Auxiliary
Department of California
205 13th Street, Suite 3300
San Francisco, CA 94103-2461
(415) 861-5092   Fax: (415) 861-8365
E-mail: calegionaux@calegionaux.org
Web: www.calegionaux.org/scholarships.htm

Summary To provide financial assistance to California residents who are veterans or members of their families and interested in studying nursing at a school in the state.

Eligibility This program is open to California residents who are veterans with wartime service or the spouse, widow(er), or child of such a veteran. Applicants must be entering or currently enrolled in an accredited nursing school in California and working on a licensed vocational nurse, registered nurse, or other recognized nursing degree. Selection is based on the application (25%), scholarship (25%), character and leadership (25%), and financial need (25%).

Financial data Stipends range up to $4,000.

Duration 1 year.

Number awarded Varies each year.

Deadline April of each year.

[418]
CALIFORNIA LEGION AUXILIARY SCHOLARSHIPS FOR CONTINUING AND/OR REENTRY STUDENTS

American Legion Auxiliary
Department of California
205 13th Street, Suite 3300
San Francisco, CA 94103-2461
(415) 861-5092   Fax: (415) 861-8365
E-mail: calegionaux@calegionaux.org
Web: www.calegionaux.org/scholarships.htm

Summary To provide financial assistance to California residents who are active-duty military personnel, veterans, or children of veterans and require assistance to continue their education.

Eligibility This program is open to California residents who are 1) active-duty military personnel; 2) veterans of World War I, World War II, Korea, Vietnam, Grenada/Lebanon, Panama, or Desert Shield/Desert Storm; and 3) children of veterans who served during those periods of war. Applicants must be continuing or reentry students at a college, university, or business/trade school in California. Selection is based on the application (25%), scholarship (25%), character and leadership (25%), and financial need (25%).

Financial data The stipend is $1,000 or $500.

Duration 1 year.

Additional information This program includes 1 scholarship designated as the Mel Foronda Memorial Scholarship.

Number awarded 5 each year: 3 at $1,000 and 2 at $500.

Deadline March of each year.

[419]
CALIFORNIA NON-RESIDENT COLLEGE FEE WAIVER PROGRAM FOR MILITARY PERSONNEL AND DEPENDENTS

California Department of Veterans Affairs
Attn: Division of Veterans Services
1227 O Street, Room 101
P.O. Box 942895
Sacramento, CA 94295
(916) 653-2573   Toll Free: (877) 741-8532
Fax: (916) 653-2563   TDD: (800) 324-5966
Web: www.calvet.ca.gov

Summary To waive non-resident fees at public institutions in California for undergraduate or graduate students from other states who are active-duty military personnel, recently-discharged veterans, or dependents of active-duty military personnel.

Eligibility This program is open to residents of states outside California who are 1) veterans of the U.S. armed forces who spent more than 1 year on active duty in California immediately prior to being discharged; 2) members of the U.S. armed forces stationed in California on active duty; or 3) the natural or adopted child, stepchild, or spouse of a member of the U.S. armed forces stationed in California on active duty. Applicants must be attending or planning to attend a community college, branch of the California State University system, or campus of the University of California as an undergraduate or graduate student.

Financial data This program waives non-resident fees of qualifying military personnel, veterans, and families who attend publicly-supported community or state colleges or universities in California.

Duration 1 year; may be renewed until completion of an undergraduate degree or for 1 additional year for military personnel working on a graduate degree; nonrenewable for graduate students who are children or spouses.

Number awarded Varies each year.

Deadline Deadline not specified.

[420]
CAPTAIN CALIENDO COLLEGE ASSISTANCE FUND SCHOLARSHIP

U.S. Coast Guard Chief Petty Officers Association
Attn: CCCAF Scholarship Committee
5520-G Hempstead Way
Springfield, VA 22151-4009
(703) 941-0395   Fax: (703) 941-0397
E-mail: cgcpoa@aol.com
Web: www.uscgcpoa.org/resources/cccaf.aspx

Summary To recognize and reward, with college scholarships, children of members or deceased members of the U.S. Coast Guard Chief Petty Officers Association (CPOA) or the Coast Guard Enlisted Association (CGEA) who submit outstanding essays.

Eligibility This competition is open to children of members or deceased members of the CPOA or CGEA who are attending or planning to attend a college, university, or vocational school. Applicants may not be older than 24 years of age (the age limit does not apply to disabled children). They must submit an essay, up to 500 words, on a topic that changes annually; recently, students were asked to write on the impact on the military of the policy changes regarding women in combat

and "don't ask/don't tell." The author of the essay judged most outstanding receives this scholarship.

Financial data The award is a $5,000 scholarship.

Duration The competition is held annually.

Number awarded 1 each year.

Deadline February of each year.

[421]
CAPTAIN GERARD COOK SCHOLARSHIP

National Guard Association of Florida
Attn: Scholarship Committee
P.O. Box 3446
St. Augustine, FL 32085-3446
(904) 823-0628   Fax: (904) 839-2068
E-mail: ngafl1903@floridaguard.org
Web: www.floridaguard.org/index.php/scholarships

Summary To provide financial assistance to children of members of the Florida National Guard who are studying architecture or engineering at a college in any state.

Eligibility This program is open to children of members of the Florida National Guard who are attending an accredited college or university in any state. Applicants must be working on a degree in architecture or engineering. Along with their application, they must submit a 500-word essay explaining why they need the award and what they plan to do with their architecture or engineering degree. Selection is based on academic achievement, civic and moral leadership, character, and financial need.

Financial data The stipend is $1,000.

Duration 1 year.

Additional information This program is jointly sponsored by the National Guard Association of Florida (NGOA-FL) and the Enlisted National Guard Association of Florida (ENGAF).

Number awarded 1 each year.

Deadline May of each year.

[422]
CAPTAIN SALLY TOMPKINS NURSING AND APPLIED HEALTH SCIENCES SCHOLARSHIP

United Daughters of the Confederacy-Virginia Division
c/o Patt Graves, Second Vice President
838 Crymes Road
Keysville, VA 23947-2815
(434) 696-2202   E-mail: thebargthree@aol.com
Web: www.vaudc.org

Summary To provide financial assistance for college to women who are Confederate descendants from Virginia and working on a degree in nursing at a school in the state.

Eligibility This program is open to women residents of Virginia interested in working on a degree in nursing at a school in the state. Applicants must be 1) lineal descendants of Confederates; or 2) collateral descendants and also members of the Children of the Confederacy or the United Daughters of the Confederacy. They must submit proof of the Confederate military record of at least 1 ancestor, with the company and regiment in which he served. They must also submit a personal letter pledging to make the best possible use of the scholarship; describing their health, social, family, religious, and fraternal connections within the community; and reflecting on what a Southern heritage means to them (using the term "War Between the States" in lieu of "Civil War"). They must have a GPA of 3.0 or higher and be able to demonstrate financial need.

Financial data The amount of the stipend depends on the availability of funds. Payment is made directly to the college or university the recipient attends.

Duration 1 year; may be renewed up to 3 additional years if the recipient maintains a GPA of 3.0 or higher.

Number awarded This scholarship is offered whenever a prior recipient graduates or is no longer eligible.

Deadline March of the years in which a scholarship is available.

[423]
CARING FOR AMERICA SCHOLARSHIPS

North Carolina Federation of Republican Women
c/o Holly Grange, Scholarship Committee
8316 Bald Eagle Lane
Wilmington, NC 28411
Web: www.ncfederationofrepublicanwomen.org

Summary To provide financial assistance to high school seniors in North Carolina who are the child of a military servicemember and plan to attend college in the state.

Eligibility This program is open to seniors graduating from high schools in North Carolina who are the dependent child of an active-duty servicemember who was wounded or killed while serving in a combat zone from September 11, 2001 to the present. Applicants must be planning to attend an accredited North Carolina college, university, or vocational/technical school. Their military sponsor must have been a North Carolina resident at the time of service. Along with their application, they must submit an essay on their academic plans, how they plan to reach their educational and career goals, and how having a parent in the military has impacted those goals. Financial need is not considered in the selection process.

Financial data The stipend is $1,000.

Duration 1 year.

Number awarded 2 each year.

Deadline March of each year.

[424]
CGMA EDUCATION LOAN PROGRAM

Coast Guard Mutual Assistance
4200 Wilson Boulevard, Suite 610
Arlington, VA 20598-7180
(202) 872-6716   Toll Free: (800) 881-2462
E-mail: ARL-DG-CGMA@uscg.mil
Web: www.cgmahq.org

Summary To provide loans to members of Coast Guard Mutual Assistance (CGMA) and their families who are working on an undergraduate or graduate degree.

Eligibility This program is open to 1) active-duty or retired Coast Guard personnel; 2) members of the Coast Guard Selected Reserve and retirement-eligible members of the IRR; 3) Coast Guard permanent and term civilian employees; 4) Coast Guard Auxiliary members; 5) U.S. Public Health Service officers serving with the Coast Guard; 6) unremarried widowed spouses of any of those; and 7) unmarried dependent children under 23 years of age and not enrolled in any military service of any of those. Applicants must be enrolled in an associate, bachelor's, or graduate degree program or an approved vocational/technical training program.

Financial data The maximum loan is $2,000.

Duration Loans must be repaid by the end of the month in which the course is completed.

Number awarded Varies each year.

Deadline Applications must be submitted no later than 30 days after the course begins.

[425]
CHAN-PADGETT SPECIAL FORCES MEMORIAL SCHOLARSHIP

American Academy of Physician Assistants-Veterans Caucus
Attn: Veterans Caucus
P.O. Box 362
Danville, PA 17821-0362
Fax: (302) 526-7154 E-mail: fbrace@veteranscaucus.org
Web: www.veteranscaucus.org

Summary To provide financial assistance to children and spouses of veterans of the Army Special Forces who are studying to become physician assistants.

Eligibility This program is open to U.S. citizens who are currently enrolled in a physician assistant program. The program must be approved by the Commission on Accreditation of Allied Health Education. Applicants must be children or surviving spouses of honorably discharged members of the Army Special Forces. Selection is based on military honors and awards received, civic and college honors and awards received, professional memberships and activities, and GPA. An electronic copy of the sponsor's DD Form 214 must accompany the application.

Financial data The stipend is $2,000.

Duration 1 year.

Additional information This program began in 2002.

Number awarded 1 each year.

Deadline February of each year.

[426]
CHAPPIE HALL MEMORIAL SCHOLARSHIP PROGRAM

101st Airborne Division Association
32 Screaming Eagle Boulevard
P.O. Box 929
Fort Campbell, KY 42223-0929
(931) 431-0199   Fax: (931) 431-0195
E-mail: 101stairbornedivisionassociation@comcast.net
Web: www.screamingeaglefoundation.org

Summary To provide financial assistance for college to the spouses, children, and grandchildren of members of the 101st Airborne Division Association.

Eligibility This program is open to graduating high school seniors and current college students who maintained a GPA of 2.0 or higher during the preceding school year and whose parent, grandparent, or spouse is (or, if deceased, was) a regular or life (not associate) member of the 101st Airborne Division. Applicants must submit a 150-word essay on patriotism and a letter on their career objectives, community service, hobbies, interests, personal achievements, and how a higher education for them in their chosen field can benefit our nation. Selection is based on the letter, career objectives, academic record, and letters of recommendation.

Financial data A stipend is awarded (amount not specified).

Duration 1 year; may be renewed.

Additional information This program includes the Pratt Scholarships, the Lencioni Family Scholarship, the Martin Family Scholarships, the Catherine and Charles Kratz Scholarships, the Phil and Laverne Blottenberger Scholarship, the 327th Infantry Regiment Scholarship, and the Knapp Family Scholarship.

Number awarded Varies each year; recently, 24 were awarded.

Deadline May of each year.

[427]
CHARLES C. BLANTON AFBA FAMILY SURVIVOR COLLEGE SCHOLARSHIP

Armed Forces Benefit Association
AFBA Building
909 North Washington Street
Alexandria, VA 22314-1556
(703) 549-4455   Toll Free: (800) 776-2322
E-mail: info@afba.com
Web: www.afba.com

Summary To provide financial assistance for college to surviving spouses and children of members of the Armed Forces Benefit Association (AFBA) who were killed on duty.

Eligibility This program is open to surviving spouses and children of deceased members of AFBA. Membership in AFBA is open to active-duty, National Guard, or Reserve members of the armed forces; those who are retired or separated from service; and emergency service providers (law enforcement officers, firefighters, and emergency medical service providers). The AFBA member's death must have been in a combat zone, as a result of combat action, as a result of acts of foreign or domestic terrorism, or at an event to which an emergency service provider is dispatched in a situation where there is the potential for loss of life. Applicants must be attending or planning to attend an undergraduate college or university.

Financial data The stipend is $10,000 per year.

Duration 1 year; may be renewed for up to 3 additional years.

Number awarded 1 or more each year.

Deadline Deadline not specified.

[428]
CHARLES W. AND ANNETTE HILL SCHOLARSHIP FUND

American Legion
Department of Kansas
1314 S.W. Topeka Boulevard
Topeka, KS 66612-1886
(785) 232-9315   Fax: (785) 232-1399
Web: www.ksamlegion.org

Summary To provide financial assistance to the children of members of the Kansas American Legion, particularly those interested in majoring in science, engineering, or business at a college in the state.

Eligibility This program is open to graduating seniors at high schools in Kansas and freshmen and sophomores at colleges in the state. Applicants must be a descendant of a member of the American Legion and have a GPA of 3.0 or higher. Preference is given to applicants planning to major in science, engineering, or business administration at a Kansas college, university, junior college, or trade school. Selection is

based on high school transcripts, 3 letters of recommendation, an essay of 250 to 500 words on "Why I Want to Go to College," and financial need.

Financial data The stipend is $1,000 per year.

Duration 1 year; may be renewed if the recipient maintains a GPA of 3.0 or higher.

Number awarded 1 each year.

Deadline February of each year.

[429]
CHIEF MASTER SERGEANTS OF THE AIR FORCE SCHOLARSHIPS

Air Force Sergeants Association
Attn: Membership and Field Relations
5211 Auth Road
Suitland, MD 20746
(301) 899-3500   Toll Free: (800) 638-0594
Fax: (301) 899-8136   E-mail: balsobrooks@hqafsa.org
Web: www.hqafsa.org/scholarships.html

Summary To provide financial assistance for college to the dependent children of enlisted Air Force personnel.

Eligibility This program is open to the unmarried children (including stepchildren and legally adopted children) of enlisted active-duty, retired, or veteran members of the U.S. Air Force, Air National Guard, or Air Force Reserves. Applicants must be attending or planning to attend an accredited academic institution. They must have an unweighted GPA of 3.5 or higher. Along with their application, they must submit 1) a paragraph on their life objectives and what they plan to do with the education they receive; and 2) an essay on the most urgent problem facing society today. High school seniors must also submit a transcript of all high school grades and a record of their SAT or ACT scores. Selection is based on academic record, character, leadership skills, writing ability, versatility, and potential for success. Financial need is not a consideration. A unique aspect of these scholarships is that applicants may supply additional information regarding circumstances that entitle them to special consideration; examples of such circumstances include student disabilities, financial hardships, parent disabled and unable to work, parent missing in action/killed in action/prisoner of war, or other unusual extenuating circumstances.

Financial data Stipends range from $1,000 to $3,000; funds may be used for tuition, room and board, fees, books, supplies, and transportation.

Duration 1 year; may be renewed if the recipient maintains full-time enrollment.

Additional information The Air Force Sergeants Association administers this program on behalf of the Airmen Memorial Foundation. It was established in 1987 and named in honor of CMSAF Richard D. Kisling, the late third Chief Master Sergeant of the Air Force. In 1997, following the deaths of CMSAF's (Retired) Andrews and Harlow, it was given its current name. The highest-ranked applicant receives the Paul W. Airey Memorial Scholarship.

Number awarded Varies each year; recently, 11 were awarded: 1 at $3,000, 1 at $2,000, and 9 at $1,000. Since this program began, it has awarded more than $350,000 in scholarships.

Deadline March of each year.

[430]
CHILDREN AND SPOUSES OF INDIANA NATIONAL GUARD PROGRAM

Indiana Commission for Higher Education
Attn: Division of Student Financial Aid
W462 Indiana Government Center South
402 West Washington Street
Indianapolis, IN 46204
(317) 232-2355   Toll Free: (888) 528-4719 (within IN)
Fax: (317) 232-3260   E-mail: awards@sfa.che.in.gov
Web: www.in.gov/sfa/2528.htm

Summary To provide financial assistance to residents of Indiana who are children or spouses of deceased members of the National Guard and interested in attending college or graduate school in the state.

Eligibility This program is open to residents of Indiana whose father, mother, or spouse was a member of the Indiana National Guard and suffered a service-connected death while serving on state active duty. Applicants must be interested in working on an undergraduate, graduate, or professional degree at an eligible institution in Indiana.

Financial data Qualified applicants receive a 100% remission of tuition and all mandatory fees for undergraduate, graduate, or professional degrees at eligible postsecondary schools and universities in Indiana. Support is not provided for such fees as room and board.

Duration Up to 124 semester hours of study.

Number awarded Varies each year.

Deadline Applications must be submitted at least 30 days before the start of the college term.

[431]
CHILDREN OF FALLEN PATRIOTS FOUNDATION ASSISTANCE

Children of Fallen Patriots Foundation
419 Third Street North
Jacksonville Beach, FL 32250
Toll Free: (866) 917-CFPF   Fax: (904) 853-6981
E-mail: contact@fallenpatriots.org
Web: www.fallenpatriots.org/who-we-are

Summary To provide financial assistance to the children of military personnel killed in combat or training.

Eligibility This program is open to the children (natural, by marriage, or adopted) of military personnel who died in the line of duty. Applicants must be enrolled or planning to enroll at a college, university, community college, or vocational school. Applicants must submit documentation of their relationship to the deceased military member, bills or receipts for all covered expenses, transcripts that include GPA, and information on their U.S. Department of Veterans Affairs benefits.

Financial data The foundation attempts to pay for all costs of higher education not covered by other grants or scholarships.

Duration Until completion of a college degree or certificate.

Additional information This program began in 1990.

Number awarded Varies each year. Since this program began, it has provided more than $7.5 million in assistance to families.

Deadline Applications may be submitted at any time.

[432]
CHILDREN OF FALLEN SOLDIERS RELIEF FUND COLLEGE GRANTS

Children of Fallen Soldiers Relief Fund
P.O. Box 1099
Temple Hills, MD 20757
(301) 685-3421   Toll Free: (866) 96-CFSRF
Fax: (301) 630-0592   E-mail: yellowribbon7@msn.com
Web: www.cfsrf.org

Summary To provide financial assistance for college to children and spouses of military personnel killed or severely disabled during service in Iraq or Afghanistan.

Eligibility This program is open to spouses and children of military personnel killed or severely disabled as a result of service in Operation Iraqi Freedom or Operation Enduring Freedom. Applicants must be enrolled or planning to enroll at a college or university. They must have a GPA of 2.75 or higher and be able to demonstrate financial need.

Financial data Grants have ranged from $1,000 to $28,000, depending on the need of the recipient.

Duration These are 1-time grants.

Additional information This organization was founded in 2003.

Number awarded Varies each year; since the organization was founded, it has awarded 14 of these college grants.

Deadline October of each year for fall; April of each year for spring.

[433]
CHILDREN OF WARRIORS NATIONAL PRESIDENTS' SCHOLARSHIP

American Legion Auxiliary
8945 North Meridian Street
Indianapolis, IN 46260
(317) 569-4500   Fax: (317) 569-4502
E-mail: alahq@alaforveterans.org
Web: www.alaforveterans.org

Summary To provide financial assistance for college to the descendants of war veterans.

Eligibility This program is open to children, stepchildren, grandchildren, and great-grandchildren of veterans who served during wartime. Applicants must be high school seniors who have completed at least 50 hours of volunteer service within their community and plan to attend an accredited 4-year college or university. Each Department (state) organization of the American Legion Auxiliary nominates 1 candidate for this scholarship annually. Nominees must submit a 1,000-word essay on a topic that changes annually; recently, students were asked to write on "How I Can Help Children of Military Families." Selection is based on the essay (25%), character and leadership (25%), scholarship, (25%), and financial need (25%).

Financial data Stipends are $3,500, $3,000, or $2,500. Funds are paid directly to the recipient's school.

Duration 1 year; recipients may not reapply.

Additional information Applications are available from the local Unit or from the Department Secretary or Department Education Chair of the state in which the applicant resides. This program was previously named the American Legion Auxiliary National President's Scholarship.

Number awarded 15 each year: in each of the 5 divisions of the Auxiliary, 1 scholarship at $3,500, 1 at $3,000, and 1 at $2,500 are awarded.

Deadline February of each year.

[434]
CLAIRE OLIPHANT MEMORIAL SCHOLARSHIP

American Legion Auxiliary
Department of New Jersey
c/o Marion Heller, Secretary
1540 Kuser Road, Suite A-8
Hamilton, NJ 08619
(609) 581-9580   Fax: (609) 581-8429
E-mail: newjerseyala1@optimum.net
Web: www.alanj.org/box_widget.html

Summary To provide financial assistance to New Jersey residents who are the descendants of veterans and planning to attend college in any state.

Eligibility This program is open to the children, grandchildren, and great-grandchildren of veterans who served in the U.S. armed forces during specified periods of wartime. Applicants must be graduating high school seniors who have been residents of New Jersey for at least 2 years. They must be planning to attend a college or university in any state. Along with their application, they must submit a 1,000-word essay on a topic that changes annually; recently, students were asked to write on the topic, "Pass it On-How I Can be a Leader in My Community." Selection is based on academic achievement (40%), character (15%), leadership (15%), Americanism (15%), and financial need (15%).

Financial data The stipend is $2,500.

Duration 1 year.

Number awarded 1 each year.

Deadline April each year.

[435]
CMSGT GERALD R. GUILD MEMORIAL SCHOLARSHIPS

Enlisted Association National Guard of Arizona
Attn: Scholarship Chair
5636 East McDowell Road
Phoenix, AZ 85008-3495
(602) 267-2467   Fax: (602) 267-2509
E-mail: scholarship@eanga.org
Web: www.eanga.org

Summary To provide financial assistance to members of the Enlisted Association National Guard of Arizona (EANGA) and to members of their families who plan to attend college in any state.

Eligibility This program is open to EANGA members, the unmarried sons and daughters of EANGA members, the spouses of EANGA members, and the unremarried spouses and unmarried dependent sons and daughters of deceased EANGA members (who were in good standing at their time of death). Qualifying EANGA members must have at least 1 year remaining on their enlistment or have served 20 or more years of service. Applicants may be high school seniors or current college students who are enrolled or planning to enroll full time at a college or university in any state. Graduate students are not eligible. Selection is based on academic record, character, leadership, and financial need.

Financial data Stipends are $1,000 or $750. Funds are made payable to the recipient's school and sent directly to the recipient.

Duration 1 year; nonrenewable.

Number awarded Varies each year; recently, 3 were awarded: 1 at $1,000 and 2 at $750.

Deadline April of each year.

[436]
COAST GUARD FOUNDATION ENLISTED RESERVE SCHOLARSHIPS

U.S. Coast Guard
Attn: COMDT (CG-1311)
2703 Martin Luther King, Jr. Avenue, S.E., Stop 7907
Washington, DC 20593-7907
(202) 475-5459   E-mail: travis.p.thornell@uscg.mil
Web: www.uscg.mil/reserve/awards

Summary To provide financial assistance for college or graduate school to members of the Coast Guard Reserves and their dependents.

Eligibility This program is open to Coast Guard enlisted reservists (Selected Reserve or Individual Ready Reserve) and their dependents who are registered in the Defense Enrollment Eligibility Reporting System (DEERS). Applicants must be enrolled or accepted for enrollment at 1) an accredited institution in a program leading to an associate, bachelor's, master's, or doctoral degree; or 2) a 2- or 4-year course of study at an accredited technical or vocational training school. Along with their application, they must submit a 1-page essay on how the participation of themselves, their spouse, or their parent in the Coast Guard Reserve has contributed to their success. Selection is based on that essay and academic achievement.

Financial data The stipend is $1,000.

Duration 1 year.

Additional information This program is sponsored by the United States Automobile Association (USAA) Insurance Corporation.

Number awarded 6 each year.

Deadline July of each year.

[437]
COL CARL F. BASWELL FALLEN ENGINEER MEMORIAL SCHOLARSHIP

Army Engineer Association
Attn: Program Coordinator
P.O. Box 30260
Alexandria, VA 22310-8260
(703) 428-7084   Fax: (703) 428-6043
E-mail: execasst@armyengineer.com
Web: www.armyengineer.com/scholarships.htm

Summary To provide financial assistance for college to children and spouses of U.S. Army Engineers who were killed in Iraq or Afghanistan.

Eligibility This program is open to the children and spouses of U.S. Army Engineers who were killed in combat during Operation Iraqi Freedom or Operation Enduring Freedom. Applicants must be working on or planning to work on an associate, bachelor's, or master's degree at an accredited college or university. Selection is based primarily on financial need, although potential for academic success and personal references are also considered.

Financial data The stipend is $2,500.
Duration 1 year.
Additional information This program began in 2010.
Number awarded 1 each year.
Deadline June of each year.

[438]
COL CHUCK JONES MEMORIAL AWARD

Hanscom Spouses' Club
Attn: Scholarship Committee Chair
General Delivery
75 Grenier Street, Unit 888
Hanscom AFB, MA 01731
(781) 538-5811   E-mail: scholarships@hanscomsc.org
Web: www.hanscomsc.org/scholarships.html

Summary To provide financial assistance to high school seniors who are children of military personnel or veterans in the Hanscom Air Force Base area of New England and interested in studying fields related to space or aeronautics at a college in any state.

Eligibility This program is open to dependents of active-duty, retired, and deceased members of any branch of the armed forces, including Reservists and National Guard members who were activated during the school year. Applicants must be graduating high school seniors who have a valid military identification card and reside within a 60-mile radius of Hanscom Air Force Base (includes eastern Massachusetts, Rhode Island, and southern New Hampshire) or be a dependent whose military sponsor is stationed at Hanscom Air Force Base. They must be planning to attend a 2- or 4-year college or university in any state to work on a degree in a field related to space or aeronautics, including communications, meteorology, air/space maintenance, manufacturing processing, or engineering. Along with their application, they must submit a 2-page essay on their educational goals, how their educational experience will help prepare them to pursue future goals, and how they intend to apply their education to better their community. Selection is based on merit.

Financial data Recently, the stipend was $4,000.
Duration 1 year; nonrenewable.
Additional information This program was established to honor a victim of an airplane crash on September 11, 2001. It is sponsored by the Paul Revere Chapter of the Air Force Association.
Number awarded 1 each year.
Deadline March of each year.

[439]
COLD WAR VETERANS ENGINEERING AND SCIENCE SCHOLARSHIPS

Marines' Memorial Association
c/o Marines Memorial Club and Hotel
609 Sutter Street
San Francisco, CA 94102
(415) 673-6672, ext. 293   Fax: (415) 441-3649
E-mail: scholarship@marineclub.com
Web: www.marineclub.com/membership/scholarship.php

Summary To provide financial assistance to members of the Marines' Memorial Association from all branches of the armed forces and their descendants who are interested in studying a field of science, technology, engineering, or mathematics (STEM) in college.

Eligibility This program is open to active members of the association and their children and grandchildren. Applicants must be high school seniors or students currently enrolled full time in an undergraduate degree program in a field of STEM. Along with their application, they must submit an essay of 250 to 500 words on the science of engineering and how they hope to contribute to its progression. Graduating high school seniors must submit a high school transcript and SAT or ACT scores; continuing college students must submit a college transcript. Selection is based on the essay, academic merit, references, and financial need.

Financial data The stipend is $2,500 per year.
Duration 1 year; recipients may reapply for up to 3 additional years.
Additional information Membership in the association is open to veterans of the Marines, Army, Navy, Air Force, or Coast Guard and to personnel currently serving in a branch of the armed forces. This program began in 2014.
Number awarded 2 each year.
Deadline April of each year.

[440]
COLONEL CHARLES L. SCHMIDT LEADERSHIP SCHOLARSHIP

11th Armored Cavalry Veterans of Vietnam and Cambodia
Attn: National Headquarters
P.O. Box 956
Coffeyville, TX 76034-0956
Web: www.11thcavnam.com/scholarship/scholar.html

Summary To provide financial assistance for college to members of the 11th Armored Cavalry Veterans of Vietnam and Cambodia (11ACVVC) and to their children who demonstrate leadership.

Eligibility This program is open to 1) current members of the 11ACVVC; 2) children and stepchildren of current members of the 11ACVVC; 3) children whose legal guardian is a current member of the 11ACVVC; 4) children of 11th Armored Cavalry troopers who were killed in action, died of wounds, or died as a result of service in Vietnam or Cambodia; and 5) children and stepchildren of 11th Armored Cavalry Regiment veterans who served in Vietnam or Cambodia but are not members of the 11ACVVC. There is no age limit. Applicants must be enrolled or planning to enroll as an undergraduate student. Along with their application, they must submit brief essays on 1) the field of study they plan to enter and why; and 2) why they would be a worthy recipient of this scholarship. Selection is based on criteria established by members of Colonel Schmidt's family and may change each year, but emphasis is given to demonstrated leadership.

Financial data The stipend is $1,000 in addition to the $4,000 paid for all the sponsor's scholarships; funds are paid directly to the recipient's school, in 2 equal installments.
Duration 1 year; nonrenewable.
Additional information This program began in 2008. Recipients must use the awarded money within 44 months of being notified.
Number awarded 1 each year.
Deadline May of each year.

[441]
COLONEL HAROLD M. BEARDSLEE MEMORIAL SCHOLARSHIP AWARDS

Army Engineer Association
Attn: Program Coordinator
P.O. Box 30260
Alexandria, VA 22310-8260
(703) 428-7084   Fax: (703) 428-6043
E-mail: execasst@armyengineer.com
Web: www.armyengineer.com/scholarships.htm

Summary To provide financial assistance for college to children and spouses of members of the Army Engineer Association (AEA).

Eligibility This program is open to spouses and children of AEA members in the following 4 categories: 1) graduating high school seniors who are children of active-duty or civilian members (including active-duty retired); 2) graduating high school seniors who are children of Reserve or National Guard members (including Reserve or National Guard retired); 3) children and spouses of members in the second, third, or fourth year of a baccalaureate degree program; and 4) the next best qualified applicant, regardless of category, not receiving any of those awards. Applicants must be enrolled or planning to enroll full time at an accredited college or university. Along with their application, they must submit an essay on their reasons for seeking this award. Selection is based on the essay, scholastic aptitude, and letters of recommendation.

Financial data The stipend is $1,000.

Duration 1 year; nonrenewable.

Number awarded 4 each year: 1 in each category.

Deadline April of each year.

[442]
COLONEL HAZEL ELIZABETH BENN, USMC SCHOLARSHIP

Fleet Reserve Association
Attn: FRA Education Foundation
125 North West Street
Alexandria, VA 22314-2754
(703) 683-1400   Toll Free: (800) FRA-1924
Fax: (703) 549-6610   E-mail: scholars@fra.org
Web: www.fra.org

Summary To provide financial assistance for college to children of members of the Fleet Reserve Association (FRA) serving in the Navy as an enlisted medical rating assigned to the United States Marine Corps (USMC).

Eligibility This program is open to the dependent children of members of the association or persons who were members at the time of death. Applicants must be entering their freshman or sophomore year of college. Their parent must be serving and have served in the U.S. Navy as an enlisted medical rating assigned to the USMC. Selection is based on academic record, financial need, extracurricular activities, leadership skills, and participation in community activities. U.S. citizenship is required.

Financial data The stipend is $2,000.

Duration 1 year.

Number awarded 1 or more each year.

Deadline April of each year.

[443]
COLONEL RICHARD HALLOCK SCHOLARSHIPS

Marines' Memorial Association
c/o Marines Memorial Club and Hotel
609 Sutter Street
San Francisco, CA 94102
(415) 673-6672, ext. 293   Fax: (415) 441-3649
E-mail: scholarship@marineclub.com
Web: www.marineclub.com/membership/scholarship.php

Summary To provide financial assistance for college to members of the Marines' Memorial Association from all branches of the armed forces and their descendants.

Eligibility This program is open to active members of the association and their children and grandchildren. Applicants must be high school seniors or students currently enrolled full time in an undergraduate degree program at a college or university. Along with their application, they must submit an essay of 250 to 500 words on their conception of "fairness" and its impact on society and in their life. Graduating high school seniors must submit a high school transcript and SAT or ACT scores; continuing college students must submit a college transcript. Selection is based on the essay, academic merit, references, and financial need.

Financial data The stipend is $2,500 per year.

Duration 1 year; recipients may reapply for up to 3 additional years.

Additional information Membership in the association is open to veterans of the Marines, Army, Navy, Air Force, or Coast Guard and to personnel currently serving in a branch of the armed forces.

Number awarded 2 each year.

Deadline April of each year.

[444]
COLORADO DEPENDENTS TUITION ASSISTANCE PROGRAM

Colorado Commission on Higher Education
1560 Broadway, Suite 1600
Denver, CO 80202
(303) 866-2723   Fax: (303) 866-4266
E-mail: cche@state.co.us
Web: highered.colorado.gov

Summary To provide financial assistance for college to the dependents of disabled or deceased Colorado National Guardsmen, law enforcement officers, and firefighters.

Eligibility Eligible for the program are dependents of Colorado law enforcement officers, firefighters, and National Guardsmen disabled or killed in the line of duty, as well as dependents of prisoners of war or service personnel listed as missing in action. Students must be Colorado residents under 22 years of age enrolled at 1) a state-supported 2- or 4-year Colorado college or university; 2) a private college, university, or vocational school in Colorado approved by the commission; or 3) an out-of-state 4-year college. Financial need is considered in the selection process.

Financial data Eligible students receive free tuition at Colorado public institutions of higher education. If the recipient wishes to attend a private college, university, or proprietary school, the award is limited to the amount of tuition at a comparable state-supported institution. Students who have applied to live in a dormitory, but have not been accepted because there is not enough space, may be provided supplemental assistance. Students who choose to live off-campus are not eligible for room reimbursement or a meal plan. Students who attend a non-residential Colorado institution and do not live at home are eligible for a grant of $1,000 per semester to assist with living expenses. Students who attend an out-of-state institution are eligible for the amount of tuition equivalent to that at a comparable Colorado public institution, but they are not eligible for room and board.

Duration Up to 6 years or until completion of a bachelor's degree, provided the recipient maintains a GPA of 2.5 or higher.

Additional information Recipients must attend accredited postsecondary institutions in Colorado.

Number awarded Varies each year; recently, nearly $365,000 was allocated to this program.

Deadline Deadline not specified.

[445]
COLORADO LEGION AUXILIARY DEPARTMENT PRESIDENT'S SCHOLARSHIP FOR JUNIOR AUXILIARY MEMBERS

American Legion Auxiliary
Department of Colorado
7465 East First Avenue, Suite D
Denver, CO 80230
(303) 367-5388   Fax: (303) 367-5388
E-mail: dept-sec@alacolorado.com
Web: www.alacolorado.com/Forms.html

Summary To provide financial assistance to junior members of the American Legion Auxiliary in Colorado who plan to attend college in the state.

Eligibility This program is open to seniors at high schools in Colorado who have been junior members of the auxiliary for the past 3 years. Applicants must be Colorado residents planning to attend college in the state. Along with their application, they must submit a 1,000-word essay on the topic, "My Obligations as an American." Selection is based on character (20%), Americanism (20%), leadership (20%), scholarship (20%), and financial need (20%).

Financial data The stipend is $1,000.

Duration 1 year; nonrenewable.

Number awarded 1 each year.

Deadline February of each year.

[446]
COLORADO LEGION AUXILIARY DEPARTMENT PRESIDENT'S SCHOLARSHIPS

American Legion Auxiliary
Department of Colorado
7465 East First Avenue, Suite D
Denver, CO 80230
(303) 367-5388   Fax: (303) 367-5388
E-mail: dept-sec@alacolorado.com
Web: www.alacolorado.com/Forms.html

Summary To provide financial assistance to children and grandchildren of veterans in Colorado who plan to attend college in the state.

Eligibility This program is open to children and grandchildren of veterans who served in the armed forces during wartime eligibility dates for membership in the American Legion. Applicants must be residents of Colorado who are high school seniors planning to attend a college in the state. Along

with their application, they must submit a 1,000-word essay on the topic, "My Obligations as an American." Selection is based on character (15%), Americanism (15%), leadership (15%), scholarship (15%), and financial need (40%).

Financial data Stipends are $1,000 or $500.

Duration 1 year.

Number awarded 4 each year: 2 at 1,000 and 2 at $500.

Deadline February of each year.

[447]
COLORADO LEGION AUXILIARY PAST PRESIDENT'S PARLEY NURSES TRAINING SCHOLARSHIP

American Legion Auxiliary
Department of Colorado
7465 East First Avenue, Suite D
Denver, CO 80230
(303) 367-5388   Fax: (303) 367-5388
E-mail: dept-sec@alacolorado.com
Web: www.alacolorado.com/Forms.html

Summary To provide financial assistance to wartime veterans and their descendants in Colorado who are interested in attending school in the state to prepare for a career in nursing.

Eligibility This program is open to 1) daughters, sons, spouses, granddaughters, and great-granddaughters of veterans; and 2) veterans who served in the armed forces during eligibility dates for membership in the American Legion. Applicants must be Colorado residents who have been accepted by an accredited school of nursing in the state. Along with their application, they must submit a 500-word essay on the topic, "Americanism." Selection is based on that essay (25%), scholastic ability (25%), financial need (25%), references (13%), and dedication to chosen field (12%).

Financial data Stipends range from $500 to $1,000.

Duration 1 year; nonrenewable.

Number awarded Varies each year, depending on the availability of funds.

Deadline April of each year.

[448]
COMMANDER WILLIAM S. STUHR SCHOLARSHIPS

Commander William S. Stuhr Scholarship Fund
Attn: Executive Director
3292 Thompson Bridge Road, Suite 120
Gainesville, GA 30506
E-mail: stuhrstudents@earthlink.net

Summary To provide financial assistance for college to the dependent children of retired or active-duty military personnel.

Eligibility This program is open to the dependent children of military personnel who are serving on active duty or retired with pay after 20 years' service (not merely separated from service). Applicants must be high school seniors who rank in the top 10% of their class and have an SAT score of at least 1900 or an ACT score of at least 27. They must plan to attend a 4-year accredited college. Selection is based on academic performance, extracurricular activities, demonstrated leadership potential, and financial need.

Financial data The stipend is $2,000 per year.

Duration 4 years, provided the recipient makes the dean's list at their college at least once during their first 2 years.

Additional information This program began in 1965. Recipients and their families attend a scholarship awards function in late May or early June; the fund pays air transportation to the event. Applications may be obtained only by writing and enclosing a self-addressed stamped envelope. The fund does not respond to telephone, fax, or e-mail inquiries.

Number awarded 6 each year: 1 for a child of a military servicemember from each of the 6 branches (Air Force, Army, Coast Guard, Marine Corps, Navy, and Reserves/National Guard).

Deadline January of each year.

[449]
COMMISSIONED OFFICERS' ASSOCIATION DEPENDENT SCHOLARSHIPS

PHS Commissioned Officers Foundation for the
    Advancement of Public Health
8201 Corporate Drive, Suite 200
Landover, MD 20785
(301) 731-9080   Fax: (301) 731-9084
E-mail: info@phscof.org
Web: www.phscof.org/education/cof-scholarship-program

Summary To provide financial assistance for college or graduate school to dependents of officers of the United States Public Health Service (USPHS) Commissioned Corps who are also members of the Commissioned Officers' Association (COA).

Eligibility This program is open to dependent children and spouses of active-duty, retired, or deceased officers of the USPHS Commissioned Corps who are also COA members. Applicants must be entering or continuing full-time students at a college or graduate school. They must be U.S. citizens and have a GPA of 3.0 or higher. Along with their application, they must submit an essay on why they want to go to college and what they intend to accomplish with their degree. Financial need is not considered in the selection process.

Financial data Stipends range up to $1,000.

Duration 1 year.

Additional information The highest-ranked applicant receives the Ronald Lessing Memorial Scholarship.

Number awarded Varies each year; recently, 13 were awarded.

Deadline May of each year.

[450]
CONGRESSMAN DAVID L. HOBSON CIVIL ENGINEERING SCHOLARSHIP

Army Engineer Association
Attn: Program Coordinator
P.O. Box 30260
Alexandria, VA 22310-8260
(703) 428-7084   Fax: (703) 428-6043
E-mail: execasst@armyengineer.com
Web: www.armyengineer.com/scholarships.htm

Summary To provide financial assistance to members of the Army Engineer Association (AEA) and their families interested in studying civil engineering in college.

Eligibility This program is open to AEA members and their families who are U.S. citizens. Applicants must be enrolled full time at an accredited college or university and working on

a bachelor's degree in civil engineering. Along with their application, they must submit a 600-word essay that lists their academic and professional goals, extracurricular activities, and military service (if applicable). Selection is based on that essay, scholastic aptitude, and letters of recommendation.

Financial data The stipend is $3,000.

Duration 1 year; nonrenewable.

Additional information This program is sponsored by the engineering firm, Trimble.

Number awarded 4 each year.

Deadline July of each year.

[451]
CONNECTICUT IRAQ AND AFGHANISTAN SERVICE GRANTS

Connecticut Office of Higher Education
Attn: Education and Employment Information Center
61 Woodland Street
Hartford, CT 06105-2326
(860) 947-1810   Toll Free: (800) 842-0229 (within CT)
Fax: (860) 947-1311   E-mail: edinfo@ctohe.org
Web: www.ctohe.org/sfa/sfa.shtml

Summary To provide financial assistance to residents of Connecticut whose military parent was killed in Iraq or Afghanistan and who wish to attend college in the state.

Eligibility This program is open to residents of Connecticut whose parent or guardian was a member of the U.S. armed forces and died as a result of service performed in Iraq or Afghanistan after September 11, 2001. Applicants must be ineligible for a federal Pell Grant because they cannot meet the financial need requirement. They must be younger than 24 years of age or have been enrolled in college at least part-time at the time of their parent's or guardian's death.

Financial data The stipend is the same as that of a federal Pell Grant (currently, $5,645 per year).

Duration 1 year; may be renewed.

Number awarded Varies each year.

Deadline Deadline not specified.

[452]
CONNECTICUT NATIONAL GUARD FOUNDATION SCHOLARSHIPS

Connecticut National Guard Foundation, Inc.
Attn: Scholarship Committee
360 Broad Street
Hartford, CT 06105-3795
(860) 241-1550   Fax: (860) 293-2929
E-mail: ctngfi@sbcglobal.net
Web: www.ctngfoundation.org/Scholarship.asp

Summary To provide financial assistance for college to members of the Connecticut National Guard and their families.

Eligibility This program is open to members of the Connecticut Army National Guard and Organized Militia, their children, and their spouses. Applicants must be enrolled or planning to enroll in an accredited college or technical program. Along with their application, they must submit a letter of recommendation, a list of extracurricular activities, high school or college transcripts, and a 200-word statement on their educational and future goals. Selection is based on achievement and citizenship.

Financial data Stipends are $2,000 or $1,000.
Duration 1 year.
Number awarded 10 each year: 5 at $2,000 and 5 at $1,000.
Deadline March of each year.

[453]
CONNECTICUT TUITION WAIVER FOR VETERANS

Connecticut Board of Regents for Higher Education
39 Woodland Street
Hartford, CT 06105
(860) 723-0013 E-mail: fitzgerald2@ct.edu
Web: www.ct.edu/admission/veterans

Summary To provide financial assistance for college or graduate school to certain Connecticut military servicemembers, veterans, and their dependents.

Eligibility This program is open to 1) honorably-discharged Connecticut veterans who served at least 90 days during specified periods of wartime; 2) active members of the Connecticut Army or Air National Guard; 3) Connecticut residents who are a dependent child or surviving spouse of a member of the armed forces killed in action on or after September 11, 2001 who was also a Connecticut resident; and 4) Connecticut residents who are a dependent child or surviving spouse of a person officially declared missing in action or a prisoner of war while serving in the armed forces after January 1, 1960. Applicants must be attending or planning to attend a public college or university in the state.

Financial data The program provides a waiver of 100% of tuition for students working on an undergraduate or graduate degree at the University of Connecticut (including summer sessions and winter intersession), 100% of tuition for general fund courses at campuses of Connecticut State University, 50% of tuition for extension and summer courses at campuses of Connecticut State University, 100% of tuition at all Connecticut community colleges, and 50% or fees at Charter Oak State College.

Duration Up to 4 years.

Additional information This is an entitlement program; applications are available at the respective college financial aid offices.

Number awarded Varies each year.
Deadline Deadline not specified.

[454]
CONNIE SETTLES SCHOLARSHIP

American Legion Auxiliary
Department of California
205 13th Street, Suite 3300
San Francisco, CA 94103-2461
(415) 861-5092 Fax: (415) 861-8365
E-mail: calegionaux@calegionaux.org
Web: www.calegionaux.org/scholarships.htm

Summary To provide financial assistance to members of the American Legion Auxiliary in California who are attending college or graduate school in the state.

Eligibility This program is open to residents of California who are currently working on an undergraduate or graduate degree at a college or university in the state. Applicants must have been members of the American Legion Auxiliary for at least the 2 preceding years and be current members. Each unit of the Auxiliary may nominate only 1 member. Selection

is based on transcripts, 2 letters of recommendation, a letter from the applicant about themselves and their goals, and financial need. Support is not provided for programs of study deemed to be nonessential (e.g., sewing classes, aerobics, sculpting).

Financial data The stipend is $5,000. Funds are paid directly to the recipient's college or university.

Duration 1 year.

Number awarded 1 each year.

Deadline Applications must be submitted to Auxiliary units by February of each year.

[455]
COUDRET TRUST SCHOLARSHIPS

American Legion
Department of Arkansas
702 Victory Street
P.O. Box 3280
Little Rock, AR 72203
(501) 375-1104 Toll Free: (877) 243-9799
Fax: (501) 375-4236 E-mail: alegion@swbell.net
Web: www.arlegion.org

Summary To provide financial assistance for college to descendants of members of the American Legion in Arkansas.

Eligibility This program is open to the children, grandchildren, and great-grandchildren of living or deceased members of the American Legion in Arkansas. The Legionnaire, except veterans of Operation Enduring Freedom and Operation Iraqi Freedom era, must have been a member for at least 2 years. Applicants must be high school seniors or graduates of a 2-year college in Arkansas. They must sign a drug free pledge and a declaration of support for the Preamble to the Constitution of the American Legion. Selection is based on American spirit, character, leadership quality, scholastic endeavor, and financial need.

Financial data The stipend is $1,000 per year.

Duration 2 years.

Number awarded 4 each year.

Deadline March of each year.

[456]
CPO SCHOLARSHIP FUND

Senior Enlisted Academy Alumni Association
Attn: CPO Scholarship Fund
1269 Elliot Avenue
Newport, RI 02841-1525
E-mail: cposfboard@cposf.org
Web: www.cposf.org/How_to_Apply.html

Summary To provide financial assistance for college to the dependents of Navy Chief Petty Officers (CPOs).

Eligibility This program is open to the spouses and children (natural born, adopted, or step) of active, Reserve, or retired Navy CPOs. Applicants must be high school seniors or students currently enrolled at a college, university, or vocational/technical school with the goal of obtaining an associate or bachelor's degree or certificate. Along with their application, they must submit an autobiographical essay of 200 to 500 words that discusses their significant experiences, community involvement, and qualities of character and leadership important in achieving their goals. Selection is based on the essay, honors and awards received during high school, extracurricular activities, community activities, and employment experience; financial need is not considered. Members of the armed services are not eligible.

Financial data The stipend is $2,000.

Duration 1 year.

Additional information The applicant judged most outstanding receives the Tom Crow Memorial Scholarship.

Number awarded Varies each year; recently, 45 were awarded.

Deadline March of each year.

[457]
CSM HARRY AND MARY HENSELL SCHOLARSHIP PROGRAM

Enlisted Association National Guard of Arizona
Attn: Scholarship Chair
5636 East McDowell Road
Phoenix, AZ 85008-3495
(602) 267-2467 Fax: (602) 267-2509
E-mail: scholarship@eanga.org
Web: www.eanga.org

Summary To provide financial assistance to members of the Enlisted Association National Guard of Arizona (EANGA) and to members of their families who plan to attend college in any state.

Eligibility This program is open to EANGA members, the unmarried sons and daughters of EANGA members, the spouses of EANGA members, and the unremarried spouses and unmarried dependent sons and daughters of deceased EANGA members (who were in good standing at their time of death). Qualifying EANGA members must have at least 1 year remaining on their enlistment or have served 20 or more years of service. Applicants may be high school seniors or current college students who are enrolled or planning to enroll full time at a college or university in any state. Graduate students are not eligible. Selection is based on academic record, character, leadership, and financial need.

Financial data The stipend is $1,000. Funds are made payable to the recipient's school and sent directly to the recipient.

Duration 1 year; nonrenewable.

Additional information This program, sponsored by USAA Insurance Corporation, was established in 1998 and given its current name in 2009.

Number awarded 1 each year.

Deadline April of each year.

[458]
CSM VINCENT BALDASSARI MEMORIAL SCHOLARSHIPS

Enlisted Association National Guard of New Jersey
Attn: Scholarship Chair
3650 Saylors Pond Road
Fort Dix, NJ 08640
(609) 432-9820 E-mail: npdsgt618@yahoo.com
Web: www.eang-nj.org/scholarships.html

Summary To provide financial assistance to New Jersey National Guard members and their children who are interested in attending college in any state.

Eligibility This program is open to 1) children of New Jersey National Guard members (active, inactive, or retired) who

are also members of the Enlisted Association National Guard of New Jersey; and 2) drilling Guard members who are also members of the Association. Applicants must be attending or planning to attend a college or university in any state. Along with their application, they must submit 1) information on their church, school, and community activities; 2) a list of honors they have received; 3) letters of recommendation; 4) transcripts; and 5) a letter with specific facts about their desire to continue their education and specifying their career goals. Financial need is not considered in the selection process.

Financial data The stipend is $1,000.

Duration 1 year.

Number awarded Varies each year; recently, 2 were awarded.

Deadline May of each year.

[459]
CSM VIRGIL R. WILLIAMS SCHOLARSHIP PROGRAM

Enlisted Association of the National Guard of the United States
3133 Mount Vernon Avenue
Alexandria, VA 22305-2640
(703) 519-3846 Toll Free: (800) 234-EANG
Fax: (703) 519-3849 E-mail: eangus@eangus.org
Web: www.eangus.org/?page=GrantsScholarships

Summary To provide financial assistance to National Guard members and their dependents who are members of the Enlisted Association of the National Guard of the United States (EANGUS) and entering or continuing in college.

Eligibility This program is open to high school seniors and current college students who are enrolled or planning to enroll as full-time undergraduate students. They must be 1) National Guard members who belong to EANGUS; 2) unmarried sons and daughters of EANGUS members; 3) spouses of EANGUS members; or 4) unremarried spouses and unmarried dependent children of deceased EANGUS members who were in good standing at the time of their death. Honorary, associate, or corporate membership alone does not qualify. Applicants must submit a copy of their school transcript, 3 letters of recommendation, a letter of academic reference (from their principal, dean, or counselor), a photocopy of the qualifying state and/or national membership card (parent's, spouse's or applicant's), and a personal letter with specific facts as to their desire to continue their education and why financial assistance is necessary. Application packets must be submitted to the state EANGUS association; acceptable packets are then sent to the national offices for judging. Selection is based on academic achievement, character, leadership, and financial need.

Financial data The stipend is $2,000.

Duration 1 year; nonrenewable.

Additional information Recent sponsors of this program included USAA Insurance Corporation, GEICO Insurance, the Armed Forces Benefit Association, and the Armed Forces Insurance Company.

Number awarded Varies each year; recently, 10 were awarded.

Deadline Applications must first be verified by the state office and then submitted by June to the national office.

[460]
DAEDALIAN FOUNDATION DESCENDANTS' SCHOLARSHIP PROGRAM

Daedalian Foundation
Attn: Scholarship Committee
55 Main Circle (Building 676)
P.O. Box 249
Randolph AFB, TX 78148-0249
(210) 945-2113   Fax: (210) 945-2112
E-mail: daedalus@daedalians.org
Web: www.daedalians.org/scholarships.htm

Summary   To provide financial assistance to descendants of members of the Order of Daedalians who wish to prepare for a career in military aviation or space.

Eligibility   This program is open to descendants of members of the order who are working on or planning to work on a baccalaureate or higher degree. Applicants must be interested in and willing to commit to a career as a commissioned military pilot, flight crew member, astronaut, or commissioned officer in 1 of the armed forces of the United States in a discipline directly supporting aeronautics or astronautics. They must be physically and mentally qualified for flight and/or space; if they intend to pursue a non-flying career as a commissioned officer in a scientific or engineering discipline supporting aviation or space, they must pass a physical examination qualifying for active commissioned duty in the U.S. armed forces. Nominations must be submitted by a local chapter (Flight) of Daedalian. Selection is based on academic achievement and recognition, extracurricular activities, honors, and employment experience. Financial need may be considered if all other factors are equal.

Financial data   The stipend is $2,000.

Duration   1 year.

Additional information   The Order of Daedalians was founded in 1934 as an organization of the nearly 14,000 aviators who served as military pilots during World War I and are still listed and designated as Founder Members. In the 1950s, the organization expanded eligibility to include 1) on a sponsorship basis, current and former commissioned military pilots from all services; and 2) on a hereditary basis, descendants of Founder Members.

Number awarded   Up to 3 each year.

Deadline   July of each year.

[461]
DANIEL E. LAMBERT MEMORIAL SCHOLARSHIP

American Legion
Department of Maine
P.O. Box 900
Waterville, ME 04903-0900
(207) 873-3229   Fax: (207) 872-0501
E-mail: legionme@mainelegion.org
Web: www.mainelegion.org

Summary   To provide financial assistance to the children of veterans in Maine who plan to attend college in any state.

Eligibility   This program is open to residents of Maine who are the child or grandchild of a veteran. Applicants must be attending or planning to attend an accredited college or vocational/technical school in any state. They must have demonstrated, by their past behavior, that they believe in the American way of life. U.S. citizenship is required. Financial need is considered in the selection process.

Financial data   The stipend is $1,000.

Duration   1 year.

Number awarded   1 or 2 each year.

Deadline   April of each year.

[462]
DARRELL THIBAULT VFW STATE MEMORIAL SCHOLARSHIP

Veterans of Foreign Wars of the United States-
  Department of Nebraska
Attn: Scholarship Committee
2431 North 48th Street
P.O. Box 4552
Lincoln, NE 68504-0552
(402) 464-0674   Fax: (402) 464-0675
E-mail: johnl@vfwne.org
Web: www.vfwne.org

Summary   To provide financial assistance to members of the Veterans of Foreign Wars (VFW), its Ladies Auxiliary, and their families in Nebraska who wish to attend college in any state.

Eligibility   This program is open to members of the Nebraska chapter of the VFW, its Ladies Auxiliary, and their spouses, children, stepchildren, and grandchildren. Applicants must have completed at least 1 year of full-time study at a college or university in any state. They must be able to demonstrate financial need.

Financial data   A stipend is awarded (amount not specified).

Duration   1 year.

Number awarded   1 or more each year.

Deadline   March of each year.

[463]
DAUGHTERS OF THE CINCINNATI SCHOLARSHIP PROGRAM

Daughters of the Cincinnati
Attn: Scholarship Administrator
20 West 44th Street, Suite 508
New York, NY 10036
(212) 991-9945
E-mail: scholarships@daughters1894.org
Web: www.daughters1894.org/scholarship.htm

Summary   To provide financial assistance for college to high school seniors who are the daughters of active-duty, deceased, or retired military officers.

Eligibility   This program is open to high school seniors who are the daughters of career commissioned officers of the regular Army, Navy, Air Force, Coast Guard, or Marine Corps on active duty, deceased, or retired. Applicants must be planning to enroll at a college or university in any state. Along with their application, they must submit an official school transcript, SAT or ACT scores, a letter of recommendation, an essay on their choice of 3 assigned topics, and documentation of financial need.

Financial data   Scholarship amounts have recently averaged $4,000 per year. Funds are paid directly to the college of the student's choice.

Duration   1 year; may be renewed up to 3 additional years, provided the recipient remains in good academic standing.

Additional information This program was originally established in 1906. It currently includes scholarships designated as the Ann Finch Cox Prize and the Acorn Foundation Scholar's Prize.

Number awarded Approximately 12 each year.

Deadline March of each year.

[464]
DELAWARE EDUCATIONAL BENEFITS FOR CHILDREN OF DECEASED VETERANS AND OTHERS

Delaware Department of Education
Attn: Higher Education Office
401 Federal Street
Dover, DE 19901-3639
(302) 735-4120   Toll Free: (800) 292-7935
Fax: (302) 739-5894   E-mail: dheo@doe.k12.de.us
Web: www.doe.k12.de.us

Summary To provide financial assistance for undergraduate education to dependents of deceased Delaware veterans, state police officers, and Department of Transportation employees and members of the armed forces declared prisoners of war or missing in action.

Eligibility Applicants for this assistance must have been Delaware residents for at least 3 consecutive years and be the children, between 16 and 24 years of age, of members of the armed forces 1) whose cause of death was service-related; 2) who are being held or were held as a prisoner of war; or 3) who are officially declared missing in action. The parent must have been a resident of Delaware at the time of death or declaration of missing in action or prisoner of war status. Also eligible are children of Delaware state police officers whose cause of death was service-related and employees of the state Department of Transportation routinely employed in job-related activities upon the state highway system whose cause of death was job related. U.S. citizenship or eligible noncitizen status is required.

Financial data Eligible students receive full tuition at any state-supported institution in Delaware or, if the desired educational program is not available at a state-supported school, at any private institution in Delaware. If the desired educational program is not offered at either a public or private institution in Delaware, this program pays the full cost of tuition at the out-of-state school the recipient attends. Students who wish to attend a private or out-of-state school even though their program is offered at a Delaware public institution receive the equivalent of the average tuition and fees at the state school.

Duration 1 year; may be renewed for 3 additional years.

Number awarded Varies each year.

Deadline Applications may be submitted at any time, but they must be received 6 to 8 weeks before the beginning of classes.

[465]
DELLA VAN DEUREN MEMORIAL SCHOLARSHIPS

American Legion Auxiliary
Department of Wisconsin
Attn: Education Chair
2930 American Legion Drive
P.O. Box 140
Portage, WI 53901-0140
(608) 745-0124   Toll Free: (866) 664-3863
Fax: (608) 745-1947   E-mail: alawi@amlegionauxwi.org
Web: www.amlegionauxwi.org/Scholarships.htm

Summary To provide financial assistance to Wisconsin residents who are members or children of members of the American Legion Auxiliary and interested in attending college in any state.

Eligibility This program is open to members and children of members of the American Legion Auxiliary in Wisconsin. Applicants must be high school seniors or graduates attending or planning to attend a college or university in any state. They must have a GPA of 3.5 or higher and be able to demonstrate financial need. Along with their application, they must submit a 300-word essay on "Education—An Investment in the Future."

Financial data The stipend is $1,000.

Duration 1 year; nonrenewable.

Number awarded 2 each year.

Deadline March of each year.

[466]
DENNIS COMAI SCHOLARSHIPS

Sons of the American Legion
Detachment of Vermont
c/o John Waite, Scholarship Chair
1034 Main Street
North Walpole, NH 03609

Summary To provide financial assistance to high school seniors in Vermont whose family has a connection to the American Legion and who are planning to attend a trade/technical school in any state.

Eligibility This program is open to seniors graduating from high schools in Vermont whose grandparent, parent, or sibling is a member of the American Legion, American Legion Auxiliary, or Sons of the American Legion. Applicants must be planning to attend a trade school or technical college in any state. Along with their application, they must submit a brief essay on what the American veteran means to them. Financial need is considered in the selection process.

Financial data Stipends are $1,000 or $500.

Duration 1 year.

Number awarded 4 each year: 2 at $1,000 (1 in the northern part of the state and 1 in the southern part of the state) and 2 at $500 (1 in the northern part of the state and 1 in the southern part of the state).

Deadline April of each year.

[467]
DISABLED AMERICAN VETERANS AUXILIARY NATIONAL EDUCATION SCHOLARSHIP FUND

Disabled American Veterans Auxiliary
Attn: National Education Scholarship Fund
3725 Alexandria Pike
Cold Spring, KY 41076
(859) 441-7300   Toll Free: (877) 426-2838, ext. 4020
Fax: (859) 442-2095   E-mail: dava@davmail.org
Web: www.davauxiliary.org/membership/Programs.aspx

Summary To provide financial assistance to members of the Disabled American Veterans (DAV) Auxiliary who are interested in attending college or graduate school.

Eligibility This program is open to paid life members of the auxiliary who are attending or planning to attend a college, university, or vocational school as a full- or part-time undergraduate or graduate student. Applicants must be at least seniors in high school, but there is no maximum age limit. Selection is based on academic achievement; participation in DAV activities; participation in other activities for veterans in their school, community, or elsewhere; volunteer work; membership in clubs or organizations; honors and awards; a statement of academic goals; and financial need.

Financial data Stipends are $1,500 per year for full-time students or $750 per year for part-time students.

Duration 1 year; may be renewed for up to 4 additional years, provided the recipient maintains a GPA of 2.5 or higher.

Additional information Membership in the DAV Auxiliary is available to extended family members of veterans eligible for membership in Disabled American Veterans (i.e., any man or woman who served in the armed forces during a period of war or under conditions simulating war and was wounded, disabled to any degree, or left with long-term illness as a result of military service and was discharged or retired from military service under honorable conditions). This program was established in September 2010 as a replacement for the educational loan program that the DAV Auxiliary operated from 1931 until August 2010.

Number awarded Varies each year.

Deadline March of each year.

[468]
DISTINGUISHED FLYING CROSS SOCIETY SCHOLARSHIPS

Distinguished Flying Cross Society
Attn: Scholarship Program
P.O. Box 502408
San Diego, CA 92150
Toll Free: (866) 332-6332
Web: www.dfcsociety.org/?page_id=790

Summary To provide financial assistance for college to descendants of members of the Distinguished Flying Cross Society (DFCS).

Eligibility This program is open to descendants (including legally adopted children) of DFCS members. Applicants must be working on an undergraduate degree at an accredited institution of higher education. Along with their application, they must submit a list of memberships in school-related organizations, a list of elected leadership positions they have held, information on activities that demonstrate community

involvement, transcripts (including SAT scores), and a 500-word essay on why they feel they deserve this scholarship.

Financial data The stipend is $1,000.

Duration 1 year.

Additional information Membership in the sponsoring organization, founded in 1994, is limited to members of the U.S. armed forces who have been awarded the Distinguished Flying Cross as a result of deeds accomplished during aerial flight.

Number awarded 4 each year.

Deadline November of each year.

[469]
DKF VETERANS ASSISTANCE FOUNDATION SCHOLARSHIPS

DKF Veterans Assistance Foundation
P.O. Box 7166
San Carlos, CA 94070
(650) 595-3896   E-mail: admin@dkfveterans.com
Web: www.dkfveterans.com/apply.html

Summary To provide financial assistance for college in any state to California residents who are veterans of Operation Enduring Freedom (OEF) in Afghanistan or Operation Iraqi Freedom (OIF) or the dependents of deceased or disabled veterans of those actions.

Eligibility This program is open to 1) veterans of the U.S. armed forces (including the Coast Guard) who served in support of OEF or OIF within the central command area of responsibility; and 2) dependents of those veterans who were killed in action or incurred disabilities rated as 75% or more. Applicants must be residents of California enrolled or planning to enroll full time at a college, university, community college, or trade institution in any state. Along with their application, they must submit a cover letter introducing themselves and their educational goals.

Financial data The stipend is $5,000 per year for students at universities and state colleges or $1,500 per year for students at community colleges and trade institutions.

Duration 1 year; may be renewed up to 3 additional years, provided the recipient maintains a GPA of 3.0 or higher.

Additional information This foundation was established in 2005.

Number awarded A limited number of these scholarships are awarded each year.

Deadline Deadline not specified.

[470]
DOLPHIN SCHOLARSHIPS

Dolphin Scholarship Foundation
Attn: Scholarship Administrator
4966 Euclid Road, Suite 109
Virginia Beach, VA 23462
(757) 671-3200, ext. 111   Fax: (757) 671-3330
E-mail: scholars@dolphinscholarship.org
Web: www.dolphinscholarship.org/?PAGEID=ELIGIBILITY

Summary To provide financial assistance for college to the children of members or former members of the Submarine Force.

Eligibility This program is open to the unmarried children and stepchildren under 24 years of age of 1) members or former members of the Submarine Force who qualified in submarines and served in the submarine force for at least 8 years; 2) Navy members who served in submarine support activities for at least 10 years; and 3) Submarine Force members who died on active duty. Applicants must be working or intending to work toward a bachelor's degree at an accredited 4-year college or university. Selection is based on academic proficiency, commitment and excellence in school and community activities, and financial need.

Financial data The stipend is $3,400 per year.

Duration 1 year; may be renewed for 3 additional years.

Additional information Since this program was established in 1961, it has awarded more than $8 million to more than 1,000 students. It includes awards previously offered by U.S. Submarine Veterans of World War II. In 1991, that organization agreed to turn over its funds to the Dolphin Scholarship Foundation with the stipulation that it would award 3 scholarships each year, designated the U.S. Submarine Veterans of World War II Scholarship, the Wives of the U.S. Submarine Veterans of World War II Scholarship, and the Arnold Krippendorf Scholarship.

Number awarded Varies each year; recently, 30 were awarded.

Deadline March of each year.

[471]
DONALDSON D. FRIZZELL MEMORIAL SCHOLARSHIPS

First Command Educational Foundation
Attn: Scholarship Programs Manager
1 FirstComm Plaza
Fort Worth, TX 76109-4999
(817) 569-2634   Toll Free: (877) 872-8289
Fax: (817) 569-2970   E-mail: Scholarships@fcef.com
Web: www.fcef.com

Summary To provide financial assistance to students, especially those with ties to the military (including ROTC), who are entering or attending college or graduate school.

Eligibility This program is open to 1) members of a U.S. uniformed service and their spouses and dependents; 2) clients of First Command Financial Services and their family members; 3) dependent family members of First Command Advisors or field office staff members; or 4) non-contractual ROTC students. Applicants may be traditional students (high school seniors and students already enrolled at a college, university, or accredited trade school) or nontraditional students (those defined by their institution as nontraditional and adult students planning to return to a college, university, or accredited trade school. They must have a GPA of 3.0 or higher and be working on a trade school certification or associate, undergraduate, or graduate degree. Applicants must submit 1-page essays on 1) their active involvement in community service programs; 2) the impact of financial literacy on their future; and 3) why they need this scholarship. Selection is based primarily on the essays, academic merit, and financial need.

Financial data Stipends are $5,000 or $2,500. Funds are disbursed directly to the recipient's college, university, or trade school.

Duration 1 year.

Additional information The sponsoring organization was formerly known as the USPA & IRA Educational Foundation, founded in 1983 to provide scholarships to the children of active, retired, or deceased military personnel. In addition to these scholarships, for which students may apply directly, it supports scholarships offered by a number of partner organizations. Since its establishment, it has awarded scholarships worth nearly $4 million.

Number awarded 6 each year: 2 at $5,000 and 4 at $2,500. Awards are split evenly between the 2 categories.

Deadline The online application process begins in February of each year and continues until 200 applications have been received in each category.

[472]
DOROTHY KELLERMAN SCHOLARSHIP

American Legion Auxiliary
Department of New Jersey
c/o Marion Heller, Secretary
1540 Kuser Road, Suite A-8
Hamilton, NJ 08619
(609) 581-9580   Fax: (609) 581-8429
E-mail: newjerseyala1@optimum.net
Web: www.alanj.org/box_widget.html

Summary To provide financial assistance to New Jersey residents who are the descendants of veterans and planning to attend college in any state.

Eligibility This program is open to the children, grandchildren, and great-grandchildren of veterans who served in the U.S. armed forces during specified periods of wartime. Applicants must be graduating high school seniors who have been residents of New Jersey for at least 2 years. They must be planning to attend a college or university in any state. Along with their application, they must submit a 1,000-word essay on a topic that changes annually; recently, students were asked to write on the topic, "Pass it On-How I Can be a Leader in My Community." Selection is based on academic achievement (40%), character (15%), leadership (15%), Americanism (15%), and financial need (15%).

Financial data Stipends range from $1,000 to $2,500.

Duration 1 year; nonrenewable.

Number awarded 1 each year.

Deadline April of each year.

[473]
DR. HANNAH K. VUOLO MEMORIAL SCHOLARSHIP

American Legion
Department of New York
112 State Street, Suite 1300
Albany, NY 12207
(518) 463-2215   Toll Free: (800) 253-4466
Fax: (518) 427-8443   E-mail: info@nylegion.org
Web: nylegion.net/programs-services/#h28

Summary To provide financial assistance to descendants of members of the American Legion in New York who are interested in becoming secondary school teachers.

Eligibility This program is open to the natural or adopted direct descendants of members or deceased members of the American Legion's New York Department. Applicants must be high school seniors or graduates under 21 years of age entering an accredited college in any state as freshmen with a commitment to earning a degree in secondary education. Preference is given to residents of New York. Selection is based on financial need (11 points), academic record (10 points), Americanism (9 points), participation in projects to help the elderly, needy, or disabled (8 points), self-help as demonstrated by work record (7 points), participation in social, political, religious, or athletic groups (6 points), neatness and correctness of letter (5 points), and New York residency (4 points).

Financial data The stipend is $1,000.

Duration 1 year.

Number awarded 1 each year.

Deadline April of each year.

[474]
DRAGON HILL CHAPTER NCOA SCHOLARSHIPS

Non Commissioned Officers Association of the United
 States of America-Dragon Hill Chapter 1507
PSC 450
Box 705
APO AP 96206-0705
E-mail: Chairman.joe@gmail.com
Web: your.ncoakorea.org/?page_id=463

Summary To provide financial assistance for college to seniors at Department of Defense Dependents Schools (DoDDS) in Korea who are children of enlisted military personnel or of members of the Non Commissioned Officers Association (NCOA).

Eligibility This program is open to seniors at DoDDS high schools in Korea who have a cumulative GPA of 3.25 or higher and are planning to attend college. Applicants must be the child of either a U.S. military enlisted servicemember or an NCOA member. They must have performed at least 40 hours of community or volunteer service during their junior or senior year of high school. Along with their application, they must submit a 250-word autobiography that closes with a paragraph on why they want to go to college, letters of recommendation, certification of community or volunteer service, a copy of their high school transcript, and a copy of their SAT/ACT scores.

Financial data A stipend is awarded (amount not specified).

Duration 1 year.

Number awarded Up to 4 each year.

Deadline April of each year.

[475]
DRS GUARDIAN SCHOLARSHIP FUND

National Guard Educational Foundation
Attn: Scholarship Fund
One Massachusetts Avenue, N.W.
Washington, DC 20001
(202) 789-0031   Fax: (202) 682-9358
E-mail: ngef@ngaus.org
Web: www.ngef.org

Summary To provide financial assistance for college to children of members of the National Guard who died in service.

Eligibility This program is open to 1) high school juniors and seniors who have been accepted to an accredited community college, technical school, or 4-year college or university and have a GPA of 3.0 or higher; and 2) students who are currently enrolled full time at an accredited community college, technical school, or 4-year college or university and have a GPA of 2.5 or higher. Applicants must be the dependent child of a National Guard member who died in an opera-

tional or training mission in support of Operation Enduring Freedom, Operation Iraqi Freedom, or Operation New Dawn. The educational institution they are attending or planning to attend must be located in the 50 states, the District of Columbia, Puerto Rico, the U.S. Virgin Islands, or Guam. Along with their application, they must submit a 1-page essay on their deceased parent, transcripts, and documentation of financial need.

Financial data The stipend is $6,250 per year.

Duration 1 year; may be renewed 1 additional year by students at community colleges and technical schools and up to 3 additional years by students at 4-year colleges and universities.

Additional information This program began in 2011 by DRS Technologies, Inc., a defense contractor headquartered in Arlington, Virginia.

Number awarded Varies each year; recently, 7 new and 5 renewal scholarships were awarded. Since the program began, it has awarded scholarships to 33 students.

Deadline June of each year.

[476]
E.A. BLACKMORE SCHOLARSHIP

American Legion
Department of Wyoming
1320 Hugur Avenue
Cheyenne, WY 82001-4817
(307) 634-3035   Fax: (307) 635-7093
E-mail: wylegion@qwest.net
Web: www.wylegion.org/awards.htm

Summary To provide financial assistance to the children and grandchildren of members of the American Legion in Wyoming who are interested in attending college in any state.

Eligibility This program is open to the children and grandchildren of members and deceased members of the American Legion in Wyoming. Applicants must rank in the top 20% of their high school graduating class and be able to demonstrate financial need. They must be attending or planning to attend a college or university in any state.

Financial data The stipend is $1,000 per year. Funds are paid directly to the recipient's school to be used for tuition, room and board, textbooks, and other fees.

Duration 1 year; may be renewed up to 3 additional years.

Number awarded 1 each year.

Deadline May of each year.

[477]
EAGLES MEMORIAL FOUNDATION EDUCATIONAL GRANTS FOR MILITARY AND OTHER SERVICE PERSONNEL

Fraternal Order of Eagles
Attn: Eagles Memorial Foundation
1623 Gateway Circle South
Grove City, OH 43123
(614) 883-2200   Fax: (613) 883-2201
E-mail: memorialfoundation@foe.com
Web: www.foe.com/Charities/MemorialFoundation.aspx

Summary To provide financial assistance for college to the children of deceased members of the Fraternal Order of Eagles or its Ladies Auxiliary who died in action.

Eligibility Applicants must be the minor (under 25 years of age) unmarried children of a deceased parent who was a member of the Fraternal Order of Eagles or its Ladies Auxiliary at the time of death; the member must have died from injuries or diseases incurred or aggravated in the line of duty while serving 1) in the armed forces of the United States or Canada; 2) as volunteer law enforcement officers in the United States; 3) as volunteer firefighters; or 4) as volunteer emergency medical service officers.

Financial data Stipends up to $6,000 per school year are provided. Funds must be used for tuition, fees, books, and course-related supplies. Room and board expenses are not covered.

Duration 1 year; may be renewed for up to 4 additional years, provided the recipient maintains a GPA of 2.0 or higher and remains an unmarried dependent.

Number awarded Varies each year.

Deadline Deadline not specified.

[478]
EANGUS AUXILIARY SCHOLARSHIP PROGRAM

Enlisted Association of the National Guard of the United
 States
Attn: Auxiliary
3133 Mount Vernon Avenue
Alexandria, VA 22305-2640
(703) 519-3846   Toll Free: (800) 234-EANG
Fax: (703) 519-3849   E-mail: eangus@eangus.org
Web: www.eangus.org/?page=AuxScholarships

Summary To provide financial assistance to members of the Auxiliary of the Enlisted Association of the National Guard of the United States (EANGUS) and their dependents who are entering or continuing in college.

Eligibility This program is open to high school seniors and currently-enrolled college students who are EANGUS Auxiliary members, their unmarried children or grandchildren younger than 26 years of age, or their spouses. Applicants must be enrolled or planning to enroll at a college, university, business school, or trade school and taking at least 8 accredited hours. Graduate students are not eligible. Along with their application, they must submit a copy of their school transcript, 3 letters of recommendation, a letter of academic reference (from their principal, dean, or counselor), and a letter with specific goals for continuing their education and why financial assistance is necessary. The sponsor's State Auxiliary must have made a donation to the EANGUS Auxiliary Scholarship fund for the current and prior years. Selection is based on academic achievement, character, leadership, and financial need.

Financial data Stipends are $1,250 or $1,000.

Duration 1 year; nonrenewable.

Additional information This program includes 1 scholarship donated by USAA Insurance Corporation.

Number awarded 4 each year: 1 at $1,250 and 3 at $1,000.

Deadline June of each year.

[479]
EANGUT SCHOLARSHIPS

Enlisted Association of the National Guard of Utah
Attn: Scholarship Committee
12953 South Minuteman Drive
Draper, UT 84020
(801) 699-1680   E-mail: eangut@hotmail.com
Web: www.eangut.org/Scholarship

Summary To provide financial assistance to National Guard members belonging to the Enlisted Association National Guard of Utah (EANGUT) and their family members who are beginning or continuing their college studies in the state.

Eligibility This program is open to members of EANGUT, their spouses, their children, and the spouses and unmarried dependent children of deceased members. Applicants must be attending or planning to attend a college, university, or vocational/technical school in Utah. EANGUT members must have at least 1 year remaining on their enlistment or have completed 20 or more years of service. Along with their application, they must submit 3 essays on 1) their educational and career goals; 2) their leadership and extracurricular activities; and 3) how the military has influenced their life.

Financial data The stipend is $1,500 or $1,000.

Duration 1 year.

Additional information This program receives support from the USAA Insurance Corporation.

Number awarded 2 each year: 1 at $1,500 and 1 at $1,000.

Deadline March of each year.

[480]
EARLINE MAYBERRY SCHOLARSHIP

Ladies Auxiliary to the Veterans of Foreign Wars-
 Department of North Carolina
c/o Lynn Edwards, Scholarship Chair
917 New Bern Avenue
Raleigh, NC 27601-1603
(919) 828-5058
Web: www.lavfwnc.org/downloadable-forms

Summary To provide financial assistance to children and grandchildren of members of the Veterans of Foreign Wars (VFW) and its Ladies Auxiliary in North Carolina who plan to attend college in the state.

Eligibility This program is open to seniors graduating from high schools in North Carolina and planning to enroll at a junior or senior college in the state. Applicants must be the child, grandchild, or stepchild of a member of the VFW or its Ladies Auxiliary, or, if deceased, was a member at time of death.

Financial data The stipend is $1,000 per year. Funds are paid directly to the recipient's institution.

Duration 1 year; may be renewed up to 3 additional years.

Number awarded 4 each year.

Deadline February of each year.

[481]
EDMUND K. GROSS SCHOLARSHIP

Marines' Memorial Association
c/o Marines Memorial Club and Hotel
609 Sutter Street
San Francisco, CA 94102
(415) 673-6672, ext. 293   Fax: (415) 441-3649
E-mail: scholarship@marineclub.com
Web: www.marineclub.com/membership/scholarship.php

Summary To provide financial assistance to members of the Marines' Memorial Association from all branches of the armed forces and their descendants who are interested in studying education in college.

Eligibility This program is open to active members of the association and their children and grandchildren. Applicants must be enrolled or planning to enroll in an undergraduate degree program in education at a college or university. Along with their application, they must submit an essay of 250 to 500 words on what they value enough to promote to a wider audience. Graduating high school seniors must submit a high school transcript and SAT or ACT scores; continuing college students must submit a college transcript. Selection is based on the essay, academic merit, references, and financial need.

Financial data The stipend is $2,500 per year.

Duration 1 year; recipients may reapply for up to 3 additional years.

Additional information Membership in the association is open to veterans of the Marines, Army, Navy, Air Force, or Coast Guard and to personnel currently serving in a branch of the armed forces.

Number awarded 1 each year.

Deadline April of each year.

[482]
EDUCATION FOUNDATION FOR THE COLORADO NATIONAL GUARD GRANTS

National Guard Association of Colorado
Attn: Education Foundation, Inc.
P.O. Box 440889
Aurora, CO 80044-0889
(303) 909-6369   Fax: (720) 535-5925
E-mail: BernieRogoff@comcast.net
Web: www.efcong.org/Grants

Summary To provide financial assistance to members of the Colorado National Guard and their families who are interested in attending college or graduate school in any state.

Eligibility This program is open to current and retired members of the Colorado National Guard and their dependent unmarried children and spouses. Applicants must be enrolled or planning to enroll full or part time at a college, university, trade school, business school, or graduate school in any state. Along with their application, they must submit an essay, up to 2 pages in length, on their desire to continue their education, what motivates them, their financial need, their commitment to academic excellence, and their current situation. Selection is based on academic achievement, community involvement, and financial need.

Financial data Stipends are generally at least $1,000 per year.

Duration 1 year; may be renewed.

Number awarded Normally, 15 to 25 of these grants are awarded each semester.

Deadline August of each year for fall semester; January of each year for spring semester.

[483]
EDUCATIONAL GRANTS FOR SPOUSES OF ACTIVE-DUTY SERVICE MEMBERS

Corvias Foundation
1405 South County Trail, Suite 539
East Greenwich, RI 02818
(401) 228-2836   Fax: (401) 336-2523
E-mail: info@CorviasFoundation.org
Web: www.corviasfoundation.org

Summary To provide financial assistance for college or graduate school to spouses of active-duty military personnel assigned to specified Army or Air Force installations throughout the United States.

Eligibility This program is open to spouses of active-duty service members stationed at 1 of 13 designated Air Force or Army installations. Applicants must be enrolled or planning to enroll at a university, community college, or technical college in any state. Selection is based on academic performance, community involvement, plan for use of the grant, and financial need.

Financial data The stipend is $5,000.

Duration 1 year; nonrenewable.

Additional information The designated installations are Aberdeen Proving Ground (Maryland), Edwards AFB (California), Eglin AFB (Florida), Eielson AFB (Alaska), Fort Bragg (North Carolina), Fort Meade (Maryland), Fort Polk (Louisiana), Fort Riley (Kansas), Fort Rucker (Alabama), Fort Sill (Oklahoma), Hurlburt Field (Florida), McConnell AFB (Kansas), or Seymour Johnson AFB (North Carolina).

Number awarded Up to 20 each year.

Deadline May of each year.

[484]
EDWARD T. CONROY MEMORIAL SCHOLARSHIP PROGRAM

Maryland Higher Education Commission
Attn: Office of Student Financial Assistance
6 North Liberty Street, Ground Suite
Baltimore, MD 21201
(410) 767-3301   Toll Free: (800) 974-0203
Fax: (410) 332-0250   TDD: (800) 735-2258
E-mail: osfamail@mhec.state.md.us
Web: www.mhec.state.md.us

Summary To provide financial assistance for college or graduate school in Maryland to children and spouses of victims of the September 11, 2001 terrorist attacks and specified categories of veterans, public safety employees, and their children or spouses.

Eligibility This program is open to entering and continuing undergraduate and graduate students in the following categories: 1) children and surviving spouses of victims of the September 11, 2001 terrorist attacks who died in the World Trade Center in New York City, in the Pentagon in Virginia, or on United Airlines Flight 93 in Pennsylvania; 2) veterans who have, as a direct result of military service, a disability of 25% or greater and have exhausted or are no longer eligible for federal veterans' educational benefits; 3) children of armed forces members whose death or 100% disability was directly caused by military service; 4) POW/MIA veterans of the Vietnam Conflict and their children; 5) state or local public safety officers or volunteers who became 100% disabled in the line of duty; and 6) children and unremarried surviving spouses of state or local public safety employees or volunteers who died or became 100% disabled in the line of duty. The parent, spouse, veteran, POW, or public safety officer or volunteer must have been a resident of Maryland at the time of death or when declared disabled. Applicants must be planning to enroll at a 2- or 4-year Maryland college or university as a full-time or part-time degree-seeking undergraduate or graduate student or attend a private career school. Financial need is not considered.

Financial data The amount of the award is equal to tuition and fees at a Maryland postsecondary institution, to a maximum of $10,085. The total amount of all Maryland scholarship awards from all sources may not exceed the cost of attendance or $19,000, whichever is less.

Duration Up to 5 years of full-time study or 8 years of part-time study.

Number awarded Varies each year.

Deadline July of each year.

[485]
EDWIN J. MCGLOTHIN MEMORIAL SCHOLARSHIP

Veterans of Foreign Wars of the United States-
Department of Oregon
12440 N.E. Halsey Street
Portland, OR 97230
(503) 255-5808   Fax: (503) 255-5817
E-mail: admin@vfworegon.org
Web: www.vfworegon.org/scholarships.htm

Summary To provide financial assistance to descendants of members of the Veterans of Foreign Wars (VFW) in Oregon who plan to attend college in any state.

Eligibility This program is open to seniors graduating from high schools in Oregon and planning to enroll full time at a 2- or 4-year college, university, or vocational school in any state. Applicants must be the child, grandchild, or great-grandchild of a VFW member who is presently, or was at the time of death, a member in good standing. They must have a GPA of 2.5 or higher and a record of involvement in community service activities. Along with their application, they must submit a 300-word essay on the topic, "Why I'm Optimistic About our Nation's Future."

Financial data The stipend is $1,000.

Duration 1 year.

Number awarded Up to 5 each year.

Deadline February of each year.

[486]
E.E. MIXON SECOND DRAGOON FOUNDATION SCHOLARSHIPS

E.E. Mixon Second Dragoon Foundation
c/o Scott C. Pierce
217 Painted Fall Way
Cary, NC 27513
(203) 979-7083   E-mail: scott@2nddragoons.org
Web: www.2nddragoons.org/index/?q=node/27

Summary To provide financial assistance for college to former members of the U.S. Army's Second Cavalry Regiment and the children of current and former members.

Eligibility This program is open to former members of the Second Cavalry Regiment and the children of current or former members. Members of other Army units and their children may also be considered, especially if they have a previous connection with the Second Cavalry Regiment or other U.S. Cavalry Regiments. Applicants must submit a 500-word essay on 1 of the following topics: 1) how our military presence in Europe contributed to the end of the Cold War; 2) the role of the non-commissioned officer corps in the U.S. military; 3) what America means to them; or 4) their strategy for the way forward in Afghanistan. They must be attending or planning to attend a college or university. Selection is based on the essay and a statement of their educational goals, projected or current field of study, and personal or family affiliation with a cavalry unit.

Financial data Stipends range from $250 to $1,000 per year. Funds are deposited directly into the recipient's college tuition account.

Duration 1 semester; may be renewed.

Number awarded Varies each year; recently, 3 were awarded.

Deadline July of each year.

[487]
ELIZABETH AND WALLACE KINGSBURY SCHOLARSHIP

United Daughters of the Confederacy
Attn: Second Vice President General
328 North Boulevard
Richmond, VA 23220-4008
(804) 355-1636   Fax: (804) 353-1396
E-mail: jamieretired@sbcglobal.net
Web: www.hqudc.org/Scholarships/index.htm

Summary To provide financial assistance for college to lineal descendants of Confederate veterans who have been members of the Children of the Confederacy for at least 3 years.

Eligibility Eligible to apply for these scholarships are lineal descendants of worthy Confederates or collateral descendants who have been members of the Children of the Confederacy for at least 3 years. Applicants must submit a family financial report and certified proof of the Confederate record of 1 ancestor, with the company and regiment in which he served. They must have at least a 3.0 GPA in high school.

Financial data The amount of the scholarship depends on the availability of funds.

Duration 1 year; may be renewed for up to 3 additional years.

Number awarded 1 each year.

Deadline April of each year.

[488]
ELIZABETH SHALLOW PRIZE

Daughters of the Cincinnati
Attn: Scholarship Administrator
20 West 44th Street, Suite 508
New York, NY 10036
(212) 991-9945
E-mail: scholarships@daughters1894.org
Web: www.daughters1894.org/scholarship.htm

Summary To provide financial assistance for college to high school seniors who are the daughters of active-duty, deceased, or retired Coast Guard officers.

Eligibility This program is open to high school seniors who are the daughters of career commissioned officers of the regular Coast Guard on active duty, deceased, or retired. Applicants must be planning to enroll at a college or university in any state. Along with their application, they must submit an official school transcript, SAT or ACT scores, a letter of recommendation, an essay on their choice of 3 assigned topics, and documentation of financial need.

Financial data Scholarship amounts have recently averaged $4,000 per year. Funds are paid directly to the college of the student's choice.

Duration 1 year; may be renewed up to 3 additional years, provided the recipient remains in good academic standing.

Number awarded 1 each year.

Deadline March of each year.

[489]
ELOISE CAMPBELL MEMORIAL SCHOLARSHIPS

United Daughters of the Confederacy
Attn: Second Vice President General
328 North Boulevard
Richmond, VA 23220-4008
(804) 355-1636   Fax: (804) 353-1396
E-mail: jamieretired@sbcglobal.net
Web: www.hqudc.org/Scholarships/index.htm

Summary To provide financial assistance for college to women, particularly in selected areas of Arkansas or Texas, who are lineal descendants of Confederate veterans.

Eligibility Eligible to apply for these scholarships are lineal descendants of worthy Confederates or collateral descendants who are members of the Children of the Confederacy or the United Daughters of the Confederacy. Applicants must be female and have at least a 3.0 GPA in high school. Preference is given to candidates from Bowie County, Texas and Miller County, Arkansas. Applications must be accompanied by a family financial report and certified proof of the Confederate military record of 1 ancestor, with the company and regiment in which he served.

Financial data The amount of the scholarship depends on the availability of funds.

Duration 1 year; may be renewed for up to 3 additional years.

Number awarded 1 each year.

Deadline April of each year.

[490]
ENLISTED ASSOCIATION NATIONAL GUARD OF KANSAS SCHOLARSHIPS

Enlisted Association National Guard of Kansas
Attn: Executive Director
P.O. Box 841
Topeka, KS 66601-0841
(785) 242-5678   Fax: (785) 242-3765
E-mail: eangks@earthlink.net
Web: www.eangks.org/benefits/scholarships

Summary To provide financial assistance to members of the Enlisted Association National Guard of Kansas and their families who are interested in attending college in any state.

Eligibility This program is open to members of the association who are also currently serving in the Kansas National Guard and their families. Spouses and dependents of associate members are not eligible. Applicants must submit high school and/or college transcripts (including SAT and/or ACT scores); 4 letters of recommendation; information on their awards and recognition, community service, extracurricular activities, and work experience; documentation of financial need; and a brief essay on their goals and career objectives. They must be enrolled or planning to enroll full time at an accredited institution of higher learning in any state.

Financial data The stipend ranges up to $1,000.

Duration 1 year.

Additional information This program includes 1 scholarship supported by USAA Insurance Corporation.

Number awarded Varies each year.

Deadline May of each year.

[491]
EOD WARRIOR FOUNDATION SCHOLARSHIPS

EOD Warrior Foundation
Attn: Executive Director
33735 Snickersville Turnpike, Suite 201
P.O. Box 309
Bluemont, VA 20135
(540) 554-4550   Fax: (540) 554-2681
E-mail: scholarship@eodwarriorfoundation.org
Web: www.eodwarriorfoundation.org/scholarship

Summary To provide financial assistance for college to spouses and other family members of technicians or military officers who have worked in explosive ordnance disposal (EOD).

Eligibility This program is open to children, stepchildren, spouses, grandchildren, and other recognized dependents of graduates of Naval School Explosive Ordnance Disposal (NAVSCOLEOD) who served or are serving in the Army, Navy, Air Force, or Marine Corps. Active-duty personnel and NAVSCOLEOD graduates are not eligible. Children or other dependents must be 23 years of age or younger; spouses may be of any age. Selection is based on GPA, community involvement and volunteerism, extracurricular activities, awards, paid employment, an essay, future goals, letters of recommendation, and overall impression. Applicants who are family members of an EOD Wounded Warrior or an EOD Memorial Honoree are automatically granted scholarships.

Financial data A stipend is awarded (amount not specified). Funds are paid directly to the academic institution for the student's tuition, books, fees, and on-campus housing.

Duration 1 year; may be renewed up to 3 additional years.

Additional information This sponsor was formerly named the Explosive Ordnance Disposal Memorial Foundation.

Number awarded Varies each year; recently, 42 were awarded.

Deadline February of each year.

[492]
ERNIE WILSON JR. SCHOLARSHIP

Sons of the American Legion
Detachment of New Jersey
135 West Hanover Street
Trenton, NJ 08618
(609) 695-5418   Fax: (609) 394-1532
Web: www.njsal.org/cgi/generalinfo.php#tabs-forms

Summary To provide financial assistance to members of the Sons of the American Legion who are high school seniors in New Jersey and planning to attend college in any state.

Eligibility This program is open to seniors graduating from high schools in New Jersey who are members of the Sons of the American Legion. Applicants must be planning to enroll at a college or university in any state. Selection is based on scholarship (20%), character (20%), leadership (20%), Americanism and community service (20%), and financial need (20%).

Financial data The stipend is $3,500.

Duration 1 year.

Number awarded 1 each year.

Deadline April of each year.

[493]
ESSAY COMPETITION FOR CHILDREN OF PUBLIC EMPLOYEES

Civil Service Employees Insurance Group
Attn: Scholarship Contest
2121 North California Boulevard, Suite 555
Walnut Creek, CA 94596-3501
(925) 817-6394   Toll Free: (800) 282-6848
E-mail: SFerrucci@cseinsurance.com
Web: www.cse-insurance.com

Summary To recognize and reward, with college scholarships, the best essays written on teenage automobile safety by the children of full-time public employees (including military personnel) in selected states.

Eligibility This competition is open to high school seniors in 3 geographic regions: southern California, northern California, and Arizona/Nevada/Utah. Applicants must have been accepted as a full-time student at an accredited 2- or 4-year college, university, or trade school in the United States. They must have a cumulative GPA of 3.0 or higher. Their parent or legal guardian must be currently employed full time (or if retired or deceased, must have been employed full time) by a government entity, including, but not limited to, peace officers, firefighters, educators, postal employees, military personnel, or federal, state, and local government workers. Qualified students are invited to write an essay (up to 500 words) that discusses the ways the teenage automobile accident rate can be reduced. Essays are evaluated on the basis of practicality, creativity, and written skill. Also required in the application process are an official transcript and letters of recommendation.

Financial data Prizes in each region are $1,500 scholarships for first place, $1,000 scholarships for second place, $500 scholarships for third place, and $250 scholarships for fourth place.

Duration The prizes are awarded annually.

Number awarded 12 each year: 4 in each region.

Deadline April of each year.

[494]
EUGENIA WATERS STILLMAN PRIZE

Daughters of the Cincinnati
Attn: Scholarship Administrator
20 West 44th Street, Suite 508
New York, NY 10036
(212) 991-9945
E-mail: scholarships@daughters1894.org
Web: www.daughters1894.org/scholarship.htm

Summary To provide financial assistance for college to high school seniors who are the daughters of active-duty, deceased, or retired military officers and have a record of outstanding community service.

Eligibility This program is open to high school seniors who are the daughters of career commissioned officers of the regular Army, Navy, Air Force, Coast Guard, or Marine Corps on active duty, deceased, or retired. Applicants must be planning to enroll at a college or university in any state. They must be able to demonstrate an outstanding record in community service. Along with their application, they must submit an official school transcript, SAT or ACT scores, a letter of recommendation, an essay on their choice of 3 assigned topics, and documentation of financial need.

Financial data Scholarship amounts have recently averaged $4,000 per year. Funds are paid directly to the college of the student's choice.

Duration 1 year; may be renewed up to 3 additional years, provided the recipient remains in good academic standing.

Number awarded 1 each year.

Deadline March of each year.

[495]
EVELYN BUKOVAC HAMILTON HEALTH CARE SCHOLARSHIP

Marines' Memorial Association
c/o Marines Memorial Club and Hotel
609 Sutter Street
San Francisco, CA 94102
(415) 673-6672, ext. 293   Fax: (415) 441-3649
E-mail: scholarship@marineclub.com
Web: www.marineclub.com/membership/scholarship.php

Summary To provide financial assistance to members of the Marines' Memorial Association from all branches of the armed forces and their descendants who are interested in studying health care in college.

Eligibility This program is open to active members of the association and their children and grandchildren. Applicants must be high school seniors or students currently enrolled full time in an undergraduate degree program in a discipline within the field of health care. Along with their application, they must submit an essay of 250 to 500 words in which they compare and contrast scientific advances to literary education. Graduating high school seniors must submit a high school transcript and SAT or ACT scores; continuing college students must submit a college transcript. Selection is based on the essay, academic merit, references, and financial need.

Financial data The stipend is $2,500 per year.

Duration 1 year; recipients may reapply for up to 3 additional years.

Additional information Membership in the association is open to veterans of the Marines, Army, Navy, Air Force, or Coast Guard and to personnel currently serving in a branch of the armed forces.

Number awarded 1 each year.

Deadline April of each year.

[496]
EXEMPTION FROM TUITION FEES FOR DEPENDENTS OF KENTUCKY VETERANS

Kentucky Department of Veterans Affairs
Attn: Tuition Waiver Coordinator
321 West Main Street, Suite 390
Louisville, KY 40202
(502) 595-4447   Toll Free: (800) 928-4012 (within KY)
Fax: (502) 595-3369
Web: www.veterans.ky.gov

Summary To provide financial assistance for undergraduate or graduate studies to the children or unremarried widow(er)s of deceased Kentucky veterans.

Eligibility This program is open to the children, stepchildren, adopted children, and unremarried widow(er)s of veterans who were residents of Kentucky when they entered military service or joined the Kentucky National Guard. The qualifying veteran must have been killed in action during a wartime period or died as a result of a service-connected disability incurred during a wartime period. Applicants must be attending or planning to attend a state-supported college or university in Kentucky to work on an undergraduate or graduate degree.

Financial data Eligible dependents and survivors are exempt from tuition and matriculation fees at any state-supported institution of higher education in Kentucky.

Duration The exemption continues until completion of an undergraduate or graduate degree. There are no age or time limits.

Number awarded Varies each year.

Deadline Deadline not specified.

[497]
FAIRFAX-LEE AUSA SCHOLARSHIPS

Association of the United States Army-Fairfax-Lee
   Chapter
Attn: Scholarship Committee Chair
7542 Laurel Creek Lane
Springfield, VA 22150
E-mail: scholars@ausafairfaxlee.org
Web: www.ausafairfaxlee.org

Summary To provide financial assistance to residents of the National Capital Region who have an affiliation with the Fairfax-Lee Chapter of the Association of the United States Army (AUSA) and are interested in attending college in any state.

Eligibility This program is open to graduating high school seniors and current full- and part-time undergraduates who fall into 1 of the following categories: 1) National Capital Region active-duty, Army Reserve, and Army National Guard

soldiers and their family members; 2) Warrior Transition Battalion soldiers and family members; 3) students enrolled in a senior ROTC or JROTC program; 4) National Capital Region Department of the Army civilian employees; 5) current Fairfax-Lee Chapter members and their families; or 6) students who fall into any of those categories and are majoring in a field of science, technology, engineering, or mathematics (STEM). Applicants must submit a 500-word essay on why they believe they are deserving of this scholarship, including any special family considerations.

Financial data Stipends range from $750 to $1,500.

Duration 1 year.

Additional information This program receives support from GEICO, Lockheed Martin, Peduzzi Associates, and other corporate sponsors. The National Capital Region is defined to include Washington, D.C.; the Maryland counties of Charles, Frederick, Montgomery, and Prince George's; the Virginia counties of Arlington, Fairfax, Loudoun, and Prince William; and the Virginia cities of Alexandria, Fairfax, Falls Church, Manassas, and Manassas Park.

Number awarded Varies each year; recently, 24 of these scholarships, with a total value of $20,000, were awarded.

Deadline April of each year.

[498]
FIFTH MARINE DIVISION ASSOCIATION SCHOLARSHIP

Fifth Marine Division Association Scholarship Fund
c/o Marine Corps Scholarship Foundation
909 North Washington Street, Suite 400
Alexandria, VA 22314
(703) 549-0060   Toll Free: (866) 496-5462
Fax: (703) 549-9474   E-mail: students@mcsf.org
Web: www.mcsf.org/apply/eligibility

Summary To provide financial assistance for college to the grandchildren of veterans who served with the Fifth Marine Division.

Eligibility This program is open to grandchildren of veterans who served with the Fifth Marine Division during World War II or Vietnam and are or were members of the Sixth Marine Division Association. Applicants must be high school seniors, high school graduates, or current college students. Along with their application, they must submit academic transcripts, a copy of their grandparent's honorable discharge, and a 500-word essay on a topic that changes periodically. The family income of applicants must be less than $93,000 per year.

Financial data Stipends range from $500 to $2,500 per year.

Duration 1 year; may be renewed for up to 3 additional years.

Additional information Recipients may also accept scholarship aid from other sources.

Number awarded Varies each year; recently, 3 were awarded.

Deadline February of each year.

[499]
FIRST CAVALRY DIVISION ASSOCIATION SCHOLARSHIPS

First Cavalry Division Association
Attn: Foundation
302 North Main Street
Copperas Cove, TX 76522-1703
(254) 547-6537   Fax: (254) 547-8853
E-mail: firstcav@1cda.org
Web: www.1cda.org/Foundation_Overview.htm

Summary   To provide financial assistance for undergraduate education to soldiers currently or formerly assigned to the First Cavalry Division and their families.

Eligibility   This program is open to children of soldiers who died or have been declared totally and permanently disabled from injuries incurred while serving with the First Cavalry Division during any armed conflict; children of soldiers who died while serving in the First Cavalry Division during peacetime; and active-duty soldiers currently assigned or attached to the First Cavalry Division and their spouses and children.

Financial data   The stipend is $1,200 per year. The checks are made out jointly to the student and the school and may be used for whatever the student needs, including tuition, books, and clothing.

Duration   1 year; may be renewed up to 3 additional years.

Additional information   Requests for applications must be accompanied by a self-addressed stamped envelope.

Number awarded   Varies each year; since the program was established, it has awarded more than $760,000 to 481 children of disabled and deceased Cavalry members and more than $255,000 to 275 current members of the Division and their families.

Deadline   June of each year.

[500]
FIRST LIEUTENANT DMITRI A. DEL CASTILLO SCHOLARSHIPS

U.S. Army Ranger Association
Attn: Scholarship Fund
P.O. Box 52126
Fort Benning, GA 31995-2126
Web: www.ranger.org/page-1263672

Summary   To provide financial assistance for college to children and spouses of deceased soldiers recognized by the Army as Rangers.

Eligibility   This program is open to the unmarried children under 23 years of age and unremarried spouses of deceased tabbed Rangers (graduated from Ranger school and awarded the Ranger Tab) or scrolled Rangers (served with the 75th Ranger Regiment in a Ranger slot). The parent or spouse must have been killed in action or during training or have died in a hospital as a result of critical wounds related to combat or training. Applicants must be attending or planning to attend an accredited college, university, or technical school.

Financial data   The stipend is $5,000; funds are disbursed directly to the recipient's institution.

Duration   1 year.

Number awarded   Varies each year; recently, 3 were awarded.

Deadline   Deadline not specified.

[501]
FIRST LIEUTENANT SCOTT MCCLEAN LOVE MEMORIAL SCHOLARSHIP

Army Scholarship Foundation
11700 Preston Road, Suite 660-301
Dallas, TX 75230
E-mail: ContactUs@armyscholarshipfoundation.org
Web: www.armyscholarshipfoundation.org

Summary   To provide financial assistance for undergraduate study to the children and spouses of Army personnel, especially those who major in the fine arts.

Eligibility   This program is open to 1) children of regular active-duty, active-duty Reserve, and active-duty Army National Guard members in good standing; 2) spouses of serving enlisted regular active-duty, active-duty Reserve, and active-duty Army National Guard members in good standing; and 3) children of former U.S. Army members who received an honorable or medical discharge or were killed while serving in the U.S. Army. Preference is given to students who are majoring or planning to major in the fine arts. Applicants must be high school seniors, high school graduates, or undergraduates enrolled at an accredited college, university, or vocational/technical institute. They must be U.S. citizens and have a GPA of 2.0 or higher; children must be younger than 24 years of age. Financial need is considered in the selection process.

Financial data   The stipend ranges from $500 to $2,000 per year.

Duration   1 year; recipients may reapply.

Additional information   The Army Scholarship Foundation was established in 2001.

Number awarded   1 each year.

Deadline   April of each year.

[502]
FIRST MARINE DIVISION ASSOCIATION SCHOLARSHIPS

First Marine Division Association
403 North Freeman Street
Oceanside, CA 92054
(760) 967-8561   Toll Free: (877) 967-8561
Fax: (760) 967-8567   E-mail: oldbreed@sbcglobal.net
Web: www.1stmarinedivisionassociation.org

Summary   To provide financial assistance for college to dependents of deceased or disabled veterans of the First Marine Division.

Eligibility   This program is open to dependents of veterans who served in the First Marine Division or in a unit attached to that Division, are honorably discharged, and now are either totally and permanently disabled or deceased from any cause. Applicants must be attending or planning to attend an accredited college, university, or trade school as a full-time undergraduate student. Graduate students and students still in high school or prep school are not eligible.

Financial data   The stipend is $1,750 per year.

Duration   1 year; may be renewed up to 3 additional years.

Additional information   Award winners who marry before completing the course or who drop out for non-scholastic reasons must submit a new application before benefits can be resumed.

Number awarded Varies each year; recently, 33 were awarded.

Deadline Deadline not specified.

[503]
FISHER CATS FOUNDATION SCHOLAR-ATHLETE SCHOLARSHIPS

New Hampshire Charitable Foundation
37 Pleasant Street
Concord, NH 03301-4005
(603) 225-6641   Toll Free: (800) 464-6641
Fax: (603) 225-1700   E-mail: info@nhcf.org
Web: www.nhcf.org/page.aspx?pid=958

Summary To provide financial assistance to high school seniors in New Hampshire and Massachusetts who have participated in athletics and plan to attend college in any state.

Eligibility This program is open to seniors graduating from high schools in New Hampshire and Massachusetts and planning to enroll at a 4-year college or university in any state or a local community college or technical school. Applicants must have participated in athletics while in high school. Selection is based on academic performance, athletic achievement, and citizenship.

Financial data The stipend is $2,500.

Duration 1 year.

Additional information This program, which began in 2007, is sponsored by the Fisher Cats Foundation. It includes the Swymer Family Scholarship, for a student who has overcome a barrier; the Chris Carpenter Scholarship, named in honor of a member of the 2011 World Series Champion St. Louis Cardinals; and the Easter Seals Veterans Count Scholarship, for a New Hampshire high school senior whose parent or guardian is an active, reserve, or veteran member of the U.S. military.

Number awarded 12 each year: 10 to students from New Hampshire and 2 to students from Massachusetts.

Deadline April of each year.

[504]
FLEET ADMIRAL CHESTER W. NIMITZ COLLEGE SCHOLARSHIP PROGRAM

USS Nimitz (CVN-68) Association
c/o David Wood, Scholarship Committee Chair
1304 East Harrison Avenue
Wheaton, IL 60187
E-mail: wood@uhc.edu
Web: www.ussnimitzassociation.org

Summary To provide financial assistance for college to members of the USS Nimitz (CVN-68) Association, their children and grandchildren, and the children of crewmembers currently serving on the USS Nimitz.

Eligibility This program is open to active members of the association, dependent children of crewmembers currently serving on the USS Nimitz, and dependent children and grandchildren of association members. Applicants must be graduating high school seniors or students currently enrolled full time at an accredited college, university, or community college. Along with their application, they must submit a transcript, SAT and/or ACT scores (for high school seniors) or GPA (for college students), 3 reference letters, and an essay of 250 to 500 words on a topic that changes annually. Selection is based on that essay (15 points for the quality of the

message and 15 points for grammar, spelling, and punctuation), GPA (multiplied by 10 points), volunteer work times (number of hours times 1 point, to maximum of 15 points), sponsor involvement in the association (up to 10 points), and honor awards (up to 10 points).

Financial data The stipend is $3,000.

Duration 1 year.

Number awarded 1 each year.

Deadline September of each year.

[505]
FLEET RESERVE ASSOCIATION MEMBER SCHOLARSHIPS

Fleet Reserve Association
Attn: FRA Education Foundation
125 North West Street
Alexandria, VA 22314-2754
(703) 683-1400   Toll Free: (800) FRA-1924
Fax: (703) 549-6610   E-mail: scholars@fra.org
Web: www.fra.org

Summary To provide financial assistance for college or graduate school to members of the Fleet Reserve Association (FRA) and their families.

Eligibility This program is open to members of the FRA and the dependent children, grandchildren, and spouses of living or deceased members. Applicants must be enrolled as full-time undergraduate or graduate students. Along with their application, they must submit an essay on why they want to go to college and what they intend to accomplish with their degree. Selection is based on academic record, financial need, extracurricular activities, leadership skills, and participation in community activities. U.S. citizenship is required.

Financial data The stipend is $5,000 per year.

Duration 1 year; may be renewed.

Additional information Membership in the FRA is restricted to active-duty, retired, and reserve members of the Navy, Marines, and Coast Guard. This program includes awards designated as the Robert M. Treadwell Annual Scholarship and the Donald Bruce Pringle Family Scholarship.

Number awarded 6 each year.

Deadline April of each year.

[506]
FLEET RESERVE ASSOCIATION NON-MEMBER SCHOLARSHIPS

Fleet Reserve Association
Attn: FRA Education Foundation
125 North West Street
Alexandria, VA 22314-2754
(703) 683-1400   Toll Free: (800) FRA-1924
Fax: (703) 549-6610   E-mail: scholars@fra.org
Web: www.fra.org

Summary To provide financial assistance for college or graduate school to sea service personnel and their families.

Eligibility This program is open to 1) active-duty, Reserve, honorably-discharged veterans, and retired members of the U.S. Navy, Marine Corps, and Coast Guard; and 2) their spouses, children, and grandchildren. Applicants must be enrolled as full-time undergraduate or graduate students, but neither they nor their family member are required to be members of the sponsoring organization. Along with their application, they must submit an essay on why they want to go to college and what they intend to accomplish with their degree. Selection is based on academic record, financial need, extracurricular activities, leadership skills, and participation in community activities. U.S. citizenship is required.

Financial data Stipends range up to $5,000 per year.

Duration 1 year; may be renewed.

Number awarded 1 or more each year.

Deadline April of each year.

[507]
FLORENCE LEMKE MEMORIAL SCHOLARSHIP IN FINE ARTS

American Legion Auxiliary
Department of Washington
Attn: Education Chair
3600 Ruddell Road S.E.
P.O. Box 5867
Lacey, WA 98509-5867
(360) 456-5995   Fax: (360) 491-7442
E-mail: secretary@walegion-aux.org
Web: www.walegion-aux.org/EducationScholarships.html

Summary To provide financial assistance to descendants of Washington veterans who are interested in studying the fine arts at a college in any state.

Eligibility This program is open to residents of Washington who are high school seniors and the children, grandchildren, or great-grandchildren of veterans. Applicants must be interested in studying fine arts (including painting, drawing, photography, literature, architecture, sculpture, poetry, music, dance, or drama) at a college in any state. Selection is based on an essay on their proposed course of study and educational goals in the field of fine arts, character, leadership, academic record, and financial need.

Financial data The stipend is $1,000.

Duration 1 year.

Number awarded 1 each year.

Deadline February of each year.

[508]
FLORIDA AMERICAN LEGION GENERAL SCHOLARSHIPS

American Legion
Department of Florida
Attn: Programs Director
1912A Lee Road
P.O. Box 547859
Orlando, FL 32854-7859
(407) 295-2631, ext. 235
Toll Free: (800) 393-3378 (within FL)
Fax: (407) 299-0901   E-mail: carol@floridalegion.org
Web: www.floridalegion.org/fal-programs-main/scholarships

Summary To provide financial assistance to the descendants of American Legion members in Florida who plan to attend college in any state.

Eligibility This program is open to the direct descendants (children, grandchildren, great-grandchildren, and legally adopted children) of a member of the American Legion's Department of Florida or of a deceased U.S. veteran who would have been eligible for membership in the American Legion. Applicants must be seniors graduating from a Florida high school and planning to attend an accredited college or

university in any state. Financial need is not considered in the selection process.

Financial data Stipends are $2,500, $2,000, $1,000, or $500.

Duration 1 year; nonrenewable.

Number awarded 7 each year: 1 at $2,500, 1 at $2,500, 1 at $1,000, and 4 at $500.

Deadline February of each year.

[509]
FLORIDA EAGLE SCOUT OF THE YEAR SCHOLARSHIPS

American Legion
Department of Florida
Attn: Programs Director
1912A Lee Road
P.O. Box 547859
Orlando, FL 32854-7859
(407) 295-2631, ext. 235
Toll Free: (800) 393-3378 (within FL)
Fax: (407) 299-0901   E-mail: carol@floridalegion.org
Web: www.floridalegion.org/fal-programs-main/scholarships

Summary To recognize and reward, with scholarships for college in any state, Eagle Scouts who are members of a troop associated with the American Legion in Florida or a son or grandson of a member of the Legion in the state.

Eligibility This program is open to Florida high school students who have earned the Eagle Scout award and religious emblem. Applicants must 1) be a registered, active member of a Boy Scout troop, Varsity Scout team, or Venturing Crew chartered to an American Legion Post or Auxiliary unit; or 2) be a registered active member of a duly chartered Boy Scout troop, Varsity Scout team, or Venturing Crew and the son or grandson of a Legionnaire or Auxiliary member. Applicants must be interested in attending a college or university in any state. They must be able to demonstrate practical citizenship in church, school, Scouting, and community.

Financial data The winner receives a $2,500 scholarship, first runner-up a $1,500 scholarship, second runner-up a $1,000 scholarship, and third runner-up a $500 scholarship.

Duration The awards are presented annually.

Number awarded 4 each year.

Deadline February of each year.

[510]
FLORIDA LEGION AUXILIARY DEPARTMENT SCHOLARSHIP

American Legion Auxiliary
Department of Florida
1912A Lee Road
P.O. Box 547917
Orlando, FL 32854-7917
(407) 293-7411   Toll Free: (866) 710-4192
Fax: (407) 299-6522   E-mail: contact@alafl.org
Web: www.alafl.org

Summary To provide financial assistance to the children of Florida veterans who are interested in attending college in the state.

Eligibility This program is open to children and stepchildren of honorably-discharged veterans who are Florida residents. Applicants must be enrolled or planning to enroll full time at a postsecondary school in the state. Financial need is considered in the selection process.

Financial data The stipends are up to $2,000 for a 4-year university or up to $1,000 for a community college or vocational/technical school. All funds are paid directly to the institution.

Duration 1 year; may be renewed if the recipient needs further financial assistance and has maintained a GPA of 2.5 or higher.

Number awarded Varies each year, depending on the availability of funds.

Deadline January of each year.

[511]
FLORIDA LEGION AUXILIARY MEMORIAL SCHOLARSHIP

American Legion Auxiliary
Department of Florida
1912A Lee Road
P.O. Box 547917
Orlando, FL 32854-7917
(407) 293-7411   Toll Free: (866) 710-4192
Fax: (407) 299-6522   E-mail: contact@alafl.org
Web: www.alafl.org

Summary To provide financial assistance to members and female dependents of members of the Florida American Legion Auxiliary who are interested in attending college in any state.

Eligibility Applicants must be members of the Florida Auxiliary or daughters or granddaughters of members who have at least 3 years of continuous membership. They must be sponsored by their local units, be Florida residents, and be enrolled or planning to enroll full time at a college, university, community college, or vocational/technical school in any state. Selection is based on academic record and financial need.

Financial data The stipends are up to $2,000 for a 4-year university or up to $1,000 for a community college or vocational/technical school. All funds are paid directly to the institution.

Duration 1 year; may be renewed if the recipient needs further financial assistance and has maintained at least a 2.5 GPA.

Number awarded Varies each year, depending on the availability of funds.

Deadline January of each year.

[512]
FLORIDA NAVY NURSE CORPS ASSOCIATION SCHOLARSHIPS

Florida Navy Nurse Corps Association
c/o Margaret Holder, Scholarship Committee
1033 Inverness Drive
St. Augustine, FL 32092
E-mail: maholder@me.com

Summary To provide financial assistance to undergraduate and graduate nursing students, especially residents of Florida with ties to the military.

Eligibility This program is open to students, including registered nursing continuing their studies, who are working on an undergraduate or graduate degree in nursing. Applicants must have completed at least 1 clinical nursing course and

have a GPA of 3.0 or higher. They may be full- or part-time students. Preference is given to current active-duty and Reserve service members, veterans of military service, family members of current or former military service personnel, civil service employees, and residents of Florida. Financial need is considered in the selection process.

Financial data The stipend is $1,000. Funds are paid directly to the student.

Duration 1 year.

Additional information This program includes the Captain Miki Iwata Memorial Scholarship.

Number awarded Approximately 3 each year.

Deadline October of each year.

[513]
FLORIDA SCHOLARSHIPS FOR CHILDREN AND SPOUSES OF DECEASED OR DISABLED VETERANS

Florida Department of Education
Attn: Office of Student Financial Assistance
State Scholarship and Grant Programs
325 West Gaines Street, Suite 1314
Tallahassee, FL 32399-0400
(850) 410-5160   Toll Free: (888) 827-2004
Fax: (850) 487-1809   E-mail: osfa@fldoe.org
Web: www.floridastudentfinancialaid.org

Summary To provide financial assistance for college to the children and spouses of Florida veterans who are disabled, deceased, or officially classified as prisoners of war (POW) or missing in action (MIA).

Eligibility This program is open to residents of Florida who are U.S. citizens or eligible noncitizens and the dependent children or spouses of veterans or servicemembers who 1) died as a result of service-connected injuries, diseases, or disabilities sustained while on active duty during a period of war; 2) have a service-connected 100% total and permanent disability; or 3) were classified as POW or MIA by the U.S. armed forces or as civilian personnel captured while serving with the consent or authorization of the U.S. government during wartime service. The veteran or servicemember must have been a U.S. citizen or eligible noncitizens and a resident of Florida for at least 1 year before death, disability, or POW/MIA status. Children must be between 16 and 22 years of age. Spouses of deceased veterans or servicemembers must be unremarried and must apply within 5 years of their spouse's death. Spouses of disabled veterans must have been married for at least 1 year.

Financial data Recently, stipends for full-time students were $2,452 per semester at 4-year institutions, $1,248 at 2-year institutions, or $1,000 at vocational/technical institutions. Part-time students received prorated amounts.

Duration 1 quarter or semester; may be renewed for up to 110% of the required credit hours of an initial associate, baccalaureate, diploma, or certificate program, provided the student maintains a GPA of 2.0 or higher.

Number awarded Varies each year; recently, 214 new and 550 renewal scholarships were awarded.

Deadline March of each year.

[514]
FOLDS OF HONOR SCHOLARSHIPS

Folds of Honor Foundation
Attn: Scholarship Department
5800 North Patriot Drive
Owasso, OK 74055
(918) 274-4700   Fax: (918) 274-4709
E-mail: scholarships@foldsofhonor.org
Web: scholarships.foldsofhonor.org

Summary To provide financial assistance for college to the spouses and children of servicemembers killed or disabled as a result of service in the Global War on Terror.

Eligibility This program is open to the spouses and children of 1) an active-duty or Reserve component soldier, sailor, airman, Marine, or Coast Guardsman killed or disabled in the Global War on Terror; 2) an active-duty or Reserve component soldier, sailor, airman, Marine, or Coast Guardsman who is currently classified as a POW or MIA; 3) a veteran who died from any cause after having been classified as having a service-connected disability; 4) a servicemember missing in action or captured in the line of duty by a hostile force; 5) a servicemember forcibly detained or interned in the line of duty by a foreign government or power; or 6) a servicemember who received a Purple Heart medal. Applicants must submit a 1-page personal essay that includes a short biography, a description of the servicemembers disability or death, and a statement of what the scholarship would mean to them and how it will help them achieve their career goals. Immediate-use scholarships are available to spouses or dependents currently attending or accepted into a 2- or 4-year college or university or a vocational, technical, or other certification program. Future-use scholarships are available to children of servicemembers from birth through grade 11 and held for them until they are ready to attend college.

Financial data Stipends range up to $2,500 per semester ($5,000 per year), depending on the need of the recipient. Funds are dispersed directly to the recipient's institution.

Duration 1 year.

Additional information This program began in 2008.

Number awarded Varies each year; since the program was established, it has awarded 3,873 immediate-use scholarships and 254 future-use scholarships.

Deadline January of each year.

[515]
FORCE RECON ASSOCIATION SCHOLARSHIPS

Force Recon Association
c/o Al Sniadecki, Scholarship Committee Chair
P.O. Box 111000
Carrollton, TX 75011
E-mail: commchief@forcerecon.com
Web: www.forcerecon.com/join.htm

Summary To provide financial assistance for college to members of the Force Recon Association and their dependents.

Eligibility This program is open to members of the Force Recon Association and family members of a relative who served both in the U.S. Marine Corps and was or is assigned to a Force Reconnaissance Company. The relative must be either an active or deceased member of the Force Recon Association. Family members include wives and widows, sons and daughters (including adopted and stepchildren),

grandchildren, and great-grandchildren. Applicants may be pursuing scholastic, vocational, or technical education. Along with their application, they must submit a personal statement on why they desire this scholarship, their proposed course of study, their progress in their current course of study, and their long-range career goals. Selection is based on academic achievement, letters of recommendation, demonstrated character, and the written statements.

Financial data A stipend is awarded (amount not specified).

Duration 1 year; may be renewed.

Number awarded 1 or more each year.

Deadline July of each year.

[516]
FOURTH MARINE DIVISION ASSOCIATION OF WWII SCHOLARSHIP

Fourth Marine Division Association of WWII
c/o Marine Corps Scholarship Foundation
909 North Washington Street, Suite 400
Alexandria, VA 22314
(703) 549-0060   Toll Free: (866) 496-5462
Fax: (703) 549-9474   E-mail: students@mcsf.org
Web: www.mcsf.org/apply/eligibility

Summary To provide financial assistance for college to the grandchildren of veterans who served with the Fourth Marine Division during World War II.

Eligibility This program is open to grandchildren of veterans who served with the Fourth Marine Division during World War II and are or were members of the Fourth Marine Division Association of World War II. Applicants must be high school seniors, high school graduates, or current college students. Along with their application, they must submit academic transcripts, a copy of their grandparent's honorable discharge, and a 500-word essay on a topic that changes periodically. Only undergraduate study is supported. The family income of applicants must be less than $93,000 per year.

Financial data Stipends depend on the need of the recipient and the availability of funds, but generally range from $500 to $2,500 per year.

Duration 1 year; may be renewed for up to 3 additional years.

Additional information The highest-ranked applicant receives an award that is designated the Thomas W. Morrow Scholarship.

Number awarded Varies each year; recently, 6 were awarded.

Deadline February of each year.

[517]
FRANCIS P. MATTHEWS AND JOHN E. SWIFT EDUCATIONAL TRUST SCHOLARSHIPS

Knights of Columbus
Attn: Department of Scholarships
P.O. Box 1670
New Haven, CT 06507-0901
(203) 752-4332   Fax: (203) 772-2696
E-mail: info@kofc.org
Web: www.kofc.org/en/scholarships/matthews_swift.html

Summary To provide financial assistance at Catholic colleges or universities in any country to children of disabled or deceased veterans, law enforcement officers, or firemen who are/were also Knights of Columbus members.

Eligibility This program is open to children of members of the sponsoring organization who are high school seniors in any country planning to attend a 4-year Catholic college or university in their country. The parent must be a member of Knights of Columbus who 1) was serving in the military forces of their country and was killed by hostile action or wounded by hostile action, resulting within 2 years in permanent and total disability; 2) was a full-time law enforcement officer who became disabled or died as a result of criminal violence; or 3) was a firefighter who became disabled or deceased in the line of duty.

Financial data The amounts of the awards vary but are designed to cover tuition, to a maximum of $25,000 per year, at the Catholic college or university of the recipient's choice in the country of their residence. Funds are not available for room, board, books, fees, transportation, dues, computers, or supplies.

Duration 1 year; may be renewed up to 3 additional years.

Additional information This program began in 1944 to provide scholarships to the children of Knights who became totally and permanently disabled through service during World War II. It has been modified on many occasions, most recently in 2007 to its current requirements.

Number awarded Varies each year.

Deadline February of each year.

[518]
FREE TUITION FOR NORTH DAKOTA DEPENDENTS

North Dakota University System
Attn: Director of Financial Aid
State Capitol, Tenth Floor
600 East Boulevard Avenue, Department 215
Bismarck, ND 58505-0230
(701) 328-4114 Fax: (701) 328-2961
E-mail: nathan.stratton@ndus.edu
Web: www.ndus.edu

Summary To waive tuition and fees for dependents of deceased or other veterans at public institutions in North Dakota.

Eligibility Eligible for this benefit are the dependents of veterans who were North Dakota residents when they entered the armed forces and died of service-related causes, were killed in action, became totally disabled, or were declared missing in action. Applicants must be attending or planning to attend a public college or university in North Dakota.

Financial data Qualified students are entitled to a waiver of all tuition and fees (except fees charged to retire outstanding bonds) at public institutions in North Dakota.

Duration Up to 45 months.

Number awarded Varies each year.

Deadline Deadline not specified.

[519]
FREEDOM ALLIANCE SCHOLARSHIPS

Freedom Alliance
Attn: Scholarship Fund
22570 Markey Court, Suite 240
Dulles, VA 20166-6915
(703) 444-7940 Toll Free: (800) 475-6620
Fax: (703) 444-9893 E-mail: info@freedomalliance.org
Web: www.fascholarship.com

Summary To provide financial assistance for college to the children of deceased and disabled military personnel.

Eligibility This program is open to high school seniors, high school graduates, and undergraduate students under 26 years of age who are dependent children of military personnel (soldier, sailor, airman, Marine, or Guardsman). The military parent must 1) have been killed or permanently disabled as a result of an operational mission or training accident; or 2) be currently classified as a POW or MIA. For disabled parents, the disability must be permanent, service-connected, and rated at 100% by the U.S. Department of Veterans Affairs. Applicants must submit a 500-word essay on what their parent's service means to them.

Financial data Stipends range up to $6,000 per year.

Duration 1 year; may be renewed up to 3 additional years, provided the recipient remains enrolled full time with a GPA of 2.0 or higher.

Number awarded Varies each year; recently, 240 were awarded. Since the program was established, it has awarded more than $7 million in scholarships.

Deadline July of each year.

[520]
GAMEWARDENS ASSOCIATION SCHOLARSHIP

Gamewardens Association, Vietnam to Present
c/o Glen Fry, Scholarship Program
230 P.R. 182 West
Heloted, TX 78023
(210) 301-4497 E-mail: normlguy@gmail.com
Web: www.tf116.org/scholarship.html

Summary To provide financial assistance for college to the children or grandchildren of members of Gamewardens Association, Vietnam to Present.

Eligibility This program is open to the children and grandchildren of living or deceased members of Gamewardens Association, Vietnam to Present. High school students (under 21 years of age) planning to enter college as full-time students and students already enrolled in college (under 23 years of age) are eligible. Selection is based on SAT or ACT scores, extracurricular activities, leadership positions held, work or volunteer experience, and financial need.

Financial data Stipends are $1,500. Awards are paid directly to the college the student is attending.

Duration 1 year.

Additional information Membership in Gamewardens Association, Vietnam to Present is open to 1) veterans who served in Vietnam in Task Force 116 or in support of Task Force 116, River Patrol Force; or 2) veterans or current Navy personnel serving as a Special Warfare Combatant-craft Crewman (SWCC) or Riverine Operator in any operation subsequent to Vietnam (including in Iraq). This program includes the YNC John Williams Scholarship.

Number awarded 2 each year.

Deadline July of each year.

[521]
GENERAL HENRY H. ARNOLD EDUCATION GRANT PROGRAM

Air Force Aid Society
Attn: Education Assistance Department
241 18th Street South, Suite 202
Arlington, VA 22202-3409
(703) 972-2647   Toll Free: (866) 896-5637
Fax: (703) 972-2646   E-mail: ed@afas-hq.org
Web: www.afas.org/education-grants

Summary To provide need-based financial assistance for college to dependents of active-duty, retired, disabled, or deceased Air Force personnel.

Eligibility This program is open to 1) dependent children of Air Force personnel who are active duty, Reservists on extended active duty, retired due to length of active-duty service or disability, or deceased while on active duty or in retired status; 2) spouses of active-duty Air Force members and Reservists on extended active duty; and 3) surviving spouses of Air Force members who died while on active duty or in retired status. Applicants must be enrolled or planning to enroll as full-time undergraduate students at an accredited college, university, or vocational/trade school. Spouses must be attending school within the 48 contiguous states. Selection is based on family income and education costs.

Financial data The stipend is $2,000.

Duration 1 year; may be renewed if the recipient maintains a GPA of 2.0 or higher.

Additional information Since this program was established in the 1988-89 academic year, it has awarded nearly 100,000 grants.

Number awarded Varies each year.

Deadline March of each year.

[522]
GENERAL JIM AND PAT BOSWELL MERIT SCHOLARSHIP PROGRAM

7th Infantry Regiment Association
c/o David Spanburg
P.O. Box 3181
Merrifield, VA 22116
(570) 409-9265   E-mail: edajack@ptd.net
Web: www.cottonbalers.com

Summary To provide financial assistance for college to descendants of members of the 7th Infantry Regiment Association.

Eligibility This program is open to the children, grandchildren, and great grandchildren of members of the association who served a duty assignment with the 7th Infantry Regiment or a component or attached unit while on active duty in the United States Army and who has been a member of the association in good standing for at least the past year. Applicants must be enrolled or planning to enroll full time in an undergraduate program. They must be U.S. citizens and have a cumulative GPA of 2.5 or higher. Along with their application, they must submit a resume, transcripts, ACT or SAT scores, 3 letters of recommendation, and a 1-page essay on why they want and/or deserve this scholarship. Selection is based on

academic excellence, leadership, and demonstrated achievement.

Financial data A stipend is awarded (amount not specified).

Duration 1 year; recipients may reapply for 1 additional year.

Number awarded 1 or more each year.

Deadline April of each year.

[523]
GENERAL JOHN PAUL RATAY EDUCATIONAL FUND GRANTS

Military Officers Association of America
Attn: Educational Assistance Program
201 North Washington Street
Alexandria, VA 22314-2539
(703) 549-2311   Toll Free: (800) 234-MOAA
Fax: (703) 838-5819   E-mail: edassist@moaa.org
Web: www.moaa.org/main_simplelist.aspx?id=1172

Summary To provide financial assistance to dependent children of surviving spouses of deceased members of Military Officers Association of America (MOAA) who are working on an undergraduate degree.

Eligibility This program is open to children of surviving spouses of deceased retired military officers (applicants for the MOAA Educational Assistance Program loans will be automatically considered for these scholarships; no separate application is necessary). All applicants must be younger than 24 years of age. Selection is based on scholastic ability (GPA of 3.0 or higher), participation, character, leadership, and financial need.

Financial data The stipend is $5,000 per year.

Duration 1 year; may be renewed for up to 4 additional years if the recipient remains enrolled full time and has not yet graduated.

Additional information The MOAA was formerly named The Retired Officers Association (TROA). No grants are made for graduate study.

Number awarded Varies each year.

Deadline February of each year.

[524]
GENERAL WILLIAM E. DEPUY MEMORIAL SCHOLARSHIP PROGRAM

Society of the First Infantry Division
Attn: 1st Infantry Division Foundation
P.O. Box 607
Ambler, PA 19002
(215) 654-1969   Fax: (215) 654-0392
E-mail: Fdn1IDChair@aol.com
Web: www.1stid.org/scholarships.php

Summary To provide financial assistance for college to the children of certain deceased members of the First Infantry Division.

Eligibility This program is open to the children of soldiers who served in the First Infantry Division and were killed while serving in combat with the Division or in peacetime training accidents. This is an entitlement program. All eligible applicants receive an award.

Financial data The stipend is $2,500 per year.

Duration 1 year; may be renewed up to 3 additional years.

Additional information This program was established during the Vietnam war to provide scholarships to children of soldiers killed while on duty with the active division; more than 1,300 children whose fathers died while serving in Vietnam received scholarships.

Number awarded Varies each year.

Deadline Deadline not specified.

[525]
GEORGIA DEPARTMENT AMERICAN LEGION SCHOLARSHIP

American Legion
Department of Georgia
3035 Mt. Zion Road
Stockbridge, GA 30281-4101
(678) 289-8883 Fax: (678) 289-8885
E-mail: amerlegga@bellsouth.net
Web: www.galegion.org/forms.html

Summary To provide financial assistance to children and grandchildren of members of the American Legion in Georgia who plan to attend college in any state.

Eligibility This program is open to seniors graduating from high schools in Georgia who have a GPA of 3.0 or higher in core subjects. Applicants must be children or grandchildren of members of the American Legion in the Department of Georgia who served in the military. They must be sponsored by a Georgia post of the American Legion. Financial need is not considered in the selection process.

Financial data The stipend is $1,000.

Duration 1 year.

Number awarded 6 each year.

Deadline June of each year.

[526]
GEORGIA LEGION AUXILIARY PAST DEPARTMENT PRESIDENTS SCHOLARSHIPS

American Legion Auxiliary
Department of Georgia
Attn: Department Secretary/Treasurer
3035 Mt. Zion Road
Stockbridge, GA 30281-4101
(678) 289-8446 Fax: (678) 289-9496
E-mail: secretary@galegionaux.org
Web: www.galegionaux.org/forms/forms.html

Summary To provide financial assistance to descendants of veterans in Georgia who are interested in attending college in any state to major in any field.

Eligibility This program is open to Georgia residents who are the descendants of veterans who served during specified periods of wartime. Applicants must be sponsored by a local unit of the American Legion Auxiliary. Selection is based on a statement explaining why they want to further their education and why they need a scholarship, a transcript of all high school or college grades, an essay on a topic of their choice, and 4 letters of recommendation (1 from a high school principal or superintendent, 1 from the sponsoring American Legion Auxiliary local unit, and 2 from other responsible people).

Financial data The stipend is $1,000.

Duration 1 year.

Number awarded 2 each year.

Deadline May of each year.

[527]
GEORGIA LEGION AUXILIARY PAST PRESIDENT PARLEY NURSING SCHOLARSHIP

American Legion Auxiliary
Department of Georgia
Attn: Department Secretary/Treasurer
3035 Mt. Zion Road
Stockbridge, GA 30281-4101
(678) 289-8446 Fax: (678) 289-9496
E-mail: secretary@galegionaux.org
Web: www.galegionaux.org/forms/forms.html

Summary To provide financial assistance to descendants of veterans in Georgia who are interested in attending college in any state to prepare for a career in nursing.

Eligibility This program is open to Georgia residents who are 1) interested in nursing education; and 2) the descendants of veterans. Applicants must be sponsored by a local unit of the American Legion Auxiliary. Selection is based on a statement explaining why they want to become a nurse and why they need a scholarship, a transcript of all high school or college grades, and 4 letters of recommendation (1 from a high school principal or superintendent, 1 from the sponsoring American Legion Auxiliary local unit, and 2 from other responsible people).

Financial data The amount of the award depends on the availability of funds.

Duration 1 year.

Number awarded Varies each year, depending upon availability of funds.

Deadline May of each year.

[528]
GEORGIA'S HERO SCHOLARSHIP PROGRAM

Georgia Student Finance Commission
Attn: Scholarships and Grants Division
2082 East Exchange Place, Suite 200
Tucker, GA 30084-5305
(770) 724-9000 Toll Free: (800) 505-GSFC
Fax: (770) 724-9089 E-mail: gacollege411@gsfc.org
Web: secure.gacollege411.org

Summary To provide financial assistance for college to members of the National Guard or Reserves in Georgia and their children and spouses.

Eligibility This program is open to Georgia residents who are active members of the Georgia National Guard or U.S. Military Reserves, were deployed outside the United States for active-duty service on or after February 1, 2003 to a location designated as a combat zone, and served in that combat zone for at least 181 consecutive days. Also eligible are 1) the children, younger than 25 years of age, of Guard and Reserve members who completed at least 1 term of service (of 181 days each) overseas on or after February 1, 2003; 2) the children, younger than 25 years of age, of Guard and Reserve members who were killed or totally disabled during service overseas on or after February 1, 2003, regardless of their length of service; and 3) the spouses of Guard and Reserve members who were killed in a combat zone, died as a result of injuries, or became 100% disabled as a result of injuries received in a combat zone during service overseas on or after February 1, 2003, regardless of their length of service. Applicants must be interested in attending a unit of the University System of Georgia, a unit of the Georgia Department of Technical and Adult Education, or an eligible private college or university in Georgia.

Financial data The stipend for full-time study is $2,000 per academic year, not to exceed $8,000 during an entire program of study. The stipend for part-time study is prorated appropriately.

Duration 1 year; may be renewed (if satisfactory progress is maintained) for up to 3 additional years.

Additional information This program, which stands for Helping Educate Reservists and their Offspring, was established in 2005.

Number awarded Varies each year.

Deadline June of each year.

[529]
GERALDINE K. MORRIS AWARD

Army Engineer Spouses' Club
c/o Laura Putnam, Chair
P.O. Box 6332
Alexandria, VA 22306-6332
E-mail: scholarships@armyengineerspouses.com
Web: www.armyengineerspouses.com

Summary To provide financial assistance to the children of officers and civilians who served in the Army Corps of Engineers and are interested in studying nursing in college.

Eligibility This program is open to children of 1) U.S. Army Corps of Engineers officers and warrant officers who are on active duty, retired, or deceased while on active duty or after retiring from active duty; or 2) current Department of the Army employees of the U.S. Army Corps of Engineers. Applicants must be high school seniors planning to enroll in a program leading to a nursing degree or certification. Selection is based on academic and extracurricular achievement during high school. U.S. citizenship is required.

Financial data The stipend is $1,000.

Duration 1 year; may be renewed, provided the recipient remains enrolled full time in a nursing program.

Additional information This program began in 2006.

Number awarded 1 each year.

Deadline February of each year.

[530]
GERTRUDE BOTTS SAUCIER SCHOLARSHIP

United Daughters of the Confederacy
Attn: Second Vice President General
328 North Boulevard
Richmond, VA 23220-4008
(804) 355-1636   Fax: (804) 353-1396
E-mail: jamieretired@sbcglobal.net
Web: www.hqudc.org/Scholarships/index.htm

Summary To provide financial assistance for college to lineal descendants of Confederate veterans who are residents of Texas, Mississippi, or Louisiana.

Eligibility Eligible to apply for these scholarships are lineal descendants of worthy Confederates or collateral descendants who are members of the Children of the Confederacy or the United Daughters of the Confederacy. Applicants must reside in Texas, Mississippi, or Louisiana and must submit a

family financial report and certified proof of the Confederate record of 1 ancestor, with the company and regiment in which he served. They must have at least a 3.0 GPA in high school.

Financial data The amount of the scholarship depends on the availability of funds.

Duration 1 year; may be renewed for up to 3 additional years.

Number awarded 1 each year.

Deadline April of each year.

[531]
GLADYS MCPARTLAND SCHOLARSHIPS

United States Marine Corps Combat Correspondents
    Association
Attn: Executive Director
110 Fox Court
Wildwood, FL 34785
(352) 748-4698   E-mail: usmccca@cfl.rr.com
Web: www.usmccca.org/archives/4941

Summary To provide financial assistance to members of the U.S. Marine Corps Combat Correspondents Association (USMCCCA) or their dependents and to Marines in designated occupational fields who are interested in studying any field in college.

Eligibility This program is open to 1) members of USMCCCA, their dependents, and their spouses; and 2) active-duty Marines in Occupational Fields 4300 and 4600 and their dependents who are USMCCCA members or will agree to become members if awarded a scholarship. Applicants must be enrolled or planning to enroll in an undergraduate program in any field. Along with their application, they must submit 500-word essays on 1) their noteworthy achievements and long-range goals; and 2) the United States I want to see in 15 years and my role in the transformation. Financial need is not considered in the selection process.

Financial data Stipends range up to $3,000; funds are disbursed directly to the recipient's institution to be used exclusively for tuition, books, and/or fees.

Duration 1 year.

Number awarded 1 or more each year.

Deadline May of each year.

[532]
GOLD STAR SCHOLARSHIP PROGRAMS

Navy-Marine Corps Relief Society
Attn: Education Division
875 North Randolph Street, Suite 225
Arlington, VA 22203-1757
(703) 696-4960   Fax: (703) 696-0144
E-mail: education@nmcrs.org
Web: www.nmcrs.org

Summary To provide financial assistance for college to the children and spouses of Navy or Marine Corps personnel who died while serving on active duty or after retirement.

Eligibility This program is open to 1) children under 23 years of age of sailors or marines who died while serving on active duty or after retirement; and 2) unremarried spouses of members of the Navy or Marine Corps who died as a result of the attack on the USS Stark, the attack on the Pentagon, or during service in Operation Iraqi Freedom, Operation Enduring Freedom, or Operation New Dawn. Applicants must be enrolled or planning to enroll full time at a college, university, or vocational/technical school. They must have a GPA of 2.0 or higher and be able to demonstrate financial need.

Financial data Stipends range from $500 to $2,500 per year. Funds are disbursed directly to the financial institution.

Duration 1 year; recipients may reapply.

Number awarded Varies each year.

Deadline April of each year.

[533]
GROGAN MEMORIAL SCHOLARSHIP

American Academy of Physician Assistants-Veterans
 Caucus
Attn: Veterans Caucus
P.O. Box 362
Danville, PA 17821-0362
Fax: (302) 526-7154 E-mail: fbrace@veteranscaucus.org
Web: www.veteranscaucus.org

Summary To provide financial assistance to veterans and their dependents who are studying to become physician assistants.

Eligibility This program is open to U.S. citizens who are currently enrolled in a physician assistant program. The program must be approved by the Commission on Accreditation of Allied Health Education. Applicants must be honorably discharged members of any branch of the military or the dependents of those members. Selection is based on military honors and awards received, civic and college honors and awards received, professional memberships and activities, and GPA. An electronic copy of the applicant's DD Form 214 must accompany the application.

Financial data The stipend is $2,000.

Duration 1 year.

Number awarded 1 each year.

Deadline February of each year.

[534]
HAD RICHARDS UDT-SEAL MEMORIAL SCHOLARSHIP

Navy Seal Foundation
Attn: Chief Financial Officer
1619 D Street, Building 5326
Virginia Beach, VA 23459
(757) 363-7490   Fax: (757) 363-7491
E-mail: info@navysealfoundation.org
Web: www.navysealfoundation.org

Summary To provide financial assistance for college to children of members of the UDT-SEAL Association.

Eligibility This program is open to children of members who are single, under 24 years of age, and a dependent of a sponsoring member of the association. Sponsors must be serving or have served in the armed forces and the Naval Special Warfare Community, been an association member for the last 4 consecutive years, and paid their dues for the current year. Applicants may be high school seniors, high school graduates, or full-time undergraduate students. Selection is based on GPA, SAT scores, class ranking, extracurricular activities, volunteer community involvement, leadership positions held, military service record, and employment (as appropriate).

Financial data Stipends are $15,000 or $7,500 per year.

Duration 1 year; may be renewed.

Additional information Membership in the association is open to all officers and enlisted personnel of the armed forces (active, retired, discharged, or separated) who have served with a Navy Combat Demolition Unit (NCDU), Underwater Demolition Team (UDT), or SEAL Team.

Number awarded Varies each year; recently, the Navy Seal Foundation awarded 12 dependent scholarships for all of its programs: 3 for 4 years at $15,000 per year to high school seniors and graduates, 3 for 1 year at $7,500 to high school seniors and graduates, 3 for 1 year at $15,000 to current college students, and 3 for 1 year at $7,500 to current college students.

Deadline February of each year.

[535]
HANSCOM SPOUSES' CLUB SCHOLARSHIPS FOR HIGH SCHOOL SENIORS

Hanscom Spouses' Club
Attn: Scholarship Committee Chair
General Delivery
75 Grenier Street, Unit 888
Hanscom AFB, MA 01731
(781) 538-5811   E-mail: scholarships@hanscomsc.org
Web: www.hanscomsc.org/scholarships.html

Summary To provide financial assistance to high school seniors who are children of military personnel or veterans in the Hanscom Air Force Base area of New England and interested in attending college in any state.

Eligibility This program is open to dependents of active-duty, retired, and deceased members of any branch of the armed forces, including Reservists and National Guard members who were activated during the school year. Applicants must be graduating high school seniors who have a valid military identification card and reside within a 60-mile radius of Hanscom Air Force Base (includes eastern Massachusetts, Rhode Island, and southern New Hampshire) or be a dependent whose military sponsor is stationed at Hanscom Air Force Base. They must be planning to attend a 2- or 4-year college or university in any state. Along with their application, they must submit a 2-page essay on their educational goals, how their educational experience will help prepare them to pursue future goals, and how they intend to apply their education to better their community. Selection is based on merit. The highest ranked applicant receives the Chief of Staff Award.

Financial data Recently, stipends of all scholarships offered by this sponsor averaged more than $2,000.

Duration 1 year; nonrenewable.

Number awarded Varies each year; recently, the sponsor awarded a total of 19 high school senior scholarships.

Deadline March of each year.

[536]
HANSCOM SPOUSES' CLUB SCHOLARSHIPS FOR SPOUSES

Hanscom Spouses' Club
Attn: Scholarship Committee Chair
General Delivery
75 Grenier Street, Unit 888
Hanscom AFB, MA 01731
(781) 538-5811   E-mail: scholarships@hanscomsc.org
Web: www.hanscomsc.org/scholarships.html

Summary   To provide financial assistance to spouses of military personnel and veterans in the Hanscom Air Force Base area of New England.

Eligibility   This program is open to spouses of active-duty, retired, or deceased military members of any branch of service the armed forces, including Reservists and National Guard members who were activated during the school year. Applicants must have a valid military identification card and reside within a 60-mile radius of Hanscom Air Force Base (includes eastern Massachusetts, Rhode Island, and southern New Hampshire) or be a spouse of a military member who is stationed at Hanscom Air Force Base. They must be planning to attend a 2- or 4-year college or university in any state. Applicants must demonstrate responsibility, leadership, scholastics, citizenship, and diversity of interest. They must have a valid military identification card and be working on or planning to work on a bachelor's or associate degree. Along with their application, they must submit a 2-page essay on their educational goals, how their educational experience will help prepare them to pursue future goals, and how they intend to apply their education to better their community. The Carmen Schipper Memorial Award is presented to the highest-ranked applicant.

Financial data   Recently, stipends of all scholarships offered by this sponsor averaged more than $2,000.

Duration   1 year; nonrenewable.

Number awarded   Varies each year; recently, 4 were awarded.

Deadline   March of each year.

[537]
HARDY WOLF & DOWNING SCHOLARSHIP AWARDS

Hardy Wolf & Downing
Attn: Scholarship Awards
477 Congress Street, 15th Floor
Portland, ME 04101
Toll Free: (800) 992-7333   E-mail: stepler@hwdlaw.com
Web: www.hardywolf.com/scholarships

Summary   To provide financial assistance for college or law school to students who have a connection to the U.S. military or to law enforcement.

Eligibility   This program is open to 1) high school seniors who plan to attend an accredited U.S. college; 2) college students attending an accredited U.S. college; and 3) law students currently entering or enrolled at an ABA-accredited law school. Applicants must be active, retired, or immediate family members of any branch of the U.S. military or any branch of law enforcement. They must have a GPA of 3.0 or higher. Along with their application, they must submit essays of 1,500 to 2,000 words on the following topics: for members and family members of the military, the greatest challenges facing veterans when they return home from serving their country; for members and family members of law enforcement, the greatest challenges facing law enforcement personnel today; for all law students, the area of law they intend to practice and why.

Financial data   Stipends range from $100 to $2,500.

Duration   1 year.

Number awarded   13 each year: 1 at $2,500, 1 at $1,000, 1 at $500, and 10 at $100.

Deadline   December of each year.

[538]
HATTIE TEDROW MEMORIAL FUND SCHOLARSHIP

American Legion
Department of North Dakota
405 West Main Street, Suite 4A
P.O. Box 5057
West Fargo, ND 58078
(701) 293-3120   Fax: (701) 293-9951
E-mail: Programs@ndlegion.org
Web: www.ndlegion.org/?page_id=111

Summary   To provide financial assistance to high school seniors in North Dakota who are direct descendants of veterans and interested in attending college in any state.

Eligibility   This program is open to seniors graduating from high schools in North Dakota and planning to attend a college, university, trade school, or technical school in any state. Applicants must be the children, grandchildren, or great-grandchildren of veterans who served honorably in the U.S. armed forces. Along with their application, they must submit a 500-word essay on why they should receive this scholarship. Selection is based on the essay and academic performance; financial need is not considered.

Financial data   The stipend is $2,000.

Duration   1 year; nonrenewable.

Number awarded   1 each year.

Deadline   March of each year.

[539]
HAZLEWOOD ACT EXEMPTIONS FOR DEPENDENTS

Texas Veterans Commission
1700 North Congress Avenue, Suite 800
P.O. Box 12277
Austin, TX 78711-2277
(512) 463-5538   Toll Free: (800) 252-VETS (within TX)
Fax: (512) 475-2395   E-mail: VetsEd@tvc.texas.gov
Web: www.tvc.texas.gov/Hazlewood-Act.aspx

Summary   To exempt children and spouses of disabled or deceased U.S. veterans from payment of tuition at public universities in Texas.

Eligibility   This program is open to residents of Texas whose parent or spouse was a resident of the state at the time of entry into the U.S. armed forces, the Texas National Guard, or the Texas Air National Guard. The veteran parent or spouse must have died as a result of service-related injuries or illness, be missing in action, or have become totally disabled as a result of service-related injury or illness. Applicants must have no remaining federal education benefits. They must be attending or planning to attend a public college or university in the state and have no available federal veterans educational benefits. Children of veterans must be 25 years of age or younger.

Financial data   Eligible students are exempt from payment of tuition, dues, fees, and charges at state-supported colleges and universities in Texas.

Duration   1 year; may be renewed.

Additional information   This program was previously administered by the Texas Higher Education Coordinating Board but was transferred to the Texas Veterans Commission in 2013.

Number awarded Varies each year; recently, 9 were granted.

Deadline Deadline not specified.

[540]
HAZLEWOOD LEGACY ACT EXEMPTIONS FOR VETERANS' CHILDREN

Texas Veterans Commission
1700 North Congress Avenue, Suite 800
P.O. Box 12277
Austin, TX 78711-2277
(512) 463-5538   Toll Free: (800) 252-VETS (within TX)
Fax: (512) 475-2395   E-mail: VetsEd@tvc.texas.gov
Web: www.tvc.texas.gov/Hazlewood-Act.aspx

Summary To exempt the children of certain Texas veterans from payment of tuition for undergraduate or graduate study at public universities in the state.

Eligibility This program is open to the dependent children under 25 years of age of veterans who are current residents of Texas and were legal residents of the state at the time they entered the U.S. armed forces and served for at least 181 days of active military duty, excluding basic training, during specified periods of wartime. The veteran parent must have received an honorable discharge or separation or a general discharge under honorable conditions. They must have unused hours of exemption from tuition under the Hazlewood Act that they can assign to a dependent child. The dependent children must be enrolled or planning to enroll at a public college or university in Texas and all their other federal veterans education benefits (not including Pell and SEOG grants) may not exceed the value of this exemption.

Financial data Dependent children who are eligible for this benefit are entitled to free tuition and fees at state-supported colleges and universities in Texas.

Duration The combined exemptions for veteran and child may be claimed up to a cumulative total of 150 credit hours, including undergraduate and graduate study.

Additional information This program was previously administered by the Texas Higher Education Coordinating Board but was transferred to the Texas Veterans Commission in 2013.

Number awarded Varies each year; recently, 8,885 were granted.

Deadline Deadline not specified.

[541]
HEAVY CONSTRUCTION ACADEMY VFW NEW HAMPSHIRE SCHOLARSHIP

Veterans of Foreign Wars of the United States-
  Department of New Hampshire
Attn: State Adjutant
P.O. Box 6025
East Rochester, NH 03868-6025
(603) 335-5923   Fax: (603) 335-5936
E-mail: stateheadquarters@nh.vfwwebmail.com
Web: www.nhvfw.org

Summary To provide financial assistance to high school seniors in New Hampshire who have a connection to the Veterans of Foreign Wars (VFW) and plan to attend vocational school in the state.

Eligibility This program is open to seniors graduating from high schools in New Hampshire who are the children or grandchildren of members of the VFW or its Ladies Auxiliary. Applicants must be planning to attend a vocational school in the state.

Financial data Stipends range from $250 to $1,500. Funds are paid directly to the recipient's vocational school.

Duration 1 year.

Additional information This program is sponsored by the Heavy Construction Academy, but recipients may attend any vocational school in New Hampshire.

Number awarded 7 each year: 1 each at $1,500, $1,000, and $500 plus 4 at $250.

Deadline Deadline not specified.

[542]
HELEN DYAR KING SCHOLARSHIP

Arizona Community Foundation
Attn: Director of Scholarships
2201 East Camelback Road, Suite 405B
Phoenix, AZ 85016
(602) 381-1400   Toll Free: (800) 222-8221
Fax: (602) 381-1575   E-mail: jmedina@azfoundation.org
Web: azfoundation.academicworks.com/opportunities/628

Summary To provide financial assistance to high school seniors and current college students, especially residents of Arizona, who are members or dependents of members of the armed services or a law enforcement agency and are interested in attending college in any state.

Eligibility This program is open to graduating high school seniors and current full-time students at colleges or universities in any state. Applicants must be an active-duty or retired member or dependent of such a member of the armed services (Air Force, Army, Coast Guard, Marine Corps, National Guard, Navy) or law enforcement agency. They must be U.S. citizens and have a GPA of 2.75 or higher. Preference is given to women and to residents of Arizona. Financial need is considered in the selection process.

Financial data The stipend is $2,000 for students at 2-year colleges or $4,000 for students at 4-year colleges and universities.

Duration 1 year.

Number awarded Varies each year.

Deadline April of each year.

[543]
HELEN JAMES BREWER SCHOLARSHIP

United Daughters of the Confederacy
Attn: Second Vice President General
328 North Boulevard
Richmond, VA 23220-4008
(804) 355-1636   Fax: (804) 353-1396
E-mail: jamieretired@sbcglobal.net
Web: www.hqudc.org/Scholarships/index.htm

Summary To provide financial assistance to lineal descendants of Confederate veterans in certain southern states who are interested in majoring in English or southern history or literature.

Eligibility Eligible to apply for these scholarships are lineal descendants of worthy Confederates or collateral descendants who are current or former members of the Children of the Confederacy or current members of the United Daughters of the Confederacy. Applicants must intend to study English history and literature or southern history and literature and must submit a family financial report and certified proof of the Confederate record of 1 ancestor, with the company and regiment in which he served. They must have at least a 3.0 GPA in high school. Residency in Alabama, Florida, Georgia, South Carolina, Tennessee, or Virginia is required.

Financial data The amount of this scholarship depends on the availability of funds.

Duration 1 year; may be renewed.

Number awarded 1 each year.

Deadline April of each year.

[544]
HELEN KLIMEK STUDENT SCHOLARSHIP

American Legion Auxiliary
Department of New York
112 State Street, Suite 1310
Albany, NY 12207
(518) 463-1162   Toll Free: (800) 421-6348
Fax: (518) 449-5406
E-mail: alanykathleen@nycap.rr.com
Web: www.deptny.org/scholarships

Summary To provide financial assistance to New York residents who are the descendants of veterans and interested in attending college in any state.

Eligibility This program is open to residents of New York who are high school seniors or graduates and attending or planning to attend an accredited college or university in any state. Applicants must be the children, grandchildren, or great-grandchildren of veterans who served during specified periods of wartime. Along with their application they must submit a 700-word statement on the significance or value of volunteerism as a resource towards the positive development of their personal and professional future. Selection is based on character (20%), Americanism (15%), volunteer involvement (20%), leadership (15%), scholarship (15%), and financial need (15%). U.S. citizenship is required.

Financial data The stipend is $1,000. Funds are paid directly to the recipient's school.

Duration 1 year.

Number awarded 1 each year.

Deadline February of each year.

[545]
HEROES LEGACY SCHOLARSHIPS

Fisher House Foundation
111 Rockville Pike, Suite 420
Rockville, MD 20850
Toll Free: (888) 294-8560
E-mail: bgawne@fisherhouse.org
Web: www.militaryscholar.org/legacy/index.html

Summary To provide financial assistance for college to the children of deceased and disabled veterans and military personnel.

Eligibility This program is open to the unmarried sons and daughters of U.S. military servicemembers (including active duty, retirees, Guard/Reserves, and survivors) who are high school seniors or full-time students at an accredited college, university, or community college and younger than 23 years of age. Applicants must have at least 1 parent who, while serving on active duty after September 11, 2001, either died or became disabled, defined as qualified for receipt of Traumatic Servicemembers Group Life Insurance (TSGLI) or

rated as 100% permanently and totally disabled by the U.S. Department of Veterans Affairs. High school applicants must have a GPA of 3.0 or higher and college applicants must have a GPA of 2.5 or higher. Along with their application, they must submit a 500-word essay on a topic that changes annually; recently, students were asked to write on the greatest challenge military families face. Selection is based on merit.

Financial data The stipend is $5,000 per year.

Duration 1 year; recipients may reapply.

Additional information This program began in 2010 with proceeds from the sale of the book *Of Thee I Sing: A Letter to My Daughters* by President Barack Obama.

Number awarded Varies each year, depending on the availability of funds. In its first 3 years, the program awarded 130 scholarships.

Deadline March of each year.

[546]
HEROES TRIBUTE SCHOLARSHIP PROGRAM FOR CHILDREN OF THE FALLEN

Marine Corps Scholarship Foundation, Inc.
Attn: Scholarship Office
909 North Washington Street, Suite 400
Alexandria, VA 22314
(703) 549-0060   Toll Free: (866) 496-5462
Fax: (703) 549-9474   E-mail: students@mcsf.org
Web: www.mcsf.org

Summary To provide financial assistance for college to the children of Marines and Navy Corpsmen serving with the Marines who were killed on September 11, 2001 or in combat since that date.

Eligibility This program is open to the children of 1) Marines and former Marines killed in the terrorist attacks on September 11, 2001; 2) Marines and U.S. Navy Corpsmen serving with the Marines who were killed in combat after September 11, 2001; 3) children of Navy Religious Program Specialists attached to a Marine unit who were killed in combat on or after September 27, 2008; and 4) children of Marines who were killed in training after September 27, 2008. Applicants must be high school seniors, high school graduates, or current undergraduates in an accredited college, university, or postsecondary vocational/technical school. They must submit academic transcripts (GPA of 2.0 or higher), documentation of their parent's service, and a 500-word essay on a topic that changes periodically. Only undergraduate study is supported. There is no maximum family income limitation. All qualified applicants receive scholarships.

Financial data The stipend is $7,500 per year.

Duration 4 years.

Number awarded Varies each year; recently, 4 were awarded.

Deadline February of each year.

[547]
HICKAM OFFICERS' SPOUSES' CLUB SCHOLARSHIPS

Hickam Officers' Spouses' Club
Attn: Scholarship Coordinator
PMB 168
P.O. Box 30800
Honolulu, HI 96820-0800
E-mail: scholarships@hickamosc.com
Web: www.hickamosc.com/page-1313406

Summary To provide financial assistance to dependents of current and former military personnel in Hawaii who are interested in attending college or graduate school in any state.

Eligibility This program is open to dependents of 1 of the following: 1) active-duty military members permanently stationed in Hawaii; 2) active-duty military members on a remote assignment from Hawaii; 3) retired military members resident in Hawaii; 4) full-time Hawaii National Guard and U.S. military Reserve members residing in Hawaii; and 5) survivors of deceased military members residing in Hawaii. Applicants must be seniors graduating from a Hawaii high school or accredited home school program based in Hawaii and planning to enroll at an accredited 2- or 4-year college, university, or vocational/technical school in any state; dependent children currently working on an undergraduate or graduate degree at a college or university in any state; or spouses currently working on an undergraduate or graduate degree at a college or university in any state. Selection is based on an essay, educational information, employment information, volunteer service and club activities, school activities, leadership roles, awards and honors, and a letter of recommendation.

Financial data A stipend is awarded (amount not specified).

Duration 1 year.

Number awarded 1 or more each year.

Deadline March of each year.

[548]
HNGEA SCHOLARSHIP

Hawaii National Guard Enlisted Association
c/o 1SG Jacob Magarro, Scholarship Committee Chair
96-1230 Waihona Street
Pearl City, HI 96782
E-mail: jacob.magarro@ng.army.mil
Web: www.hngea.net/organization.htm

Summary To provide financial assistance for college to members of the Hawaii National Guard Enlisted Association (HNGEA) and their dependents.

Eligibility This program is open to HNGEA members and their dependent spouses and children. Applicants must be attending or interested in attending a college or university in Hawaii as an undergraduate student. They must have a GPA of at least 2.5 for the current semester and 2.0 overall. Along with their application, they must submit a letter describing their educational goals and need for the scholarship.

Financial data Stipends range up to $2,000.

Duration 1 year.

Number awarded Varies each year.

Deadline May of each year.

[549]
HONOLULU POST SAME SCHOLARSHIPS

Society of American Military Engineers-Honolulu Post
P.O. Box 201445
Honolulu, HI 96820
Web: www.samehonolulu.org

Summary To provide financial assistance to residents of Hawaii (particularly military servicemembers, military dependents, and ROTC students) who are interested in attending college or graduate school in any state to work on a degree in engineering or architecture.

Eligibility This program is open to residents of Hawaii who are graduating high school seniors or current undergraduates enrolled or planning to enroll full time at an accredited college or university in any state. Applicants must be planning to work on an undergraduate or graduate degree in engineering or architecture. They must be U.S. citizens and have a GPA of 3.0 or higher. Military affiliation or experience (i.e., ROTC, member or dependent of a member of the Society of Military Engineers (SAME), military dependent, Junior ROTC) is not required but is given preference. Along with their application, they must submit a transcript; a resume of work experience, academic activities, and extracurricular accomplishments; and a 1-page essay on how their engineering or architecture degree will impact our nation.

Financial data The stipend is $2,000 or $1,500 per year.

Duration 1 year for the $2,000 scholarships; 4 years for the $1,500 scholarships.

Number awarded Varies each year; recently, 6 were awarded: 2 at $2,000 for 1 year and 4 at $1,500 per year for 4 years.

Deadline March of each year.

[550]
HOPE FOR THE WARRIORS SPOUSE/CAREGIVER SCHOLARSHIPS

Hope for the Warriors
Attn: Spouse/Caregiver Scholarships Director
5101C Backlick Road
Annandale, VA 22003
Toll Free: (877) 246-7349
E-mail: scholarships@hopeforthewarriors.org
Web: www.hopeforthewarriors.org

Summary To provide financial assistance for college or graduate school to the spouses and caregivers of wounded or deceased military personnel or veterans.

Eligibility This program is open to spouses and caregivers of current and former servicemembers who were wounded or killed in the line of duty while serving in support of Operation Enduring Freedom, Operation Iraqi Freedom, or Operation New Dawn. Applicants must be enrolled or planning to enroll full or part time at an accredited college, university, or trade school to work on a bachelor's degree, master's degree, or vocational certification. They must have a high school GPA of 2.6 or higher or a GED score of 650 or higher. Along with their application, they must submit a 500-word essay on how this scholarship will impact their ability to complete their degree. Selection is based on that essay, academic achievement, personal goals, and letters of recommendation.

Financial data The stipend is $1,000 per year.

Duration 1 year; may be renewed up to 3 additional years.

Number awarded 1 or more each year.

Deadline March of each year for fall; October of each year for spring.

[551]
H.S. AND ANGELINE LEWIS SCHOLARSHIPS

American Legion Auxiliary
Department of Wisconsin
Attn: Education Chair
2930 American Legion Drive
P.O. Box 140
Portage, WI 53901-0140
(608) 745-0124   Toll Free: (866) 664-3863
Fax: (608) 745-1947   E-mail: alawi@amlegionauxwi.org
Web: www.amlegionauxwi.org/Scholarships.htm

Summary To provide financial assistance to Wisconsin residents who are related to veterans or members of the American Legion Auxiliary and interested in working on an undergraduate or graduate degree at a school in any state.

Eligibility This program is open to the children, wives, and widow(er)s of veterans who are high school seniors or graduates and have a GPA of 3.5 or higher. Grandchildren and great-grandchildren of members of the American Legion Auxiliary are also eligible. Applicants must be residents of Wisconsin and interested in working on an undergraduate or graduate degree at a school in any state. Along with their application, they must submit a 300-word essay on "Education—An Investment in the Future." Financial need is considered in the selection process.

Financial data The stipend is $1,000.

Duration 1 year; nonrenewable.

Number awarded 6 each year: 1 to a graduate student and 5 to undergraduates.

Deadline March of each year.

[552]
HUI O'WAHINE MERIT SCHOLARSHIP FOR CONTINUING EDUCATION

Hui O'Wahine Fort Shafter Spouses Club
Attn: Scholarships
4285 Lawehana Street
PMB A-8
Honolulu, HI 96818-3128
E-mail: huiowahinescholarships@gmail.com
Web: www.huispirit.com/scholarshipwelfare.html

Summary To provide financial assistance to members and spouses of members of Hui O'Wahine (the Fort Shafter Spouses Club) in Hawaii who are interested in returning to college in any state after taking a break in their education.

Eligibility This program is open to Hui O'Wahine members and their spouses who are active-duty, Reserve, or retired military members or Department of Defense civilians residing in or assigned to Hawaii. Applicants must have taken a break in their education and be entering or continuing full- or part-time students at a qualifying college, university, or vocational school in any state. Selection is based on academic merit and community involvement.

Financial data A stipend is awarded (amount not specified).

Duration 1 year.

Number awarded Several each year.

Deadline March of each year.

[553]
HUI O'WAHINE MERIT SCHOLARSHIP FOR TRADITIONAL STUDENTS

Hui O'Wahine Fort Shafter Spouses Club
Attn: Scholarships
4285 Lawehana Street
PMB A-8
Honolulu, HI 96818-3128
E-mail: huiowahinescholarships@gmail.com
Web: www.huispirit.com/scholarshipwelfare.html

Summary To provide financial assistance to children of members of Hui O'Wahine (the Fort Shafter Spouses Club) in Hawaii who are interested in attending college or graduate school in any state.

Eligibility This program is open to children of members of Hui O'Wahine who are graduating high school seniors or currently enrolled as full- or part-time undergraduate or graduate students at a qualifying college, university, or vocational school in any state. Applicants must be younger than 23 years of age and have at least 1 parent who is an active-duty, Reserve, or retired military member or Department of Defense civilian residing in or assigned to Hawaii. They must submit transcripts that, for high school seniors, include ACT and/or SAT scores. Selection is based on academic merit and community involvement.

Financial data A stipend is awarded (amount not specified).

Duration 1 year.

Number awarded Several each year.

Deadline March of each year.

[554]
I. BEVERLY LAKE SCHOLARSHIP ENDOWMENT

North Carolina Community Foundation
Attn: Program Associate
4601 Six Forks Road, Suite 524
Raleigh, NC 27609
(919) 828-4387   Toll Free: (800) 201-9533
Fax: (919) 828-5495
E-mail: sltaylor@nccommunityfoundation.org
Web: www.nccommunityfoundation.org

Summary To provide financial assistance to residents of North Carolina who are eligible for membership in the Sons of Confederate Veterans or the United Daughters of the Confederacy and interested in attending college in any state.

Eligibility This program is open to residents of North Carolina who are currently enrolled at a postsecondary institution in any state. Applicants must be eligible for membership in the Sons of Confederate Veterans (SCV) or the United Daughters of the Confederacy (UDC). Along with their application, they must submit a 300-word letter pledging to make the best possible use of the opportunity offered by this scholarship, outlining their goals and their plans for meeting those, and evaluating the significance of a southern heritage in today's world.

Financial data A stipend is awarded (amount not specified).

Duration 1 year.

Additional information This program is sponsored by the Bennett Place Chapter of UDC.

Number awarded 1 or more each year.

Deadline April of each year.

[555]
IA DRANG SCHOLARSHIP PROGRAM

First Cavalry Division Association
Attn: Foundation
302 North Main Street
Copperas Cove, TX 76522-1703
(254) 547-6537   Fax: (254) 547-8853
E-mail: firstcav@1cda.org
Web: www.1cda.org/Foundation_Overview.htm

Summary To provide financial assistance for undergraduate education to descendants of Army and Air Force personnel who fought in the battle of Ia Drang in 1965.

Eligibility This program is open to the children and grandchildren of members of designated Army and Air Force units who actually fought in the battle of the Ia Drang valley from November 3 through 19, 1965. For a list of the qualifying units, contact the sponsor. Children and grandchildren of personnel who were assigned to a unit that fought in the battles but were themselves at other locations during the specified dates are not eligible.

Financial data The stipend is $1,200 per year. The checks are made out jointly to the student and the school and may be used for whatever the student needs, including tuition, books, and clothing.

Duration 1 year; may be renewed up to 3 additional years.

Additional information This program began in 1994. Requests for applications must be accompanied by a self-addressed stamped envelope.

Number awarded Varies each year. Since the program was established, 275 of these scholarships, worth more than $473,000, have been awarded.

Deadline June of each year.

[556]
IDAHO ARMED FORCES AND PUBLIC SAFETY OFFICER DEPENDENT SCHOLARSHIPS

Idaho State Board of Education
Attn: Scholarships Program Manager
650 West State Street, Room 307
P.O. Box 83720
Boise, ID 83720-0037
(208) 334-2270   Fax: (208) 334-2632
E-mail: scholarshiphelp@osbe.idaho.gov
Web: www.boardofed.idaho.gov

Summary To provide financial assistance for college in Idaho to dependents of certain members of the armed forces and of disabled or deceased public safety officers.

Eligibility This program is open to spouses and children of 1) Idaho residents determined by the federal government to have been prisoners of war, missing in action, or killed in action or died of injuries or wounds sustained in any area of armed conflict to which the United States was a party; 2) any member of the armed forces stationed in Idaho and deployed from Idaho to any area of armed conflict to which the United States was a party and who has been determined by the federal government to be a prisoner of war or missing action or to have died of or become totally and permanently disabled by injuries or wounds sustained in action as a result of such deployment; or 3 full- or part-time Idaho public safety officers employed by or volunteering for the state or a political subdivision who were killed or totally and permanently disabled in the line of duty. Applicants must be Idaho residents enrolled or planning to enroll at a public institution of higher education in the state.

Financial data Each scholarship provides a full waiver of tuition and fees at public institutions of higher education or public vocational schools within Idaho, an allowance of $500 per semester for books, on-campus housing, and a campus meal plan.

Duration Benefits are available for a maximum of 36 months (4 academic years).

Number awarded Varies each year.

Deadline Deadline not specified.

[557]
IDAHO ENLISTED ASSOCIATION YOUNG PATRIOT SCHOLARSHIP

Idaho Enlisted Association of the National Guard of the United States
c/o Steve Vinsonhaler, President
7054 West Saxton Drive
Boise, ID 83714-2366
(208) 407-4887   E-mail: svinsonhaler@imd.idaho.gov
Web: www.eangusidaho.org/Scholarships.php

Summary To provide financial assistance to members of the Idaho Enlisted Association of the National Guard of the United States and their family who are interested in attending college in any state.

Eligibility This program is open to 1) members of the association; 2) dependent unmarried children of members; 3) spouses of members; and 4) unmarried spouses and unmarried dependent children of deceased members who were in good standing at the time of death. Association members must also be enlisted members of the Idaho National Guard with at least 1 year remaining on their enlistment or have 20 or more years of military service. Applicants must be enrolled or planning to enroll full time at a college, university, trade school, or business school in any state. Along with their application, they must submit a 2-page essay about an activity or interest that has been meaningful to them, a personal letter providing information about themselves and their families, 2 letters of recommendation, an academic letter of recommendation, and a copy of the sponsor's current membership card or number. Family income is considered in the selection process.

Financial data The stipend is $1,500.

Duration 1 year; nonrenewable.

Number awarded 2 each year.

Deadline August of each year.

[558]
IDAHO LEGION AUXILIARY GENERAL STUDIES SCHOLARSHIP

American Legion Auxiliary
Department of Idaho
905 Warren Street
Boise, ID 83706-3825
(208) 342-7066   Fax: (208) 342-7066
E-mail: idalegionaux@msn.com
Web: www.idahoala.org/14301.html

Summary To provide financial assistance to Idaho veterans and their descendants who are interested in attending college in any state and majoring in any field.

Eligibility This program is open to veterans and the children and grandchildren of veterans who are residents of Idaho. Applicants must be attending or planning to attend a college or university in any state and major in any field. They may be traditional or nontraditional students between 17 and 35 years of age. Selection is based on financial need, scholarship, and deportment.

Financial data The stipend is $1,000.

Duration 1 year.

Number awarded 1 each year.

Deadline May of each year.

[559]
IDAHO LEGION AUXILIARY NURSES SCHOLARSHIP

American Legion Auxiliary
Department of Idaho
905 Warren Street
Boise, ID 83706-3825
(208) 342-7066   Fax: (208) 342-7066
E-mail: idalegionaux@msn.com
Web: www.idahoala.org/14301.html

Summary To provide financial assistance to Idaho veterans and their descendants who are interested in studying nursing at a school in any state.

Eligibility This program is open to student nurses who are veterans or the children or grandchildren of veterans and are residents of Idaho. Applicants must be attending or planning to attend a school of nursing in any state. They may be traditional or nontraditional students between 17 and 35 years of age. Selection is based on financial need, scholarship, and deportment.

Financial data The stipend is $1,000.

Duration 1 year.

Number awarded 1 each year.

Deadline May of each year.

[560]
ILLINOIS AMERICAN LEGION AUXILIARY PAST PRESIDENTS PARLEY NURSES SCHOLARSHIP

American Legion Auxiliary
Department of Illinois
2720 East Lincoln Street
P.O. Box 1426
Bloomington, IL 61702-1426
(309) 663-9366   Fax: (309) 663-5827
E-mail: karen.boughan@ilala.org
Web: www.ilala.org/education.html

Summary To provide financial assistance to Illinois veterans and their descendants who are attending college in any state to prepare for a career as a nurse.

Eligibility This program is open to veterans who served during designated periods of wartime and their children, grandchildren, and great-grandchildren. Applicants must be currently enrolled full time at a college or university in any state and studying nursing. They must be residents of Illinois or members of the American Legion Family, Department of Illinois. Selection is based on commitment to a nursing career (25%) character (25%), academic rating (20%), and financial need (30%).

Financial data The stipend is $1,000.

Duration 1 year.

Additional information Applications may be obtained only from a local unit of the American Legion Auxiliary.

Number awarded 1 or more each year.

Deadline April of each year.

[561]
ILLINOIS AMVETS JUNIOR ROTC SCHOLARSHIPS

AMVETS-Department of Illinois
2200 South Sixth Street
Springfield, IL 62703
(217) 528-4713   Toll Free: (800) 638-VETS (within IL)
Fax: (217) 528-9896   E-mail: info@ilamvets.org
Web: www.ilamvets.org

Summary To provide financial assistance for college to high school seniors in Illinois who have participated in Junior ROTC (JROTC), especially children and grandchildren of veterans.

Eligibility This program is open to seniors graduating from high schools in Illinois who have taken the ACT or SAT and have participated in the JROTC program. Financial need is considered in the selection process. Priority is given to children and grandchildren of veterans.

Financial data A stipend is awarded (amount not specified).

Duration 1 year; nonrenewable.

Number awarded 5 each year: 1 in each of the sponsor's divisions.

Deadline February of each year.

[562]
ILLINOIS AMVETS SERVICE FOUNDATION SCHOLARSHIPS

AMVETS-Department of Illinois
2200 South Sixth Street
Springfield, IL 62703
(217) 528-4713   Toll Free: (800) 638-VETS (within IL)
Fax: (217) 528-9896   E-mail: info@ilamvets.org
Web: www.ilamvets.org

Summary To provide financial assistance for college to high school seniors in Illinois, especially children and grandchildren of veterans.

Eligibility This program is open to seniors graduating from high schools in Illinois who have taken the ACT or SAT. Financial need is considered in the selection process. Priority is given to children and grandchildren of veterans.

Financial data The stipend is $1,000.

Duration 1 year; nonrenewable.

Number awarded Up to 30 each year: 6 in each of the sponsor's 5 divisions.

Deadline February of each year.

[563]
ILLINOIS AMVETS TRADE SCHOOL SCHOLARSHIPS

AMVETS-Department of Illinois
2200 South Sixth Street
Springfield, IL 62703
(217) 528-4713   Toll Free: (800) 638-VETS (within IL)
Fax: (217) 528-9896   E-mail: info@ilamvets.org
Web: www.ilamvets.org

Summary To provide financial assistance to high school seniors in Illinois, especially children and grandchildren of veterans, who are interested in attending trade school.
Eligibility This program is open to seniors graduating from high schools in Illinois who have been accepted at an approved trade school. Financial need is considered in the selection process. Priority is given to children and grandchildren of veterans.
Financial data The stipend is $1,000.
Duration 1 year; nonrenewable.
Number awarded 5 each year: 1 in each of the sponsor's divisions.
Deadline February of each year.

[564]
ILLINOIS CHILDREN OF VETERANS SCHOLARSHIPS

Illinois Department of Veterans' Affairs
833 South Spring Street
P.O. Box 19432
Springfield, IL 62794-9432
(217) 782-6641   Toll Free: (800) 437-9824 (within IL)
Fax: (217) 524-0344   TDD: (217) 524-4645
E-mail: webmail@dva.state.il.us
Web: www2.illinois.gov

Summary To provide financial assistance for college to the children of Illinois veterans (with preference given to the children of disabled or deceased veterans).
Eligibility Each county in the state is entitled to award an honorary scholarship to the child of a veteran of World War I, World War II, the Korean Conflict, the Vietnam Conflict, or any time after August 2, 1990. Preference is given to children of disabled or deceased veterans.
Financial data Students selected for this program receive free tuition at any branch of the University of Illinois.
Duration Up to 4 years.
Number awarded Each county in Illinois is entitled to award 1 scholarship. The Board of Trustees of the university may, from time to time, add to the number of honorary scholarships (when such additions will not create an unnecessary financial burden on the university).
Deadline Deadline not specified.

[565]
ILLINOIS FALLEN HEROES SCHOLARSHIP

Office of the State Treasurer
Attn: Bright Start Account Representative
400 West Monroe Street, Suite 401
Springfield, IL 62704
(217) 782-6540   Fax: (217) 524-3822
E-mail: fallenheroes@treasurer.state.il.us
Web: www.treasurer.il.gov

Summary To provide financial assistance for college to the children of Illinois servicemembers killed in Iraq.
Eligibility This program is open to the children of fallen Illinois servicemembers who served in Operation Iraqi Freedom or Operation Enduring Freedom. Applicants must be U.S. citizens of any age under 30 years. They may be planning to attend an accredited college or university anywhere in the United States or at selected institutions abroad. Children of all Illinois active and Reserve servicemen and women are eligible.

Financial data The stipend is $2,500. Funds are deposited into an age-based Bright Start portfolio (the Illinois 529 program) and are available when the student reaches college age. The older the child, the more conservative the investment becomes. Funds may be used only for tuition, fees, room, and board, and must be spent before the child reaches 30 years of age.
Duration 1 year.
Additional information This program began in 2008.
Number awarded Varies each year.
Deadline Deadline not specified.

[566]
ILLINOIS LEGION SCHOLARSHIPS

American Legion
Department of Illinois
2720 East Lincoln Street
P.O. Box 2910
Bloomington, IL 61702-2910
(309) 663-0361   Fax: (309) 663-5783
E-mail: hdqs@illegion.org
Web: www.illegion.org/scholarship.html

Summary To provide financial assistance to the children and grandchildren of members of the American Legion in Illinois who plan to attend college in any state.
Eligibility This program is open to students graduating from high schools in Illinois who plan to further their education at an accredited college, university, technical school, or trade school in any state. Applicants must be the children or grandchildren of living or deceased members of American Legion posts in Illinois. Selection is based on academic performance and financial need. U.S. citizenship is required.
Financial data The stipend is $1,000.
Duration 1 year; nonrenewable.
Number awarded 20 each year: 4 in each of the Illinois department's 5 divisions.
Deadline March of each year.

[567]
ILLINOIS LEGION TRADE SCHOOL SCHOLARSHIPS

American Legion
Department of Illinois
2720 East Lincoln Street
P.O. Box 2910
Bloomington, IL 61702-2910
(309) 663-0361   Fax: (309) 663-5783
E-mail: hdqs@illegion.org
Web: www.illegion.org/scholarship.html

Summary To provide financial assistance to the children and grandchildren of members of the American Legion in Illinois who plan to attend trade school in any state.
Eligibility This program is open to students graduating from high schools in Illinois who plan to further their education through a private career school, on-the-job training, apprenticeship, or cooperative training at a program in any state. Applicants must be the children or grandchildren of members of American Legion posts in Illinois. Selection is based on academic performance and financial need.
Financial data The stipend is $1,000.
Duration 1 year; nonrenewable.

Number awarded 5 each year: 1 in each of the Illinois department's 5 divisions.

Deadline March of each year.

[568]
ILLINOIS MIA/POW SCHOLARSHIP

Illinois Department of Veterans' Affairs
833 South Spring Street
P.O. Box 19432
Springfield, IL 62794-9432
(217) 782-3564   Toll Free: (800) 437-9824 (within IL)
Fax: (217) 524-0344   TDD: (217) 524-4645
E-mail: webmail@dva.state.il.us
Web: www2.illinois.gov

Summary To provide financial assistance for 1) the undergraduate education of Illinois dependents of disabled or deceased veterans or those listed as prisoners of war or missing in action; and 2) the rehabilitation or education of disabled dependents of those veterans.

Eligibility This program is open to the spouses, natural children, legally adopted children, or stepchildren of a veteran or servicemember who 1) has been declared by the U.S. Department of Defense or the U.S. Department of Veterans Affairs to be permanently disabled from service-connected causes with 100% disability, deceased as the result of a service-connected disability, a prisoner of war, or missing in action; and 2) at the time of entering service was an Illinois resident or was an Illinois resident within 6 months of entering such service. Special support is available for dependents who have a physical, mental, or developmental disability.

Financial data An eligible dependent is entitled to full payment of tuition and certain fees at any Illinois state-supported college, university, or community college. In lieu of that benefit, an eligible dependent who has a disability is entitled to receive a grant to be used to cover the cost of treating the disability at 1 or more appropriate therapeutic, rehabilitative, or educational facilities. For all recipients, the total benefit cannot exceed the cost equivalent of 4 calendar years of full-time enrollment, including summer terms, at the University of Illinois.

Duration This scholarship may be used for a period equivalent to 4 calendar years, including summer terms. Dependents have 12 years from the initial term of study to complete the equivalent of 4 calendar years. Disabled dependents who elect to use the grant for rehabilitative purposes may do so as long as the total benefit does not exceed the cost equivalent of 4 calendar years of full-time enrollment at the University of Illinois.

Number awarded Varies each year.

Deadline Deadline not specified.

[569]
ILLINOIS SCHOLARSHIPS FOR JUNIOR MEMBERS

American Legion Auxiliary
Department of Illinois
2720 East Lincoln Street
P.O. Box 1426
Bloomington, IL 61702-1426
(309) 663-9366   Fax: (309) 663-5827
E-mail: karen.boughan@ilala.org
Web: www.ilala.org/education.html

Summary To provide financial assistance to high school seniors or graduates in Illinois who are junior members of the American Legion Auxiliary and planning to attend college in any state.

Eligibility This program is open to junior members of the Illinois American Legion Auxiliary who are daughters, granddaughters, great-granddaughters, or sisters of veterans who served during eligibility dates for membership in the American Legion. Applicants must have been members for at least 3 years. They must be high school seniors or graduates who have not yet attended an institution of higher learning and are planning to attend college in any state. Along with their application, they must submit a 1,000-word essay on "The Veteran in My Life." Selection is based on that essay (25%) character and leadership (25%), scholarship (25%), and financial need (25%).

Financial data The stipend is $1,000.

Duration 1 year.

Number awarded Varies each year.

Deadline March of each year.

[570]
ILLINOIS SCV/MOS&B SCHOLARSHIP

Illinois Sons of Confederate Veterans/Military Order of the Stars and Bars
c/o James F. Barr, Scholarship Chair
3162 North Broadway, Suite 200
Chicago, IL 60657
(773) 755-2748   E-mail: jim@tax-acct.net

Summary To provide financial assistance to high school seniors in Illinois who are descendants of Confederate veterans and plan to attend college in any state.

Eligibility This program is open to seniors (male or female) graduating from high schools in Illinois and planning to attend a college, university, or community college in any state. Applicants must be a descendant of a male who served honorably in the army, navy, judicial, executive, or civil service of the Confederate States of America. Along with their application, they must submit 1) a transcript of grades; 2) an autobiography that includes a genealogical chart showing lineal or collateral family lines to a Confederate ancestor; and 3) a 500-word essay on an event, person, philosophy, or ideal associated with the Confederate Cause during the War Between the States. Financial need is not considered in the selection process.

Financial data The stipend is $1,000.

Duration 1 year.

Additional information This scholarship is offered jointly by the Illinois Division of Sons of Confederate Veterans (SCV) and Illinois Society, Military Order of the Stars and Bars (MOS&B).

Number awarded 1 each year.

Deadline March of each year.

[571]
INDIANA AMERICAN LEGION FAMILY SCHOLARSHIP

American Legion
Department of Indiana
777 North Meridian Street, Suite 104
Indianapolis, IN 46204
(317) 630-1264   Fax: (317) 630-1277
Web: www.indianalegion.org

Summary To provide financial assistance to children and grandchildren of members of the American Legion family in Indiana who are interested in attending college in the state.

Eligibility This program is open to residents of Indiana who are the children or grandchildren of members of the American Legion, American Legion Auxiliary, Sons of the American Legion, or deceased members of those organizations who, at the time of death, were in current paid status. Applicants must be enrolled or accepted for enrollment at an Indiana college, university, junior college, community college, or technical school. Along with their application, they must submit a 500-word essay describing the reasons they wish to be considered for this scholarship, the purpose to which the funds will be put, their relationship to the Legion family and what it has meant to them, and how the citizens of Indiana and the members of the American Legion family will benefit in the future from their having achieved their educational goals with the assistance of this scholarship. Financial need is not considered in the selection process.

Financial data The stipend is $1,500.

Duration 1 year.

Number awarded 5 each year: 1 to a high school senior who plans to attend a 4-year college or university, 1 to a high school senior who plans to attend a 2-year college, and 1 to a college freshman who plans to continue in that program.

Deadline March of each year.

[572]
INDIANA CHILDREN OF VETERANS PROGRAM

Indiana Commission for Higher Education
Attn: Division of Student Financial Aid
W462 Indiana Government Center South
402 West Washington Street
Indianapolis, IN 46204
(317) 232-2355   Toll Free: (888) 528-4719 (within IN)
Fax: (317) 232-3260   E-mail: awards@sfa.che.in.gov
Web: www.in.gov/sfa/2526.htm

Summary To provide financial assistance to residents of Indiana who are the children of specified categories of veterans and interested in attending college in the state.

Eligibility This program is open to residents of Indiana whose parent 1) served in the U.S. armed forces during a war or performed duty equally hazardous that was recognized by the award of a U.S. service or campaign medal, suffered a service-connected death or disability, and received a discharge or separation other than dishonorable; 2) served in the U.S. armed forces, received the Purple Heart decoration or wounds as a result of enemy action, and received a discharge or separation other than dishonorable; or 3) was declared a POW or MIA while serving in the U.S. armed forces after January 1, 1960.

Financial data Qualified applicants receive a 100% remission of tuition and all mandatory fees for undergraduate or professional degrees at eligible postsecondary schools and universities in Indiana. Support is not provided for such fees as room and board.

Duration Up to 124 semester hours of study.

Number awarded Varies each year.

Deadline Applications must be submitted at least 30 days before the start of the college term.

[573]
INDIANA EAGLE SCOUT OF THE YEAR SCHOLARSHIPS

American Legion
Department of Indiana
777 North Meridian Street, Suite 104
Indianapolis, IN 46204
(317) 630-1264   Fax: (317) 630-1277
Web: www.indianalegion.org

Summary To recognize and reward, with scholarships for college in any state, Eagle Scouts who are members of a troop associated with the American Legion in Indiana or a son or grandson of a member of the Legion in the state.

Eligibility Applicants for this award must be either 1) a registered, active member of a Boy Scout Troop, Varsity Scout Team, or Venturing Crew chartered to an Indiana American Legion Post, Auxiliary Unit, or Sons of the American Legion Squadron; or 2) a registered active member of an Indiana Boy Scout Troop, Varsity Scout Team, or Venturing Crew and also the son or grandson of a member of the American Legion or American Legion Auxiliary. Candidates must also 1) have received the Eagle Scout Award; 2) be active members of their religious institution and have received the appropriate religious emblem; 3) have demonstrated practical citizenship in church, school, Scouting, and community; 4) be at least 15 years of age and enrolled in high school; and 5) submit at least 4 letters of recommendation, including 1 each from leaders of their religious institution, school, community, and Scouting. They must be planning to attend college in any state.

Financial data District winners receive $200 scholarships; the state winner receives a $1,000 scholarship.

Duration The awards are presented annually.

Number awarded 12 each year: 1 state winner and 11 district winners.

Deadline February of each year.

[574]
INDIANA SONS OF THE AMERICAN LEGION SCHOLARSHIP

Sons of the American Legion
Detachment of Indiana
Attn: Adjutant
777 North Meridian Street, Suite 104
Indianapolis, IN 46204
(317) 630-1363   Fax: (317) 237-9891
Web: www.in-sal.org

Summary To provide financial assistance to members of the Sons of the American Legion in Indiana who are interested in attending college in the state.

Eligibility This program is open to active members of a Squadron within the Indiana Detachment of the Sons of the American Legion. Applicants must be 1) seniors graduating from high school and planning to attend an accredited col-

lege, university, or trade school in Indiana; or 2) high school graduates attending or planning to attend an accredited college, university, or trade school in the state. Along with their application, they must submit an essay (up to 1,800 words) on the reasons why they feel they should receive this scholarship. Selection is based entirely on involvement in activities of the Sons of the American Legion.
Financial data The stipend is $1,000.
Duration 1 year; nonrenewable.
Number awarded 1 each year.
Deadline May of each year.

[575]
IOWA EAGLE SCOUT OF THE YEAR SCHOLARSHIP
American Legion
Department of Iowa
720 Lyon Street
Des Moines, IA 50309-5481
(515) 282-5068   Toll Free: (800) 365-8387
Fax: (515) 282-7583   E-mail: programs@ialegion.org
Web: www.ialegion.org/eagle_scout_of_the_year.htm
Summary To recognize and reward, with scholarships for college in any state, Eagle Scouts who are members of a troop associated with the American Legion in Iowa or a son or grandson of a member of the Legion.
Eligibility Applicants for this award must be either 1) a registered, active member of a Boy Scout Troop, Varsity Scout Team, or Venturing Crew chartered to an Iowa American Legion Post, Auxiliary Unit, or Sons of the American Legion Squadron; or 2) a registered active member of an Iowa Boy Scout Troop, Varsity Scout Team, or Venturing Crew and also the son or grandson of a member of the American Legion or American Legion Auxiliary. Candidates must also 1) have received the Eagle Scout Award; 2) be active members of their religious institution and have received the appropriate religious emblem; 3) have demonstrated practical citizenship in church, school, Scouting, and community; 4) be at least 15 years of age and enrolled in high school; and 5) submit at least 4 letters of recommendation, including 1 each from leaders of their religious institution, school, community, and Scouting. They must be planning to attend college in any state.
Financial data The first-place winner receives a $2,000 scholarship, second a $1,500 scholarship, and third a $1,000 scholarship. All awards must be used for payment of tuition at the recipient's college or university.
Duration The awards are presented annually.
Number awarded 3 each year.
Deadline January of each year.

[576]
IRAQ AND AFGHANISTAN SERVICE GRANTS
Department of Education
Attn: Federal Student Aid Information Center
P.O. Box 84
Washington, DC 20044-0084
(319) 337-5665   Toll Free: (800) 4-FED-AID
TDD: (800) 730-8913
Web: studentaid.ed.gov
Summary To provide financial assistance for undergraduate education to students whose parent was killed as a result of service in Iraq or Afghanistan.

Eligibility This program is open to students younger than 24 years of age whose parent or guardian was a member of the U.S. armed forces and died as a result of service performed in Iraq or Afghanistan after September 11, 2001. Applicants must be enrolled at least part time. The program is designed for students who do not qualify for Federal Pell Grants because of their family's financial situation.
Financial data The amount of the grant ranges up to that of a Federal Pell Grant, currently $5,654 per year.
Duration Up to 5 years of undergraduate study.
Number awarded Varies each year; recently, approximately 1,000 students qualified for this program.
Deadline Students may submit applications between January of the current year through June of the following year.

[577]
ISABELLA M. GILLEN MEMORIAL SCHOLARSHIP
Aviation Boatswain's Mates Association
c/o Terry L. New, Scholarship Chair
3193 Glastonbury Drive
Virginia Beach, VA 23453
E-mail: Scholarship@abma-usn.org
Web: www.abma-usn.org
Summary To provide financial assistance for college to the spouses and children of paid-up members of the Aviation Boatswains Mates Association (ABMA).
Eligibility Applicants must be dependents whose sponsor has been an active, dues-paying member of the ABMA for at least 2 years. They must prepare a statement describing their vocational or professional goals and relating how their past, present, and future activities make the accomplishment of those goals probable. Other submissions include transcripts, SAT or ACT scores, letters of recommendation, and honors received in scholarship, leadership, athletics, dramatics, community service, or other activities. Selection is based on financial need, character, leadership, and academic achievement.
Financial data The stipend is $3,500 per year.
Duration 1 year; may be renewed.
Additional information This program began in 1976. Membership in ABMA is open to all U.S. Navy personnel (active, retired, discharged, or separated) who hold or held the rating of aviation boatswains mate.
Number awarded 1 or 2 each year.
Deadline May of each year.

[578]
JACK E. BARGER, SR. MEMORIAL NURSING SCHOLARSHIPS
Nursing Foundation of Pennsylvania
3605 Vartan Way, Suite 204
Harrisburg, PA 17110
(717) 827-4369   Toll Free: (888) 707-7762
Fax: (717) 657-3796   E-mail: info@theNFP.org
Web: www.thenfp.webs.com/vfw-scholarship
Summary To provide financial assistance to military personnel, veterans, and their dependents who are studying nursing in Pennsylvania.
Eligibility This program is open to veterans, active-duty military personnel, and the children and spouses of veterans and active-duty military personnel. Applicants must be residents of Pennsylvania and currently enrolled in an undergrad-

uate professional school of nursing in the state. Recipients are selected by lottery from among the qualified applicants.

Financial data   The stipend is $1,000.

Duration   1 year.

Additional information   This program is sponsored by the Department of Pennsylvania Veterans of Foreign Wars (VFW). Recipients must attend the VFW Convention to accept the scholarship; travel, meals, and overnight expenses are paid by the VFW.

Number awarded   6 each year.

Deadline   April of each year.

[579]
JAN GWATNEY SCHOLARSHIP

United Daughters of the Confederacy
Attn: Second Vice President General
328 North Boulevard
Richmond, VA 23220-4008
(804) 355-1636   Fax: (804) 353-1396
E-mail: jamieretired@sbcglobal.net
Web: www.hqudc.org/Scholarships/index.htm

Summary   To provide financial assistance to female lineal descendants of Confederate Veterans, especially those from designated southern states.

Eligibility   Eligible to apply for these scholarships are female lineal descendants of worthy Confederates or collateral descendants who are current or former members of the Children of the Confederacy or current members of the United Daughters of the Confederacy. Applicants must submit a family financial report and certified proof of the Confederate record of 1 ancestor, with the company and regiment in which he served. They must have at least a 3.0 GPA in high school. Preference is given to residents of Georgia, Louisiana, or Texas.

Financial data   The amount of this scholarship depends on the availability of funds.

Duration   1 year; may be renewed.

Number awarded   1 each year.

Deadline   April of each year.

[580]
JANE HAWKES LIDDELL PRIZE

Daughters of the Cincinnati
Attn: Scholarship Administrator
20 West 44th Street, Suite 508
New York, NY 10036
(212) 991-9945
E-mail: scholarships@daughters1894.org
Web: www.daughters1894.org/scholarship.htm

Summary   To provide financial assistance to high school seniors who are the daughters of active-duty, deceased, or retired military officers and plan to study the arts in college.

Eligibility   This program is open to high school seniors who are the daughters of career commissioned officers of the regular Army, Navy, Air Force, Coast Guard, or Marine Corps on active duty, deceased, or retired. Applicants must be planning to enroll at a college or university in any state and major in the arts. Along with their application, they must submit an official school transcript, SAT or ACT scores, a letter of recommendation, an essay on their choice of 3 assigned topics, and documentation of financial need.

Financial data   Scholarship amounts have recently averaged $4,000 per year. Funds are paid directly to the college of the student's choice.

Duration   1 year; may be renewed up to 3 additional years, provided the recipient remains in good academic standing.

Number awarded   1 each year.

Deadline   March of each year.

[581]
JANET RUSSELL WHITMAN PRIZE

Daughters of the Cincinnati
Attn: Scholarship Administrator
20 West 44th Street, Suite 508
New York, NY 10036
(212) 991-9945
E-mail: scholarships@daughters1894.org
Web: www.daughters1894.org/scholarship.htm

Summary   To provide financial assistance to high school seniors who are the daughters of active-duty, deceased, or retired military officers and plan to attend college to prepare for a career in public service.

Eligibility   This program is open to high school seniors who are the daughters of career commissioned officers of the regular Army, Navy, Air Force, Coast Guard, or Marine Corps on active duty, deceased, or retired. Applicants must be planning to enroll at a college or university in any state to prepare for a career in public service. Along with their application, they must submit an official school transcript, SAT or ACT scores, a letter of recommendation, an essay on their choice of 3 assigned topics, and documentation of financial need.

Financial data   Scholarship amounts have recently averaged $4,000 per year. Funds are paid directly to the college of the student's choice.

Duration   1 year; may be renewed up to 3 additional years, provided the recipient remains in good academic standing.

Number awarded   1 each year.

Deadline   March of each year.

[582]
JAPANESE AMERICAN VETERANS ASSOCIATION MEMORIAL SCHOLARSHIPS

Japanese American Veterans Association
c/o Terry Shima, Outreach and Education Committee
  Chair
415 Russell Avenue, Number 1005
Gaithersburg, MD 20877
(301) 987-6746   E-mail: ttshima@comcast.net
Web: www.javadc.org

Summary   To provide financial assistance for college or graduate school to relatives of Japanese American veterans and military personnel.

Eligibility   This program is open to graduating high school seniors and students currently working on an undergraduate or graduate degree at a college, university, or school of specialized study. Applicants must be related, by blood or marriage, to 1) a person who served with the 442nd Regimental Combat Team, the 100th Infantry Battalion, or other unit associated with those; 2) a person who served in the U.S. Military Intelligence Service during or after World War II; 3) a person of Japanese ancestry who is serving or has served in the U.S. armed forces and been honorable discharged; or 4) a member of the Japanese American Veterans Association (JAVA) whose membership extends back at least 1 year.

Financial data The stipend is $1,500.

Duration 1 year; recipients may reapply.

Additional information These scholarships, first awarded in 2008, include the following named awards: the Orville C. Shirey Memorial Scholarship, the Joseph Ichiuji Memorial Scholarship, the Phil and Douglas Ishio Scholarship, the Kiyoko Tsuboi Taubkin Scholarship, the Ranger Grant Hirabayashi Memorial Scholarship, the Victor and Teru Matsui Scholarship, the Betty Shima Scholarship, the Mitsugi Kasai Scholarship, and the U.S. Senator Daniel K. Inouye Scholarship.

Number awarded 10 each year.

Deadline April of each year.

[583]
JEANNE RICHTER MEMORIAL SCHOLARSHIP

Hanscom Spouses' Club
Attn: Scholarship Committee Chair
General Delivery
75 Grenier Street, Unit 888
Hanscom AFB, MA 01731
(781) 538-5811   E-mail: scholarships@hanscomsc.org
Web: www.hanscomsc.org/scholarships.html

Summary To provide financial assistance to high school seniors who are children of military personnel or veterans in the Hanscom Air Force Base area of New England and interested in studying education at a college in any state.

Eligibility This program is open to dependents of active-duty, retired, and deceased members of any branch of the armed forces, including Reservists and National Guard members who were activated during the school year. Applicants must be graduating high school seniors who have a valid military identification card and reside within a 60-mile radius of Hanscom Air Force Base (includes eastern Massachusetts, Rhode Island, and southern New Hampshire) or be a dependent whose military sponsor is stationed at Hanscom Air Force Base. They must be planning to attend a 2- or 4-year college or university in any state to work on a degree in education. Along with their application, they must submit a 2-page essay on their educational goals, how their educational experience will help prepare them to pursue future goals, and how they intend to apply their education to better their community. Selection is based on merit.

Financial data Recently, the stipend was $2,500.

Duration 1 year; nonrenewable.

Number awarded 1 each year.

Deadline March of each year.

[584]
JEWELL HILTON BONNER SCHOLARSHIP

Navy League of the United States
Attn: Scholarships
2300 Wilson Boulevard, Suite 200
Arlington, VA 22201-5424
(703) 528-1775   Toll Free: (800) 356-5760
Fax: (703) 528-2333
E-mail: scholarships@navyleague.org
Web: www.navyleague.org/aboutus/scholarship.html

Summary To provide financial assistance for college to dependent children of sea service personnel, especially Native Americans.

Eligibility This program is open to U.S. citizens who are 1) dependents or direct descendants of an active, Reserve, retired, or honorably discharged member of the U.S. sea service (including the Navy, Marine Corps, Coast Guard, or Merchant Marines); or 2) current active members of the Naval Sea Cadet Corps. Applicants must be entering their freshman year at an accredited college or university. They must have a GPA of 3.0 or higher. Along with their application, they must submit transcripts, 2 letters of recommendation, SAT/ACT scores, documentation of financial need, proof of qualifying sea service duty, and a 1-page personal statement on why they should be considered for this scholarship. Preference is given to applicants of Native American heritage.

Financial data The stipend is $2,500 per year.

Duration 4 years, provided the recipient maintains a GPA of 3.0 or higher.

Number awarded 1 each year.

Deadline February of each year.

[585]
JEWISH WAR VETERANS NATIONAL YOUTH ACHIEVEMENT PROGRAM

Jewish War Veterans of the U.S.A.
1811 R Street, N.W.
Washington, DC 20009-1659
(202) 265-6280   Fax: (202) 234-5662
E-mail: jwv@jwv.org
Web: www.jwv.org

Summary To provide financial assistance for college to descendants of members of the Jewish War Veterans of the U.S.A.

Eligibility This program is open to children, grandchildren, and great-grandchildren of members or of deceased members of Jewish War Veterans in good standing who are high school seniors. Applicants must have been accepted by an accredited college, university, community college, or hospital school of nursing as a freshman. Selection is based on academic achievement, SAT and/or ACT test scores, class standing, and extracurricular and community activities.

Financial data This program awards the Seymour and Phyllis Shore Memorial Grant of $1,500, the Robert and Rebecca Rubin Memorial Grant of $1,250, the Bernard Rotberg Memorial Grant of $1,000, and the Edith, Louis, and Max S. Millen Memorial Athletic Grant of $1,000.

Duration 1 year; nonrenewable.

Number awarded 4 each year.

Deadline Applications must be submitted to the department commander by April of each year.

[586]
JOAN KATKUS MEMORIAL SCHOLARSHIP

Ladies Auxiliary to the Veterans of Foreign Wars-
  Department of Alaska
c/o Benitia Johnson
35765 Edginton Road
Soldotna, AK 99669
(907) 262-1262   E-mail: benitia55@yahoo.com
Web: www.aklavfw.org/Forms.html

Summary To provide financial assistance to children of veterans in Alaska who are interested in attending college in any state.

Eligibility This program is open to the children of veterans in Alaska who are attending or planning to attend a college or university in any state. Applicants must submit a letter than includes a description of their commitment to higher education, why receiving this scholarship would be important to them, the course of study they plan to pursue, when they will be utilizing the funding, where they plan to study, their financial need, and how the scholarship will help them achieve their educational goals.

Financial data The stipend is $2,000.

Duration 1 year.

Additional information This program began in 2011.

Number awarded 1 each year.

Deadline February of each year.

[587]
JOANNE HOLBROOK PATTON MILITARY SPOUSE SCHOLARSHIP PROGRAM

National Military Family Association, Inc.
Attn: Spouse Scholarship Program
2500 North Van Dorn Street, Suite 102
Alexandria, VA 22302-1601
(703) 931-NMFA　　　　　Toll Free: (800) 260-0218
Fax: (703) 931-4600
E-mail: scholarships@militaryfamily.org
Web: www.militaryfamily.org

Summary To provide financial assistance for undergraduate or graduate study to spouses of active and retired military personnel.

Eligibility This program is open to the spouses of military personnel (active, retired, Reserve, Guard, or survivor). Applicants must be attending or planning to attend an accredited postsecondary institution to work on an undergraduate or graduate degree, professional certification, vocational training, GED or ESL, or other postsecondary training. They may enroll part or full time and on-campus or online. Along with their application, they must submit an essay on a question that changes annually; recently, applicants were asked to write about what they like most about the health care they are receiving as a military family member, what they like the least, and what they would recommend to change it. Selection is based on that essay, community involvement, and academic achievement.

Financial data The stipend is $1,000. Funds are paid directly to the educational institution to be used for tuition, fees, and school room and board. Support is not provided for books, rent, or previous education loans.

Duration 1 year; recipients may reapply.

Additional information This program began in 2004.

Number awarded Varies each year; recently, 254 were awarded.

Deadline January of each year.

[588]
JOHN A. HIGH CHILD WELFARE SCHOLARSHIP ENDOWMENT FUND

American Legion
Department of New Hampshire
121 South Fruit Street
Concord, NH 03301
(603) 856-8951　　　　　Fax: (603) 856-8943
E-mail: adjutantnh@nhlegion.com
Web: www.nhlegion.com/page215.html

Summary To provide financial assistance to the sons of members of the New Hampshire Department of the American Legion or American Legion Auxiliary who plan to attend college in any state.

Eligibility This program is open to male seniors graduating from high schools in New Hampshire who plan to attend college in any state. Applicants must be the son of a deceased veteran or of parents who have been members of the American Legion or the American Legion Auxiliary in New Hampshire for 3 continuous years. Along with their application, they must submit a 300-word essay on what this scholarship would mean to them. Selection is based on academic record (20%), Americanism (10%), financial need (50%), and character (20%).

Financial data The stipend is $2,000.

Duration 1 year.

Number awarded 1 each year.

Deadline April of each year.

[589]
JOHN CORNELIUS/MAX ENGLISH MEMORIAL SCHOLARSHIP AWARD

Marine Corps Tankers Association
c/o Stephen Chambers, Scholarship Chair
1922 Freeman Street
Oceanside, CA 92054
Web: www.usmarinetankers.org/scholarship-program

Summary To provide financial assistance for college or graduate school to children and grandchildren of members of the Marine Corps Tankers Association and to Marine and Navy personnel currently serving in tank units.

Eligibility This program is open to high school seniors and graduates who are children, grandchildren, or under the guardianship of an active, Reserve, retired, or honorably discharged Marine who served in a tank unit. Marine or Navy Corpsmen currently assigned to tank units are also eligible. Applicants must be enrolled or planning to enroll full time at a college or graduate school. Their parent or grandparent must be a member of the Marine Corps Tankers Association or, if not a member, must join if the application is accepted. Along with their application, they must submit an essay on their educational goals, future aspirations, and concern for the future of our society and for the peoples of the world. Selection is based on that essay, academic record, school activities, leadership potential, and community service.

Financial data The stipend is at least $2,000 per year.

Duration 1 year; recipients may reapply.

Number awarded Varies each year; recently, 15 were awarded.

Deadline March of each year.

[590]
JOHN J. GUENTHER MERIT SCHOLARSHIP

Marine Corps Intelligence Association, Inc.
Attn: Marine Corps Intelligence Educational Foundation
P.O. Box 1028
Quantico, VA 22134-1028
E-mail: scholarship@mcia-inc.org
Web: www.mcia-inc.org/MCIEFINC.html

Summary To provide financial assistance for college to members of the Marine Corps Intelligence Association (MCIA) and their dependent children.

Eligibility This program is open to current MCIA members, their dependent children, and their survivors. Applicants must be attending or planning to attend an accredited 4-year college or university as a full-time student. They must submit a 300-word essay on a risk that has led to a significant change in their personal or intellectual life, the most challenging obstacles they have had to overcome and what they learned from the experience, and where they envision themselves in 10 years. Selection is based on the essay, academic achievement, extracurricular activities, and work experience. Financial need is not considered.

Financial data The stipend is at least $1,000.

Duration 1 year.

Additional information Membership in the MCIA is open to Marine Corps intelligence personnel, including active duty, Reserve, and retired.

Number awarded At least 1 each year.

Deadline July of each year.

[591]
JOHN KEYS KENTUCKY SONS OF THE AMERICAN LEGION SCHOLARSHIP

Sons of the American Legion
Detachment of Kentucky
Independence Squadron 275
P.O. Box 18791
Erlanger, KY 41018-0791
E-mail: SAL275@fuse.net
Web: moonbrothers275.org

Summary To provide financial assistance for college in designated states to members of Kentucky squadrons of the Sons of the American Legion and to veterans who are residents of Kentucky.

Eligibility This program is open to 1) members of the Sons of the American Legion who belong to a squadron in Kentucky; and 2) honorably-discharged veterans of the U.S. armed forces who are residents of Kentucky (regardless of length or period of service). Applicants must be enrolled (and have completed some course work) at a postsecondary institution in Kentucky or a bordering state (Illinois, Indiana, Missouri, Ohio, Tennessee, Virginia, or West Virginia). Along with their application, they must submit a letter explaining their background, career objectives, current educational program, and financial need.

Financial data The stipend varies, depending on the availability of funds; recently, they averaged $1,000. Awards are made directly to the recipient's institution.

Duration 1 year.

Additional information This program began in 1988.

Number awarded 1 or 2 each year; since the program began, it has awarded more than 60 scholarships.

Deadline Applications may be submitted at any time.

[592]
JOLLY GREEN MEMORIAL SCHOLARSHIP

Jolly Green Association
Attn: Secretary
P.O. Box 965
O'Fallon, IL 62269-0965
E-mail: bill6100@aol.com
Web: www.jollygreen.org

Summary To provide financial assistance for college to dependents of current and former members of the Air Force Combat Rescue or Support Forces.

Eligibility This program is open to high school seniors who are dependents of current or former uniformed members of the USAF Combat Rescue or Support Forces. Applicants must have taken the ACT or SAT examinations and be eligible for admission to the college or university of their choice. Selection is based on academic achievement (40%), scholastic or public service achievements (10%), and financial need (50%).

Financial data A stipend is awarded (amount not specified).

Duration 1 year.

Number awarded 1 or more each year.

Deadline April of each year.

[593]
JOSEPH A. MCALINDEN DIVERS SCHOLARSHIP

Navy-Marine Corps Relief Society
Attn: Education Division
875 North Randolph Street, Suite 225
Arlington, VA 22203-1757
(703) 696-4960   Fax: (703) 696-0144
E-mail: education@nmcrs.org
Web: www.nmcrs.org

Summary To provide financial assistance to current and former Navy and Marine Corps divers and their families who are interested in completing diver training or working on an undergraduate degree in a field related to ocean agriculture.

Eligibility This program is open to 1) active-duty and retired sailors and Marines (including Reservists serving on active duty for more than 90 days) completing a program for advanced diver training, certification, or licensure; 2) the children and spouses of active-duty or retired sailors and Marines (including Reservists serving on active duty for more than 90 days) completing a program for advanced diver training, certification, or licensure; and 3) the children and spouses of active-duty or retired sailors and Marines (including Reservists serving on active duty for more than 90 days) working full time on their first undergraduate degree in oceanography, ocean agriculture, aquaculture, or a related field. Financial need is considered in the selection process.

Financial data The stipend ranges from $500 to $3,000, depending on the need of the recipient.

Duration 1 year.

Number awarded 1 or more each year.

Deadline Applications may be submitted at any time.

[594]
JOSEPH H. ELLINWOOD SCHOLARSHIP

American Legion
Department of Massachusetts
State House
24 Beacon Street, Room 546-2
Boston, MA 02133-1044
(617) 727-2966 Fax: (617) 727-2969
E-mail: masslegion@verizon.net
Web: www.masslegion.org

Summary To provide financial assistance to the children and grandchildren of members of the American Legion in Massachusetts who plan to study nursing at a school in any state.

Eligibility This program is open to the children and grandchildren of members in good standing in the American Legion's Department of Massachusetts (or who were members in good standing at the time of death). Applicants must be entering their freshman year at a college or university in any state to prepare for a career as a nurse. Along with their application, they must submit a 100-word essay on their long-range goal and why they want to go to college. Financial need is considered in the selection process.

Financial data The stipend is $1,000. Funds are paid directly to the recipient.

Duration 1 year.

Number awarded 1 each year.

Deadline March of each year.

[595]
JOSEPH P. GAVENONIS SCHOLARSHIPS

American Legion
Department of Pennsylvania
Attn: Scholarship Endowment Fund
P.O. Box 2324
Harrisburg, PA 17105-2324
(717) 730-9100 Fax: (717) 975-2836
E-mail: hq@pa-legion.com
Web: www.pa-legion.com

Summary To provide financial assistance to the children of members of the American Legion in Pennsylvania who plan to attend college in the state.

Eligibility This program is open to seniors at high schools in Pennsylvania who are planning to attend a 4-year college or university in the state. Applicants must have a parent who has been in the military or is in the military and is a member of an American Legion Post in Pennsylvania. First preference is given to the children of Legion members who are deceased, killed in action, or missing in action. Financial need is considered in the selection process.

Financial data The stipend is $1,000 per year.

Duration 4 years, provided the recipient maintains a GPA of 2.5 or higher each semester.

Number awarded 1 or more each year.

Deadline May of each year.

[596]
JUDITH HAUPT MEMBER'S CHILD SCHOLARSHIP

Navy Wives Clubs of America
c/o NSA Mid-South
P.O. Box 54022
Millington, TN 38054-0022
Toll Free: (866) 511-NWCA
E-mail: nwca@navywivesclubsofamerica.org
Web: www.navywivesclubsofamerica.org/scholarships

Summary To provide financial assistance for college to the children of members of the Navy Wives Clubs of America (NWCA).

Eligibility This program is open to students currently enrolled at accredited college or university whose parent has been an NWCA member for at least 1 year. Along with their application, they must submit a brief statement on why they feel they should be awarded this scholarship and any special circumstances (financial or other) they wish to have considered. Financial need is also considered in the selection process.

Financial data A stipend is provided (amount not specified).

Duration 1 year.

Additional information Membership in the NWCA is open to spouses of enlisted personnel serving in the Navy, Marine Corps, Coast Guard, and the active Reserve units of those services; spouses of enlisted personnel who have been honorably discharged, retired, or transferred to the Fleet Reserve on completion of duty; and widows of enlisted personnel in those services.

Number awarded 1 or more each year.

Deadline May of each year.

[597]
JUNIOR GIRLS SCHOLARSHIPS

Ladies Auxiliary to the Veterans of Foreign Wars
Attn: Director of Programs
406 West 34th Street, Tenth Floor
Kansas City, MO 64111
(816) 561-8655 Fax: (816) 931-4753
E-mail: info@ladiesauxvfw.org
Web: www.ladiesauxvfw.org/programs-page/scholarships

Summary To provide financial assistance for college to outstanding members of a Junior Girls Unit of the Ladies Auxiliary to the Veterans of Foreign Wars.

Eligibility Applicants must have been active members of a unit for 1 year, have held an office in the unit, and be between 13 and 16 years of age. Previous winners are not eligible, although former applicants who did not receive scholarships may reapply. Selection is based on participation in the Junior Girls Unit (40 points), school activities (30 points), and academic achievement (30 points).

Financial data The winner receives a $7,500 scholarship. Funds are paid directly to the college of the recipient's choice. In addition, $100 is awarded to each Junior Girl who is selected as the department winner and entered in the national competition.

Duration 1 year.

Number awarded 1 each year.

Deadline March of each year.

[598]
KANSAS TUITION WAIVER FOR DEPENDENTS AND SPOUSES OF DECEASED MILITARY PERSONNEL

Kansas Board of Regents
Attn: Student Financial Assistance
1000 S.W. Jackson Street, Suite 520
Topeka, KS 66612-1368
(785) 296-3518   Fax: (785) 296-0983
E-mail: loldhamburns@ksbor.org
Web: www.kansasregents.org/scholarships_and_grants

Summary To provide financial assistance for college to residents of Kansas whose parent or spouse died on active military service after September 11, 2001.

Eligibility This program is open to residents of Kansas who are the dependent children or spouses of members of the U.S. armed forces who died on or after September 11, 2001 while, and as a result of, serving on active military duty. The deceased military member must have been a resident of Kansas at the time of death. Applicants must be enrolled or planning to enroll at a public educational institution in Kansas, including area vocational/technical schools and colleges, community colleges, the state universities, and Washburn University.

Financial data Qualifying students are permitted to enroll at an approved Kansas institution without payment of tuition or fees. They are responsible for other costs, such as books, room, and board.

Duration 1 year; may be renewed for a total of 10 semesters of undergraduate study.

Additional information This program began in 2005.

Number awarded Varies each year.

Deadline Deadline not specified.

[599]
KANSAS VFW ENDOWMENT SCHOLARSHIP

Veterans of Foreign Wars of the United States-
    Department of Kansas
Attn: VFW Endowment Association
115 S.W. Gage Boulevard
P.O. Box 1008
Topeka, KS 66601-1008
(785) 272-6463   Fax: (785) 272-2629
E-mail: ksvfwhq@kvfw.kscoxmail.com
Web: www.ksvfw.org/programs.html

Summary To provide financial assistance to residents of Kansas who are related to members of the Veterans of Foreign Wars (VFW) or its Ladies Auxiliary and interested in attending college in any state.

Eligibility This program is open to residents of Kansas who are graduating high school seniors, holders of a high school diploma equivalent, or students already enrolled at a college, university, or vocational school in any state. Applicants must be the child or grandchild of an active or deceased member of the VFW or its Ladies Auxiliary. Along with their application, they must submit transcripts that include ACT scores (the ACT score requirement may be waived if the applicant is 25 years of age or older), information on extracurricular activities, statements on their career plans reasons for furthering their education, and documentation of financial need.

Financial data Stipends range from $500 to $2,000.

Duration 1 year; may be renewed up to 3 additional years.

Number awarded 1 or more each year.

Deadline January of each year.

[600]
KATHERN F. GRUBER SCHOLARSHIPS

Blinded Veterans Association
477 H Street, N.W.
Washington, DC 20001-2694
(202) 371-8880   Toll Free: (800) 669-7079
Fax: (202) 371-8258   E-mail: temanuel@bva.org
Web: www.bva.org/services.html

Summary To provide financial assistance for undergraduate or graduate study to immediate family members of blinded veterans and servicemembers.

Eligibility This program is open to dependent children, grandchildren, and spouses of blinded veterans and active-duty blinded servicemembers of the U.S. armed forces. The veteran or servicemember must be legally blind; the blindness may be either service-connected or nonservice-connected. Applicants must have been accepted or be currently enrolled as a full-time student in an undergraduate or graduate program at an accredited institution of higher learning. Along with their application, they must submit a 300-word essay on their career goals and aspirations. Financial need is not considered in the selection process.

Financial data The stipend is $2,000; funds are intended to be used to cover the student's expenses, including tuition, other academic fees, books, dormitory fees, and cafeteria fees. Funds are paid directly to the recipient's school.

Duration 1 year; recipients may reapply for up to 3 additional years.

Number awarded 6 each year.

Deadline April of each year.

[601]
KENTUCKIANA POST SAME SCHOLARSHIP

Society of American Military Engineers-Kentuckiana Post
c/o Kristen Crumpton, Scholarship Committee Co-Chair
URS Corporation
325 West Main Street, Suite 1200
Louisville, KY 40202
(502) 569-2301   Fax: (502) 569-2304
E-mail: kristen.crumpton@urs.com
Web: posts.same.org/kentuckiana

Summary To provide financial assistance to residents of Indiana and Kentucky who are majoring in engineering in college (especially those who are 1) currently serving in the military, 2) the family members of current service personnel, or ROTC students).

Eligibility This program is open to students who fall into 1 of the following categories: a dependent of a current Society of American Military Engineers (SAME) Kentuckiana Post member; an employee or dependent of an employee of a Kentuckiana Post sustaining member firm; an employee or dependent of an employee of the Louisville District Corps of Engineers; a current student member of the Kentuckiana Post; a student whose permanent home address is within the Kentuckiana Post's geographic boundary (Kentucky and Indiana) and who is enrolled in an ROTC program or military academy; or an individual on active duty or the dependent of an individual on active duty who is assigned to an installation within the Kentuckiana Post's geographic boundary. Applicants must be U.S. citizens accepted at an undergraduate ABET-accredited engineering program; undergraduates enrolled in engineering technology programs are not eligible. Along with their application, they must submit an essay of 300 to 500 words on a topic that changes annually; recently, applicants were invited to write on how winning this scholarship would promote a promising future for their engineering career and how they might envision that career supporting the mission of SAME. Financial need is not considered in the selection process.

Financial data The stipend is $4,000 per year.

Duration 1 year; may be renewed 1 additional year.

Additional information Recipients are required to attend the scholarship luncheon ceremony in Louisville in May.

Number awarded Varies each year; recently, 6 were awarded.

Deadline March of each year.

[602]
KENTUCKY VETERANS TUITION WAIVER PROGRAM

Kentucky Department of Veterans Affairs
Attn: Tuition Waiver Coordinator
321 West Main Street, Suite 390
Louisville, KY 40202
(502) 595-4447   Toll Free: (800) 928-4012 (within KY)
Fax: (502) 595-3369
Web: www.veterans.ky.gov

Summary To provide financial assistance for college to the children, spouses, or unremarried widow(er)s of disabled or deceased Kentucky veterans.

Eligibility This program is open to the children, stepchildren, spouses, and unremarried widow(er)s of veterans who are residents of Kentucky (or were residents at the time of their death). The qualifying veteran must meet 1 of the following conditions: 1) died on active duty (regardless of wartime service); 2) died as a result of a service-connected disability (regardless of wartime service); 3) has a 100% service-connected disability; 4) is totally disabled (nonservice-connected) with wartime service; or 5) is deceased and served during wartime. The military service may have been as a member of the U.S. armed forces, the Kentucky National Guard, or a Reserve component; service in the Guard or Reserves must have been on state active duty, active duty for training, inactive duty training, or active duty with the U.S. armed forces. Children of veterans must be under 26 years of age; no age limit applies to spouses or unremarried widow(er)s. All applicants must be attending or planning to attend a 2-year, 4-year, or vocational technical school operated and funded by the Kentucky Department of Education.

Financial data Eligible dependents and survivors are exempt from tuition and matriculation fees at any state-supported institution of higher education in Kentucky.

Duration Tuition is waived until the recipient completes 45 months of training, receives a college degree, or (in the case of children of veterans) reaches 26 years of age, whichever comes first. Spouses and unremarried widow(er)s are not subject to the age limitation.

Number awarded Varies each year.

Deadline Deadline not specified.

[603]
KIM AND HAROLD LOUIE FAMILY FOUNDATION SCHOLARSHIPS

Kim and Harold Louie Family Foundation
445 Pullman Road
Hillsborough, CA 94010
(650) 491-3434   Fax: (650) 490-3153
E-mail: louiefoundation@gmail.com
Web: www.louiefamilyfoundation.org

Summary To provide financial assistance for college to high school seniors who have faced special challenges in completing their education.

Eligibility This program is open to graduating high school seniors who plan to enroll either full time or at least substantial part time at an accredited college, university, or vocational program in any state. Applicants must be able to demonstrate outstanding personal achievements, academic merit, leadership qualities, and/or community service. They must have a GPA of 3.2 or higher and an SAT score of at least 1800 or an ACT score of at least 25. Special consideration is given to students who have a demonstrated financial need, whose parents did not attend college, who have a documented disability, who have overcome significant adversity, or who have parents that are U.S. veterans or are currently in the U.S. military. U.S. citizenship or legal resident status is required.

Financial data Stipends vary each year; recently, they averaged approximately $3,000.

Duration 1 year.

Number awarded Varies each year; recently, 33 were awarded. The foundation expects to award $100,000 in scholarships each year.

Deadline March of each year.

[604]
KOREAN WAR VETERAN DESCENDANT SCHOLARSHIPS

Korean American Scholarship Foundation
Eastern Region
1952 Gallows Road, Suite 310
Vienna, VA 22182
(703) 748-5935   Fax: (703) 748-1874
E-mail: erc.scholarship@kasf.org
Web: www.kasf.org/eastern

Summary To provide financial assistance to the descendants of the Korean War from any state who are working on an undergraduate or graduate degree in any field at a school in eastern states.

Eligibility This program is open to direct descendants of veterans who served in Korea from June 25, 1950 to January 31, 1955. Applicants may reside in any state but they must be enrolled as full-time undergraduate or graduate students at a college or university in Delaware, District of Columbia, Kentucky, Maryland, North Carolina, Pennsylvania, Virginia, or West Virginia. Selection is based on academic achievement (40%), an essay (40%), and recommendations (20%).

Financial data The stipend is $2,000.

Duration 1 year.

Additional information This program began in 2013.

Number awarded Varies each year.

Deadline July of each year.

[605]
KOREAN WAR VETERANS ASSOCIATION SCHOLARSHIPS

Korean War Veterans Association
Attn: Scholarship Coordinator
13730 Loumont Street
Whittier, CA 90601

Summary To provide financial assistance for college to descendants of Army veterans who served in Korea during or prior to the war there.

Eligibility This program is open to the children, grandchildren, and great-grandchildren of veterans who served on active duty in the U.S. Army in Korea between August 15, 1945 and December 31, 1955. Applicants must be attending or planning to attend an accredited college or university. Along with their application, they must submit an essay describing their educational and career goals, why they think they should receive this scholarship, and where they learned about it. Selection is based on academic achievement (GPA of 2.75 or higher), extracurricular activities, and financial need.

Financial data The stipend depends on the need of the recipient, to a maximum of $5,000 per year.

Duration 1 year; may be renewed up to 3 additional years or until completion of a bachelor's degree.

Number awarded Varies each year; recently, 5 were awarded.

Deadline April of each year.

[606]
LA FRA NATIONAL PRESIDENT'S SCHOLARSHIP

Ladies Auxiliary of the Fleet Reserve Association
c/o Sandra Robbins, National Scholarship Chair
2712 Holly Ridge Road
Orange Park, FL 32073
(904) 269-2136   E-mail: slgr@bellsouth.net
Web: www.la-fra.org/scholarship.html

Summary To provide financial assistance for college to the children and grandchildren of naval personnel.

Eligibility Eligible to apply for these scholarships are the children and grandchildren of Navy, Marine, Coast Guard, active Fleet Reserve, Fleet Marine Corps Reserve, and Coast Guard Reserve personnel on active duty, retired with pay, or deceased while on active duty or retired with pay. Applicants must submit an essay on their life experiences, career objectives, and what motivated them to select those objectives. Selection is based on academic record, financial need, extracurricular activities, leadership skills, and participation in community activities. U.S. citizenship is required.

Financial data The stipend is $2,500.

Duration 1 year; may be renewed.

Number awarded 1 each year.

Deadline April of each year.

[607]
LA FRA SCHOLARSHIP

Ladies Auxiliary of the Fleet Reserve Association
c/o Sandra Robbins, National Scholarship Chair
2712 Holly Ridge Road
Orange Park, FL 32073
(904) 269-2136   E-mail: slgr@bellsouth.net
Web: www.la-fra.org/scholarship.html

Summary To provide financial assistance for college to the daughters and granddaughters of naval personnel.

Eligibility Eligible to apply for these scholarships are the daughters and granddaughters of Navy, Marine, Coast Guard, active Fleet Reserve, Fleet Marine Corps Reserve, and Coast Guard Reserve personnel on active duty, retired with pay, or deceased while on active duty or retired with pay. Applicants must submit an essay on their life experiences, career objectives, and what motivated them to select those objectives. Selection is based on academic record, financial need, extracurricular activities, leadership skills, and participation in community activities. U.S. citizenship is required.

Financial data The stipend is $2,500.

Duration 1 year; may be renewed.

Number awarded 1 each year.

Deadline April of each year.

[608]
LADIES AUXILIARY VFW CONTINUING EDUCATION SCHOLARSHIPS

Ladies Auxiliary to the Veterans of Foreign Wars
Attn: Director of Programs
406 West 34th Street, Tenth Floor
Kansas City, MO 64111
(816) 561-8655   Fax: (816) 931-4753
E-mail: info@ladiesauxvfw.org
Web: www.ladiesauxvfw.org/programs-page/scholarships

Summary To provide financial assistance for college to members of Ladies Auxiliary to the Veterans of Foreign Wars (VFW) and their families.

Eligibility This program is open to members of the Ladies Auxiliary VFW and their children and spouses. Applicants must be 18 years of age or older and planning to work on a college degree or a career direction at a technical school. Along with their application, they must submit a 300-word essay describing their commitment to their goals and how this scholarship will help them attain those goals. The qualifying member must have belonged to the Auxiliary for at least 1 year prior to application. Financial need is considered in the selection process.

Financial data The stipend is $1,000. Funds are paid directly to the college or vocational school.

Duration 1 year.

Number awarded 4 each year: 1 in each Ladies Auxiliary VFW Conference.

Deadline February of each year.

[609]
LAURA BLACKBURN MEMORIAL SCHOLARSHIP

American Legion Auxiliary
Department of Kentucky
P.O. Box 5435
Frankfort, KY 40602-5435
(502) 352-2380   Fax: (502) 352-2381
Web: www.kyamlegionaux.org/page17.html

Summary   To provide financial assistance to descendants of veterans in Kentucky who plan to attend college in any state.

Eligibility   This program is open to the children, grandchildren, and great-grandchildren of veterans who served in the armed forces during eligibility dates for membership in the American Legion. Applicants must be Kentucky residents enrolled in their senior year at an accredited high school. They must be planning to attend a college or university in any state. Selection is based on academic achievement (40%), character (20%), leadership (20%), and Americanism (20%).

Financial data   The stipend is $1,000.

Duration   1 year.

Number awarded   1 each year.

Deadline   March of each year.

[610]
LEO A. SEIGEL-DR. PHILIP SHAPIRO EDUCATION GRANT

Jewish War Veterans of the U.S.A.-New Jersey Chapter
Attn: Department Commander
135 West Hanover Street, Second Floor
Trenton, NJ 08618
(609) 396-2508   E-mail: jwv.new.jersey@gmail.com
Web: www.jwv-nj.org/forms.html

Summary   To provide financial assistance to high school seniors in New Jersey who are descendants of members of the Jewish War Veterans (JWV) of the U.S.A and planning to attend college in any state.

Eligibility   This program is open to seniors graduating from public or private high schools in New Jersey and planning to attend an accredited college. university, community college, or hospital school of nursing in any state. Applicants must be the child, grandchild, or great-grandchild of a veteran who has been a JWV member for at least 3 consecutive years or, if deceased, was a member at time of death. They must rank in the top 25% of their class. Selection is based on class standing, SAT or ACT scores, GPA, and participation in extracurricular activities (school, Jewish community, and community at large).

Financial data   Stipends are $2,000, $1,500, or $1,000.

Duration   1 year.

Number awarded   3 each year: 1 each at $2,000, $1,500, and $1,000.

Deadline   May of each year.

[611]
LIEUTENANT GENERAL CHUBB AWARD

Hanscom Spouses' Club
Attn: Scholarship Committee Chair
General Delivery
75 Grenier Street, Unit 888
Hanscom AFB, MA 01731
(781) 538-5811   E-mail: scholarships@hanscomsc.org
Web: www.hanscomsc.org/scholarships.html

Summary   To provide financial assistance to high school seniors who are children of military personnel or veterans in the Hanscom Air Force Base area of New England and interested in studying engineering or computer science at a college in any state.

Eligibility   This program is open to dependents of active-duty, retired, and deceased members of any branch of the armed forces, including Reservists and National Guard members who were activated during the school year. Applicants must be graduating high school seniors who have a valid military identification card and reside within a 60-mile radius of Hanscom Air Force Base (includes eastern Massachusetts, Rhode Island, and southern New Hampshire) or be a dependent whose military sponsor is stationed at Hanscom Air Force Base. They must be planning to attend a 2- or 4-year college or university in any state to work on a degree in engineering or computer science. Along with their application, they must submit a 2-page essay on their educational goals, how their educational experience will help prepare them to pursue future goals, and how they intend to apply their education to better their community. Selection is based on merit.

Financial data   Recently, the stipend was $2,000.

Duration   1 year; nonrenewable.

Additional information   This program is sponsored by the Military Affairs Council/North Suburban Chamber of Commerce.

Number awarded   1 each year.

Deadline   March of each year.

[612]
LIEUTENANT GENERAL CLARENCE L. HUEBNER SCHOLARSHIPS

Society of the First Infantry Division
Attn: 1st Infantry Division Foundation
P.O. Box 607
Ambler, PA 19002
(215) 654-1969   Fax: (215) 654-0392
E-mail: Fdn1IDChair@aol.com
Web: www.1stid.org/scholarships.php

Summary   To provide financial support for college to the children or grandchildren of members of the First Infantry Division.

Eligibility   This program is open to high school seniors who are the children or grandchildren of soldiers who served in the First Infantry Division of the U.S. Army. Applicants must submit academic transcripts, letters of recommendation, and a 200-word essay on a major problem facing the country today and their recommendations for the solution of the problem. Selection is based on the essay, academic achievement, extracurricular activities, community service, and work experience.

Financial data   The stipend is $2,500 per year, payable to the recipient's school annually.

Duration 4 years.

Number awarded Varies each year; recently, 5 were awarded.

Deadline May of each year.

[613]
LILLIAN CAMPBELL MEDICAL SCHOLARSHIP

Veterans of Foreign Wars of the United States-
    Department of Wisconsin
P.O. Box 6128
Monona, WI 53716-0128
(608) 221-5276   Fax: (608) 221-5277
E-mail: wivfw@att.net
Web: www.vfwofwi.com/downloadable-forms

Summary To provide financial assistance to students working on a degree in a medical field in Wisconsin who served in the military or are related to a person who did.

Eligibility This program is open to students who have completed at least 1 year of study in Wisconsin in a program in nursing, pharmacy, physician assistant, medical or surgical technology, physical or occupational therapy, dental assisting, radiology, or other related medical profession. Applicants or a member of their immediate family (parent, sibling, child, spouse, or grandparent) must have served in the military. They must have a high school diploma or GED but may be of any age. Along with their application, they must submit a 200-word essay on why they are studying this medical profession. Financial need is considered in the selection process.

Financial data The stipend is $1,000.

Duration 1 year.

Number awarded 1 or more each year.

Deadline April of each year.

[614]
LILLIE LOIS FORD SCHOLARSHIPS

American Legion
Department of Missouri
3341 American Avenue
P.O. Box 179
Jefferson City, MO 65102-0179
(573) 893-2353   Toll Free: (800) 846-9023
Fax: (573) 893-2980   E-mail: info@missourilegion.org
Web: www.missourilegion.org/molegion_019.htm

Summary To provide financial assistance for college to descendants of Missouri veterans who have participated in specified American Legion programs.

Eligibility This program is open to the unmarried children, grandchildren, and great-grandchildren under 21 years of age of honorably-discharged Missouri veterans who served at least 90 days on active duty. Applicants must be enrolled or planning to enroll at an accredited college or university in any state as a full-time student. Boys must have attended a complete session of Missouri Boys State or Cadet Patrol Academy. Girls must have attended a complete session of Missouri Girls State or Cadet Patrol Academy. Financial need is considered in the selection process.

Financial data The stipend is $1,000.

Duration 1 year (the first year of college).

Number awarded 2 each year: 1 for a boy and 1 for a girl.

Deadline April of each year.

[615]
LITTLE ROCK SPOUSES' CLUB HIGH SCHOOL SCHOLARSHIPS

Little Rock Spouses' Club
Attn: Scholarship Committee
P.O. Box 1264
Jacksonville, AR 72078
E-mail: littlerockspousesclub@gmail.com
Web: www.littlerockspouses.com/?page_id=37

Summary To provide financial assistance to high school seniors in Arkansas who are children of current or former members of the armed forces and are planning to attend college in any state.

Eligibility This program is open to seniors graduating from high schools in Arkansas who are planning to enroll full time at an accredited college or university in any state. Applicants must be a dependent child of an active duty or retired member of the armed services, including full-time Guard or Reserves. Selection is based on transcripts (including ACT/SAT scores), 2 letters of recommendation, and a 500-word essay on their goals and how this scholarship would help them achieve those.

Financial data A stipend is awarded (amount not specified).

Duration 1 year.

Number awarded Varies each year; recently, this organization awarded $11,000 in scholarships.

Deadline March of each year.

[616]
LITTLE ROCK SPOUSES' CLUB SPOUSES SCHOLARSHIPS

Little Rock Spouses' Club
Attn: Scholarship Committee
P.O. Box 1264
Jacksonville, AR 72078
E-mail: littlerockspousesclub@gmail.com
Web: www.littlerockspouses.com/?page_id=37

Summary To provide financial assistance to residents of Arkansas who are spouses of current or former members of the armed forces and interested in attending college in any state.

Eligibility This program is open to residents of Arkansas who have a high school diploma or GED equivalent and are enrolled or planning to enroll at an accredited college or university in any state. Applicants must be a spouse of a full-time active duty, Guard, Reserve, or retired member of the armed services, stationed at Little Rock Air Force Base. Selection is based on transcripts (including ACT/SAT scores if graduated from high school less than 3 years ago), 2 letters of recommendation, and a 500-word essay on their goals and how this scholarship would help them achieve those.

Financial data A stipend is awarded (amount not specified).

Duration 1 year.

Number awarded Varies each year; recently, this organization awarded $11,000 in scholarships.

Deadline March of each year.

[617]
LOLA B. CURRY SCHOLARSHIP

United Daughters of the Confederacy
Attn: Second Vice President General
328 North Boulevard
Richmond, VA 23220-4008
(804) 355-1636   Fax: (804) 353-1396
E-mail: jamieretired@sbcglobal.net
Web: www.hqudc.org/Scholarships/index.htm

Summary To provide financial assistance to lineal descendants of Confederate veterans in Alabama who are interested in attending college in the state.

Eligibility Eligible to apply for these scholarships are Alabama residents who are lineal descendants of worthy Confederates or collateral descendants who are members of the Children of the Confederacy or the United Daughters of the Confederacy. Applicants must submit a family financial report and certified proof of the Confederate record of 1 ancestor, with the company and regiment in which he served. They must have a GPA of 3.0 or higher in high school and be attending college in Alabama.

Financial data The amount of the scholarship depends on the availability of funds.

Duration 1 year; may be renewed.

Number awarded 1 each year.

Deadline April of each year.

[618]
LORETTA CORNETT-HUFF SCHOLARSHIPS

Council of College and Military Educators
c/o Kenneth D. McRae, Scholarship Committee Chair
Mississippi State University
G.V. "Sonny" Montgomery Center for America's Veterans
126 Magruder Street
P. O. Drawer 6283
Mississippi State, MS 39762
(662) 325-6719   Fax: (662) 325-6723
E-mail: scholarship@ccmeonline.aspx
Web: www.ccmeonline.org/scholarships

Summary To provide financial assistance to spouses of members of the armed services who are interested in working on an undergraduate or master's degree.

Eligibility This program is open to spouses of members of the uniformed services, including active, National Guard, and Reserves. Applicants must be currently enrolled full time at an accredited institution that is a member of the Council of College and Military Educators (CCME) and working on an associate, bachelor's, or master's degree. Undergraduates must have a GPA of 2.5 or higher and graduate students must have a GPA of 3.0 or higher. Along with their application, they must submit an essay of 400 to 750 words on their most meaningful achievements and how those relate to their field of study and their future goals. Financial need is not considered in the selection process.

Financial data The stipend is $1,000.

Duration 1 year.

Number awarded 5 each year.

Deadline September of each year.

[619]
LOUIS J. SCHOBER MEMORIAL SCHOLARSHIP

Society of American Military Engineers-Louisiana Post
c/o Chris Dunn, Young Members Committee Chair
U.S. Army Corps of Engineers, New Orleans District
7400 Leake Avenue
P.O. Box 60267
New Orleans, LA 70160
(504) 862-1799
E-mail: Christopher.L.Dunn@usace.army.mil
Web: posts.same.org/louisiana/YoungMembers.htm

Summary To provide financial assistance to students from Louisiana majoring in engineering, particularly those who are enrolled in ROTC, are serving or have served in the armed forces, or are children of members of the Society of American Military Engineers (SAME) Louisiana Post.

Eligibility This program is open to students currently working on an undergraduate degree in engineering. Applicants must be either 1) enrolled at a college or university in Louisiana; or 2) the children of a member of the SAME Louisiana Post (who may be studying at a college or university in any state). Graduate students are not eligible; high school seniors may be considered if no suitable college students apply. Selection is based primarily on academic record and demonstration of leadership characteristics; other factors considered are participation in SAME posts and activities, enrollment in an ROTC program, former or current military service, and participation in school and community activities.

Financial data The stipend is $2,000.

Duration 1 year; nonrenewable.

Number awarded 1 or more each year.

Deadline May of each year.

[620]
LOUISIANA EDUCATIONAL BENEFITS FOR CHILDREN, SPOUSES, AND SURVIVING SPOUSES OF VETERANS

Louisiana Department of Veterans Affairs
Attn: Education Program
1885 Wooddale Boulevard, Room 1013
P.O. Box 94095, Capitol Station
Baton Rouge, LA 70804-9095
(225) 219-5000   Toll Free: (877) GEAUX-VA
Fax: (225) 219-5590   E-mail: veteran@la.gov
Web: www.vetaffairs.la.gov/Programs/Education.aspx

Summary To provide financial assistance to children, spouses, and surviving spouses of certain disabled or deceased Louisiana veterans who plan to attend college in the state.

Eligibility This program is open to children (between 16 and 25 years of age), spouses, or surviving spouses of veterans who served during specified periods of wartime and 1) were killed in action or died in active service; 2) died of a service-connected disability; 3) are missing in action (MIA) or a prisoner of war (POW); 4) sustained a disability rated as 90% or more by the U.S. Department of Veterans Affairs; or 5) have been determined to be unemployable as a result of a service-connected disability. Deceased, MIA, and POW veterans must have resided in Louisiana for at least 12 months prior to entry into service. Living disabled veterans must have resided in Louisiana for at least 24 months prior to the child's or spouse's admission into the program.

Financial data Eligible persons accepted as full-time students at Louisiana state-supported colleges, universities, trade schools, or vocational/technical schools are admitted free and are exempt from payment of tuition, laboratory, athletic, medical, and other special fees. Free registration does not cover books, supplies, room and board, or fees assessed by the student body on themselves (such as yearbooks and weekly papers).

Duration Support is provided for a maximum of 4 school years, to be completed in not more than 5 years from date of original entry.

Additional information Attendance must be on a full-time basis. Surviving spouses must remain unremarried and must take advantage of the benefit within 10 years after eligibility is established.

Number awarded Varies each year.

Deadline Applications must be received no later than 3 months prior to the beginning of a semester.

[621]
LT. COL. ROMEO AND JOSEPHINE BASS FERRETTI SCHOLARSHIP

Air Force Association
Attn: Manager, Awards and Scholarships
1501 Lee Highway
Arlington, VA 22209-1198
(703) 247-5800, ext. 4807
Toll Free: (800) 727-3337, ext. 4807
Fax: (703) 247-5853　　　　E-mail: awards@afa.org
Web: www.afa.org

Summary To provide financial assistance to dependents of Air Force enlisted personnel who are high school seniors planning to attend college to major in a field of science, technology, engineering, or mathematics (STEM).

Eligibility This program is open to dependents of Air Force active duty, Reserve, or Air National Guard enlisted personnel who are graduating high school seniors. Applicants must be planning to enroll full time at an accredited institute of higher education to work on an undergraduate degree in any area of STEM. Selection is based on academic achievement, character, and financial need.

Financial data The stipend is $2,500.

Duration 1 year; nonrenewable.

Number awarded Varies each year; recently, 4 were awarded.

Deadline June of each year.

[622]
LT. JOHN J. GRIFFIN/USS EMMONS MEMORIAL SCHOLARSHIP

USS Emmons Association
c/o Thomas Hoffman, Scholarship Committee Chair
3136 Northampton Street
Bethlehem, PA 18020
E-mail: ussemmons@gmail.com
Web: www.ussemmons.org/scholarship

Summary To provide financial assistance for college or graduate school to descendants of crewmembers of the USS Emmons who were killed during World War II.

Eligibility This program is open to 1) direct lineal descendants of crewmembers aboard the USS Emmons when it was destroyed on April 6, 1945 during the battle of Okinawa; and

2) direct lineal descendants of siblings of childless crewmembers of the USS Emmons when it was lost. Applicants must be enrolled or planning to enroll as full-time undergraduate or graduate students. Along with their application, they must submit an essay of 500 to 750 words on a topic that changes annually but relates to the history of the USS Emmons.

Financial data Stipends are $2,000 or $500.

Duration 1 year.

Number awarded 2 each year: 1 at $2,000 and 1 at $500.

Deadline May of each year.

[623]
LT. JON C. LADDA MEMORIAL FOUNDATION SCHOLARSHIP

Lt. Jon C. Ladda Memorial Foundation
P.O. Box 55
Unionville, CT 06085
E-mail: info@jonladda.org
Web: www.jonladda.org/scholarship.htm

Summary To provide financial assistance for college to children of deceased and disabled U.S. Naval Academy graduates and members of the Navy submarine service.

Eligibility This program is open to children of U.S. Naval Academy graduates and members of the U.S. Navy submarine service. The parent must have died on active duty or been medically retired with a 100% disability. Applicants must be enrolled or accepted at a 4-year college or university, including any of the service academies. Along with their application, they must submit an essay on a topic that changes annually. Selection is based on academic achievement, financial need, and merit.

Financial data A stipend is awarded (amount not specified). Funds are disbursed directly to the recipient's institution.

Duration 1 year; may be renewed.

Number awarded 1 or more each year.

Deadline March of each year.

[624]
LT. MICHAEL L. LEWIS, JR. MEMORIAL FUND

Sons of the American Legion
Detachment of New York
112 State Street, Suite 1300
Albany, NY 12207
(518) 463-2215　　　　　　　Fax: (518) 427-8443
E-mail: info@nylegion.org
Web: www.sonsdny.org

Summary To provide financial assistance to high school seniors and graduates in New York who are members of the Sons of the American Legion and plan to attend college in any state.

Eligibility This program is open to members of the Sons of the American Legion in New York. Applicants must be high school seniors or graduates and planning to attend college or trade school in any state. Along with their application, they must submit a 200-word essay either on why a college education is important to them or why they want to continue their postsecondary education in a business trade school. Selection is based on academics (25%), character (25%), leadership (25%), and Americanism (25%).

Financial data The stipend is $1,000.

Duration 1 year.
Number awarded 2 each year.
Deadline April of each year.

[625]
LTC KAREN J. WAGNER SCHOLARSHIP

Courtney Owens Educational Foundation, Inc.
1460 A Fifth Avenue
Fort Knox, KY 40121
(703) 328-2077　　　　　　Fax: (502) 942-9013
Web: coeficup.org/Scholarships.html

Summary To provide financial assistance for college to high school seniors who are the children of active, retired, or deceased members of the armed forces.

Eligibility This program is open to graduating high school seniors who are the children of active-duty, retire, National Guard, Reserve, or deceased members of the armed forces (any branch). Applicants must be entering a college or university and majoring in any field. They must have taken the ACT or SAT. Selection is based on academic merit, demonstration of social commitment, leadership potential, and financial need.

Financial data The stipend is $1,000.

Duration 1 year.

Number awarded 1 each year.

Deadline May of each year.

[626]
LYNDON F. MURRAY, SR. COLLEGE SCHOLARSHIP GRANT

Northwestern Vermont Vietnam Veterans of America
Attn: Scholarship Committee
P.O. Box 965
St. Albans, VT 05478-0965
(802) 849-9230　　　　E-mail: scw9250@myfairpoint.net

Summary To provide financial assistance to high school seniors in Vermont who are relatives of current or former military personnel, especially Vietnam veterans, and planning to attend college in any state.

Eligibility This program is open to seniors graduating from high schools in Vermont and planning to enrolled at a college or university in any state. First preference is given to relatives of Vietnam-Era veterans; second preference is given to relatives of U.S. military servicemembers currently serving on active duty or who have been honorably discharged. The relative must also be a resident of Vermont. Applicants must submit a 500-word essay on a topic that changes annually; recently, students were asked to write on the topic, "A Noble Endeavor: The American Serviceman and the Cause of Freedom."

Financial data The stipend is $1,500.

Duration 1 year.

Number awarded 1 each year.

Deadline March of each year.

[627]
M. LOUISE WILSON LOAN FUND

American Legion Auxiliary
Department of Wisconsin
Attn: Loan Fund
2930 American Legion Drive
P.O. Box 140
Portage, WI 53901-0140
(608) 745-0124　　　　　Toll Free: (866) 664-3863
Fax: (608) 745-1947　　E-mail: alawi@amlegionauxwi.org
Web: www.amlegionauxwi.org

Summary To loan money to Wisconsin women veterans or female relatives of veterans who plan to attend college in any state.

Eligibility This program is open to Wisconsin residents who are women veterans or the wives, daughters, granddaughters, great-granddaughters, mothers, grandmothers, or sisters of honorably-discharged veterans. The veteran relative must have served during specified periods of wartime. Applicants must be planning to attend college in any state.

Financial data Up to $400 per year may be borrowed, to a lifetime total of $2,000. Repayment begins 3 months after graduation at the rate of at least $35 per month, but no interest is charged.

Duration Up to 5 years.

Additional information This program began in 1925.

Number awarded Varies each year.

Deadline March of each year.

[628]
MADELINE PICKETT (HALBERT) COGSWELL NURSING SCHOLARSHIP

Daughters of the American Revolution-National Society
Attn: Committee Services Office, Scholarships
1776 D Street, N.W.
Washington, DC 20006-5303
(202) 628-1776
Web: www.dar.org

Summary To provide financial assistance for nursing education to active members of the Daughters of the American Revolution (DAR) and their descendants.

Eligibility This program is open to undergraduate students currently enrolled at accredited schools of nursing who are members, eligible for membership, or descendants of a member of DAR. Applicants must have completed at least 1 year of nursing school. They must be sponsored by a local chapter of DAR. Selection is based on academic excellence, commitment to field of study, and financial need. U.S. citizenship is required.

Financial data The stipend is $1,000.

Duration 1 year; nonrenewable.

Number awarded Varies each year.

Deadline February of each year.

[629]
MAINE VETERANS DEPENDENTS EDUCATIONAL BENEFITS

Bureau of Veterans' Services
117 State House Station
Augusta, ME 04333-0117
(207) 430-6035   Toll Free: (800) 345-0116 (within ME)
Fax: (207) 626-4471   E-mail: mainebvs@maine.gov
Web: www.maine.gov/dvem/bvs/educational_benefits.htm

Summary To provide financial assistance for undergraduate or graduate education to dependents of disabled and other Maine veterans.

Eligibility Applicants for these benefits must be children (high school seniors or graduates under 22 years of age), non-divorced spouses, or unremarried widow(er)s of veterans who meet 1 or more of the following requirements: 1) living and determined to have a total permanent disability resulting from a service-connected cause; 2) killed in action; 3) died from a service-connected disability; 4) died while totally and permanently disabled due to a service-connected disability but whose death was not related to the service-connected disability; or 5) a member of the armed forces on active duty who has been listed for more than 90 days as missing in action, captured, forcibly detained, or interned in the line of duty by a foreign government or power. The veteran parent must have been a resident of Maine at the time of entry into service or a resident of Maine for 5 years preceding application for these benefits. Children may be working on an associate or bachelor's degree. Spouses, widows, and widowers may work on an associate, bachelor's, or master's degree.

Financial data Recipients are entitled to free tuition at institutions of higher education supported by the state of Maine.

Duration Children may receive up to 8 semesters of support; they have 6 years from the date of first entrance to complete those 8 semesters. Continuation in the program is based on their earning a GPA of 2.0 or higher each semester. Spouses are entitled to receive up to 120 credit hours of educational benefits and have 10 years from the date of first entrance to complete their program.

Additional information College preparatory schooling and correspondence courses are not supported under this program.

Number awarded Varies each year.

Deadline Deadline not specified.

[630]
MAINE VIETNAM VETERANS SCHOLARSHIP FUND

Maine Community Foundation
Attn: Program Director
245 Main Street
Ellsworth, ME 04605
(207) 667-9735   Toll Free: (877) 700-6800
Fax: (207) 667-0447   E-mail: info@mainecf.org
Web: www.mainecf.org/statewidescholars.aspx ·

Summary To provide financial assistance for college or graduate school to Vietnam veterans or the dependents of Vietnam or other veterans in Maine.

Eligibility This program is open to residents of Maine who are Vietnam veterans or the descendants of veterans who served in the Vietnam Theater. As a second priority, children

of veterans from other time periods are also considered. Graduating high school seniors, nontraditional students, undergraduates, and graduate students are eligible to apply. Selection is based on financial need, extracurricular activities, work experience, academic achievement, and a personal statement of career goals and how the applicant's educational plans relate to them.

Financial data The stipend is $1,000 per year.

Duration 1 year.

Additional information This program began in 1985. There is a $3 processing fee.

Number awarded 3 to 6 each year.

Deadline April of each year.

[631]
MAJOR GENERAL DUANE L. "DUKE" CORNING MEMORIAL SCHOLARSHIP

South Dakota National Guard Enlisted Association
c/o Nancy Ausland, Scholarship Committee Chair
517 North Euclid Avenue
Sioux Falls, SD 57104
(605) 988-5946   E-mail: nancy.ausland@ang.af.mil
Web: www.sdngea.com/programs/scholarships

Summary To provide financial assistance to current and retired members of the South Dakota National Guard Enlisted Association (SDNGEA), the National Guard Association of South Dakota (NGASD), or their dependents who are interested in attending college in any state.

Eligibility This program is open to current and retired members of the SDNGEA and the NGASD and the dependents of current and retired members of those associations. Applicants must be graduating high school seniors or full-time undergraduate students at a college or university in any state. They must submit a 300-page autobiography that includes their experiences to date and their hopes and plans for the future. Selection is based on the essay; awards, honors, and offices in high school, college, or trade school; GPA and ACT/SAT scores; letters of recommendation; and extracurricular and community activities and honors.

Financial data The stipend is $1,000.

Duration 1 year; nonrenewable.

Number awarded 1 each year.

Deadline March of each year.

[632]
MAJOR SAMUEL WOODFILL CHAPTER AUSA SCHOLARSHIP PROGRAM

Association of the United States Army-Major Samuel
  Woodfill Chapter
c/o LTC Robert F. Sprague, Retired
1326 Cayton Road
Florence, KY 41042-9335
(859) 525-1082   E-mail: spraguer@fuse.net
Web: www3.ausa.org/chapweb/wcc/index.html

Summary To provide financial assistance to Army personnel and their families, especially those from Indiana, Kentucky, and Ohio, who have served in the Global War on Terror and are interested in attending college in any state.

Eligibility This program is open to (in order of preference) 1) children and spouses of U.S. Army soldiers (active-duty, Reserve, or National Guard) who are currently serving, or have served in the Global War on Terrorism; 2) Army soldiers and veterans who are currently serving or have served in the Global War on Terrorism; and 3) children, grandchildren, and spouses of members of the Major Samuel Woodfill Chapter of the Association of the United States Army (AUSA). Priority is given to residents of Indiana, Kentucky, and Ohio. Applicants may be attending or accepted at an accredited college or university in any state. Along with their application, they must submit a 500-word essay on the greatest challenge they have faced and how it has impacted them. High school seniors must also submit information on their GPA, extracurricular activities, honors and/or awards, and SAT/ACT scores. Financial need is not considered in the selection process.

Financial data The stipend is $1,000. Funds are disbursed directly to the recipient's college or university.

Duration 1 year.

Number awarded Varies each year; recently, 5 were awarded.

Deadline March of each year.

[633]
MARCELLA ARNOLD NURSING SCHOLARSHIP

Ladies Auxiliary to the Veterans of Foreign Wars-
 Department of Minnesota
Attn: Scholarship Committee
20 West 12th Street, Floor 3
St. Paul, MN 55155-2002
(651) 291-1759   Fax: (661) 291-7932

Summary To provide financial assistance to residents of Minnesota who are either eligible for membership in the Veterans of Foreign Wars (VFW) or its Ladies Auxiliary or the child or grandchild of a member and interested in studying nursing at a school in the state.

Eligibility This program is open to residents of Minnesota enrolled full time at a school or nursing in the state and working on an associate degree, bachelor's degree, or L.P.N. certificate; the scholarship is designed to help fund the final year of study. Applicants must be eligible to join the VFW or its Ladies Auxiliary or be the child or grandchild of a VFW or Auxiliary member. Along with their application, they must submit essays on how the scholarship will make a difference for them and if they would be willing to work at a Veterans Administration medical center or veterans home. Selection is based on nursing goals (25 points), interest in working with veterans (20 points), extenuating circumstances (15 points), and financial need (40 points).

Financial data A stipend is awarded (amount not specified).

Duration 1 year.

Additional information This program began in 1981.

Number awarded 1 each year.

Deadline March of each year.

[634]
MARGUERITE MC'ALPIN MEMORIAL SCHOLARSHIP

American Legion Auxiliary
Department of Washington
Attn: Education Chair
3600 Ruddell Road S.E.
P.O. Box 5867
Lacey, WA 98509-5867
(360) 456-5995   Fax: (360) 491-7442
E-mail: secretary@walegion-aux.org
Web: www.walegion-aux.org/EducationScholarships.html

Summary To provide financial assistance to Washington veterans or their descendants who are interested in working on an undergraduate or graduate degree in nursing at a school in any state.

Eligibility This program is open to Washington veterans and their children, grandchildren, and great-grandchildren. Applicants must be interested in studying nursing on the undergraduate or graduate level at a school in any state. Selection is based on an essay on their desire to study nursing, character, leadership, scholastic history, and financial need.

Financial data The stipend is $1,000.

Duration 1 year.

Number awarded 1 each year.

Deadline February of each year.

[635]
MARIA C. JACKSON/GENERAL GEORGE A. WHITE SCHOLARSHIP

Oregon Student Access Commission
Attn: Grants and Scholarships Division
1500 Valley River Drive, Suite 100
Eugene, OR 97401-2146
(541) 687-7395   Toll Free: (800) 452-8807, ext. 7395
Fax: (541) 687-7414   TDD: (800) 735-2900
E-mail: awardinfo@osac.state.or.us
Web: www.oregonstudentaid.gov/scholarships.aspx

Summary To provide financial assistance to veterans and children of veterans and military personnel in Oregon who are interested in attending college or graduate school in the state.

Eligibility This program is open to residents of Oregon who served, or whose parents are serving or have served, in the U.S. armed forces. Applicants or their parents must have resided in Oregon at the time of enlistment. They must be enrolled or planning to enroll at a college or graduate school in the state. College and university undergraduates must have a GPA of 3.75 or higher, but there is no minimum GPA requirement for graduate students or those attending a technical school. Selection is based on scholastic ability and financial need.

Financial data Stipends for scholarships offered by the Oregon Student Access Commission (OSAC) range from $200 to $10,000 but recently averaged $5,200.

Duration 1 year.

Number awarded Varies each year.

Deadline February of each year.

[636]
MARIE KLUGOW MEMORIAL SCHOLARSHIPS

Ladies Auxiliary to the Veterans of Foreign Wars-
 Department of California
Attn: Scholarship Chair
9136 Elk Grove Boulevard
Elk Grove, CA 95624
(916) 361-0932   E-mail: dioldmo@msn.com
Web: www.lavfwca.org

Summary To provide financial assistance to children and grandchildren of members of the Veterans of Foreign Wars (VFW) or its Ladies Auxiliary in California who are interested in attending college or nursing school in any state.

Eligibility This program is open to the children and grandchildren of members in good standing in a California VFW Post or Ladies Auxiliary and to members of an Auxiliary. Applicants may be 1) graduating high school seniors; 2) students graduating from a community college or continuing as a full-time student at a 4-year college or university in any state; or 3) students preparing for a nursing career. They must have a GPA of 2.5 or higher and not have received a failing grade in any class. Graduating high school seniors must submit their SAT and/or ACT scores. Financial need is considered in the selection process. U.S. citizenship is required.

Financial data The stipend is $3,000 per year;.

Duration 1 year; recipients may reapply for 1 additional year.

Number awarded 3 each year: 1 to a graduating high school senior, 1 to a community college graduate or continuing university student, and 1 to a nursing student.

Deadline April of each year.

[637]
MARINE CORPS COUNTERINTELLIGENCE ASSOCIATION SCHOLARSHIPS

Marine Corps Counterintelligence Association
c/o Samuel L. Moyer, Scholarship Committee Chair
315 Palmdale Drive
Oldsmar, FL 34677
E-mail: oldjarhd@aol.com
Web: www.mccia.org/Public/Scholarship/default.aspx

Summary To provide financial assistance for college to dependents of members of the Marine Corps Counterintelligence Association (MCCIA).

Eligibility This program is open to children, grandchildren, and spouses of 1) current MCCIA members; 2) deceased Marines who were MCCIA members at the time of death; and 3) counterintelligence Marines who lost their lives in the line of duty (whether they were a member of MCCIA or not). Spouses of deceased Marines must also be MCCIA Auxiliary members. Applicants must be enrolled or planning to enroll as a full-time undergraduate student at an accredited college or university and have a GPA of 3.0 or higher. Along with their application, they must submit a 1-page essay on a topic of their choice, letters of recommendation, SAT or ACT scores, transcripts, copies of awards and other honors, and evidence of acceptance at a college or university. Financial need is not considered.

Financial data Stipends range up to $1,000. Funds must be used to help pay for tuition, books, fees, and materials; they may not be used for personal or living expenses.

Duration 1 year; may be renewed up to 4 additional years (need not be consecutive).

Number awarded Varies each year; recently, 6 were awarded.

Deadline June of each year.

[638]
MARINE CORPS LEAGUE SCHOLARSHIPS

Marine Corps League
Attn: National Executive Director
P.O. Box 3070
Merrifield, VA 22116-3070
(703) 207-9588   Toll Free: (800) MCL-1775
Fax: (703) 207-0047   E-mail: mcl@mcleague.org
Web: www.mcleague.com

Summary To provide college aid to students whose parents served in the Marines and to members of the Marine Corps League or Marine Corps League Auxiliary.

Eligibility This program is open to 1) children of Marines who lost their lives in the line of duty; 2) spouses, children, grandchildren, great-grandchildren, and stepchildren of active Marine Corps League and/or Auxiliary members; and 3) members of the Marine Corps League and/or Marine Corps League Auxiliary who are honorably discharged and in need of rehabilitation training not provided by government programs. Applicants must be seeking further education and training as a full-time student and be recommended by the commandant of an active chartered detachment of the Marine Corps League or the president of an active chartered unit of the Auxiliary. They must have a GPA of 3.0 or higher. Financial need is not considered in the selection process.

Financial data A stipend is awarded (amount not specified). Funds are paid directly to the recipient.

Duration 1 year; may be renewed up to 3 additional years (all renewals must complete an application and attach a transcript from the college or university).

Number awarded Varies, depending upon the amount of funds available each year.

Deadline June of each year.

[639]
MARINE CORPS SCHOLARSHIPS

Marine Corps Scholarship Foundation, Inc.
Attn: Scholarship Office
909 North Washington Street, Suite 400
Alexandria, VA 22314
(703) 549-0060   Toll Free: (866) 496-5462
Fax: (703) 549-9474   E-mail: students@mcsf.org
Web: www.mcsf.org/newapplicants

Summary To provide financial assistance for college to the children of present or former members of the U.S. Marine Corps.

Eligibility This program is open to the children of 1) Marines on active duty or in the Reserves; 2) veteran Marines who have received an honorable discharge or were killed while serving in the U.S. Marines; 3) active-duty or Reserve U.S. Navy Corpsmen who are serving or have served with a U.S. Marine unit; and 4) U.S. Navy Corpsmen who have served with a U.S. Marine unit and have received an honorable discharge or were killed while serving in the U.S. Navy. Applicants must be high school seniors, high school graduates, or current undergraduates in an accredited college, university, or postsecondary vocational/technical school. They must submit academic transcripts (GPA of 2.0 or higher); a written statement of service from their parent's commanding officer or a copy of their parent's honorable discharge; and a 500-word essay on a topic that changes periodically. Only undergraduate study is supported. The family income of applicants must be less than $93,000 per year.

Financial data   Stipends range from $1,500 to $10,000 per year.

Duration   1 year; may be renewed upon reapplication.

Additional information   Students pursuing their second bachelor's degree, enrolling in graduate school of any kind, or attending Federal Service Academies are not eligible.

Number awarded   Varies each year; recently, 2,040 of these scholarships, worth more than $6,600,000, were awarded.

Deadline   February of each year.

[640]
MARINE GUNNERY SERGEANT JOHN DAVID FRY SCHOLARSHIP

Department of Veterans Affairs
Attn: Veterans Benefits Administration
810 Vermont Avenue, N.W.
Washington, DC 20420
(202) 418-4343   Toll Free: (888) GI-BILL1
Web: www.benefits.va.gov/gibill/post911_gibill.asp

Summary   To provide financial assistance to children of military personnel who died in the line of duty on or after September 11, 2001.

Eligibility   This program is open to the children of active-duty members of the Armed Forces who have died in the line of duty on or after September 11, 2001. Applicants must be planning to enroll as undergraduates at a college or university. They must be at least 18 years of age, even if they have completed high school.

Financial data   Eligible students receive full payment of tuition and fees at public schools in their state of residence. For students attending a private or foreign university, the maximum payment for tuition and fees in most states is $19,198.31; students at private institutions in Arizona, Michigan, New Hampshire, New York, Pennsylvania, South Carolina, and Texas may be eligible for a higher tuition reimbursement rate. A monthly living stipend based on the military housing allowance for the zip code where the school is located and an annual book and supplies allowance of $1,000 are also provided.

Duration   Participants receive up to 36 months of entitlement. They have 15 years in which to utilize the benefit.

Additional information   This program began in 2009 as a component of the Post-9/11 GI Bill.

Number awarded   Varies each year.

Deadline   Deadline not specified.

[641]
MARION STEWART LINS PRIZE

Daughters of the Cincinnati
Attn: Scholarship Administrator
20 West 44th Street, Suite 508
New York, NY 10036
(212) 991-9945
E-mail: scholarships@daughters1894.org
Web: www.daughters1894.org/scholarship.htm

Summary   To provide financial assistance to high school seniors who are the daughters of active-duty, deceased, or retired military officers and plan to study music in college.

Eligibility   This program is open to high school seniors who are the daughters of career commissioned officers of the regular Army, Navy, Air Force, Coast Guard, or Marine Corps on active duty, deceased, or retired. Applicants must be planning to enroll at a college or university in any state and major in music. Along with their application, they must submit an official school transcript, SAT or ACT scores, a letter of recommendation, an essay on their choice of 3 assigned topics, and documentation of financial need.

Financial data   Scholarship amounts have recently averaged $4,000 per year. Funds are paid directly to the college of the student's choice.

Duration   1 year; may be renewed up to 3 additional years, provided the recipient remains in good academic standing.

Number awarded   1 each year.

Deadline   March of each year.

[642]
MARITIME PATROL ASSOCIATION SCHOLARSHIPS

Wings Over America Scholarship Foundation
Attn: Scholarship Administrator
4966 Euclid Road, Suite 109
Virginia Beach, VA 23462
(757) 671-3200, ext. 117
E-mail: scholarship@wingsoveramerica.us
Web: wingsoveramerica.us

Summary   To provide financial assistance for college to dependents of Navy personnel who have served or are serving in the Maritime Patrol and Reconnaissance community.

Eligibility   This program is open to 1) children of a military sponsor who are graduating high school seniors planning to enroll in college full time to work on a bachelor's degree or who are already enrolled in such a program; and 2) spouses of a military sponsor currently enrolled full or part time and working on an associate or bachelor's degree at an accredited college or university. Children must be unmarried and younger than 22 years of age. The military sponsor must have completed at least 8 years of active-duty service in the Maritime Patrol and Reconnaissance community and be currently on active duty, honorably discharged, retired, or deceased. Also eligible are children of members of the U.S. Navy who died while on active duty serving with a Naval air force unit, regardless of the length of service of the deceased parent. Selection is based on academic proficiency, extracurricular activities, community contributions, and life experience and character of the applicant.

Financial data   A stipend is awarded (amount not specified).

Duration   1 year.

Additional information This program, which began in 2013, is sponsored by the Maritime Patrol Association.

Number awarded 2 each year.

Deadline Pre-qualification forms must be submitted by January of each year.

[643]
MARY ANNE WILLIAMS SCHOLARSHIP

United Daughters of the Confederacy-Virginia Division
c/o Patt Graves, Second Vice President
838 Crymes Road
Keysville, VA 23947-2815
(434) 696-2202   E-mail: thebargthree@aol.com
Web: www.vaudc.org

Summary To provide financial assistance to Confederate descendants from Virginia who are interested in working on an undergraduate or graduate degree in engineering or medicine at a school in the state.

Eligibility This program is open to residents of Virginia who are 1) lineal descendants of Confederates; or 2) collateral descendants and also members of the Children of the Confederacy or the United Daughters of the Confederacy. Applicants must be interested in working on an undergraduate or graduate degree in medicine or engineering at a college or university in Virginia. They must submit proof of the Confederate military record of at least 1 ancestor, with the company and regiment in which he served. They must also submit a personal letter pledging to make the best possible use of the scholarship; describing their health, social, family, religious, and fraternal connections within the community; and reflecting on what a Southern heritage means to them (using the term "War Between the States" in lieu of "Civil War"). They must have a GPA of 3.0 or higher and be able to demonstrate financial need.

Financial data The amount of the stipend depends on the availability of funds. Payment is made directly to the college or university the recipient attends.

Duration 1 year; may be renewed up to 3 additional years if the recipient maintains a GPA of 3.0 or higher.

Number awarded This scholarship is offered whenever a prior recipient graduates or is no longer eligible.

Deadline March of the years in which the scholarship is available.

[644]
MARY BARRETT MARSHALL SCHOLARSHIP

American Legion Auxiliary
Department of Kentucky
P.O. Box 5435
Frankfort, KY 40602-5435
(502) 352-2380   Fax: (502) 352-2381
Web: www.kyamlegionaux.org/committies.html

Summary To provide financial assistance to female dependents of veterans in Kentucky who plan to attend college in the state.

Eligibility This program is open to the daughters, wives, sisters, widows, granddaughters, or great-granddaughters of veterans eligible for membership in the American Legion who are high school seniors or graduates and 5-year residents of Kentucky. Applicants must be planning to attend a college or university in Kentucky.

Financial data The stipend is $1,000. The funds may be used for tuition, registration fees, laboratory fees, and books, but not for room and board.

Duration 1 year.

Number awarded 1 each year.

Deadline March of each year.

[645]
MARY BARRETT MARSHALL STUDENT LOAN FUND

American Legion Auxiliary
Department of Kentucky
P.O. Box 5435
Frankfort, KY 40602-5435
(502) 352-2380   Fax: (502) 352-2381
Web: www.kyamlegionaux.org

Summary To provide loans to female dependents or descendants of veterans who need financial assistance to attend college in Kentucky.

Eligibility This program is open to the daughters, wives, sisters, widows, granddaughters, or great-granddaughters of veterans eligible for membership in the American Legion. Applicants must be high school graduates with financial need, 5-year residents of Kentucky, and planning to attend college in Kentucky.

Financial data Loans may be made up to $1,000 per year (but usually do not exceed $800). Funds may be used for books, tuition, and laboratory fees, but not for room and board. Repayment begins after graduation or upon securing employment, with monthly payments of the principal but no interest for 5 years, after which interest is 6%.

Duration 1 year; renewable.

Number awarded Varies each year.

Deadline Deadline not specified.

[646]
MARY PAOLOZZI MEMBER'S SCHOLARSHIP

Navy Wives Clubs of America
c/o NSA Mid-South
P.O. Box 54022
Millington, TN 38054-0022
Toll Free: (866) 511-NWCA
E-mail: nwca@navywivesclubsofamerica.org
Web: www.navywivesclubsofamerica.org/scholarships

Summary To provide financial assistance for undergraduate or graduate study to members of the Navy Wives Clubs of America (NWCA).

Eligibility This program is open to NWCA members who can demonstrate financial need. Applicants must be 1) a high school graduate or senior planning to attend college full time next year; 2) currently enrolled in an undergraduate program and planning to continue as a full-time undergraduate; 3) a college graduate or senior planning to be a full-time graduate student next year; or 4) a high school graduate or GED recipient planning to attend vocational or business school next year. Along with their application, they must submit a brief statement on why they feel they should be awarded this scholarship and any special circumstances (financial or other) they wish to have considered. Financial need is also considered in the selection process.

Financial data Stipends range from $500 to $1,000 each year (depending upon the donations from the NWCA chapters).

Duration 1 year.

Additional information Membership in the NWCA is open to spouses of enlisted personnel serving in the Navy, Marine Corps, Coast Guard, and the active Reserve units of those services; spouses of enlisted personnel who have been honorably discharged, retired, or transferred to the Fleet Reserve on completion of duty; and widows of enlisted personnel in those services.

Number awarded 1 or more each year.

Deadline May of each year.

[647]
MARY ROWENA COOPER SCHOLARSHIP

Winston-Salem Foundation
Attn: Student Aid Department
860 West Fifth Street
Winston-Salem, NC 27101-2506
(336) 714-3445   Toll Free: (866) 227-1209
Fax: (336) 727-0581
E-mail: StudentAid@wsfoundation.org
Web: www.wsfoundation.org/page.aspx?pid=745

Summary To provide financial assistance for college to children of veterans who served in Vietnam.

Eligibility This program is open to students currently enrolled at least half time at an accredited 2- or 4-year college, university, or vocational/technical school. Applicants must be the child of a living or deceased veteran who served in Vietnam. They must have a GPA of 2.0 or higher and have a family income less than 300% above the federal poverty guidelines. U.S. citizenship is required.

Financial data A stipend is awarded (amount not specified).

Duration 1 year; nonrenewable.

Additional information This program began in 1998. There is a $20 application fee (waived if the applicant is unable to pay).

Number awarded 1 or more each year.

Deadline August of each year.

[648]
MARYANN K. MURTHA MEMORIAL SCHOLARSHIP

American Legion Auxiliary
Department of New York
112 State Street, Suite 1310
Albany, NY 12207
(518) 463-1162   Toll Free: (800) 421-6348
Fax: (518) 449-5406
E-mail: alanykathleen@nycap.rr.com
Web: www.deptny.org/scholarships

Summary To provide financial assistance to New York residents who are the descendants of veterans and interested in attending college in any state.

Eligibility This program is open to residents of New York who are high school seniors or graduates and attending or planning to attend an accredited college or university in any state. Applicants must be the children, grandchildren, or great-grandchildren of veterans who served during specified periods of wartime. Along with their application, they must submit a 700-word article describing their plans and goals for

the future and how they hope to use their talent and education to help others. Selection is based on character (20%), Americanism (15%), community involvement (15%), leadership (15%), scholarship (20%), and financial need (15%). U.S. citizenship is required.

Financial data The stipend is $1,000. Funds are paid directly to the recipient's school.

Duration 1 year.

Number awarded 1 each year.

Deadline February of each year.

[649]
MARYLAND LEGION AUXILIARY CHILDREN AND YOUTH FUND SCHOLARSHIP

American Legion Auxiliary
Department of Maryland
1589 Sulphur Spring Road, Suite 105
Baltimore, MD 21227
(410) 242-9519   Fax: (410) 242-9553
E-mail: hq@alamd.org
Web: www.alamd.org/Scholarships.html

Summary To provide financial assistance for college to the daughters of veterans who are Maryland residents and wish to study designated fields at a school in the state.

Eligibility This program is open to Maryland senior high school girls with a veteran parent who wish to study arts, sciences, business, public administration, education, or a medical field other than nursing at a college or university in the state. Preference is given to children of members of the American Legion or American Legion Auxiliary. Selection is based on character (30%), Americanism (20%), leadership (10%), scholarship (20%), and financial need (20%). U.S. citizenship is required.

Financial data The stipend is $2,000.

Duration 1 year; may be renewed up to 3 additional years.

Number awarded 1 each year.

Deadline April of each year.

[650]
MARYLAND LEGION AUXILIARY PAST PRESIDENTS' PARLEY NURSING SCHOLARSHIP

American Legion Auxiliary
Department of Maryland
1589 Sulphur Spring Road, Suite 105
Baltimore, MD 21227
(410) 242-9519   Fax: (410) 242-9553
E-mail: hq@alamd.org
Web: www.alamd.org/Scholarships.html

Summary To provide financial assistance to the female descendants of Maryland veterans who wish to study nursing at a school in any state.

Eligibility This program is open to Maryland residents who are the daughters, granddaughters, great-granddaughters, step-daughters, step-granddaughters, or step-great-granddaughters of ex-servicewomen (or of ex-servicemen, if there are no qualified descendants of ex-servicewomen). Applicants must be interested in attending a school in any state to become a registered nurse and be able to show financial need. They must submit a 300-word essay on the topic "What a Nursing Career Means to Me."

Financial data The stipend is $2,000. Funds are sent directly to the recipient's school.

Duration 1 year; may be renewed for up to 3 additional years if the recipient remains enrolled full time.
Number awarded 1 each year.
Deadline April of each year.

[651]
MARYLAND SCHOLARSHIPS FOR VETERANS OF THE AFGHANISTAN AND IRAQ CONFLICTS

Maryland Higher Education Commission
Attn: Office of Student Financial Assistance
6 North Liberty Street, Ground Suite
Baltimore, MD 21201
(410) 767-3301   Toll Free: (800) 974-0203
Fax: (410) 332-0250   TDD: (800) 735-2258
E-mail: osfamail@mhec.state.md.us
Web: www.mhec.state.md.us

Summary To provide financial assistance for college to residents of Maryland who served in the armed forces in Afghanistan or Iraq and their children and spouses.
Eligibility This program is open to Maryland residents who are 1) a veteran who served at least 60 days in Afghanistan on or after October 24, 2001 or in Iraq on or after March 19, 2003; 2) an active-duty member of the armed forces who served at least 60 days in Afghanistan or Iraq on or after those dates; 3) a member of a Reserve component of the armed forces or the Maryland National Guard who was activated as a result of the Afghanistan or Iraq conflicts and served at least 60 days; and 4) the children and spouses of such veterans, active-duty armed forces personnel, or members of Reserve forces or Maryland National Guard. Applicants must be enrolled or accepted for enrollment in a regular undergraduate program at an eligible Maryland institution. In the selection process, veterans are given priority over dependent children and spouses.
Financial data The stipend is equal to 50% of the annual tuition, mandatory fees, and room and board of a resident undergraduate at a 4-year public institution within the University System of Maryland, currently capped at $10,655 per year for students who live on campus, at $6,795 for students who live with their parents, or at %7,745 for students who live off campus.
Duration 1 year; may be renewed for an additional 4 years of full-time study or 7 years of part-time study, provided the recipient remains enrolled in an eligible program with a GPA of 2.5 or higher.
Additional information This program is scheduled to expire in 2016.
Number awarded Varies each year.
Deadline February of each year.

[652]
MASSACHUSETTS LEGION DEPARTMENT GENERAL SCHOLARSHIPS

American Legion
Department of Massachusetts
State House
24 Beacon Street, Room 546-2
Boston, MA 02133-1044
(617) 727-2966   Fax: (617) 727-2969
E-mail: masslegion@verizon.net
Web: www.masslegion.org

Summary To provide financial assistance to the children and grandchildren of members of the American Legion in Massachusetts who are entering college in any state.
Eligibility This program is open to the children and grandchildren of members in good standing in the American Legion's Department of Massachusetts (or who were members in good standing at the time of death). Applicants must be entering their freshman year at a college or university in any state. Along with their application, they must submit a 100-word essay on their long-range goal and why they want to go to college. Financial need is considered in the selection process.
Financial data Stipends are $1,000 or $500.
Duration 1 year.
Additional information The $1,000 scholarships are designated as follows: the Frank R. Kelley Scholarship, the Robert (Sam) Murphy Scholarship, the H.P. Redden Scholarship, the Mayer/Murphy/Nee Scholarship, the Paul A. Morin Scholarship PNC, the Past Department Commanders Scholarship, the Daniel J. Doherty Scholarship PNC, the John P. "Jake" Comer Scholarship PNC, and the Grace Fuller Olson Scholarship.
Number awarded 19 each year: 9 at $1,000 and 10 at $500.
Deadline March of each year.

[653]
MASSACHUSETTS PUBLIC SERVICE GRANT PROGRAM

Massachusetts Office of Student Financial Assistance
454 Broadway, Suite 200
Revere, MA 02151
(617) 391-6070   Fax: (617) 727-0667
E-mail: osfa@osfa.mass.edu
Web: www.osfa.mass.edu

Summary To provide financial assistance for college to children or widow(er)s of deceased public service officers and others in Massachusetts.
Eligibility This program is open to Massachusetts residents who are enrolled or planning to enroll full time at a college or university in the state. Applicants must be 1) the children or spouses of firefighters, police officers, or corrections officers who were killed or died from injuries incurred in the line of duty; 2) children of prisoners of war or military service personnel missing in action in southeast Asia whose wartime service was credited to Massachusetts and whose service was between February 1, 1955 and the termination of the Vietnam campaign; or 3) children of veterans whose service was credited to Massachusetts and who were killed in action or died as a result of their service. U.S. citizenship or permanent resident status is required. This is an entitlement program; support is provided to all qualifying students, regardless of their academic achievement or financial need.
Financial data Scholarships provide up to the cost of tuition at a state-supported college or university in Massachusetts; if the recipient attends a private Massachusetts college or university, the scholarship is equivalent to tuition at a public institution, up to $2,500.
Duration 1 year; renewable.
Number awarded Varies each year.
Deadline April of each year.

[654]
MASSACHUSETTS SOLDIERS LEGACY FUND SCHOLARSHIPS

Massachusetts Soldiers Legacy Fund
P.O. Box 962061
Milk Street Post Office
Boston, MA 02196
(508) 630-2382   Toll Free: (866) 856-5533
E-mail: info@mslfund.org
Web: www.mslfund.org

Summary To provide financial assistance for college or professional school to the children of servicemembers from Massachusetts who were killed in Afghanistan or Iraq.

Eligibility This program is open to children of members of the U.S. armed forces who died while deployed on operations Enduring Freedom or Iraqi Freedom. The parent's home of record must have been Massachusetts. Applicants must be enrolled or planning to enroll at a 2- or 4-year college or university, professional school, or trade school in any state. All qualified children receive this assistance; there is no selection process.

Financial data The stipend is $10,000 per year.

Duration 1 year; may be renewed up to 3 additional years.

Additional information This program began in 2004.

Number awarded Varies each year.

Deadline Deadline not specified.

[655]
MERRILYN STOCK MEMORIAL SCHOLARSHIP

American Legion Auxiliary
Department of Alaska
Attn: Secretary/Treasurer
P.O. Box 670750
Chugiak, AK 99567
(907) 688-0241   Fax: (907) 688-0241
E-mail: aladepak@gci.net
Web: alaskalegionauxiliary.org/siteimage/228docs.pdf

Summary To provide financial assistance to nontraditional students in Alaska who have a tie to the American Legion.

Eligibility This program is open to residents of Alaska who are members or children of members of the American Legion, American Legion Auxiliary, or Sons of the American Legion. Applicants must be nontraditional students accepted or enrolled at an accredited college, university, or vocational/technical institution in any state to enhance their job skills so they can enter or reenter the work field at a higher level. Along with their application, they must submit brief essays on why receiving this scholarship would be important to them; the course of study they plan to pursue and why; their involvement in school, church, and community activities; and why they think United States patriotic organizations, such as the American Legion, are important to the world today. Selection is based on character (25%), Americanism (25%), leadership (25%), and financial need (25%).

Financial data A stipend is awarded (amount not specified).

Duration 1 year.

Number awarded 1 each year.

Deadline March of each year.

[656]
MG BENJAMIN J. BUTLER "CENTURY DIVISION" SCHOLARSHIP AWARD

Association of the Century, Inc.
Attn: Scholarship Committee
P.O. Box 34393
Louisville, KY 40232
Web: www.the-century.org/scholarship.htm

Summary To provide financial assistance for college to members of the United States Army 100th Infantry Division and their descendants.

Eligibility This program is open to active, retired, or former members of the Army 100th Infantry Division (or any of its successor designations), their direct lineal descendants, and their adopted dependents. Applicants must be enrolled or planning to enroll at an accredited 4-year college or university. They must have a GPA of 2.5 or higher. Along with their application, they must submit a 250-word essay on how this scholarship will help them. Selection is based on academic excellence, qualities of good citizenship and patriotism, letters of recommendation, and financial need.

Financial data The stipend is $1,000.

Duration 1 year.

Additional information This program, which began in 2008, is managed by the Community Foundation of Louisville.

Number awarded Varies each year; recently, 5 were awarded.

Deadline May of each year.

[657]
MG JAMES URSANO SCHOLARSHIP FUND

Army Emergency Relief
200 Stovall Street
Alexandria, VA 22332-0600
(703) 428-0000   Toll Free: (866) 878-6378
Fax: (703) 325-7183   E-mail: ursano@aerhq.org
Web: www.aerhq.org

Summary To provide financial assistance for college to the dependent children of Army personnel.

Eligibility This program is open to dependent unmarried children under 23 years of age (including stepchildren and legally adopted children) of soldiers on active duty, retired, or deceased while on active duty or after retirement. Applicants must be working or planning to work full time on a 4-year degree at an accredited college or university. They must have a GPA of 2.0 or higher. Selection is based primarily on financial need, but academic achievements and individual accomplishments are also considered.

Financial data The amount varies, depending on the needs of the recipient, but recently averaged $2,417. Children of soldiers who die while on active duty receive the maximum award of $3,500.

Duration 1 year; may be renewed for up to 3 additional years, provided the recipient maintains a GPA of 2.0 or higher.

Additional information Army Emergency Relief is a private nonprofit organization dedicated to "helping the Army take care of its own." Its primary mission is to provide financial assistance to Army people and their dependents in time of valid emergency need; its educational program was established as a secondary mission to meet a need of Army people for their dependents to pursue vocational training, preparation for acceptance by service academies, or an undergraduate education. It established this program in 1976.

Number awarded Varies each year; recently, 3,181 were awarded.

Deadline April of each year.

[658]
MICHAEL BAKER CORPORATION IRAQ SURVIVORS SCHOLARSHIP FUND

Pittsburgh Foundation
Attn: Scholarship Coordinator
Five PPG Place, Suite 250
Pittsburgh, PA 15222-5414
(412) 391-5122   Fax: (412) 391-7259
E-mail: turnerd@pghfdn.org
Web: www.pittsburghfoundation.org/node/1669

Summary To provide financial assistance for college in any state to children and spouses of military servicemembers killed in the war in Iraq.

Eligibility This program is open to children and surviving spouses of servicemembers who died during active military service in, or as the direct result of service in, the war in Iraq. Applicants must be enrolled or planning to enroll at a 2- or 4-year college, university, or technical school in any state. They must have a GPA of 2.8 or higher. Along with their application, they must submit a 1-page essay on how this scholarship would help them achieve their long-term career goals.

Financial data A stipend is awarded (amount not specified).

Duration 1 year.

Additional information This program is sponsored by the Michael Baker Corporation.

Number awarded 1 or more each year.

Deadline April of each year.

[659]
MICHIGAN CHILDREN OF VETERANS TUITION GRANTS

Michigan Department of Treasury
Attn: Student Scholarships and Grants
P.O. Box 30462
Lansing, MI 48909-7962
(517) 373-0457   Toll Free: (888) 4-GRANTS
Fax: (517) 241-5835   E-mail: ssg@michigan.gov
Web: www.michigan.gov

Summary To provide financial assistance for college to the children of Michigan veterans who are totally disabled or deceased as a result of service-connected causes.

Eligibility This program is open to natural and adopted children of veterans who have been totally and permanently disabled as a result of a service-connected illness or injury prior to death and have now died, have died or become totally and permanently disabled as a result of a service-connected illness or injury, have been killed in action or died from another cause while serving in a war or war condition, or are listed as missing in action in a foreign country. The veteran must have been a legal resident of Michigan immediately before entering military service and did not reside outside of Michigan for more than 2 years, or must have established legal residency in Michigan after entering military service. Applicants must be between 16 and 26 years of age and must

have lived in Michigan at least 12 months prior to the date of application. They must be enrolled or planning to enroll at least half time at a community college, public university, or independent degree-granting college or university in Michigan. U.S. citizenship or permanent resident status is required.

Financial data Full-time recipients are exempt from payment of the first $2,800 per year of tuition or any other fee that takes the place of tuition. Prorated exemptions apply to three-quarter time and half-time students.

Duration 1 year; may be renewed for up to 3 additional years if the recipient maintains full-time enrollment and a GPA of 2.25 or higher.

Additional information This program was formerly known as the Michigan Veterans Trust Fund Tuition Grants, administered by the Michigan Veterans Trust Fund within the Department of Military and Veterans Affairs. It was transferred to Student Scholarships and Grants in 2006.

Number awarded Varies each year; recently, 414 of these grants, worth $967,853, were awarded.

Deadline Deadline not specified.

[660]
MIKE AND GAIL DONLEY SPOUSE SCHOLARSHIPS

Air Force Association
Attn: Manager, Awards and Scholarships
1501 Lee Highway
Arlington, VA 22209-1198
(703) 247-5800, ext. 4807
Toll Free: (800) 727-3337, ext. 4807
Fax: (703) 247-5853   E-mail: awards@afa.org
Web: www.afa.org/donleyspousescholarship

Summary To provide financial assistance for undergraduate or graduate study to spouses of Air Force members.

Eligibility This program is open to spouses of active-duty Air Force, Air National Guard, or Air Force Reserve members. Spouses who are themselves military members or in ROTC are not eligible. Applicants must have a GPA of 3.5 or higher in college (or high school if entering college for the first time) and be able to provide proof of acceptance into an accredited undergraduate or graduate degree program. They must submit a 2-page essay on their academic and career goals, the motivation that led them to that decision, and how Air Force and other local community activities in which they are involved will enhance their goals. Selection is based on the essay and 2 letters of recommendation.

Financial data The stipend is $2,500; funds are sent to the recipients' schools to be used for any reasonable cost related to working on a degree.

Duration 1 year; nonrenewable.

Additional information This program began in 1995.

Number awarded At least 10 each year: 1 to an airman assigned to each of the 10 Air Force Major Commands.

Deadline April of each year.

[661]
MILDRED R. KNOLES SCHOLARSHIPS

American Legion Auxiliary
Department of Illinois
2720 East Lincoln Street
P.O. Box 1426
Bloomington, IL 61702-1426
(309) 663-9366   Fax: (309) 663-5827
E-mail: karen.boughan@ilala.org
Web: www.ilala.org/education.html

Summary To provide financial assistance to Illinois veterans and their descendants who are attending college in any state.

Eligibility This program is open to veterans who served during designated periods of wartime and their children, grandchildren, and great-grandchildren. Applicants must be currently enrolled at a college or university in any state and studying any field except nursing. They must be residents of Illinois or members of the American Legion Family, Department of Illinois. Along with their application, they must submit a 1,000-word essay on "What My Education Will Do for Me." Selection is based on that essay (25%) character and leadership (25%), scholarship (25%), and financial need (25%).

Financial data The stipend is $1,000.

Duration 1 year.

Additional information Applications may be obtained only from a local unit of the American Legion Auxiliary.

Number awarded Varies each year.

Deadline March of each year.

[662]
MILITARY CHILD OF THE YEAR AWARDS

Operation Homefront
8930 Fourwinds Drive, Suite 340
San Antonio, TX 78239
(210) 659-7756   Toll Free: (800) 722-6098
Fax: (210) 566-7544
E-mail: info@OperationHomefront.net
Web: www.militarychildoftheyear.org

Summary To recognize and reward outstanding military children.

Eligibility This award is available to children of military personnel in each branch of the armed forces (Air Force, Army, Coast Guard, Marine Corps, Navy). Nominees must have demonstrated resilience, strength of character, leadership within their families and communities, and ability to thrive in the face of the challenges of military life. They must be between 8 and 18 years of age and enrolled in the Defense Enrollment Eligibility Reporting System (DEERS).

Financial data In addition to a trip to our nation's capital, recipients receive a laptop computer and a $10,000 award. These funds may be used for college.

Duration The awards are presented annually.

Additional information These awards were first presented in 2011.

Number awarded 5 each year: 1 from each branch.

Deadline Nominations must be submitted by December of each year.

[663]
MILITARY COMMANDERS' SCHOLARSHIP FUND

Scholarship America
Attn: Scholarship Management Services
One Scholarship Way
P.O. Box 297
St. Peter, MN 56082
(507) 931-1682   Toll Free: (800) 537-4180
Fax: (507) 931-9168
E-mail: militarycommanders@scholarshipamerica.org
Web: sms.scholarshipamerica.org/militarycommanders

Summary To provide financial assistance for college to children of active and retired military personnel.

Eligibility This program is open to children of active-duty, Reserve, National Guard, and retired members of the U.S. military. Applicants must be high school seniors or graduates who plan to enroll full time as entering freshmen at an accredited 2- or 4-year college or university. They must have a cumulative GPA of 3.5 or higher. Selection is based on academic record, demonstrated leadership and participation in school and community activities, honors, work experience, a statement of goals and aspirations, unusual personal or family circumstances, an outside appraisal, and financial need.

Financial data The stipend is $5,000.

Duration 1 year; nonrenewable.

Additional information This program is administered by Scholarship Management Services of Scholarship America on behalf of the New York Chapter of the American Logistics Association.

Number awarded Up to 15 each year: 3 from each branch of the armed forces (Air Force, Army, Coast Guard, Marines, Navy).

Deadline February of each year.

[664]
MILITARY FAMILY SUPPORT TRUST SCHOLARSHIPS

Military Family Support Trust
1010 American Eagle Boulevard
P.O. Box 301
Sun City Center, FL 33573
(813) 634-4675   Fax: (813) 419-4944
E-mail: president@mobc-online.org
Web: www.mobc-online.org/scholarships.html

Summary To provide financial assistance for college to children and grandchildren of retired and deceased officers who served in the military or designated public service agencies.

Eligibility This program is open to graduating high school seniors who have a GPA of 3.0 and a minimum score of 21 on the ACT or 1500 on the 3-part SAT. Applicants must have a parent, guardian, or grandparent who is 1) a retired active-duty, National Guard, or Reserve officer or former officer of the U.S. Army, Navy, Marine Corps, Air Force, Coast Guard, Public Health Service, or National Oceanic and Atmospheric Administration, at the rank of O-1 through O-10, WO-1 through WO-5, or E-5 through E-9; 2) an officer who died while on active duty in service to the country; 3) a recipient of the Purple Heart, regardless of pay grade or length of service; 4) a World War II combat veteran of the Merchant Marine; 5) a federal employee at the grade of GS-7 or higher; 6) a Foreign Service Officer at the grade of FSO-8 or lower; or

7) an honorably discharged or retired foreign military officer of friendly nations meeting the service and disability retirement criteria of the respective country and living in the United States. Applicants must have been accepted to an accredited program at a college or university. Selection is based on leadership (40%), scholarship (30%), and financial need (30%).

Financial data   Stipends range from $500 to $3,000 per year.

Duration   4 years, provided the recipient maintains a GPA of 3.0 or higher.

Additional information   This foundation was established in 1992 as the Military Officers' Benevolent Corporation. It changed its name in 2008 to the current usage.

Number awarded   16 each year: 4 at $3,000 per year, 1 at $2,500 per year, 1 at $2,000 per year, 2 at $1,500 per year, 1 at $1,000 per year, and 7 at $500 per year.

Deadline   February of each year.

[665]
MILITARY FRIENDS FOUNDATION PATRIOT SCHOLAR PROGRAM

Military Friends Foundation
14 Beacon Street, Suite 706
Boston, MA 02108
(617) 733-7994   E-mail: info@militaryfriends.org
Web: www.militaryfriends.org/programs/patriot-scholar

Summary   To provide financial assistance for college or graduate school in any state to Massachusetts residents who are the children of National Guard members, Reservists, or deceased servicemembers.

Eligibility   This program is open to residents of Massachusetts who are 1) high school seniors or freshmen at a college in any state and the child of an active or honorably discharged member of the Massachusetts National Guard or Reserve component who has been activated overseas after September 11, 2001; and 2) an undergraduate, trade school, or graduate student at a school in any state and the relative of a servicemember who died as a result of military service after September 11, 2001. Selection is based on academic merit and financial need.

Financial data   The stipend is $1,000.

Duration   1 year.

Number awarded   10 each year: 1 in each Massachusetts Congressional district.

Deadline   Deadline not specified.

[666]
MILITARY INTELLIGENCE CORPS ASSOCIATION SCHOLARSHIPS

Military Intelligence Corps Association
Attn: Scholarship Committee
P.O. Box 13020
Fort Huachuca, AZ 85670-3020
(520) 227-3894   E-mail: execdir@micorps.org
Web: www.micastore.com/Scholarships.html

Summary   To provide financial assistance for college to members of the Military Intelligence Corps Association (MICA) and their immediate family.

Eligibility   This program is open to active-duty, Reserve, National Guard, and retired military intelligence soldiers who are MICA members and to their immediate family (spouses, children, or other relatives living with and supported by the

MICA member). Applicants must be attending or accepted for attendance at an accredited college, university, vocational school, or technical institution. Along with their application, they must submit a 1-page essay on their educational goals and program of study. Financial need is not considered in the selection process.

Financial data   Stipend amounts vary depending on the availability of funds and the number of qualified applicants, but recently were $5,000. Funds are to be used for tuition, books, and classroom fees; support is not provided for housing, board, travel, or administrative purposes.

Duration   1 year; recipients may reapply.

Number awarded   Varies each year; recently, 4 were awarded.

Deadline   May of each year.

[667]
MILITARY NON-RESIDENT TUITION WAIVER AFTER ASSIGNMENT IN TEXAS

Texas Higher Education Coordinating Board
Attn: Grants and Special Programs
1200 East Anderson Lane
P.O. Box 12788
Austin, TX 78711-2788
(512) 427-6340   Toll Free: (800) 242-3062
Fax: (512) 427-6420   E-mail: grantinfo@thecb.state.tx.us
Web: www.collegeforalltexans.com

Summary   To provide educational assistance to the spouses and children of Texas military personnel assigned elsewhere.

Eligibility   This program is open to the spouses and dependent children of members of the U.S. armed forces or commissioned officers of the Public Health Service who remain in Texas when the member is reassigned to duty outside of the state. The spouse or dependent child must reside continuously in Texas. Applicants must be attending or planning to attend a Texas public college or university.

Financial data   Eligible students are entitled to pay tuition and fees at the resident rate at publicly-supported colleges and universities in Texas.

Duration   The waiver remains in effect for the duration of the member's first assignment outside of Texas.

Additional information   This program became effective in 2003.

Number awarded   Varies each year.

Deadline   Deadline not specified.

[668]
MILITARY NON-RESIDENT TUITION WAIVER FOR MEMBERS, SPOUSES OR CHILDREN ASSIGNED TO DUTY IN TEXAS

Texas Higher Education Coordinating Board
Attn: Grants and Special Programs
1200 East Anderson Lane
P.O. Box 12788
Austin, TX 78711-2788
(512) 427-6340   Toll Free: (800) 242-3062
Fax: (512) 427-6420   E-mail: grantinfo@thecb.state.tx.us
Web: www.collegeforalltexans.com

Summary   To exempt military personnel stationed in Texas and their dependents from the payment of non-resident tuition at public institutions of higher education in the state.

Eligibility Eligible for these waivers are members of the U.S. armed forces and commissioned officers of the Public Health Service from states other than Texas, their spouses, and dependent children. Applicants must be assigned to Texas and attending or planning to attend a public college or university in the state.

Financial data Although persons eligible under this program are classified as non-residents, they are entitled to pay the resident tuition at Texas institutions of higher education, regardless of their length of residence in Texas.

Duration 1 year; may be renewed.

Number awarded Varies each year.

Deadline Deadline not specified.

[669]
MILITARY NON-RESIDENT TUITION WAIVER FOR MEMBERS, SPOUSES OR CHILDREN WHO REMAIN CONTINUOUSLY ENROLLED IN HIGHER EDUCATION IN TEXAS

Texas Higher Education Coordinating Board
Attn: Grants and Special Programs
1200 East Anderson Lane
P.O. Box 12788
Austin, TX 78711-2788
(512) 427-6340   Toll Free: (800) 242-3062
Fax: (512) 427-6420   E-mail: grantinfo@thecb.state.tx.us
Web: www.collegeforalltexans.com

Summary To waive non-resident tuition at Texas public colleges and universities for members of the armed forces and their families who are no longer in the military.

Eligibility Eligible for these waivers are members of the U.S. armed forces, commissioned officers of the Public Health Service (PHS), their spouses, and their children. Applicants must have previously been eligible to pay tuition at the resident rate while enrolled in a degree or certificate program at a Texas public college or university because they were a member, spouse, or child of a member of the armed forces or PHS. This waiver is available after the servicemember, spouse, or parent is no longer a member of the armed forces or a commissioned officer of the PHS. The student must remain continuously enrolled in the same degree or certificate program in subsequent terms or semesters.

Financial data The student's eligibility to pay tuition and fees at the rate provided for Texas students does not terminate because the member, spouse, or parent is no longer in the service.

Duration 1 year.

Additional information This program became effective in September 2003.

Number awarded Varies each year.

Deadline Deadline not specified.

[670]
MILITARY ORDER OF THE PURPLE HEART SCHOLARSHIP PROGRAM

Military Order of the Purple Heart
Attn: Scholarships
5413-B Backlick Road
Springfield, VA 22151-3960
(703) 642-5360   Toll Free: (888) 668-1656
Fax: (703) 642-2054
E-mail: scholarship@purpleheart.org
Web: www.purpleheart.org/Scholarships/Default.aspx

Summary To provide financial assistance for college or graduate school to members of the Military Order of the Purple Heart (MOPH) and their families.

Eligibility This program is open to 1) members of the MOPH who received a Purple Heart; 2) spouses and widows of MOPH members; 3) direct descendants (children, stepchildren, adopted children, and grandchildren) of veterans who are MOPH members or were members at the time of death; and 4) spouses, widows, and direct descendants of veterans killed in action or who died of wounds. Applicants must be graduating seniors or graduates of an accredited high school who are enrolled or accepted for enrollment in a full-time program of study in a college, university, or trade school. They must have a GPA of 2.75 or higher. U.S. citizenship is required. Along with their application, they must submit an essay of 200 to 300 words on a topic that changes annually but recently was, "The American Veteran." Financial need is not considered in the selection process.

Financial data The stipend is $3,000 per year.

Duration 1 year; may be renewed up to 2 additional years.

Additional information Membership in MOPH is open to all veterans who received a Purple Heart Medal and were discharged under conditions other than dishonorable. A processing fee of $15 is required.

Number awarded Varies each year; recently, 83 were awarded.

Deadline February of each year.

[671]
MILITARY ORDER OF THE STARS AND BARS SCHOLARSHIPS

Military Order of the Stars and Bars
P.O. Box 1700
White House, TN 37188-1700
Web: www.militaryorderofthestarsandbars.org

Summary To provide financial assistance to high school seniors and currently-enrolled college and graduate students who are the descendants of Confederate officers or public servants.

Eligibility This program is open to graduating high school seniors and currently-enrolled undergraduate and graduate students who are the genealogically proven descendants of 1) a Confederate officer; 2) a member of the Confederate executive or legislative branches of government; or 3) a member of the Confederate legislative, judiciary, or executive branches of state government. Applicants must submit a personal letter of application (describing academic and career aspirations), genealogical proof of Confederate ancestor, a completed and signed application form, and 3 letters of recommendation. Selection is based on academic performance

(70%), extracurricular activities (10%), the personal statement (10%), and letters of recommendation (10%).

Financial data The stipend is $1,000.

Duration 1 year; nonrenewable.

Additional information The Military Order of the Stars and Bars is an international genealogical, historical, and patriotic organization that was organized in 1938 and is composed of male descendants of the Confederate officer corps, Confederate civil officials, and state officials. These scholarships are designated the Major General Patrick R. Cleburne Scholarship (for students residing in the area of the Army of Trans-Mississippi), the Lt. General Nathan B. Forrest Scholarship (for students residing in the area of the Army of Tennessee), and the General Robert E. Lee Scholarship (for students residing in the area of the Army of Northern Virginia).

Number awarded Varies each year, but at least 1 in each of the 3 Confederate Army departments.

Deadline February of each year.

[672]
MILITARY SPOUSE CAREER ADVANCEMENT ACCOUNTS (MYCAA) PROGRAM

Department of Defense
Attn: Spouse Education and Career Opportunities
 Program
1400 Defense Pentagon
Washington, DC 20301-1400
(703) 253-7599   Toll Free: (800) 342-9647
TDD: (866) 607-6794
E-mail: MyCAAHELP@militaryonesource.com
Web: aiportal.acc.af.mil/mycaa/default.aspx

Summary To provide financial assistance to military spouses who are interested in obtaining additional education that will improve their employment opportunities.

Eligibility This program is open to military spouses who are enrolled or planning to enroll in educational or training courses that lead to an associate degree, license, certificate, or certification at an accredited college, university, or technical school in the United States or an approved testing organization that expands employment or portable career opportunities for military spouses. Applicants must be spouses of servicemembers on active duty in pay grades E-1 to E-5, W-1 to W-2, or O-1 to O-2 who can start and complete their course work while their military sponsor is on Title 10 military orders, including spouses married to members of the National Guard and Reserve components. Support is not available for non-academic credit or ungraded courses; academic credit by examination courses; general studies, liberal arts, or interdisciplinary associate degrees that do not have a concentration; personal enrichment courses; transportation, lodging, child care, or medical services; study abroad programs; or high school completion programs. Spouses who are themselves in the military or married to members of the Coast Guard are not eligible.

Financial data The maximum support per fiscal year is $2,000; spouses may receive a lifetime total of $4,000 from this program. Funds are paid directly to schools.

Duration Associate degrees must be completed in 12 months and licenses and certificates within 18 months. The times of study may be extended over a 3-year period.

Additional information This program began in March 2009 but was suspended in February 2010 when an unexpected large number of spouses applied. It was resumed for spouses who had already applied in March 2010 and for new enrollees in October 2010.

Number awarded More than 136,000 military spouses and more than 3,000 schools are currently participating in this program.

Deadline Applications may be submitted at any time.

[673]
MILITARY SPOUSES OF NEWPORT SCHOLARSHIPS FOR HIGH SCHOOL STUDENTS

Military Spouses of Newport
Attn: Scholarship Committee
P.O. Box 5115
Newport, RI 02841
Web: www.milspousenewport.org/page-646318

Summary To provide financial assistance for college in any state to high school seniors in Rhode Island whose parent has a tie to Naval Station Newport.

Eligibility This program is open to graduating high school seniors who plan to enroll full time at an accredited 2- or 4-year college or university in any state. Applicants must be dependent children possessing a valid military ID card of 1) active-duty military personnel (any branch, office or enlisted) attached to the Newport Naval Station in Rhode Island); 2) retired military (any branch, officer or enlisted) and a resident of Rhode Island; or 3) deceased military, while on active duty or paid retired status (any branch, officer or enlisted) and a resident of Rhode Island. Along with their application, they must submit a 1-page essay on what it's like to be a child of a military parent. Selection is based on that essay; academic achievement (based on transcripts and ACT/SAT scores); school-sponsored extracurricular activities; community involvement, experience, and volunteerism; honors and awards; achievements and/or recognitions; and letters of recommendation.

Financial data A stipend is awarded (amount not specified).

Duration 1 year.

Number awarded Varies each year.

Deadline April of each year.

[674]
MINNESOTA G.I. BILL PROGRAM

Minnesota Department of Veterans Affairs
Attn: Programs and Services Division
20 West 12th Street, Room 206
St. Paul, MN 55155
(651) 296-2562   Toll Free: (888) LINK-VET
TDD: (800) 627-3529   E-mail: MNGIBill@state.mn.us
Web: mn.gov/mdva/resources/education/minnesotagibill.jsp

Summary To provide financial assistance for college or graduate school in Minnesota to residents who 1) served in the military after September 11, 2001 or 2) are the family members of deceased or disabled military personnel.

Eligibility This program is open to residents of Minnesota enrolled at colleges and universities in the state as undergraduate or graduate students. Applicants must be 1) a veteran who is serving or has served honorably in a branch of the U.S. armed forces at any time; 2) a non-veteran who has served honorably for a total of 5 years or more cumulatively as a member of the Minnesota National Guard or other active or Reserve component of the U.S. armed forces, and any part of that service occurred on or after September 11, 2001; or 3) a surviving child or spouse of a person who has served in the military at any time on or after September 11, 2001 and who has died or has a total and permanent disability as a result of that military service. Financial need is also considered in the selection process.

Financial data The stipend is $1,000 per semester for full-time study or $500 per semester for part-time study. The maximum award is $3,000 per academic year or $10,000 per lifetime.

Duration 1 year; may be renewed, provided the recipient continues to make satisfactory academic progress.

Additional information This program was established by the Minnesota Legislature in 2007.

Number awarded Varies each year.

Deadline Deadline not specified.

[675]
MINNESOTA LEGION AUXILIARY DEPARTMENT SCHOLARSHIPS

American Legion Auxiliary
Department of Minnesota
State Veterans Service Building
20 West 12th Street, Room 314
St. Paul, MN 55155-2069
(651) 224-7634   Toll Free: (888) 217-9598
Fax: (651) 224-5243   E-mail: deptoffice@mnala.org
Web: www.mnala.org/Scholarships.aspx

Summary To provide financial assistance to the children and grandchildren of Minnesota veterans who are interested in attending college in the state.

Eligibility This program is open to the children and grandchildren of veterans who served during designated periods of wartime. Applicants must be a resident of Minnesota or a member of an American Legion post, American Legion Auxiliary unit, or Sons of the American Legion detachment in the Department of Minnesota. They must be high school seniors or graduates, have a GPA of 2.0 or higher, be able to demonstrate financial need, and be planning to attend a vocational or business school, college, or university in Minnesota. Along with their application, they must submit a brief essay, telling of their plans for college, career goals, and extracurricular and community activities.

Financial data The stipend is $1,000. Funds are to be used to pay for tuition or books and are sent directly to the recipient's school.

Duration 1 year.

Number awarded 7 each year.

Deadline March of each year.

[676]
MINNESOTA LEGION AUXILIARY PAST PRESIDENTS PARLEY HEALTH CARE SCHOLARSHIP

American Legion Auxiliary
Department of Minnesota
State Veterans Service Building
20 West 12th Street, Room 314
St. Paul, MN 55155-2069
(651) 224-7634   Toll Free: (888) 217-9598
Fax: (651) 224-5243   E-mail: deptoffice@mnala.org
Web: www.mnala.org/Scholarships.aspx

Summary To provide financial assistance for education in health care fields to members of the American Legion Auxiliary in Minnesota.

Eligibility This program is open to residents of Minnesota who have been members of the American Legion Auxiliary for at least 3 years. Applicants must have a GPA of 2.0 or higher and be planning to study in Minnesota. They must be preparing for a career in a phase of health care, including nursing assistant, registered nurse, licensed practical nurse, X-ray or other technician, dietician, physical or other therapist, dental hygienist, or dental assistant.

Financial data The stipend is $1,000. Funds are sent directly to the recipient's school after satisfactory completion of the first quarter.

Duration 1 year.

Number awarded Up to 10 each year.

Deadline March of each year.

[677]
MINNESOTA NATIONAL GUARD SURVIVOR ENTITLEMENT TUITION REIMBURSEMENT PROGRAM

Department of Military Affairs
Attn: Education Services Officer
JFMN-J1-ARED
20 West 12th Street
St. Paul, MN 55155-2098
(651) 282-4589   Toll Free: (800) 657-3848
Fax: (651) 282-4694
E-mail: ng.mn.mnarng.mbx.assets-education@mail.mil
Web: www.minnesotanationalguard.org

Summary To provide financial assistance for college or graduate school to survivors of members of the Minnesota National Guard who were killed on active duty.

Eligibility This program is open to surviving spouses and children of members of the Minnesota Army or Air National Guard who were killed while performing military duty. Dependent children are eligible until their 24th birthday; surviving spouses are eligible regardless of age or remarriage; all survivors remain eligible even if they move out of state and become residents of another state. The Guard member's death must have occurred within the scope of assigned duties while in a federal duty status or on state active service. Applicants must be enrolled as undergraduate or graduate students at colleges or universities in Minnesota. Reimbursement is provided only for undergraduate courses completed with a grade of "C" or better or for graduate courses completed with a grade of "B" or better.

Financial data The maximum reimbursement rate is 100% of the tuition rate at the University of Minnesota Twin Cities campus, with a maximum benefit of $13,000 per fiscal year for undergraduate course work or $22,000 per fiscal year for graduate course work.

Duration   1 academic term, to a maximum of 18 credits per term; may be renewed for a total of 144 semester credits or 208 quarter credits.

Additional information   This program became effective in 1992.

Number awarded   Varies each year.

Deadline   Participants must request reimbursement within 90 days of the last official day of the term.

[678]
MISSISSIPPI EDUCATIONAL ASSISTANCE FOR MIA/POW DEPENDENTS

Mississippi State Veterans Affairs Board
3466 Highway 80
P.O. Box 5947
Pearl, MS 39288-5947
(601) 576-4850   Toll Free: (877) 203-5632
Fax: (601) 576-4868
Web: www.vab.ms.gov

Summary   To provide financial assistance for college to the children of Mississippi residents who are POWs or MIAs.

Eligibility   This entitlement program is open to the children of members of the armed services whose official home of record and residence is in Mississippi and who are officially reported as being either a prisoner of a foreign government or missing in action. Applicants must be attending or planning to attend a state-supported college or university in Mississippi.

Financial data   This assistance covers all costs of college attendance.

Duration   Up to 8 semesters.

Number awarded   Varies each year.

Deadline   Deadline not specified.

[679]
MISSISSIPPI NATIONAL GUARD NCO ASSOCIATION SCHOLARSHIPS

Mississippi National Guard NCO Association
Attn: Executive Director
P.O. Box 48
Lauderdale, MS 39335
(601) 632-4535   E-mail: msccm10@gmail.com
Web: www.msncoa.org/Scholorships.php

Summary   To provide financial assistance to dependents of members of the Mississippi National Guard NCO Association who are interested in attending college in any state.

Eligibility   This program is open to the unmarried dependent children and spouses of annual, enlisted, retired, and life members of the association and of deceased members who were annual, enlisted, retired, or life members at the time of death. Applicants must be high school seniors or undergraduate students with at least 1 full semester remaining before graduation. They must be attending or planning to attend an accredited university, college, community college, vocational/technical, business, or trade school in any state. Selection is based on GPA (25 points), ACT score (25 points), a personal letter on their long-range plan (20 points), honors (10 points), school, community, church, and social activities (10 points), and letters of recommendation (10 points).

Financial data   A stipend is awarded (amount not specified).

Duration   1 year.

Number awarded   Varies each year.

Deadline   January of each year.

[680]
MISSOURI NATIONAL GUARD ASSOCIATION SCHOLARSHIPS

Missouri National Guard Association
Attn: Scholarship
2303 Militia Drive
Jefferson City, MO 65101-1203
(573) 632-4240   Toll Free: (800) 972-1164
E-mail: executivedirector@mongaonline.com
Web: www.mongaonline.com/?page=Scholarship

Summary   To provide financial assistance to members of the Missouri National Guard Association (MoNGA) and their dependents who are interested in attending college in any state.

Eligibility   This program is open to annual, associate, and lifetime members of the association and their dependents. Applicants must be interested in working on a degree at an accredited junior college or 4-year college or university in any state. They must submit high school or college transcripts, 3 letters of recommendation, and a letter describing their desire to continue their education, why they need financial assistance, and how they have demonstrated the traits (scholarship, citizenship, and leadership) upon which selection is based.

Financial data   Stipends for MoNGA members are $1,000 or $750. Stipends for dependents are $750 or $500. In addition, USAA Insurance Corporation sponsors a $500 scholarship for enlisted MoNGA members. Funds are paid directly to the recipient's college or university.

Duration   1 year.

Number awarded   5 each year: 2 for MoNGA members (1 at $1,000 and 1 at $750), 2 for dependents (1 at $750 and 1 at $500), and 1 USAA scholarship.

Deadline   February of each year.

[681]
MISSOURI PAST NATIONAL PRESIDENTS' SCHOLARSHIP

Ladies Auxiliary to the Veterans of Foreign Wars-
  Department of Missouri
c/o Brenda McCann
629 S.W. 36th Terrace
Lee's Summit, MO 64082
(816) 223-8561
E-mail: brendacollinsmccann@yahoo.com
Web: www.myvfwaux.org/moladies/programs/scholarship-2

Summary   To provide financial assistance to high school seniors in Missouri who have a tie to the Veterans of Foreign Wars (VFW) or its Ladies Auxiliary and plan to attend college in any state.

Eligibility   This program is open to seniors graduating from high schools in Missouri who are the children, grandchildren, or great-grandchildren of VFW or Ladies Auxiliary members. Applicants must be planning to enroll at a college, university, or vocational/technical school in any state. Along with their application, they must submit a 300-word essay on their community involvement, their volunteer activities, the honors they have received, and organizations outside of school in which they participate.

Financial data Stipends are $1,800 or $1,200.

Duration 1 year.

Number awarded 2 each year: 1 at $1,800 and 1 at $1,200.

Deadline April of each year.

[682]
MISSOURI VIETNAM VETERAN SURVIVOR GRANT PROGRAM

Missouri Department of Higher Education
Attn: Student Financial Assistance
205 Jefferson Street
P.O. Box 1469
Jefferson City, MO 65102-1469
(573) 526-7958   Toll Free: (800) 473-6757
Fax: (573) 751-6635   E-mail: info@dhe.mo.gov
Web: www.dhe.mo.gov/ppc/grants/vietnamveterans.php

Summary To provide financial assistance to survivors of certain deceased Missouri Vietnam veterans who plan to attend college in the state.

Eligibility This program is open to surviving spouses and children of veterans who served in the military in Vietnam or the war zone in southeast Asia, who were residents of Missouri when first entering military service and at the time of death, whose death was attributed to or caused by exposure to toxic chemicals during the Vietnam conflict, and who served in the Vietnam Theater between 1961 and 1972. Applicants must be Missouri residents enrolled in a program leading to a certificate, associate degree, or baccalaureate degree at an approved postsecondary institution in the state. Students working on a degree or certificate in theology or divinity are not eligible. U.S. citizenship or permanent resident status is required.

Financial data The maximum annual grant is the lesser of 1) the actual tuition charged at the school where the recipient is enrolled; or 2) the amount of tuition charged to a Missouri undergraduate resident enrolled full time in the same class level and in the same academic major as a student at the Missouri public 4-year regional institutions.

Duration 1 semester; may be renewed until the recipient has obtained a baccalaureate degree, has received the award for 10 semesters, or has completed 150 semester credit hours, whichever comes first. Dependent children remain eligible until they reach 25 years of age. Spouses remain eligible until the fifth anniversary of the veteran's death.

Additional information Awards are not available for summer study.

Number awarded Up to 12 each year.

Deadline There is no application deadline, but early submission of the completed application is encouraged.

[683]
MISSOURI WARTIME VETERAN'S SURVIVOR GRANT PROGRAM

Missouri Department of Higher Education
Attn: Student Financial Assistance
205 Jefferson Street
P.O. Box 1469
Jefferson City, MO 65102-1469
(573) 526-7958   Toll Free: (800) 473-6757
Fax: (573) 751-6635   E-mail: info@dhe.mo.gov
Web: www.dhe.mo.gov/ppc/grants/wartimevetsurvivor.php

Summary To provide financial assistance to survivors of deceased or disabled Missouri post-September 11, 2001 veterans who plan to attend college in the state.

Eligibility This program is open to spouses and children of veterans whose deaths or injuries were a result of combat action or were attributed to an illness that was contracted while serving in combat action, or who became at least 80% disabled as a result of injuries or accidents sustained in combat action since September 11, 2001. The veteran must have been a Missouri resident when first entering military service or at the time of death or injury. The spouse or child must be a U.S. citizen or permanent resident or otherwise lawfully present in the United States; children of veterans must be younger than 25 years of age. All applicants must be enrolled or accepted for enrollment at least half time at participating public college or university in Missouri.

Financial data The maximum annual grant is the lesser of 1) the actual tuition charged at the school where the recipient is enrolled; or 2) the amount of tuition charged to a Missouri resident enrolled in the same number of hours at the University of Missouri at Columbia. Additional allowances provide up to $2,000 per semester for room and board and the lesser of the actual cost for books or $500.

Duration 1 year. May be renewed, provided the recipient maintains a GPA of 2.5 or higher and makes satisfactory academic progress; children of veterans are eligible until they turn 25 years of age or receive their first bachelor's degree, whichever occurs first.

Number awarded Up to 25 each year.

Deadline There is no application deadline, but early submission of the completed application is encouraged.

[684]
MOAA STUDENT LOAN PROGRAM

Military Officers Association of America
Attn: Educational Assistance Program
201 North Washington Street
Alexandria, VA 22314-2539
(703) 549-2311   Toll Free: (800) 234-MOAA
Fax: (703) 838-5819   E-mail: edassist@moaa.org
Web: www.moaa.org/loans

Summary To provide interest-free loans for undergraduate education to children of former, active, or retired officers or active or retired enlisted military personnel.

Eligibility This program is open to children of active, Reserve, National Guard, and retired uniformed service personnel (Army, Navy, Air Force, Marines, Coast Guard, Public Health Service, or National Oceanic and Atmospheric Administration). Applicants must be under 24 years of age. Parents who are officers eligible for membership in the Military Officers Association of America (MOAA) must be members. Children of enlisted personnel are also eligible to apply. Selection is based on scholastic ability (GPA of 3.0 or higher), participation, leadership, and financial need.

Financial data Loans up to $5,500 per year are available. Repayment at an agreed rate begins 3 to 4 months after graduation or after leaving college, but no interest is charged.

Duration 1 year; may be renewed for 4 additional years as long as the recipient remains enrolled full time and has not yet graduated.

Additional information The MOAA was formerly named The Retired Officers Association (TROA). No loans are made for graduate study.

Number awarded Varies each year; recently, 667 students received loans through this program as first-time recipients.

Deadline February of each year.

[685]
MONTANA WAR ORPHANS WAIVER

Office of the Commissioner of Higher Education
Attn: Montana University System
State Scholarship Coordinator
2500 Broadway
P.O. Box 203201
Helena, MT 59620-3201
(406) 444-6570   Toll Free: (800) 537-7508
Fax: (406) 444-1469   E-mail: snewlun@montana.edu
Web: www.mus.edu

Summary To provide financial assistance for undergraduate education to the children of Montana veterans who died in the line of duty or as a result of service-connected disabilities.

Eligibility This program is open to children of members of the U.S. armed forces who served on active duty during World War II, the Korean Conflict, the Vietnam Conflict, the Afghanistan Conflict, or the Iraq Conflict; were legal residents of Montana at the time of entry into service; and were killed in action or died as a result of injury, disease, or other disability while in the service. Applicants must be no older than 25 years of age. Financial need is considered in the selection process.

Financial data Students eligible for this benefit are entitled to attend any unit of the Montana University System without payment of undergraduate registration or incidental fees.

Duration Undergraduate students are eligible for continued fee waiver as long as they maintain reasonable academic progress as full-time students.

Number awarded Varies each year.

Deadline Deadline not specified.

[686]
MONTFORD POINT MARINE ASSOCIATION SCHOLARSHIP

Montford Point Marine Association
c/o James Maillard, National Scholarship Director
7714 113th Street, Number 2G
Forest Hills, NY 11375-7119
(718) 261-9640   Fax: (718) 261-3021
E-mail: Scholarships@montfordpointmarines.com
Web: www.montfordpointmarines.com

Summary To provide financial assistance to high school seniors, high school graduates, and current undergraduates who have a connection to the Montford Point Marine Association (MPMA).

Eligibility This program is open to high school seniors, high school graduates, or current college students who have a connection to the MPMA. Along with their application, they must submit academic transcripts, information on their connection to MPMA, and a 500-word essay on a topic that changes periodically. Only undergraduate study is supported. The family income of applicants must be less than $90,000 per year.

Financial data Stipends depend on the need of the recipient and the availability of funds, but generally range from $500 to $2,500 per year.

Duration 1 year.

Additional information Membership in the MPMA is restricted to former Marines and the families of Marines who served at Camp Montford Point, North Carolina where African Americans trained during the days of segregation from 1942 to 1949. This scholarship program, which began in 2003, operates in coordination with the Marine Corps Scholarship Foundation.

Number awarded 1 or more each year.

Deadline Deadline not specified.

[687]
MSON SCHOLARSHIPS FOR SPOUSES

Military Spouses of Newport
Attn: Scholarship Committee
P.O. Box 5115
Newport, RI 02841
Web: www.milspousenewport.org/page-646318

Summary To provide financial assistance for college in any state to residents of Rhode Island whose spouse has a tie to Naval Station Newport.

Eligibility This program is open to residents of Rhode Island whose spouse is an active duty servicemember and assigned to Naval Station Newport, attached to Naval Station Newport, or residing within 35 miles of Newport. Applicants must be enrolled or planning to enroll at an accredited postsecondary institution or certification program in any state. They must be a high school graduate or GED recipient and have a GPA of 2.5 or higher. Along with their application, they must submit a 1-page essay on what they would do to improve the sponsoring organization. Selection is based on that essay, academic achievement, extracurricular activities, community involvement, employment experience, volunteerism, honors and awards, achievements and/or recognitions, letters of recommendation, and financial information.

Financial data A stipend is awarded (amount not specified).

Duration 1 year.

Number awarded Varies each year.

Deadline April of each year.

[688]
NANNIE W. NORFLEET SCHOLARSHIP

American Legion Auxiliary
Department of North Carolina
P.O. Box 25726
Raleigh, NC 27611-5726
(919) 832-4051　　　　　　Fax: (919) 832-1888
E-mail: ncala@ncrrbiz.com
Web: www.alanorthcarolina.com

Summary To provide financial assistance to members of the American Legion Auxiliary in North Carolina and their children and grandchildren who plan to attend college in any state.

Eligibility This program is open to North Carolina residents who are either adult members of the American Legion Auxiliary or high school seniors (with preference to the children and grandchildren of members). Applicants must be interested in attending college in any state. They must be able to demonstrate financial need.

Financial data The stipend is $1,000.

Duration 1 year.

Number awarded 1 each year.

Deadline March of each year.

[689]
NARRAGANSETT BAY POST SAME SCHOLARSHIP

Society of American Military Engineers-Narragansett Bay Post
Attn: Scholarship Committee
15 Mohegan Avenue
New London, CT 06320
(860) 444-8312　　　　　　Fax: (860) 444-8219
E-mail: Gregory.j.carabine@uscg.mil
Web: posts.same.org/Narragansett/scholarship.htm

Summary To provide financial assistance to residents of New England (particularly ROTC students and military family members) who are interested in working on a bachelor's degree in construction-related fields at colleges in any state.

Eligibility This program is open to residents of New England (preferably Connecticut, Massachusetts, and Rhode Island) who are graduating high school seniors or students currently enrolled at a college or university in any state. Applicants must be interested in working on a bachelor's degree in an accredited engineering or architectural program, preferably in civil engineering, environmental engineering, architecture, or other construction-related program. Preference is given to students who 1) are dependents of or sponsored by a member of the Narragansett Bay Post of the Society of American Military Engineers (SAME); 2) are enrolled in ROTC (preferably not a recipient of an ROTC scholarship); or 3) have prior U.S. military service and/or public service. Along with their application, they must submit a 500-word essay about themselves, their achievements, or their situation. Selection is based on that essay, grades and class rank, school or community honors, extracurricular activities, leadership, volunteer activities, and completeness and quality of the application. U.S. citizenship is required.

Financial data The stipend is $1,000.

Duration 1 year.

Number awarded 1 each year.

Deadline May of each year.

[690]
NATIONAL 4TH INFANTRY (IVY) DIVISION ASSOCIATION ANNUAL SCHOLARSHIP

National 4th Infantry (IVY) Division Association
c/o Don Kelby, Executive Director
P.O. Box 1914
St. Peters, MO 63376-0035
(314) 606-1969　　　　　E-mail: 4thidaed@swbell.net
Web: www.4thinfantry.org/content/scholarships-donations

Summary To provide financial assistance for college to members of the National 4th Infantry (IVY) Division Association and their families.

Eligibility This program is open to association members in good standing and all blood relatives of active association members in good standing. Recipients are chosen by lottery.

Financial data The stipend is $2,000.

Duration 1 year; may be renewed.

Additional information The trust fund from which these scholarships are awarded was created by the officers and enlisted men of the 4th Infantry Division as a living memorial to the men of the division who died in Vietnam. Originally, it was only open to children of members of the division who died in the line of duty while serving in Vietnam between August 1, 1966 and December 31, 1977. When all those eligible had completed college, it adopted its current requirements.

Number awarded Up to 10 each year.

Deadline June of each year.

[691]
NATIONAL 4TH INFANTRY (IVY) DIVISION ASSOCIATION MEMORIAL SCHOLARSHIP

National 4th Infantry (IVY) Division Association
c/o Don Kelby, Executive Director
P.O. Box 1914
St. Peters, MO 63376-0035
(314) 606-1969　　　　　E-mail: 4thidaed@swbell.net
Web: www.4thinfantry.org/content/scholarships-donations

Summary To provide financial assistance for college to descendants of soldiers who were killed while serving in the Fourth Infantry Division in the Global War on Terror (GWOT).

Eligibility This program is open to the children, stepchildren, and adopted children of soldiers who were killed while serving with the Fourth Infantry Division in Iraq, Afghanistan, and/or the GWOT. Membership in the sponsoring organization is not required. Recipients are chosen by lottery.

Financial data The stipend is $2,000.

Duration 1 year.

Number awarded Up to 10 each year.

Deadline June of each year.

[692]
NATIONAL ASSOCIATION FOR UNIFORMED SERVICES SCHOLARSHIP PROGRAM

National Association for Uniformed Services
Attn: Scholarship Committee
5535 Hempstead Way
Springfield, VA 22151
(703) 750-1342　　　Toll Free: (800) 842-3451, ext. 1803
Fax: (703) 354-4380　　　E-mail: scholarship@naus.org
Web: www.naus.org/benefits-scholarship.html

Summary To provide financial assistance for college to members of the National Association for Uniformed Services (NAUS) and their families.

Eligibility This program is open to NAUS members, their spouses, and their children. Applicants must be high school seniors or undergraduates enrolled full or part time in a degree- or certificate-granting program. High school seniors must have a GPA of 3.0 or higher and undergraduates must have a GPA of 2.5 or higher. Along with their application, they must submit statements, up to 100 words each, on 1) their reasons for enrolling in a postsecondary education program; and 2) a list of academic achievements, personal achievements, extracurricular activities, and any community service performed in the past 2 years. Financial need is not considered in the selection process.

Financial data The stipend is $2,500.

Duration 1 year.

Additional information Membership in NAUS is open to members of the armed forces, veterans, retirees, their spouses, and their widow(er)s.

Number awarded Varies each year; recently, 8 were awarded.

Deadline April of each year.

[693]
NATIONAL GUARD ASSOCIATION OF ARIZONA SCHOLARSHIPS

National Guard Association of Arizona
Attn: Scholarship Committee
5640 East McDowell Road
Phoenix, AZ 85008
(602) 275-8305   Fax: (602) 275-9254
E-mail: ngaofaz@aol.com
Web: www.ngaaz.org/scholarship.html

Summary To provide financial assistance to students at colleges and universities in Arizona who have a connection to the National Guard and the National Guard Association of Arizona (NGAAZ).

Eligibility This program is open to full-time students at colleges, universities, and community colleges in Arizona. Applicants must be a member of 1 of the following categories: 1) a current enlisted member of the Arizona National Guard; 2) a current officer member of the Arizona National Guard who is also a member of the NGAAZ; or 3) a child or spouse of an NGAAZ member. Applicants must submit 2 letters of recommendation and verification of good standing from the first commander in the chain of command of the Arizona National Guard. Selection is based on GPA (25%), community service (15%), letters of recommendation (15%), knowledge of National Guard philosophy (15%), and financial need (30%).

Financial data The stipend is $1,500.

Duration 1 year; nonrenewable.

Number awarded 3 each year: 1 to each category of applicant.

Deadline April of each year.

[694]
NATIONAL GUARD ASSOCIATION OF CALIFORNIA SCHOLARSHIPS

National Guard Association of California
Attn: Executive Director
3336 Bradshaw Road, Suite 230
Sacramento, CA 95827-2615
(916) 362-3411   Toll Free: (800) 647-0018
Fax: (916) 362-3707
Web: www.ngac.org

Summary To provide financial assistance to members of the National Guard Association of California (NGAC) and their dependents who are interested in attending college in any state.

Eligibility This program is open to 1) current members of the NGAC; 2) dependents of NGAC members; and 3) dependents of retired California National Guard servicemembers who are life members of the NGAC. Applicants must be attending or planning to attend a college, university, or trade school in any state. Along with their application, they must submit a 500-word essay on the greatest challenge they have faced and how it has impacted them. Selection is based on that essay; unweighted GPA; extracurricular activities, honors, and/or awards; letters of recommendation; and (if case of a tie after evaluation of those criteria) SAT or ACT scores.

Financial data Stipends range from $250 to $1,000. Funds are paid directly to the recipient.

Duration 1 year.

Number awarded Varies each year; recently, 19 were awarded.

Deadline May of each year.

[695]
NATIONAL GUARD ASSOCIATION OF CONNECTICUT SCHOLARSHIP PROGRAM

National Guard Association of Connecticut
Attn: Scholarship Committee
360 Broad Street
Hartford, CT 06105-3795
(860) 247-5000
E-mail: ngactexecutivedirector@gmail.com
Web: www.ngact.org/scholarships

Summary To provide financial assistance to members and the family of members of the National Guard Association of Connecticut (NGACT) who are interested in attending college in any state.

Eligibility This program is open to 1) NGACT members; 2) unmarried children and grandchildren of NGACT members; 3) spouses of NGACT members; and 4) unremarried spouses and unmarried dependent children and grandchildren of deceased NGACT members who were members in good standing at the time of their death. Applicants must be attending or planning to attend, on a part- or full-time basis, a college, university, trade school, or business school in any state. Graduate students are not eligible to apply. Along with their application, they must submit: an official transcript, a letter on their desire to continue their education and why financial assistance is required, 2 letters of recommendation, and 1 letter of academic reference. Selection is based on academic record, character, leadership, and need.

Financial data A stipend is awarded (amount not specified). Funds are sent to the recipient but are made payable to the recipient's choice of school. To receive the awards, proof of enrollment must be presented.

Duration 1 year.

Number awarded Varies each year.

Deadline May of each year.

[696]
NATIONAL GUARD ASSOCIATION OF INDIANA EDUCATIONAL GRANTS

National Guard Association of Indiana
Attn: Educational Grant Committee
2002 South Holt Road, Building 8
Indianapolis, IN 46241-4839
(317) 247-3196   Toll Free: (800) 219-2173
Fax: (317) 247-3575   E-mail: membership@ngai.net
Web: www.ngai.net/membership

Summary To provide financial assistance to members of the National Guard Association of Indiana (NGAI) and their dependents who plan to attend college in any state.

Eligibility This program is open to NGAI members and their dependents who are currently serving in the Indiana National Guard or are retired members of the Indiana National Guard. Applicants must be attending or planning to attend a college or university in any state. Along with their application, they must submit 2 letters of recommendation, a copy of high school or college transcripts, SAT or ACT scores (if taken), a letter of acceptance from a college or university (if not currently attending college), and a 2-page essay on the educational program they intend to pursue and the goals they wish to attain. Selection is based on academic achievement, commitment and desire to achieve, extracurricular activities, accomplishments, goals, and financial need.

Financial data The stipend is $1,000.

Duration 1 year; recipients may reapply.

Number awarded 10 each year: 5 to military members and 5 to dependents.

Deadline March of each year.

[697]
NATIONAL GUARD ASSOCIATION OF MARYLAND SCHOLARSHIPS

National Guard Association of Maryland
Attn: Scholarship Committee
P.O. Box 16675
Baltimore, MD 21221-0675
(410) 557-2606   Toll Free: (800) 844-1394
Fax: (410) 893-7529
E-mail: executivedirector@ngam.net
Web: www.ngam.net/benefits/scholarships.html

Summary To provide financial assistance to members of the National Guard Association of Maryland (NGAM) and their family members who are interested in attending college in any state.

Eligibility This program is open to NGAM members (including current and former members of the National Guard) and their spouses and children. Applicants must be enrolled or planning to enroll in an accredited college, university, or vocational/technical school in any state on either a part-time or full-time basis. They must submit a resume in which they outline their academic background, activities in which they have participated, and honors they have received;

3 letters of recommendation; the name of the college; and information on financial need.

Financial data The stipend is $1,000. Funds are paid directly to the recipient's university to be used for tuition, fees, and books.

Duration 1 year; recipients may reapply.

Number awarded Varies each year; recently, 13 were awarded.

Deadline March of each year.

[698]
NATIONAL GUARD ASSOCIATION OF MINNESOTA SCHOLARSHIPS

National Guard Association of Minnesota
Attn: Executive Director
P.O. Box 47132
Plymouth, MN 55442
(763) 202-2151   E-mail: director@ngamn.org
Web: www.ngamn.org/node/56

Summary To provide financial assistance to current and retired members of the National Guard Association of Minnesota (NGAMN) and their families who are working on an undergraduate or graduate degree at a school in any state.

Eligibility This program is open to active members and retired life members of NGAMN and their spouses, children, and grandchildren. Applicants must be currently enrolled at least half time at an accredited institution of higher learning in any state and working on a 4-year bachelor's or graduate degree. They must have a GPA of 2.75 or higher. Along with their application, they must submit an essay on a topic that describes a value of the Army or Air Force, rotating among loyalty, duty, respect, selfless service, honor, integrity, personal courage, commitment, and excellence. Financial need is not considered in the selection process.

Financial data Stipends are $1,000 or $500. Funds are paid directly to the recipient.

Duration 1 year. Recipients may reapply after 3 years.

Additional information The $1,000 scholarship is sponsored by HiWay Federal Credit Union. This program began in 2008.

Number awarded 3 each year: 1 at $1,000 and 2 at $500 (1 to a member or retired member and 1 to a spouse, child, or grandchild).

Deadline July of each year.

[699]
NATIONAL GUARD ASSOCIATION OF NEW HAMPSHIRE SCHOLARSHIPS

National Guard Association of New Hampshire
Attn: Scholarship Committee
P.O. Box 22031
Portsmouth, NH 03802-2031
(603) 227-1597   E-mail: nganhscholarship@gmail.com
Web: www.nganh.org/Archive/Scholarship

Summary To provide financial assistance to members of the National Guard Association of New Hampshire and their dependents who are interested in attending college or graduate school in any state.

Eligibility This program is open to current members of the National Guard Association of New Hampshire (officer, enlisted, or retired), their spouses, and their dependent children. Applicants must be enrolled or planning to enroll full or part time in an associate, bachelor's, graduate, professional, or doctoral degree program at an accredited college or university in any state. Along with their application, they must submit a 1-page essay on a topic that changes annually; recently, they were asked to describe what citizen service means to them.

Financial data The stipend is $1,000.

Duration 1 year.

Number awarded 1 each year.

Deadline April of each year.

[700]
NATIONAL GUARD ASSOCIATION OF NEW JERSEY SCHOLARSHIP PROGRAM

National Guard Association of New Jersey
Attn: Scholarship Committee
P.O. Box 266
Wrightstown, NJ 08562
(973) 541-6776   Fax: (973) 541-6909
E-mail: scholarship@nganj.org
Web: www.nganj.org/benefits.htm

Summary To provide financial assistance to members of the National Guard Association of New Jersey (NGANJ) or their dependents who are interested in attending college or graduate school in any state.

Eligibility This program is open to 1) active members of the NGANJ currently enrolled full time at an approved community college, school of nursing, or 4-year college in any state; and 2) the spouses, children, and grandchildren of active, retired, or deceased members entering or attending a 4-year college or university in any state. Applicants must submit transcripts, information on the civic and academic activities in which they have participated, and a list of offices, honors, awards, and special recognitions they have received. Selection is based on academic accomplishment, leadership, and citizenship.

Financial data Stipends up to $1,000 are available.

Duration 1 year; nonrenewable.

Number awarded Varies each year; recently, 10 were awarded.

Deadline April of each year.

[701]
NATIONAL GUARD ASSOCIATION OF RHODE ISLAND SCHOLARSHIPS

National Guard Association of Rhode Island
Attn: Scholarship Committee
645 New London Avenue
Cranston, RI 02920-3097
(401) 228-6586   Fax: (401) 541-9182
E-mail: ngarinews@gmail.com
Web: www.ngari.org/scholarships/

Summary To provide financial assistance to current and former members of the Rhode Island National Guard and their children who plan to attend college in any state.

Eligibility This program is open to active and retired members of the Rhode Island National Guard and their children. Applicants must be high school seniors, high school graduates, or undergraduate students. They must be attending or accepted at an accredited college, university, or vocational/technical school in any state. As part of their application, they

must describe any needs, goals, and other factors that may help the selection committee.

Financial data The stipend is $1,000.

Duration 1 year; nonrenewable.

Number awarded Varies each year; recently, 4 were awarded.

Deadline May of each year.

[702]
NATIONAL GUARD ASSOCIATION OF SOUTH CAROLINA AUXILIARY COLLEGE SCHOLARSHIP PROGRAM

National Guard Association of South Carolina Auxiliary
P.O. Box 281
Irmo, SC 29063
E-mail: nginfo@ngasc.org
Web: www.ngasc.org/services-view/scholorships

Summary To provide financial assistance to members of the National Guard Association of South Carolina Auxiliary (NGASCA) and their dependents who are interested in attending college in any state.

Eligibility This program is open to members of the auxiliary and their dependents who are related to an active, retired, or deceased member of the NGASCA. Applicants must be attending or planning to attend a college or university in any state. Along with their application, they must submit transcripts and documentation of financial need.

Financial data A stipend is awarded (amount not specified).

Duration 1 year.

Number awarded 1 or more each year.

Deadline January of each year.

[703]
NATIONAL GUARD ASSOCIATION OF SOUTH CAROLINA SCHOLARSHIPS

National Guard Association of South Carolina
Attn: NGASC Scholarship Foundation
132 Pickens Street
Columbia, SC 29205
(803) 254-8456   Toll Free: (800) 822-3235
Fax: (803) 254-3869   E-mail: nginfo@ngasc.org
Web: www.ngasc.org/services-view/scholorships

Summary To provide financial assistance to current and former South Carolina National Guard members and their dependents who are interested in attending college or graduate school in any state.

Eligibility This program is open to undergraduate students who are 1) current, retired, or deceased members of the South Carolina National Guard; 2) their dependents; and 3) members of the National Guard Association of South Carolina (NGASC). Graduate students are also eligible if they are members of the South Carolina National Guard. Applicants must be attending or interested in attending a college or university in any state as a full-time student. Several of the scholarships include additional restrictions on school or academic major; some are granted only for academic excellence, but most are based on both academics and financial need.

Financial data The stipend is $1,500 or $1,000.

Duration 1 year; may be renewed up to 3 additional years.

Number awarded Varies each year; recently, 55 were awarded.
Deadline January of each year.

[704]
NATIONAL GUARD ASSOCIATION OF TENNESSEE AUXILIARY SCHOLARSHIP PROGRAM

National Guard Association of Tennessee Auxiliary
Attn: Scholarship Committee
4332 Kenilwood Drive
Nashville, TN 37204-4401
(615) 833-9100   Toll Free: (888) 642-8448 (within TN)
Fax: (615) 833-9173   E-mail: ngatauxiliary@aol.com
Web: www.ngatn.org

Summary To provide financial assistance to spouses of members of the Tennessee National Guard who are interested in attending college in any state.
Eligibility This program is open to spouses of current members of the Tennessee National Guard who are attending or planning to attend college in any state. Applicants must submit a personal statement on their reason for requesting the scholarship, their educational and career goals, and how this award can help them attain those goals. Financial need is also considered in the selection process.
Financial data The stipends are $1,500.
Duration 1 year.
Additional information This program includes the Margene Mogan Proctor Scholarship and the General Jerry Wyatt Memorial Scholarship.
Number awarded 2 each year.
Deadline June of each year.

[705]
NATIONAL GUARD ASSOCIATION OF TENNESSEE SCHOLARSHIP PROGRAM

National Guard Association of Tennessee
Attn: Scholarship Committee
4332 Kenilwood Drive
Nashville, TN 37204-4401
(615) 833-9100   Toll Free: (888) 642-8448 (within TN)
Fax: (615) 833-9173   E-mail: Christi@ngatn.org
Web: www.ngatn.org

Summary To provide financial assistance for college to members or dependents of members of the National Guard Association of Tennessee (NGATN).
Eligibility This program is open to active Tennessee National Guard members and to active annual or life members of the NGATN. If no active Guard or association member qualifies, the scholarships may be awarded to the child of a Guard or association member, including life members who have retired or are deceased. All applicants must be high school seniors or graduates who meet entrance or continuation requirements at a Tennessee college or university. Selection is based on leadership in school and civic activities, motivation for continued higher education, academic achievement in high school and/or college, and financial need.
Financial data The stipends are $1,500.
Duration 1 year.
Number awarded 6 each year: 1 to an active National Guard member; 2 to current association members or their dependents; 2 to active National Guard members or their dependents; and 1 to a current Guard member who was

mobilized for Operations Desert Storm, Noble Eagle, Enduring Freedom, or Iraqi Freedom.
Deadline May of each year.

[706]
NATIONAL GUARD ASSOCIATION OF TEXAS SCHOLARSHIP PROGRAM

National Guard Association of Texas
Attn: Education Committee
3706 Crawford Avenue
Austin, TX 78731-6803
(512) 454-7300   Toll Free: (800) 252-NGAT
Fax: (512) 467-6803   E-mail: rlindner@ngat.org
Web: www.ngat.org/educate.php

Summary To provide financial assistance to members and dependents of members of the National Guard Association of Texas who are interested in attending college or graduate school in any state.
Eligibility This program is open to annual and life members of the association and their spouses and children (associate members and their dependents are not eligible). Applicants may be high school seniors, undergraduate students, or graduate students, either enrolled or planning to enroll at an institution of higher education in any state. Along with their application, they must submit an essay on their desire to continue their education. Selection is based on scholarship, citizenship, and leadership.
Financial data Stipends range from $700 to $5,000.
Duration 1 year (nonrenewable).
Additional information This program includes 1 scholarship sponsored by USAA Insurance Corporation.
Number awarded Varies each year; recently, 9 were awarded: 1 at $5,000, 2 at $2,000, 1 at $1,500, 1 at $1,250, 3 at $1,000, and 1 at $750.
Deadline February of each year.

[707]
NATIONAL GUARD ASSOCIATION OF VERMONT SCHOLARSHIPS

National Guard Association of Vermont
Attn: Scholarships
P.O. Box 694
Essex Junction, VT 05453
(802) 338-3185   E-mail: timothy.gariboldi@us.army.mil
Web: www.ngavt.org/scholarInfo.shtml

Summary To provide financial assistance to members of the Vermont National Guard (VTNG) or the National Guard Association of Vermont (NGA-VT) and their children or spouses who are interested in attending college or graduate school in any state.
Eligibility This program is open to current members of the VTNG or the NGA-VT, their spouses, and their unmarried children. Applicants must be working, or planning to work, on an associate, undergraduate, technical, or graduate degree as a full-time student at a school in any state. Along with their application, they must submit an essay on their commitment to selfless public service or their plan for pursuing it in the future. In the selection process, first priority is given to applicants in grades E-1 through E-6, W-1 and W-2, and O-1 through O-3; second to E-7, E-8, and W3; third to E-9, W-4 and W-5, and O-4 and above. Other factors considered include the essay, academic performance, and community

service. The program includes the COL James D. Kneeland Memorial Scholarship Award, reserved for a member of the Vermont Army National Guard Aviation Community.

Financial data Stipends range from $500 to $1,500. Funds are sent directly to the recipient.

Duration 1 year; recipients may reapply.

Number awarded 4 each year: 1 at $1,500 (the COL James D. Kneeland Memorial Scholarship Award), 1 at $1,000, and 2 at $500 (1 for a student affiliated with the Vermont Army National Guard and 1 for a student affiliated with the Vermont Air National Guard).

Deadline June of each year.

[708]
NATIONAL GUARD CHAPTER ASMC DEPENDENT SCHOLARSHIPS

American Society of Military Comptrollers-National Guard Chapter
c/o CW3 Carl Jackson, Continuing Education Committee
United States Property and Fiscal Officer for Georgia
Resource Management Division
P.O. Box 17882
Atlanta, GA 30316-0882
(678) 569-6399 E-mail: carl.stefan.jackson@us.army.mil
Web: www.ng-asmc.org

Summary To provide financial assistance to dependents of members of the National Guard Chapter of the American Society of Military Comptrollers (ASMC) who are interested in studying a field related to financial and resource management.

Eligibility This program is open to graduating high school seniors and current college students entering a field of study related to financial and resource management (e.g., accounting, business administration, computer science, economics, finance, operations research related to financial management, public administration). Applicants must be a dependent of an ASMC member who has been a member of its National Guard Chapter for at least 24 months. Along with their application, they must submit 2 letters of recommendation, transcripts that include ACT and/or SAT scores, and a 250-word essay on their career and academic goals and financial need.

Financial data Stipends are $1,500 or $1,000.

Duration 1 year.

Additional information Membership in ASMC is open to military and civilian personnel involved in the field of military comptrollership. The National Guard Chapter serves ASMC members who are associated with the Army National Guard or Air National Guard in any state.

Number awarded 2 each year: 1 at $1,500 and 1 at $1,000.

Deadline February of each year.

[709]
NATIONAL GUARD OF GEORGIA SCHOLARSHIP FUND FOR COLLEGES OR UNIVERSITIES

Georgia Guard Insurance Trust
P.O. Box 889
Mableton, GA 30126
(770) 739-9651   Toll Free: (800) 229-1053
Fax: (770) 745-0673   E-mail: director@ngaga.org
Web: www.ngaga.org/scholarships.html

Summary To provide financial assistance to members of the Georgia National Guard and their spouses, children, and grandchildren who are interested in attending college in any state.

Eligibility This program is open to policyholders with the Georgia Guard Insurance Trust (GGIT) who are members of the National Guard Association of Georgia (NGAGA) or the Enlisted Association of the National Guard of Georgia (EANGGA); spouses, children, and grandchildren of NGAGA and EANGGA members are also eligible. Applicants must be enrolled or planning to enroll full time at a college or university in any state and have received an academic honor while in high school. Graduating high school seniors must have a combined mathematics and critical reading SAT score of at least 1000 or a GPA of 3.0 or higher. Students already enrolled at a college or university must have a cumulative GPA of 3.0 or higher. Along with their application, they must submit transcripts, a letter with personal specific facts regarding their desire to continue their education, 2 letters of recommendation, a letter of academic reference, and an agreement to retain insurance with the GGIT for at least 2 years following completion of the school year for which the scholarship is awarded. Selection is based on academics, character, and moral and personal traits.

Financial data The stipend is $1,000.

Duration 1 year.

Number awarded 1 or 2 each year.

Deadline April of each year.

[710]
NATIONAL GUARD OF GEORGIA SCHOLARSHIP FUND FOR VOCATIONAL OR BUSINESS SCHOOLS

Georgia Guard Insurance Trust
P.O. Box 889
Mableton, GA 30126
(770) 739-9651   Toll Free: (800) 229-1053
Fax: (770) 745-0673   E-mail: director@ngaga.org
Web: www.ngaga.org/scholarships.html

Summary To provide financial assistance to members of the Georgia National Guard and their spouses, children, and grandchildren who are interested in attending business or vocational school in any state.

Eligibility This program is open to policyholders with the Georgia Guard Insurance Trust (GGIT) who are members of the National Guard Association of Georgia (NGAGA) or the Enlisted Association of the National Guard of Georgia (EANGGA); spouses, children, and grandchildren of NGAGA and EANGGA members are also eligible. Applicants must be interested in enrolling full time in day or evening classes at a business or vocational school in any state. They must be able to meet program-specific admission standards and institutional requirements and complete all admission procedures for admission to a degree/diploma program in regular program status. Along with their application, they must submit transcripts, a letter with personal specific facts regarding their desire to continue their education, 2 letters of recommendation, and an agreement to retain insurance with the GGIT for at least 2 years following completion of the school year for which the scholarship is awarded. Selection is based on academics, character, and moral and personal traits.

Financial data The stipend is $1,000.

Duration 1 year.

Number awarded 1 or 2 each year.
Deadline April of each year.

[711]
NAVAL CRYPTOLOGIC VETERANS ASSOCIATION SCHOLARSHIPS

Naval Cryptologic Veterans Association
c/o Bill Hickey, Executive Director
156 Barcelona Drive
Boulder, CO 80303
E-mail: wa3h@hotmail.com
Web: www.usncva.org

Summary To provide financial assistance to high school seniors and college students who are sponsored by a member of the Naval Cryptologic Veterans Association (NCVA).

Eligibility This program is open to graduating high school seniors and students currently or previously enrolled in college. Applicants must be sponsored by an NCVA member who submits their application on their behalf, although they do not need to be related to the sponsor. Along with their application, they must submit a brief written statement on their current and future educational goals as well as any special circumstances (such as financial need) they wish to have considered.

Financial data Stipends range from $1,000 to $2,000.

Duration 1 year.

Number awarded Varies each year; recently, 3 were awarded: 1 each at $2,000, $1,500, and $1,000.

Deadline June of each year.

[712]
NAVAL ENLISTED RESERVE ASSOCIATION SCHOLARSHIPS

Naval Enlisted Reserve Association
Attn: Scholarship Committee
6703 Farragut Avenue
Falls Church, VA 22042-2189
(703) 534-1329   Toll Free: (800) 776-9020
Fax: (703) 534-3617   E-mail: members@nera.org
Web: www.nera.org

Summary To provide financial assistance for college to members of the Naval Enlisted Reserve Association (NERA) and their families.

Eligibility This program is open to regular or associate NERA members, the spouses of regular members, and the unmarried children and grandchildren under 23 years of age of regular members. Applicants must be graduating high school seniors or undergraduates currently attending an accredited 2- or 4-year college or university as a full- or part-time student. Along with their application, they must submit a 500-word essay on either 1) their career goals and objectives for their education; or 2) why Reservists are important to America. Financial need is not considered in the selection process.

Financial data The stipend is $2,500.

Duration 1 year.

Additional information This program is funded in part by USAA Insurance Corporation.

Number awarded 4 each year.

Deadline June of each year.

[713]
NAVAL HELICOPTER ASSOCIATION MEMORIAL SCHOLARSHIPS

Naval Helicopter Association
Attn: Scholarship Fund
P.O. Box 180578
Coronado, CA 92178-0578
(619) 435-7139   Fax: (619) 435-7354
Web: nhascholarshipfund.org/scholarships-available.html

Summary To provide financial assistance for college or graduate school to 1) active-duty personnel who are working or have worked in rotary wing activities of the sea services and 2) members of their families.

Eligibility This program is open to 1) active-duty Navy, Marine Corps, or Coast Guard rotary wing aviators, aircrewmen, or support personnel; and 2) the children and spouses of those personnel. Applicants must be working on or planning to work on an undergraduate or graduate degree in any field. Along with their application, they must submit a personal statement on their academic and career aspirations. Selection is based on that statement, academic proficiency, scholastic achievements and awards, extracurricular activities, employment history, and letters of recommendation.

Financial data Stipends are approximately $2,000.

Duration 1 year.

Additional information This program includes the following named awards: the Edward and Veronica Ream Memorial Scholarship, the CDR Mort McCarthy Memorial Scholarship, the Charles Karman Memorial Scholarship, the LT Christian "Horse" Hescock Memorial Scholarship, and the Captain Mark Starr Memorial Scholarship.

Number awarded Varies each year; recently, 4 were awarded.

Deadline January of each year.

[714]
NAVAL HELICOPTER ASSOCIATION REGIONAL SCHOLARSHIPS

Naval Helicopter Association
Attn: Scholarship Fund
P.O. Box 180578
Coronado, CA 92178-0578
(619) 435-7139   Fax: (619) 435-7354
Web: nhascholarshipfund.org/scholarships-available.html

Summary To provide financial assistance for college to students who have an affiliation with the rotary wing activities of the sea services.

Eligibility This program is open to high school seniors and current undergraduates who are children, grandchildren, or spouses of active-duty, former, or retired Navy, Marine Corps, or Coast Guard rotary wing aviators, aircrewmen, or support personnel. Applicants must submit a personal statement on their academic and career aspirations. Selection is based on that statement, academic proficiency, scholastic achievements and awards, extracurricular activities, employment history, and letters of recommendation.

Financial data Stipends are $2,000.

Duration 1 year.

Number awarded Up to 5 each year: 1 in each of 5 regions of the country.

Deadline January of each year.

[715]
NAVAL HELICOPTER ASSOCIATION UNDERGRADUATE SCHOLARSHIPS

Naval Helicopter Association
Attn: Scholarship Fund
P.O. Box 180578
Coronado, CA 92178-0578
(619) 435-7139   Fax: (619) 435-7354
Web: nhascholarshipfund.org/scholarships-available.html

Summary To provide financial assistance for college to students who have an affiliation with the rotary wing activities of the sea services.

Eligibility This program is open to high school seniors and current undergraduates who are children, grandchildren, or spouses of active-duty, former, or retired Navy, Marine Corps, or Coast Guard rotary wing aviators, aircrewmen, or support personnel. Applicants must submit a personal statement on their academic and career aspirations. Selection is based on that statement, academic proficiency, scholastic achievements and awards, extracurricular activities, employment history, and letters of recommendation.

Financial data Stipends are approximately $2,000.

Duration 1 year.

Additional information This program includes the DPA Thousand Points of Light Award (sponsored by D.P. Associates Inc. and L-3 Communications), the Sergei Sikorsky Scholarship, and scholarships sponsored by Raytheon Corporation, Lockheed Martin, and Northrop Grumman.

Number awarded Varies each year; recently, 9 were awarded.

Deadline February of each year.

[716]
NAVAL OFFICERS' SPOUSES' CLUB OF WASHINGTON, D.C. GRADUATING SENIOR SCHOLARSHIP PROGRAM

Naval Officers' Spouses' Club of Washington, D.C.
Attn: Mary K. Page, Scholarship Committee
1122 Columbus Circle
Joint Base Andrews, MD 20762
(703) 992-8381   E-mail: scholarship@noscdc.com
Web: www.noscdc.com/Philanthrophy

Summary To provide financial assistance to high school seniors who are the children of naval personnel and veterans in Naval District Washington and plan to attend college in any state.

Eligibility This program is open to dependent children of active-duty, retired, or deceased U.S. Navy personnel who are 1) residing and serving in a command within the boundaries of Naval District Washington; 2) retired and had served in a command in Naval District Washington; or 3) deceased and had served in a command in Naval District Washington. Applicants must be high school seniors at an accredited high school in Naval District Washington, U.S. citizens, and planning to enroll full time at an accredited 2- or 4-year undergraduate college or university, visual or performing arts school, or vocational/technical school in any state. Along with their application, they must submit a 600-word essay on their choice of 3 assigned topics that change annually. Selection is based on that essay, GPA, SAT and/or ACT scores, extracurricular activities and awards, and school and community involvement; financial need is not considered.

Financial data The stipend is $2,000. Funds are paid directly to the recipient's institution to be used only for tuition.

Duration 1 year; nonrenewable.

Additional information Naval District Washington covers the District of Columbia; the Maryland counties of Anne Arundel, Calvert, Charles, Frederick, Montgomery, Prince George's, and St. Mary's; and the Virginia counties of Arlington, Fairfax, Fauquier, King George, Loudoun, Prince William, Stafford, and Westmoreland (plus the independent cities within their boundaries). This program includes the LCDR Erik S. Kristensen, USN, Memorial Scholarship and the Theressa R. French Memorial Scholarship.

Number awarded Varies each year; recently, 12 were awarded.

Deadline March of each year.

[717]
NAVAL OFFICERS' SPOUSES' CLUB OF WASHINGTON, D.C. SPOUSE SCHOLARSHIP PROGRAM

Naval Officers' Spouses' Club of Washington, D.C.
Attn: Mary K. Page, Scholarship Committee
1122 Columbus Circle
Joint Base Andrews, MD 20762
(703) 992-8381   E-mail: scholarship@noscdc.com
Web: www.noscdc.com/Philanthrophy

Summary To provide financial assistance to spouses of naval personnel in Naval District Washington who are interested in attending college in any state.

Eligibility This program is open to spouses of active-duty Navy personnel who are residing and serving in a command within the boundaries of Naval District Washington and have been on active duty for at least 9 consecutive months. Applicants must be attending or planning to attend an accredited 2- or 4-year undergraduate college or university, visual or performing arts school, or vocational/technical school in any state. Along with their application, they must submit a 600-word essay on their choice of 3 assigned topics that change annually. Selection is based on that essay, academic record, job record, volunteer work, and participation in community activities; financial need is not considered.

Financial data The stipend is $2,000. Funds are paid directly to the recipient's institution to be used only for tuition.

Duration 1 year; nonrenewable.

Additional information Naval District Washington covers the District of Columbia; the Maryland counties of Anne Arundel, Calvert, Charles, Frederick, Montgomery, Prince George's, and St. Mary's; and the Virginia counties of Arlington, Fairfax, Fauquier, King George, Loudoun, Prince William, Stafford, and Westmoreland (plus the independent cities within their boundaries).

Number awarded Varies each year; recently, 1 of these scholarships was awarded.

Deadline March of each year.

[718]
NAVAL SPECIAL WARFARE DEVELOPMENT GROUP SCHOLARSHIPS

Navy Seal Foundation
Attn: DEVGRU Scholarship Committee
1619 D Street, Building 5326
Virginia Beach, VA 23459
(757) 363-7490   Fax: (757) 363-7491
E-mail: info@navysealfoundation.org
Web: www.navysealfoundation.org

Summary To provide financial assistance for college or graduate school to the children and spouses of personnel assigned to the Naval Special Warfare Development Group (DEVGRU).

Eligibility This program is open to the dependent children and spouses of former and present Navy SEAL, Special Warfare Combatant-craft Crewmen (SWCC), or Military Direct Support person who are or have been assigned to DEVGRU. Applicants must be enrolled or planning to enroll at a trade school, technical/vocational institute, or undergraduate college. Spouses may also apply for graduate school. Along with their application, they must submit an essay on their plans as related to their educational and career objectives and long-term goals. Selection is based on merit (as measured by GPA, SAT scores, class rank, extracurricular activities, volunteer community involvement, leadership positions held, military service record, and after school employment, as appropriate) and academic potential.

Financial data Stipends are $15,000, $7,500, or $5,000 per year.

Duration 1 year; may be renewed.

Number awarded Varies each year; recently, the Navy Seal Foundation awarded 16 scholarships for all of its programs: 3 for 4 years at $15,000 per year to high school seniors and graduates, 3 for 1 year at $7,500 to high school seniors and graduates, 3 for 1 year at $15,000 to current college students, 3 for 1 year at $7,500 to current college students, and 4 for 1 year at $5,000 to spouses.

Deadline January of each year.

[719]
NAVY LEAGUE FOUNDATION SCHOLARSHIPS

Navy League of the United States
Attn: Scholarships
2300 Wilson Boulevard, Suite 200
Arlington, VA 22201-5424
(703) 528-1775   Toll Free: (800) 356-5760
Fax: (703) 528-2333
E-mail: scholarships@navyleague.org
Web: www.navyleague.org/aboutus/scholarship.html

Summary To provide financial assistance for college to dependent children of sea service personnel.

Eligibility This program is open to U.S. citizens who are 1) dependents or direct descendants of an active, Reserve, retired, or honorably discharged member of the U.S. sea service (including the Navy, Marine Corps, Coast Guard, or Merchant Marine); or 2) currently an active member of the Naval Sea Cadet Corps. Applicants must be high school seniors entering their freshman year at an accredited college or university. They must have a GPA of 3.0 or higher. Along with their application, they must submit transcripts, 2 letters of recommendation, SAT/ACT scores, documentation of financial

need, proof of qualifying sea service duty, and a 1-page personal statement on why they should be considered for this scholarship.

Financial data The stipend is $2,500 per year.

Duration 4 years, provided the recipient maintains a GPA of 3.0 or higher.

Additional information This program includes the following named awards: the Jack and Eileen Anderson Scholarship, the John G. Brokaw Scholarship, the Wesley C. Cameron Scholarship, the CAPT Ernest G. "Scotty" Campbell, USN (Ret) and Renee Campbell Scholarship, the Ann E. Clark Foundation Scholarship, the CAPT Winifred Quick Collins, USN (Ret) Scholarship, the Albert Levinson Scholarship, the Gladys Ann Smith Greater Los Angeles Women's Council Scholarship, the Subic Bay-Cubi Point Scholarship, the USS Mahan Scholarship, and the United Armed Forces Association Scholarship.

Number awarded Approximately 25 each year.

Deadline February of each year.

[720]
NAVY/MARINE CORPS/COAST GUARD ENLISTED DEPENDENT SPOUSE SCHOLARSHIP

Navy Wives Clubs of America
c/o NSA Mid-South
P.O. Box 54022
Millington, TN 38054-0022
Toll Free: (866) 511-NWCA
E-mail: nwca@navywivesclubsofamerica.org
Web: www.navywivesclubsofamerica.org/scholarships

Summary To provide financial assistance for undergraduate or graduate study to spouses of naval personnel.

Eligibility This program is open to the spouses of active-duty Navy, Marine Corps, or Coast Guard members who can demonstrate financial need. Applicants must be 1) a high school graduate or senior planning to attend college full time next year; 2) currently enrolled in an undergraduate program and planning to continue as a full-time undergraduate; 3) a college graduate or senior planning to be a full-time graduate student next year; or 4) a high school graduate or GED recipient planning to attend vocational or business school next year. Along with their application, they must submit a brief statement on why they feel they should be awarded this scholarship and any special circumstances (financial or other) they wish to have considered. Financial need is also considered in the selection process.

Financial data The stipends range from $500 to $1,000 each year (depending upon the donations from chapters of the Navy Wives Clubs of America).

Duration 1 year.

Number awarded 1 or more each year.

Deadline May of each year.

[721]
NAVY SEAL FOUNDATION SCHOLARSHIPS

Navy Seal Foundation
Attn: Chief Financial Officer
1619 D Street, Building 5326
Virginia Beach, VA 23459
(757) 363-7490   Fax: (757) 363-7491
E-mail: info@navysealfoundation.org
Web: www.navysealfoundation.org

Summary To provide financial assistance for college or graduate school to Naval Special Warfare (NSW) personnel and their families.

Eligibility This program is open to active-duty Navy SEALS, Special Warfare Combatant-craft Crewmen (SWCC), and military personnel assigned to other NSW commands. Their dependent children and spouses are also eligible. Applicants must be entering or continuing full or part-time students working on an associate or bachelor's degree. Active-duty and spouses, but not dependent children, may also work on a graduate degree. Selection is based on GPA, SAT scores, class ranking, extracurricular activities, volunteer community involvement, leadership positions held, military service record, and employment (as appropriate).

Financial data Stipends are $15,000, $7,500, or $5,000 per year.

Duration 1 year; may be renewed.

Number awarded Varies each year; recently, the Navy Seal Foundation awarded 16 scholarships for all of its programs: 3 for 4 years at $15,000 per year to high school seniors and graduates, 3 for 1 year at $7,500 to high school seniors and graduates, 3 for 1 year at $15,000 to current college students, 3 for 1 year at $7,500 to current college students, and 4 for 1 year at $5,000 to spouses.

Deadline February of each year.

[722]
NAVY SUPPLY CORPS FOUNDATION MEMORIAL SCHOLARSHIPS

Navy Supply Corps Foundation
Attn: Administrator
P.O. Box 6228
Athens, GA 30604-6228
(706) 354-4111   Fax: (706) 354-0334
E-mail: foundation@usnscf.com
Web: www.usnscf.com

Summary To provide financial assistance for college to children of Navy Supply Corps personnel who died on active duty.

Eligibility This program is open to children of Navy Supply Corps personnel who died on active duty after 2001. The program applies to Active Duty Supply Corps Officers as well as Reserve Supply Corps Officers in the following categories: Mobilization, Active Duty for Special Work (ADSW), Active Duty for Training (ADT), Annual Training (AT), and Inactive Duty for Training (IDT). Applicants must be attending or planning to attend a 2- or 4-year accredited college on a full-time basis and have a GPA of 2.5 or higher in high school and/or college. Selection is based on character, leadership, academic achievement, extracurricular activities, and financial need.

Financial data The stipend is $2,500.

Duration 1 year.

Number awarded Varies each year; recently, 7 were awarded.

Deadline March of each year.

[723]
NAVY SUPPLY CORPS FOUNDATION SCHOLARSHIPS

Navy Supply Corps Foundation
Attn: Administrator
P.O. Box 6228
Athens, GA 30604-6228
(706) 354-4111   Fax: (706) 354-0334
E-mail: foundation@usnscf.com
Web: www.usnscf.com

Summary To provide financial assistance for college to relatives of current or former Navy Supply Corps personnel.

Eligibility This program is open to dependents (child, grandchild, or spouse) of a living or deceased regular, retired, Reserve, or prior Navy Supply Corps officer, warrant officer, or enlisted personnel. Enlisted ratings that apply are AK (Aviation Storekeeper), SK (Storekeeper), MS (Mess Specialist), DK (Disbursing Clerk), SH (Ship Serviceman), LI (Lithographer), and PC (Postal Clerk). Applicants must be attending or planning to attend a 2- or 4-year accredited college on a full-time basis and have a GPA of 2.5 or higher in high school and/or college. Selection is based on character, leadership, academic achievement, extracurricular activities, and financial need.

Financial data Stipends range from $1,000 to $12,500 per year.

Duration 1 year; some scholarships may be renewed for 3 additional years.

Additional information This program began in 1971.

Number awarded Varies each year; recently, the foundation awarded 74 new scholarships (worth $163,000) and 21 renewals (worth $87,500). Since the program was established, it has awarded 2,102 scholarships with a total value of more than $4,443,000.

Deadline March of each year.

[724]
NAVY WIVES CLUBS OF AMERICA NATIONAL SCHOLARSHIPS

Navy Wives Clubs of America
c/o NSA Mid-South
P.O. Box 54022
Millington, TN 38054-0022
Toll Free: (866) 511-NWCA
E-mail: nwca@navywivesclubsofamerica.org
Web: www.navywivesclubsofamerica.org/scholarships

Summary To provide financial assistance for college or graduate school to the children of naval personnel.

Eligibility Applicants for these scholarships must be the children (natural born, legally adopted, or stepchildren) of enlisted members of the Navy, Marine Corps, or Coast Guard on active duty, retired with pay, or deceased. Applicants must be attending or planning to attend an accredited college or university as a full-time undergraduate or graduate student. They must have a GPA of 2.5 or higher. Along with their application, they must submit an essay on their career objectives and the reasons they chose those objectives. Selection is based on academic standing, moral character, and financial need. Some scholarships are reserved for students majoring in special education, medical students, and children of members of Navy Wives Clubs of America (NWCA).

Financial data The stipend is $1,500.

Duration 1 year; may be renewed up to 3 additional years.

Additional information Membership in the NWCA is open to spouses of enlisted personnel serving in the Navy, Marine Corps, Coast Guard, and the active Reserve units of those services; spouses of enlisted personnel who have been honorably discharged, retired, or transferred to the Fleet Reserve on completion of duty; and widows of enlisted personnel in those services.

Number awarded 30 each year, including at least 4 to freshmen, 4 to current undergraduates applying for the first time, 2 to medical students, 1 to a student majoring in special education, and 4 to children of NWCA members.

Deadline May of each year.

[725]
NEBRASKA VFW STATE SCHOLARSHIP

Veterans of Foreign Wars of the United States-
  Department of Nebraska
Attn: Scholarship Committee
2431 North 48th Street
P.O. Box 4552
Lincoln, NE 68504-0552
(402) 464-0674   Fax: (402) 464-0675
E-mail: johnl@vfwne.org
Web: www.vfwne.org

Summary To provide financial assistance to members of the Veterans of Foreign Wars (VFW), its Ladies Auxiliary, and their families in Nebraska who wish to attend college in the state.

Eligibility This program is open to members of the Nebraska chapter of the VFW, its Ladies Auxiliary, and their spouses, children, stepchildren, and grandchildren. Applicants must have completed at least 1 year of full-time study at a college or university in Nebraska. They must be able to demonstrate financial need.

Financial data A stipend is awarded (amount not specified).

Duration 1 year.

Number awarded 1 or more each year.

Deadline March of each year.

[726]
NEBRASKA WAIVER OF TUITION FOR VETERANS' DEPENDENTS

Department of Veterans' Affairs
State Office Building
301 Centennial Mall South, Sixth Floor
P.O. Box 95083
Lincoln, NE 68509-5083
(402) 471-2458   Fax: (402) 471-2491
E-mail: john.hilgert@nebraska.gov
Web: www.vets.state.ne.us/benefits.html

Summary To provide financial assistance for college to dependents of deceased and disabled veterans and military personnel in Nebraska.

Eligibility Eligible are spouses, widow(er)s, and children who are residents of Nebraska and whose parent, stepparent, or spouse was a member of the U.S. armed forces and 1) died of a service-connected disability; 2) died subsequent to discharge as a result of injury or illness sustained while in service; 3) is permanently and totally disabled as a result of military service; or 4) is classified as missing in action or as a

prisoner of war during armed hostilities. Applicants must be attending or planning to attend a branch of the University of Nebraska, a state college, or a community college in Nebraska.

Financial data Tuition is waived at public institutions in Nebraska.

Duration The waiver is valid for 1 degree, diploma, or certificate from a community college and 1 baccalaureate degree.

Additional information Applications may be submitted through 1 of the recognized veterans' organizations or any county service officer.

Number awarded Varies each year; recently, 311 were awarded.

Deadline Deadline not specified.

[727]
NEW HAMPSHIRE CHAPTER MOAA SCHOLARSHIP LOAN PROGRAM

Military Officers Association of America-New Hampshire
  Chapter
c/o COL Calvin Hosmer
P.O. Box 175
York, ME 03909
(207) 363-2396   E-mail: hosmerIII@aol.com
Web: www.moaa-nh.org

Summary To provide loans or other financial assistance for college in any state to the children and grandchildren of members of the New Hampshire Chapter of the Military Officers Association of America (MOAA).

Eligibility This program is open to children and grandchildren of members of the chapter who are attending or planning to attend college in any state. Selection is based on merit, not need.

Financial data The amount of the loan depends on the availability of funds and numbers of students applying. Repayment is expected to begin 6 months after completion of the recipient's academic program at the rate of 2% of the loan per month. No interest is charged. Portions of a loan may be forgiven, based on academic performance, at the discretion of the sponsor.

Duration 1 year.

Number awarded Varies each year; recently, 7 of these loans were granted.

Deadline May of each year.

[728]
NEW HAMPSHIRE SCHOLARSHIPS FOR ORPHANS OF VETERANS

New Hampshire Department of Education
Attn: Center for College Planning
Lonergan Hall, Room 100B
101 Pleasant Street
Concord, NH 03301-3494
(603) 271-0289   Toll Free: (888) 747-2382, ext. 119
Fax: (603) 271-1953 E-mail: Patricia.Moquin@doe.nh.gov
Web: www.education.nh.gov/highered/financial/index.htm

Summary To provide financial assistance for college in the state to the children of New Hampshire veterans who died of service-connected causes.

Eligibility This program is open to New Hampshire residents between 16 and 25 years of age whose parent(s) died while on active duty or as a result of a service-related disability incurred during World War II, the Korean Conflict, the southeast Asian Conflict (Vietnam), or the Gulf Wars. Parents must have been residents of New Hampshire at the time of death. Applicants must be enrolled at least half time as undergraduate students at a public college or university in New Hampshire. Financial need is not considered in the selection process.

Financial data The stipend is $2,500 per year, to be used for the payment of room, board, books, and supplies. Recipients are also eligible to receive a tuition waiver from the institution.

Duration 1 year; may be renewed for up to 3 additional years.

Additional information This program began in 1943.

Number awarded Varies each year; recently, 2 were awarded.

Deadline Deadline not specified.

[729]
NEW JERSEY AMERICAN LEGION AUXILIARY DEPARTMENT SCHOLARSHIPS

American Legion Auxiliary
Department of New Jersey
c/o Marion Heller, Secretary
1540 Kuser Road, Suite A-8
Hamilton, NJ 08619
(609) 581-9580   Fax: (609) 581-8429
E-mail: newjerseyala1@optimum.net
Web: www.alanj.org/box_widget.html

Summary To provide financial assistance to New Jersey residents who are the descendants of veterans and planning to attend college in any state.

Eligibility This program is open to the children, grandchildren, and great-grandchildren of veterans who served in the U.S. armed forces during specified periods of wartime. Applicants must be graduating high school seniors who have been residents of New Jersey for at least 2 years. They must be planning to attend a college or university in any state. Along with their application, they must submit a 1,000-word essay on a topic that changes annually; recently, students were asked to write on the topic, "Pass it On-How I Can be a Leader in My Community." Selection is based on academic achievement (40%), character (15%), leadership (15%), Americanism (15%), and financial need (15%).

Financial data Stipends range from $1,000 to $2,500.

Duration 1 year; nonrenewable.

Number awarded 3 each year: 1 each to a resident of North Jersey, Central Jersey, and South Jersey.

Deadline April of each year.

[730]
NEW JERSEY AMERICAN LEGION SCHOLARSHIPS

American Legion
Department of New Jersey
Attn: Adjutant
135 West Hanover Street
Trenton, NJ 08618
(609) 695-5418   Fax: (609) 394-1532
E-mail: newjersey@legion.org
Web: www.njamericanlegion.org/programs.htm

Summary To provide financial assistance to the descendants of members of the New Jersey Department of the American Legion who plan to attend college in any state.

Eligibility This program is open to high school seniors who are the natural or adopted children, grandchildren, or great-grandchildren of members of the American Legion's New Jersey Department. Applicants must be planning to attend a college or university in any state. Along with their application, they must submit a brief statement on the reasons for their choice of vocation. Selection is based on character (20%), Americanism and community service (20%), leadership (20%), scholarship (20%), and financial need (20%).

Financial data The stipend is $1,500 or $1,000 per year.

Duration These scholarships are for 4 years, 2 years, or 1 year.

Additional information These scholarships were formerly designated the Lawrence Luterman Memorial Scholarships and the Stutz Memorial Scholarship.

Number awarded 9 each year: 2 at $1,000 per year for 4 years, 4 at $1,000 per year for 2 years, 2 at $1,000 for 1 year, and 1 at $1,500 for 1 year (designated the John Casey Scholarship).

Deadline February of each year.

[731]
NEW JERSEY BANKERS EDUCATION FOUNDATION SCHOLARSHIPS

New Jersey Bankers Association
Attn: New Jersey Bankers Education Foundation, Inc.
411 North Avenue East
Cranford, NJ 07016-2436
(908) 272-8500, ext. 614   Fax: (908) 272-6626
E-mail: j.meredith@njbankers.com
Web: www.njbankers.com

Summary To provide financial assistance to dependents of deceased and disabled military personnel who have a connection to New Jersey and are interested in attending college in any state.

Eligibility This program is open to the spouses, children, stepchildren, and grandchildren of members of the armed services who died or became disabled while on active duty; it is not required that the military person died in combat. Applicants must have a high school or equivalency diploma and be attending college in any state. Adult dependents who wish to obtain a high school equivalency diploma are also eligible. Either the dependent or the servicemember must have a connection to New Jersey; the applicant's permanent address must be in New Jersey or the servicemember's last permanent address or military base must have been in the state. Financial need is considered in the selection process.

Financial data A stipend is awarded (amount not specified).

Duration 1 year; may be renewed if the recipient maintains a "C" average.

Additional information This program began in 2005.

Number awarded 1 or more each year.

Deadline June of each year.

[732]
NEW JERSEY LEGION AUXILIARY PAST PRESIDENTS' PARLEY NURSES SCHOLARSHIPS

American Legion Auxiliary
Department of New Jersey
c/o Marion Heller, Secretary
1540 Kuser Road, Suite A-8
Hamilton, NJ 08619
(609) 581-9580   Fax: (609) 581-8429
E-mail: newjerseyala1@optimum.net
Web: www.alanj.org/box_widget.html

Summary To provide financial assistance to New Jersey residents who are the descendants of veterans and interested in studying nursing at a school in any state.

Eligibility This program is open to the children, grandchildren, and great-grandchildren of veterans who served in the U.S. armed forces during specified periods of wartime. Applicants must be graduating high school seniors who have been residents of New Jersey for at least 2 years. They must be planning to study nursing at a school in any state. Along with their application, they must submit a 1,000-word essay on a topic that changes annually; recently, students were asked to write on the topic, "Pass it On-How I Can be a Leader in My Community." Selection is based on academic achievement (40%), character (15%), leadership (15%), Americanism (15%), and financial need (15%).

Financial data A stipend is awarded (amount not specified).

Duration 1 year.

Number awarded 1 or more each year.

Deadline April of each year.

[733]
NEW JERSEY NATIONAL GUARD TUITION PROGRAM

New Jersey Department of Military and Veterans Affairs
Attn: New Jersey Army National Guard Education Center
3650 Saylors Pond Road
Fort Dix, NJ 08640-7600
(609) 562-0654   Toll Free: (888) 859-0352
Fax: (609) 562-0201
Web: www.state.nj.us/military/education/NJNGTP.htm

Summary To provide financial assistance for college or graduate school to New Jersey National Guard members and the surviving spouses and children of deceased members.

Eligibility This program is open to active members of the New Jersey National Guard who have completed Initial Active Duty for Training (IADT). Applicants must be New Jersey residents who have been accepted into a program of undergraduate or graduate study at any of 31 public institutions of higher education in the state. The surviving spouses and children of deceased members of the Guard who had completed IADT and were killed in the performance of their duties while a member of the Guard are also eligible if the school has classroom space available.

Financial data Tuition for up to 15 credits per semester is waived for full-time recipients in state-supported colleges or community colleges in New Jersey.

Duration 1 semester; may be renewed.

Number awarded Varies each year.

Deadline Deadline not specified.

[734]
NEW JERSEY POW/MIA TUITION BENEFIT PROGRAM

New Jersey Department of Military and Veterans Affairs
Attn: Division of Veterans Programs
101 Eggert Crossing Road
P.O. Box 340
Trenton, NJ 08625-0340
(609) 530-7045   Toll Free: (800) 624-0508 (within NJ)
Fax: (609) 530-7075
Web: www.state.nj.us/military/veterans/programs.html

Summary To provide financial assistance for college to the children of New Jersey military personnel reported as missing in action or prisoners of war during the southeast Asian conflict.

Eligibility Eligible to apply for this assistance are New Jersey residents attending or accepted at a New Jersey public or independent postsecondary institution whose parents were military service personnel officially declared prisoners of war or missing in action after January 1, 1960.

Financial data This program entitles recipients to full undergraduate tuition at any public or independent postsecondary educational institution in New Jersey.

Duration Assistance continues until completion of a bachelor's degree.

Number awarded Varies each year.

Deadline February of each year for the spring term and September for the fall and spring terms.

[735]
NEW MEXICO CHILDREN OF DECEASED MILITARY PERSONNEL SCHOLARSHIPS

New Mexico Department of Veterans' Services
Attn: Benefits Division
407 Galisteo Street, Room 142
P.O. Box 2324
Santa Fe, NM 87504-2324
(505) 827-6374   Toll Free: (866) 433-VETS
Fax: (505) 827-6372   E-mail: alan.martinez@state.nm.us
Web: www.dvs.state.nm.us/benefits.html

Summary To provide financial assistance for college or graduate school to the children of deceased military personnel in New Mexico.

Eligibility This program is open to the children of military personnel killed in action or as a result of such action during a period of armed conflict. Applicants must be between the ages of 16 and 26 and enrolled in a state-supported school in New Mexico. Selection is based on merit and financial need.

Financial data The scholarships provide full waiver of tuition at state-funded postsecondary schools in New Mexico. A stipend of $150 per semester ($300 per year) provides assistance with books and fees.

Duration 1 year; may be renewed.

Number awarded Varies each year.

Deadline Deadline not specified.

[736]
NEW YORK AMERICAN LEGION PRESS ASSOCIATION SCHOLARSHIP

New York American Legion Press Association
Attn: Scholarship Chair
P.O. Box 650
East Aurora, NY 14052-0650
E-mail: CStarberry@cs.com
Web: www.nyalpa.webs.com

Summary To provide financial assistance to residents of New York who have a connection with the American Legion and are interested in careers in communications.

Eligibility This program is open to New York residents who are 1) children of members of the American Legion or American Legion Auxiliary; 2) members of the Sons of the American Legion; 3) junior members of the American Legion Auxiliary; or 4) graduates of the New York Boys State or Girls State. Applicants must be entering or attending an accredited 4-year college or university, working on a degree in communications (including public relations, journalism, reprographics, newspaper design or management, or other related fields acceptable to the scholarship committee). Along with their application, they must submit a 500-word essay on why they chose the field of communications as a future vocation. Financial need and class standing are not considered.

Financial data The stipend is $1,000.

Duration 1 year.

Number awarded 1 each year.

Deadline April of each year.

[737]
NEW YORK LEGION AUXILIARY DEPARTMENT SCHOLARSHIP

American Legion Auxiliary
Department of New York
112 State Street, Suite 1310
Albany, NY 12207
(518) 463-1162   Toll Free: (800) 421-6348
Fax: (518) 449-5406
E-mail: alanykathleen@nycap.rr.com
Web: www.deptny.org/scholarships

Summary To provide financial assistance to New York residents who are the descendants of veterans and interested in attending college in any state.

Eligibility This program is open to residents of New York who are high school seniors or graduates and attending or planning to attend an accredited college or university in any state. Applicants must be the children, grandchildren, or great-grandchildren of veterans who served during specified periods of wartime. Along with their application, they must submit a 500-word essay on a subject of their choice. Selection is based on character (20%), Americanism (20%), leadership (20%), scholarship (15%), and financial need (25%). U.S. citizenship is required.

Financial data The stipend is $1,000. Funds are paid directly to the recipient's school.

Duration 1 year.

Number awarded 1 each year.

Deadline February of each year.

[738]
NEW YORK LEGION AUXILIARY DISTRICT SCHOLARSHIPS

American Legion Auxiliary
Department of New York
112 State Street, Suite 1310
Albany, NY 12207
(518) 463-1162   Toll Free: (800) 421-6348
Fax: (518) 449-5406
E-mail: alanykathleen@nycap.rr.com
Web: www.deptny.org/scholarships

Summary To provide financial assistance to descendants of veterans in New York who are interested in attending college in any state.

Eligibility This program is open to residents of New York who are high school seniors or graduates and attending or planning to attend an accredited college or university in any state. Applicants must be the children, grandchildren, or great-grandchildren of veterans who served during specified periods of wartime. Along with their application, they must submit a 500-word essay on why they chose to further their education. Selection is based on character (30%), Americanism (20%), leadership (10%), scholarship (20%), and financial need (20%). U.S. citizenship is required.

Financial data The stipend is $1,000. Funds are paid directly to the recipient's school.

Duration 1 year.

Number awarded 10 each year: 1 in each of the 10 judicial districts in New York.

Deadline February of each year.

[739]
NEW YORK LEGION AUXILIARY PAST PRESIDENTS PARLEY STUDENT SCHOLARSHIP IN MEDICAL FIELD

American Legion Auxiliary
Department of New York
112 State Street, Suite 1310
Albany, NY 12207
(518) 463-1162   Toll Free: (800) 421-6348
Fax: (518) 449-5406
E-mail: alanykathleen@nycap.rr.com
Web: www.deptny.org/scholarships

Summary To provide financial assistance to descendants of wartime veterans in New York who are interested in attending college in any state to prepare for a career in a medical field.

Eligibility This program is open to residents of New York who are high school seniors or graduates and attending or planning to attend an accredited college or university in any state to prepare for a career in a medical field. Applicants must be the children, grandchildren, or great-grandchildren of veterans who served during specified periods of wartime. Along with their application, they must submit a 500-word essay on why they selected the medical field. Selection is based on character (30%), Americanism (20%), leadership (10%), scholarship (20%), and financial need (20%). U.S. citizenship is required.

Financial data The stipend is $1,000. Funds are paid directly to the recipient's school.

Duration 1 year.

Number awarded 2 each year.

Deadline February of each year.

[740]
NEW YORK MILITARY ENHANCED RECOGNITION INCENTIVE AND TRIBUTE (MERIT) SCHOLARSHIPS

New York State Higher Education Services Corporation
Attn: Student Information
99 Washington Avenue
Albany, NY 12255
(518) 473-1574   Toll Free: (888) NYS-HESC
Fax: (518) 473-3749   TDD: (800) 445-5234
E-mail: webmail@hesc.com
Web: www.hesc.ny.gov

Summary To provide financial assistance to disabled veterans and the family members of deceased or disabled veterans who are residents of New York and interested in attending college in the state.

Eligibility This program is open to New York residents who served in the armed forces of the United States or state organized militia at any time on or after August 2, 1990 and became severely and permanently disabled as a result of injury or illness suffered or incurred in a combat theater or combat zone or during military training operations in preparation for duty in a combat theater or combat zone of operations. Also eligible are the children, spouses, or financial dependents of members of the armed forces of the United States or state organized militia who at any time after August 2, 1990 1) died, became severely and permanently disabled as a result of injury or illness suffered or incurred, or are classified as missing in action in a combat theater or combat zone of operations; 2) died as a result of injuries incurred in those designated areas; or 3) died or became severely and permanently disabled as a result of injury or illness suffered or incurred during military training operations in preparation for duty in a combat theater or combat zone of operations. Applicants must be attending or accepted at an approved program of study as full-time undergraduates at a public college or university or private institution in New York.

Financial data At public colleges and universities, this program provides payment of actual tuition and mandatory educational fees; actual room and board charged to students living on campus or an allowance for room and board for commuter students; and allowances for books, supplies, and transportation. At private institutions, the award is equal to the amount charged at the State University of New York (SUNY) for 4-year tuition and average mandatory fees (or the student's actual tuition and fees, whichever is less) plus allowances for room, board, books, supplies, and transportation. Recently, maximum awards were $21,892 for students living on campus or $14,602 for commuter students.

Duration This program is available for 4 years of full-time undergraduate study (or 5 years in an approved 5-year bachelor's degree program).

Additional information This program was previously known as the New York State Military Service Recognition Scholarships (MSRS).

Number awarded Varies each year.

Deadline April of each year.

[741]
NGAMA SCHOLARSHIPS

National Guard Association of Massachusetts
Attn: Education Services Office
2 Randolph Road, Building 1505
Hanscom AFB, MA 01731-3001
E-mail: contact@ngama.org
Web: www.ngama.org/scholarships/

Summary To provide financial assistance to members of the Massachusetts National Guard and their dependents who are interested in attending college in any state.

Eligibility This program is open to 1) current members of the Massachusetts National Guard; 2) children and spouses of current members of the National Guard Association of Massachusetts (NGAMA); and 3) children and spouses of current members of the Massachusetts National Guard. Applicants must be enrolled in or planning to enroll in an accredited college or technical program in any state. Along with their application, they must submit a letter of recommendation, a list of extracurricular activities and other significant accomplishments, high school or college transcripts, and an essay on a topic that changes annually but relates to the National Guard.

Financial data The stipend is $2,000.

Duration 1 year.

Number awarded 2 each year.

Deadline March of each year.

[742]
NGAUT AND EANGUT "MINUTEMAN" SCHOLARSHIPS

National Guard Association of Utah
12953 South Minuteman Drive, Room 19835
P.O. Box 435
Draper, UT 84020
(801) 631-6312   E-mail: ngautah@ngaut.org
Web: www.ngaut.org/Scholarship.php

Summary To provide financial assistance to members and dependents of members of the National Guard Association of Utah (NGAAUT) and the Enlisted Association of the National Guard of Utah (EANGUT) who are interested in attending college in the state.

Eligibility This program is open to members and dependents of members of NGAUT and EANGUT who are high school seniors or students enrolled for at least 6 credit hours at a college or university in the state. Applicants must submit 1) a 150-word description of their educational and career goals; 2) a 200- to 300-word description of leadership and extracurricular activities that they may have had or currently enjoy; 3) a 300-word essay on how the military has influenced their life; 4) a 1-page cover letter or resume; and 5) 2 letters of reference.

Financial data Stipends are $1,500 or $1,000. Funds are sent to the recipient's school and must be used for tuition, laboratory fees, and curriculum-required books and supplies.

Duration 1 year.

Number awarded 12 each year: 1 at $1,500 and 4 at $1,000 sponsored by NGAUT, 1 at $1,500 and 1 at $1,000 sponsored by EANGUT, 1 at $1,000 sponsored by Boeing, and 4 at $1,000 sponsored by other corporate members.

Deadline March of each year.

[743]
NGAW SCHOLARSHIP PROGRAM

National Guard Association of Washington
Attn: Scholarship Committee
P.O. Box 5144
Camp Murray
Tacoma, WA 98430-5144
(253) 584-5411   Toll Free: (800) 588-6420
Fax: (253) 582-9521   E-mail: ngaw@ngaw.org
Web: www.ngaw.org/programs/scholarships-and-awards

Summary To provide financial assistance to members of the Washington National Guard and their dependents who are interested in attending college in the state.

Eligibility This program is open to members of the Washington National Guard and their dependents who are enrolled at an accredited college, university, or trade school in the state. Guard members may be full-time or part-time students; dependents must be enrolled full time. Applicants do not need to be members of the National Guard Association of Washington (NGAW) although members are eligible for larger awards. Along with their application, they must submit a statement that covers their educational goals, academic credits completed, honors and awards, participation in National Guard, plans for the future in the National Guard, participation in school extracurricular activities, participation in volunteer civic and community events, and financial need.

Financial data The stipend ranges from $500 to $1,000.

Duration 1 year.

Number awarded 7 each year: 1 at $1,000 (designated the Lowenberg Scholarship and reserved for a Guard member) and 6 at either $750 (if the recipient is an NGAW member) or $500 (if the recipient is not a member).

Deadline March of each year.

[744]
NGOA-FL AND ENGAF SCHOLARSHIP PROGRAM

National Guard Association of Florida
Attn: Scholarship Committee
P.O. Box 3446
St. Augustine, FL 32085-3446
(904) 823-0628   Fax: (904) 839-2068
E-mail: ngafl1903@floridaguard.org
Web: www.floridaguard.org/index.php/scholarships

Summary To provide financial assistance to members of the Florida National Guard and their families who are also members of either the National Guard Association of Florida (NGOA-FL) or the Enlisted National Guard Association of Florida (ENGAF) and interested in attending college in the state.

Eligibility This program is open to active members of the Florida National Guard (enlisted, officer, and warrant officer), their spouses, and children, but preference is given to Guard members. Applicants must be residents of Florida attending or planning to attend an accredited college, university, or vocational/technical school in the state. They must also be a member, spouse of a member, or child of a member of their respective association. Selection is based on academic achievement, civic and moral leadership, character, and financial need.

Financial data Scholarships are $1,000 for full-time students or $500 for part-time students; funds are paid directly to the recipient's institution.

Duration 1 year; may be renewed.

Additional information This program is jointly sponsored by the respective associations.

Number awarded 15 each year.

Deadline June of each year.

[745]
NISEI VETERANS COMMITTEE/WOMEN'S AUXILIARY CLUB SCHOLARSHIP

Nisei Veterans Committee
Attn: NVC Foundation
1212 South King Street
Seattle, WA 98144-2025
(206) 322-1122   E-mail: scholarship@nvcfoundation.org
Web: www.seattlenvc.org/education/scholarship

Summary To provide financial assistance for college to high school seniors who are related to a member of the Nisei Veterans Committee or the NVC Foundation.

Eligibility This program is open to high school seniors who are relatives of members of the Nisei Veterans Committee (an organization of Japanese American veterans) or of the NVC Foundation. Applicants must be planning to attend a college or university. Along with their application, they must submit essays on 1) what the Nisei veterans' legacy means to them; and 2) their future aspirations and life plans. Special consideration is given to students who have helped support the NVC organization. Financial need is considered in the selection process.

Financial data The stipend is $2,500.

Duration 1 year.

Number awarded 1 each year.

Deadline January of each year.

[746]
NON COMMISSIONED OFFICERS ASSOCIATION SCHOLARSHIP FUND

Non Commissioned Officers Association of the United
   States of America
Attn: Scholarship Fund
P.O. Box 33790
San Antonio, TX 78265-3790
(210) 653-6161   Toll Free: (800) 662-2620
Fax: (210) 637-3337   E-mail: membsvc@ncoausa.org
Web: www.ncoausa.org

Summary To provide financial assistance for college to spouses and children of members of the Non Commissioned Officers Association.

Eligibility This program is open to spouses and children (under 25 years of age) of members of the association. Children must submit 2 letters of recommendation from teachers, a personal recommendation from an adult who is not a relative, a handwritten autobiography, a certified transcript of high school or college grades, ACT or SAT scores, and a composition on Americanism. Spouses must submit a copy of their high school diploma or GED equivalent; a certified transcript of all college courses completed (if any); a certificate of completion for any other courses or training; a brief biographical background statement; and a letter of intent that includes a description of their proposed course of study for a degree, plans for completion of a degree, and a paragraph on "What a College Degree Means to Me." Financial need is not normally considered in the selection process and no applicant will be rejected because of a lack of need, but in some cases of extreme need it may be used as a factor. Each year, 2 special awards are presented: the Mary Barraco Scholarship to the student submitting the best essay on Americanism, and the William T. Green Scholarship to the student with the best high school academic record.

Financial data The scholarship stipend is $900 for children of members or $1,000 for spouses of members; the special awards are $1,000. Funds are paid directly to the designated school to be used for the recipient's room and board, tuition, library fees, textbooks, and related instructional material.

Duration 1 year; may be renewed if the student maintains a GPA of 3.0 or higher and carries at least 15 hours.

Additional information Spouses who receive a grant must apply for membership in 1 of the NCOA membership categories (regular, associate, veteran, or auxiliary).

Number awarded 15 each year: 9 scholarships to children of members, 4 scholarships to spouses of members, and 2 special awards.

Deadline March of each year.

[747]
NON-RESIDENT TUITION WAIVERS FOR VETERANS AND THEIR DEPENDENTS WHO MOVE TO TEXAS

Texas Higher Education Coordinating Board
Attn: Grants and Special Programs
1200 East Anderson Lane
P.O. Box 12788
Austin, TX 78711-2788
(512) 427-6340   Toll Free: (800) 242-3062
Fax: (512) 427-6420   E-mail: grantinfo@thecb.state.tx.us
Web: www.collegeforalltexans.com

Summary To exempt veterans who move to Texas and their dependents from the payment of non-resident tuition at public institutions of higher education in the state.

Eligibility Eligible for these waivers are former members of the U.S. armed forces and commissioned officers of the Public Health Service who are retired or have been honorably discharged, their spouses, and their dependent children. Applicants must have moved to Texas upon separation from the service and be attending or planning to attend a public college or university in the state. They must have indicated their intent to become a Texas resident by registering to vote and doing 1 of the following: owning real property in Texas, registering an automobile in Texas, or executing a will indicating that they are a resident of the state.

Financial data Although persons eligible under this program are still classified as non-residents, they are entitled to pay the resident tuition at Texas institutions of higher education on an immediate basis.

Duration 1 year.

Number awarded Varies each year.

Deadline Deadline not specified.

[748]
NORTH CAROLINA NATIONAL GUARD ASSOCIATION ACADEMIC EXCELLENCE/ LEADERSHIP AWARD

North Carolina National Guard Association
Attn: Educational Foundation, Inc.
7410 Chapel Hill Road
Raleigh, NC 27607-5047
(919) 851-3390, ext. 5
Toll Free: (800) 821-6159 (within NC)
Fax: (919) 859-4990
E-mail: peggyncngaef@bellsouth.net
Web: sites.google.com/site/ncngassociation/documents

Summary To provide financial assistance to members and dependents of members of the North Carolina National Guard Association who demonstrate academic excellence and are attending college in any state.

Eligibility This program is open to active and associate members of the association as well as the spouses, children, grandchildren, and legal dependents of active, associate, or deceased members. Applicants must be attending a 4-year college or university in any state and have a GPA of 3.5 or higher. Selection is based on academic achievement, citizenship, leadership, and other application information.

Financial data The stipend is $1,000.

Duration 1 year; may be renewed.

Number awarded 1 or 2 each year.

Deadline January of each year.

[749]
NORTH CAROLINA NATIONAL GUARD ASSOCIATION SCHOLARSHIPS

North Carolina National Guard Association
Attn: Educational Foundation, Inc.
7410 Chapel Hill Road
Raleigh, NC 27607-5047
(919) 851-3390, ext. 5
Toll Free: (800) 821-6159 (within NC)
Fax: (919) 859-4990
E-mail: peggyncngaef@bellsouth.net
Web: sites.google.com/site/ncngassociation/documents

Summary To provide financial assistance to members and dependents of members of the North Carolina National Guard Association who plan to attend college in any state.

Eligibility This program is open to active and associate members of the association as well as the spouses, children, grandchildren, and legal dependents of active, associate, or deceased members. Applicants must be high school seniors, high school graduates, or students currently enrolled at a college or university in any state. Selection is based on financial need, academic achievement, citizenship, leadership, and other application information. The most outstanding applicants receive scholarships provided by the SECU Foundation. Applicants who meet specified additional requirements qualify for various memorial and special scholarships.

Financial data Stipends are $10,000 or $5,000 for the SECU Foundation Scholarships, $1,000 for memorial and special scholarships, $1,000 for citizenship awards, $800 for general scholarships, or $400 for community college scholarships.

Duration 1 year; may be renewed.

Additional information This program, which began in 1968, includes a number of named memorial and special scholarships. Other scholarships are funded by the SECU Foundation of the State Employees' Credit Union and the USAA Insurance Corporation.

Number awarded Varies each year; recently, 37 were awarded: 2 SECU Foundation Scholarships (1 at $10,000 and 1 at $5,000), 18 memorial and special scholarships at $1,000, 2 citizenship awards are $1,000, 10 general scholarships at $800, and 5 community college scholarships at $400.

Deadline January of each year for high school graduates and college students; February of each year for high school seniors.

[750]
NORTH CAROLINA NATIONAL GUARD ASSOCIATION SPECIAL POPULATION SCHOLARSHIP

North Carolina National Guard Association
Attn: Educational Foundation, Inc.
7410 Chapel Hill Road
Raleigh, NC 27607-5047
(919) 851-3390, ext. 5
Toll Free: (800) 821-6159 (within NC)
Fax: (919) 859-4990
E-mail: peggyncngaef@bellsouth.net
Web: sites.google.com/site/ncngassociation/documents

Summary To provide financial assistance to members and dependents of members of the North Carolina National Guard Association who have a disability and are interested in attending college in any state.

Eligibility This program is open to active and associate members of the association as well as the spouses, children, grandchildren, and legal dependents of active, associate, or deceased members. Applicants must be learning disabled and/or physically disabled. They may be high school seniors, high school graduates, or students currently enrolled at a college or university in any state. Selection is based on financial need, academic achievement, citizenship, leadership, and other application information.

Financial data The stipend is $1,000.

Duration 1 year; may be renewed.

Number awarded 1 each year.

Deadline January of each year for high school graduates and college students; February of each year for high school seniors.

[751]
NORTH CAROLINA SCHOLARSHIPS FOR CHILDREN OF WAR VETERANS

North Carolina Division of Veterans Affairs
Albemarle Building
325 North Salisbury Street, Suite 1065
1315 Mail Service Center
Raleigh, NC 27699-1315
(919) 807-4250   Fax: (919) 807-4260
E-mail: ncdva.aso@ncmail.net
Web: www.doa.nc.gov

Summary To provide financial assistance to the children of disabled and other classes of North Carolina veterans who plan to attend college in the state.

Eligibility Eligible applicants come from 5 categories: Class I-A: the veteran parent died in wartime service or as a result of a service-connected condition incurred in wartime service; Class I-B: the veteran parent is rated by the U.S. Department of Veterans Affairs (VA) as 100% disabled as a result of wartime service and currently or at the time of death was drawing compensation for such disability; Class II: the veteran parent is rated by the VA as much as 20% but less than 100% disabled due to wartime service, or was awarded a Purple Heart medal for wounds received, and currently or at the time of death drawing compensation for such disability; Class III: the veteran parent is currently or was at the time of death receiving a VA pension for total and permanent disability, or the veteran parent is deceased but does not qualify under any other provisions, or the veteran parent served in a combat zone or waters adjacent to a combat zone and received a campaign badge or medal but does not qualify under any other provisions; Class IV: the veteran parent was a prisoner of war or missing in action. For all classes, applicants must 1) be under 25 years of age and have a veteran parent who was a resident of North Carolina at the time of entrance into the armed forces; or 2) be the natural child, or adopted child prior to age 15, who was born in North Carolina, has been a resident of the state continuously since birth, and is the child of a veteran whose disabilities occurred during a period of war.

Financial data Students in Classes I-A, II, III, and IV receive $4,500 per academic year if they attend a private college or junior college; if attending a public postsecondary institution, they receive free tuition, a room allowance, a board allowance, and exemption from certain mandatory fees. Students in Class I-B receive $1,500 per academic year if they attend a private college or junior college; if attending a public postsecondary institution, they receive free tuition and exemption from certain mandatory fees.

Duration 4 academic years.

Number awarded An unlimited number of awards are made under Classes I-A, I-B, and IV. Classes II and III are limited to 100 awards each year in each class.

Deadline Applications for Classes I-A, I-B, and IV may be submitted at any time; applications for Classes II and III must be submitted by February of each year.

[752]
NORTH CAROLINA VIETNAM VETERANS SCHOLARSHIP PROGRAM

North Carolina Vietnam Veterans, Inc.
c/o Bud Gross, Treasurer
601 Compton Road
Raleigh, NC 27609
(919) 787-7228   E-mail: ncvvi65@gmail.com
Web: www.ncvvi.org

Summary To provide financial assistance to North Carolina residents who are Vietnam veterans or the dependents of veterans and interested in attending college in any state.

Eligibility This program is open to current residents of Chatham, Durham, Franklin, Granville, Harnett, Johnston, Nash, or Wake counties in North Carolina who are either a Vietnam veteran or the veteran's spouse, child, foster child, adopted child, or grandchild. Families of members of North Carolina Vietnam Veterans, Inc. (NCVVI) who live in any county of the state are also eligible. Applicants must be attending or planning to attend a college, university, community college, or trade school in any state. They must submit a copy of the Department of Defense Form DD214 to document Vietnam service; a birth certificate and/or marriage license (as needed); a personal statement about themselves, including work experience, anticipated career, and goals; a list of current activities and awards; and an essay of 600 to 900 words on a topic that changes annually; recently, the topic was "Why is it important to teach the lessons of Vietnam in schools today?"

Financial data Stipends range from $500 to $1,500. Funds are paid directly to the recipients on a reimbursement basis (presentation of paid receipts for tuition, fees, and/or books).

Duration 1 year.

Additional information This program includes the Mike Hooks Memorial Scholarship.

Number awarded 1 or more each year.

Deadline February of each year.

[753]
NORTH DAKOTA EDUCATIONAL ASSISTANCE FOR DEPENDENTS OF VETERANS

Department of Veterans Affairs
4201 38th Street S.W., Suite 104
P.O. Box 9003
Fargo, ND 58106-9003
(701) 239-7165   Toll Free: (866) 634-8387
Fax: (701) 239-7166
Web: www.nd.gov

Summary To provide financial assistance for college to the spouses, widow(er)s, and children of disabled and other North Dakota veterans and military personnel.

Eligibility This program is open to the spouses, widow(er)s, and dependent children of veterans who were killed in action, died from wounds or other service-connected causes, were totally disabled as a result of service-connected causes, died from service-connected disabilities, were a prisoners of war, or were declared missing in action. Veteran parents must have been born in and lived in North Dakota until entrance into the armed forces (or must have resided in the state for at least 6 months prior to entrance into military service) and must have served during wartime.

Financial data Eligible dependents receive free tuition and are exempt from fees at any state-supported institution of higher education, technical school, or vocational school in North Dakota.

Duration Up to 45 months or 10 academic semesters.

Number awarded Varies each year.

Deadline Deadline not specified.

[754]
NORTH DAKOTA NATIONAL GUARD ENLISTED ASSOCIATION SCHOLARSHIPS

North Dakota National Guard Enlisted Association
c/o MSG Joe Lovelace
4900 107th Avenue S.E.
Minot, ND 58701-9207
E-mail: joseph.m.lovelace@us.army.mil
Web: www.ndngea.org/forms.html

Summary To provide financial assistance to members of the North Dakota National Guard Enlisted Association (NDN-

GEA) and their families who are interested in attending college in any state.

Eligibility This program is open to association members who have at least 1 year remaining on their enlistment or have completed 20 or more years in service. Also eligible are their unmarried dependent children and spouses and the unremarried spouses and unmarried dependent children of deceased NDNGEA members who were in good standing at the time of death. Applicants must be attending or planning to attend a university, college, or trade/business school in any state. Graduate students are not eligible. Selection is based on academic achievement, leadership, character, and financial need.

Financial data The stipend is $1,000. Funds are sent directly to the school in the recipient's name.

Duration 1 year.

Number awarded 1 or more each year.

Deadline November of each year.

[755]
OFFICE OF WORK-LIFE SCHOLARSHIPS

U.S. Coast Guard
Attn: Office of Work-Life (CG-111)
2100 Second Street, S.W., Stop 7902
Washington, DC 20593-7902
(202) 475-5140   Toll Free: (800) 872-4957
Fax: (202) 475-5906
E-mail: HQS.SMB.FamilySupportServices@uscg.mil
Web: www.uscg.mil/hr/cg111/scholarship.asp

Summary To provide financial assistance for college to the dependent children of Coast Guard enlisted personnel.

Eligibility This program is open to the dependent children of enlisted members of the U.S. Coast Guard on active duty, retired, or deceased, and of enlisted personnel in the Coast Guard Reserve currently on extended active duty 180 days or more. Applicants must be high school seniors or current undergraduates enrolled or planning to enroll full-time at a 4-year college, university, or vocational school. They must be under 24 years of age and registered in the Defense Enrollment Eligibility Reporting System (DEERS) system. Along with their application, they must submit their SAT or ACT scores, a letter of recommendation, transcripts, a financial information statement, and a 500-word essay on their personal and academic achievements, extracurricular activities, contributions to the community, and academic plans and career goals.

Financial data The stipend ranges from $1,000 to $5,000 per year.

Duration 1 year; some scholarships may be renewed up to 3 additional years.

Additional information This program includes several named awards, including the Coast Guard Foundation Scholarships, RADM Arnold I. Sobel Scholarships, the Captain Ernest Fox Scholarships, the Commander Daniel J. Christovich Scholarship, the Commander Ronald J. Cantin Scholarship, and the Carole Westbrook Scholarship.

Number awarded Varies each year; recently, 61 were awarded: 6 at $5,000 per year for 4 years, 17 at $5,000 per year for 1 year, 30 at $2,500 per year for 1 year, 1 at $2,000 per year for 1 year, and 7 at $1,000 for 1 year.

Deadline March of each year.

[756]
OHIO LEGION AUXILIARY DEPARTMENT PRESIDENT'S SCHOLARSHIP

American Legion Auxiliary
Department of Ohio
1100 Brandywine Boulevard, Suite D
P.O. Box 2760
Zanesville, OH 43702-2760
(740) 452-8245   Fax: (740) 452-2620
E-mail: ala_katie@rrohio.com
Web: www.alaohio.org/Scholarships

Summary To provide financial assistance to veterans and their descendants in Ohio who are interested in attending college in any state.

Eligibility This program is open to honorably-discharged veterans and the children, grandchildren, and great-grandchildren of living, deceased, or disabled honorably-discharged veterans who served during designated periods of wartime. Applicants must be residents of Ohio, seniors at an accredited high school, planning to enter a college in any state, and sponsored by an American Legion Auxiliary Unit. Along with their application, they must submit an original article (up to 500 words) written by the applicant on a topic that changes annually. Recently, students were asked to write on "Education and the American Dream." Selection is based on character, Americanism, leadership, scholarship, and financial need.

Financial data Stipends are $1,500 or $1,000. Funds are paid to the recipient's school.

Duration 1 year.

Number awarded 2 each year: 1 at $1,500 and 1 at $1,000.

Deadline March of each year.

[757]
OHIO NATIONAL GUARD ASSOCIATION LEADERSHIP GRANTS

Ohio National Guard Association
Attn: Leadership Grant Committee
1299 Virginia Avenue
P.O. Box 8070
Columbus, OH 43201
Toll Free: (800) 642-6642
E-mail: ONGAKoper@prodigy.net
Web: www.ohionga.org/schlolarship.html

Summary To provide financial assistance to members of the Ohio National Guard Association (ONGA) and their families who are interested in attending college in any state.

Eligibility This program is open to active members (either officers or warrant officers) of the ONGA and the dependents of active, life, retired, or deceased members. Applicants must be enrolled or planning to enroll at a college or university in any state. Along with their application, they must submit transcripts, SAT/ACT scores, and a 2-page essay explaining why they should be selected to receive a grant. Selection is based on grades, future plans, membership and leadership, honors and awards, need, and overall impression.

Financial data A stipend is awarded (amount not specified).

Duration 1 year; nonrenewable.

Additional information This program began in 1996.

Number awarded Varies each year; recently, 5 were awarded.

Deadline November of each year.

[758]
OHIO SAFETY OFFICERS COLLEGE MEMORIAL FUND

Ohio Board of Regents
Attn: Office of Financial Aid
25 South Front Street
Columbus, OH 43215-3414
(614) 752-9528   Toll Free: (888) 833-1133
Fax: (614) 466-5866 E-mail: abrady@regents.state.oh.us
Web: www.ohiohighered.org/safety-officers-college-fund

Summary To provide financial assistance to Ohio residents who are interested in attending college in the state and whose parent or spouse was killed in the line of duty as a safety officer or member of the armed forces.

Eligibility This program is open to Ohio residents whose parent or spouse was 1) a peace officer, firefighter, or other safety officer killed in the line of duty anywhere in the United States; or 2) a member of the U.S. armed forces killed in the line of duty during Operation Enduring Freedom, Operation Iraqi Freedom, or other designated combat zone. Applicants must be interested in attending a participating Ohio college or university. Children and spouses of military personnel are eligible for this program only if they do not qualify for the Ohio War Orphans Scholarship.

Financial data At Ohio public colleges and universities, the program provides full payment of tuition. At Ohio private colleges and universities, the stipend is equivalent to the average amounts paid to students attending public institutions, currently $7,494 per year.

Duration 1 year; may be renewed up to 3 additional years.

Additional information Eligible institutions are Ohio state-assisted colleges and universities and Ohio institutions approved by the Board of Regents. This program was established in 1980.

Number awarded Varies each year; recently, 54 students received benefits from this program.

Deadline Application deadlines are established by each participating college and university.

[759]
OHIO WAR ORPHANS SCHOLARSHIP

Ohio Board of Regents
Attn: Office of Financial Aid
25 South Front Street
Columbus, OH 43215-3414
(614) 752-9528   Toll Free: (888) 833-1133
Fax: (614) 466-5866 E-mail: abrady@regents.state.oh.us
Web: www.ohiohighered.org/ohio-war-orphans

Summary To provide financial assistance to the children of deceased or disabled Ohio veterans who plan to attend college in the state.

Eligibility This program is open to residents of Ohio who are under 25 years of age and interested in enrolling full time at an eligible college or university in the state. Applicants must be the child of a veteran who 1) was a member of the U.S. armed forces, including the organized Reserves and Ohio National Guard, for a period of 90 days or more (or discharged because of a disability incurred after less than 90 days of service); 2) served during specified periods of war-time; 3) entered service as a resident of Ohio; and 4) as a result of that service, either was killed or became at least 60% service-connected disabled. Also eligible are children of veterans who have a permanent and total nonservice-connected disability and are receiving disability benefits from the U.S. Department of Veterans Affairs. If the veteran parent served only in the organized Reserves or Ohio National Guard, the parent must have been killed or became permanently and totally disabled while at a scheduled training assembly, field training period (of any duration or length), or active duty for training, pursuant to bona fide orders issued by a competent authority. Financial need is considered in the selection process.

Financial data At Ohio public colleges and universities, the program provides payment of 77% of tuition and fees. At Ohio private colleges and universities, the stipend is $6,994 per year.

Duration 1 year; may be renewed up to 4 additional years, provided the recipient maintains a GPA of 2.0 or higher.

Additional information Eligible institutions are Ohio state-assisted colleges and universities and Ohio institutions approved by the Board of Regents. This program was established in 1957.

Number awarded Varies, depending upon the funds available. If sufficient funds are available, all eligible applicants are given a scholarship. Recently, 861 students received benefits from this program.

Deadline June of each year.

[760]
OKLAHOMA HEROES PROMISE SCHOLARSHIP

Oklahoma State Regents for Higher Education
Attn: Director of Scholarship and Grant Programs
655 Research Parkway, Suite 200
P.O. Box 108850
Oklahoma City, OK 73101-8850
(405) 225-9131   Toll Free: (800) 858-1840
Fax: (405) 225-9230   E-mail: studentinfo@osrhe.edu
Web: secure.okcollegestart.org

Summary To provide financial assistance for college to children of Oklahoma military personnel who were killed in action.

Eligibility This program is open to Oklahoma residents who are the child of a person killed after January 1, 2000 in the line of duty in a branch of the U.S. armed forces or who died after January 1, 2000 as a result of an injury sustained in the line of duty. Applicants must enroll at a college or university in Oklahoma prior to reaching 21 years of age. Their parent must have filed an individual or joint Oklahoma resident income tax return for the year prior to their death.

Financial data The program pays the tuition at a public community college or university in the state or a comparable amount at an accredited Oklahoma private college or university.

Duration Assistance continues for 5 years or until receipt of a bachelor's degree, whichever occurs first.

Additional information This program was established in 2011 as a replacement for the former program named the Oklahoma Tuition Waiver for Prisoners of War, Persons Missing in Action, and Dependents.

Number awarded Varies each year.
Deadline Deadline not specified.

[761]
OKLAHOMA NATIONAL GUARD ASSOCIATION SCHOLARSHIPS

National Guard Association of Oklahoma
Attn: Scholarship Foundation
6500 North Kelley Avenue
Oklahoma City, OK 73111
(405) 475-2152   Fax: (405) 475-2183
E-mail: ngaok@coxinet.net
Web: www.ngaok.org/scholarship

Summary To provide financial assistance to members of the National Guard Association of Oklahoma (NGAOK) and their dependents who are interested in attending college in any state.

Eligibility This program is open to NGAOK members and their dependents who are attending or planning to attend a college or university in any state. The primary next of kin of members of the Oklahoma National Guard killed in action after September 11, 2001 are considered life member of NGAOK. Applicants must submit a 2-page statement that describes their academic performance, character, demonstrated leadership and leadership ability, aspirations, and future goals or plans.

Financial data Stipends are $500 or $1,000.

Duration 1 year.

Number awarded 20 to 25 each year.

Deadline January of each year.

[762]
ONGEA SCHOLARSHIP PROGRAM

Ohio National Guard Enlisted Association
Attn: Scholarship Chair
1299 Virginia Avenue
Columbus, OH 43212
(740) 574-5932   Toll Free: (800) 642-6642
Fax: (614) 520-6146   E-mail: ongea@juno.com
Web: www.ongea.org/12.html

Summary To provide financial assistance to members of the Ohio National Guard Enlisted Association (ONGEA) and children of members of the ONGEA Auxiliary who are interested in attending college in any state.

Eligibility This program is open to 1) children of ONGEA and ONGEA Auxiliary members (ONGEA member spouses must be Auxiliary members in order for a child to be eligible); 2) unmarried dependent children of deceased ONGEA and ONGEA Auxiliary members who were in good standing the time of their death; and 3) ONGEA members (if married, the spouse must also be a member of the Auxiliary). Applicants must be enrolling as full-time undergraduate students at a college, university, trade school, or business school in any state. Selection is based on academic record, character, leadership, and financial need.

Financial data Stipends are $1,000 or $500. After verification of enrollment is provided, checks are sent to the recipient and made out to the recipient's school.

Duration 1 year; nonrenewable.

Additional information This program is sponsored jointly by ONGEA, the ONGEA Auxiliary, USAA Insurance Corporation, and the First Cleveland Cavalry Association.

Number awarded 5 to 10 each year, depending upon the availability of funds.
Deadline March of each year.

[763]
OPERATION ENDURING FREEDOM AND OPERATION IRAQI FREEDOM SCHOLARSHIP

Vermont Student Assistance Corporation
Attn: Scholarship Programs
10 East Allen Street
P.O. Box 2000
Winooski, VT 05404-2601
(802) 654-3798 Toll Free: (888) 253-4819
Fax: (802) 654-3765 TDD: (800) 281-3341 (within VT)
E-mail: info@vsac.org
Web: services.vsac.org

Summary To provide financial assistance to residents of Vermont whose parent has served or is serving in Operating Enduring Freedom in Afghanistan or Operation Iraqi Freedom.

Eligibility This program is open to residents of Vermont who are children of a member of any branch of the armed forces or National Guard whose residence or home of record is in Vermont. Applicants must plan to enroll full time in a certificate, associate degree, or bachelor's degree program at an accredited postsecondary school in any state. The parent must have served or currently be serving in Operation Enduring Freedom or Operation Iraqi Freedom. Preference is given to applicants whose parent was killed, was wounded, or became permanently disabled as a result of their service. Along with their application, they must submit 1) a 100-word essay on any significant barriers that limit their access to education; 2) a 250-word essay on their short- and long-term academic, educational, career, vocational, and/or employment goals; and 3) what they believe distinguishes their application from others that may be submitted. Selection is based on those essays, a letter of recommendation, and financial need (expected family contribution of $23,760 or less).

Financial data The stipend ranges from $3,500 to $7,000 per year.
Duration 1 year; may be renewed up to 3 additional years.
Additional information This program, established in 2007, is sponsored by the Hoehl Family Foundation.
Number awarded Varies each year; recently, 10 were awarded.
Deadline March of each year.

[764]
OREGON LEGION AUXILIARY DEPARTMENT NURSES SCHOLARSHIP FOR DEPENDENTS OF DISABLED VETERANS

American Legion Auxiliary
Department of Oregon
30450 S.W. Parkway Avenue
P.O. Box 1730
Wilsonville, OR 97070-1730
(503) 682-3162 Fax: (503) 685-5008
E-mail: alaor@pcez.com
Web: www.alaoregon.org/scholarships.php

Summary To provide financial assistance for study of nursing at a school in any state to the wives and children of disabled Oregon veterans and military personnel.

Eligibility This program is open to Oregon residents who are the wives or children of veterans or of persons still serving in the armed forces who have a disability. Applicants must have been accepted by an accredited hospital or university school of nursing in any state. Selection is based on ability, aptitude, character, determination, seriousness of purpose, and financial need.
Financial data The stipend is $1,500.
Duration 1 year; may be renewed.
Number awarded 1 each year.
Deadline May of each year.

[765]
OREGON LEGION AUXILIARY DEPARTMENT NURSES SCHOLARSHIP FOR WIDOWS

American Legion Auxiliary
Department of Oregon
30450 S.W. Parkway Avenue
P.O. Box 1730
Wilsonville, OR 97070-1730
(503) 682-3162 Fax: (503) 685-5008
E-mail: alaor@pcez.com
Web: www.alaoregon.org/scholarships.php

Summary To provide financial assistance to the widows of Oregon veterans who are interested in studying nursing at a school in any state.

Eligibility This program is open to Oregon residents who are the widows of deceased veterans. Applicants must have been accepted by an accredited hospital or university school of nursing in any state. Selection is based on ability, aptitude, character, determination, seriousness of purpose, and financial need.
Financial data The stipend is $1,500.
Duration 1 year; may be renewed.
Number awarded 1 each year.
Deadline May of each year.

[766]
OREGON LEGION AUXILIARY DEPARTMENT SCHOLARSHIPS FOR CHILDREN AND WIDOWS OF VETERANS

American Legion Auxiliary
Department of Oregon
30450 S.W. Parkway Avenue
P.O. Box 1730
Wilsonville, OR 97070-1730
(503) 682-3162 Fax: (503) 685-5008
E-mail: alaor@pcez.com
Web: www.alaoregon.org/scholarships.php

Summary To provide financial assistance to the children widows of Oregon veterans who are interested in attending college in any state.

Eligibility This program is open to Oregon residents who are children or widows of veterans. Applicants must be interested in obtaining education beyond the high school level at a college, university, business school, vocational school, or any other accredited postsecondary school in the state of Oregon. Selection is based on ability, aptitude, character, seriousness of purpose, and financial need.
Financial data The stipend is $1,000.
Duration 1 year; nonrenewable.

Number awarded 1 or more each year.

Deadline February of each year.

[767]
OREGON LEGION AUXILIARY DEPARTMENT SCHOLARSHIPS FOR WIVES OF DISABLED VETERANS

American Legion Auxiliary
Department of Oregon
30450 S.W. Parkway Avenue
P.O. Box 1730
Wilsonville, OR 97070-1730
(503) 682-3162   Fax: (503) 685-5008
E-mail: alaor@pcez.com
Web: www.alaoregon.org/scholarships.php

Summary To provide financial assistance to the wives of disabled Oregon veterans who are interested in attending college in any state.

Eligibility This program is open to Oregon residents who are wives of disabled veterans. Applicants must be interested in obtaining education beyond the high school level at a college, university, business school, vocational school, or any other accredited postsecondary school in the state of Oregon. Selection is based on ability, aptitude, character, seriousness of purpose, and financial need.

Financial data The stipend is $1,000.

Duration 1 year; nonrenewable.

Number awarded 1 or more each year.

Deadline February of each year.

[768]
OREGON NATIONAL GUARD ASSOCIATION SCHOLARSHIPS

Oregon National Guard Association
Attn: Scholarship Committee
1776 Militia Way, S.E.
P.O. Box 14350
Salem, OR 97309-5047
(503) 584-3456   Fax: (503) 584-3052
E-mail: diane.r.beach.mil/mail.mil
Web: www.ornga.org/scholarships

Summary To provide financial assistance to members of the Oregon National Guard, the Oregon National Guard Association (ORNGA), and their children and spouses who are interested in attending college in any state.

Eligibility This program is open to active members of the Oregon Army and Air National Guard, members of the ORNGA, and their children and spouses. Applicants must be high school seniors, graduates, or GED recipients and interested in working on an undergraduate degree at a college, university, or trade school in any state. The parent, spouse, or applicant must have an ETS date beyond the end of the academic year for which the scholarship is used. Selection is based on demonstrated qualities of leadership, civic action, and academic achievement.

Financial data The stipend is $1,500.

Duration 1 year.

Number awarded Up to 10 each year.

Deadline March of each year.

[769]
OTIS N. BROWN/BILLY RAY CAMERON SCHOLARSHIPS

Veterans of Foreign Wars of the United States-
  Department of North Carolina
Attn: Scholarships Committee
P.O. Box 25337
Raleigh, NC 27611
(336) 468-6257   E-mail: cdrdist11@nc.vfwweb.mail.com
Web: vfwnc.org

Summary To provide financial assistance to children and grandchildren of members of the Veterans of Foreign Wars (VFW) and its Ladies Auxiliary in North Carolina who plan to attend college in the state.

Eligibility This program is open to seniors graduating from high schools in North Carolina and planning to enroll at a junior or senior college in the state. Applicants must be the child, grandchild, or stepchild of a member of the VFW or its Ladies Auxiliary, or, if deceased, was a member at time of death.

Financial data The stipend is $1,000 per year. Funds are paid directly to the recipient's institution.

Duration 1 year; may be renewed up to 3 additional years.

Number awarded 2 each year.

Deadline February of each year.

[770]
OUR FUTURE SCHOLARSHIPS FOR GRADUATING HIGH SCHOOL SENIORS

Corvias Foundation
1405 South County Trail, Suite 539
East Greenwich, RI 02818
(401) 228-2836   Fax: (401) 336-2523
E-mail: info@CorviasFoundation.org
Web: www.corviasfoundation.org

Summary To provide financial assistance for college to high school seniors who are children of active-duty military personnel assigned to specified Army or Air Force installations throughout the United States.

Eligibility This program is open to graduating high school seniors between 16 and 19 years of age who have an unweighted GPA of 3.0 or higher and are planning to enroll full time at a 4-year college or university in any state. Applicants must be children of active-duty service members stationed at 1 of 13 designated Air Force or Army installations. They must have a GPA of 3.0 or higher. Selection is based on academic performance, community involvement, extracurricular activities, educational goals, and financial need.

Financial data The stipend is $12,500 per year.

Duration 4 years, provided the recipient remains enrolled full time and maintains a GPA of 3.0 or higher.

Additional information The designated installations are Aberdeen Proving Ground (Maryland), Edwards AFB (California), Eglin AFB (Florida), Eielson AFB (Alaska), Fort Bragg (North Carolina), Fort Meade (Maryland), Fort Polk (Louisiana), Fort Riley (Kansas), Fort Rucker (Alabama), Fort Sill (Oklahoma), Hurlburt Field (Florida), McConnell AFB (Kansas), or Seymour Johnson AFB (North Carolina).

Number awarded Up to 10 each year.

Deadline February of each year.

[771]
PAST NATIONAL PRESIDENT FRANCES BOOTH MEDICAL SCHOLARSHIP

Ladies Auxiliary to the Veterans of Foreign Wars-
  Department of Maine
c/o Sheila Webber
P.O. Box 492
Old Orchard Beach, ME 04064
(207) 934-2405   E-mail: swebber2@maine.rr.com

Summary To provide financial assistance to children and grandchildren of members of the Veterans of Foreign Wars (VFW) and its Ladies Auxiliary in Maine who are studying a medical field in college.

Eligibility This program is open to Maine residents who are the children, grandchildren, stepchildren, or foster children of current or immediate past year members of the VFW or its Ladies Auxiliary in Maine. Applicants must be enrolled at a 2- or 4-year college, university, or vocational school and majoring in a field related to medicine.

Financial data The stipend is $1,000 or $500 per year. Funds are paid to the school of the recipient's choice.

Duration 1 year; may be renewed.

Number awarded 1 or more each year.

Deadline March of each year.

[772]
PAULINE LANGKAMP MEMORIAL SCHOLARSHIP

Navy Wives Clubs of America
P.O. Box 54022
Millington, TN 38053-6022
Toll Free: (866) 511-NWCA
E-mail: nwca@navywivesclubsofamerica.org
Web: www.navywivesclubsofamerica.org/scholarships

Summary To provide financial assistance for college to the adult children of members of the Navy Wives Clubs of America (NWCA).

Eligibility This program is open to children of NWCA members who no longer carry a military ID card because they have reached adult status. Applicants must be attending or planning to attend an accredited college or university. Along with their application, they must submit a brief statement on why they feel they should be awarded this scholarship and any special circumstances (financial or other) they wish to have considered. Financial need is also considered in the selection process.

Financial data A stipend is provided (amount not specified).

Duration 1 year.

Additional information Membership in the NWCA is open to spouses of enlisted personnel serving in the Navy, Marine Corps, Coast Guard, and the active Reserve units of those services; spouses of enlisted personnel who have been honorably discharged, retired, or transferred to the Fleet Reserve on completion of duty; and widows of enlisted personnel in those services.

Number awarded 1 or more each year.

Deadline May of each year.

[773]
PENNSYLVANIA EDUCATIONAL GRATUITY FOR VETERANS' DEPENDENTS

Office of the Deputy Adjutant General for Veterans Affairs
Building S-0-47, FTIG
Annville, PA 17003-5002
(717) 865-8910   Toll Free: (800) 54 PA VET (within PA)
Fax: (717) 861-8589   E-mail: RA-VA-Info@pa.gov
Web: www.portal.state.pa.us

Summary To provide financial assistance for college to the children of disabled or deceased Pennsylvania veterans.

Eligibility This program is open to children (between 16 and 23 years of age) of honorably-discharged veterans who are rated totally and permanently disabled as a result of wartime service or who have died of such a disability. Applicants must have lived in Pennsylvania for at least 5 years immediately preceding the date of application, be able to demonstrate financial need, and have been accepted or be currently enrolled in a Pennsylvania state or state-aided secondary or postsecondary educational institution.

Financial data The stipend is $500 per semester ($1,000 per year). The money is paid directly to the recipient's school and is to be applied to the costs of tuition, board, room, books, supplies, and/or matriculation fees.

Duration The allowance is paid for up to 4 academic years or for the duration of the course of study, whichever is less.

Number awarded Varies each year.

Deadline Deadline not specified.

[774]
PENNSYLVANIA GRANTS FOR CHILDREN OF SOLDIERS DECLARED POW/MIA

Pennsylvania Higher Education Assistance Agency
Attn: Special Programs
1200 North Seventh Street
P.O. Box 8157
Harrisburg, PA 17105-8157
(717) 720-2800   Toll Free: (800) 692-7392
Fax: (717) 720-3786   TDD: (800) 654-5988
Web: www.pheaa.org

Summary To provide financial assistance for college to the children of POWs/MIAs from Pennsylvania.

Eligibility This program is open to dependent children of members or former members of the U.S. armed services who served on active duty after January 31, 1955, who are or have been prisoners of war or are or have been listed as missing in action, and who were residents of Pennsylvania for at least 12 months preceding service on active duty. Eligible children must be enrolled in a program of at least 1 year in duration on at least a half-time basis at an approved school. Financial need is not considered in the selection process.

Financial data The maximum grant is $1,200.

Duration 1 year; may be renewed for 3 additional years.

Additional information With certain exceptions, recipients may attend any accredited college in the United States. Excluded from coverage are 2-year public colleges located outside Pennsylvania and schools in states bordering Pennsylvania that do not allow their state grant recipients to attend Pennsylvania schools (i.e., New York, Maryland, and New Jersey).

Number awarded Varies each year.

Deadline April of each year for students at colleges, universities, and transferable programs at community colleges; July of each year for students at business schools, trade/technical schools, hospital schools of nursing, and non-transferable programs at community colleges.

[775]
PENNSYLVANIA NATIONAL GUARD SCHOLARSHIP FUND

Pennsylvania National Guard Associations
Attn: Pennsylvania National Guard Scholarship Fund
Biddle Hall (Building 9-109)
Fort Indiantown Gap
Annville, PA 17003-5002
(717) 865-9631   Toll Free: (800) 997-8885
Fax: (717) 861-5560   E-mail: oswalddean@aol.com
Web: www.pngas.net/news/75652

Summary To provide financial assistance to Pennsylvania National Guard members and the children of disabled or deceased members who are interested in attending college in any state.

Eligibility This program is open to active members of the Pennsylvania Army or Air National Guard. Children of members of the Guard who died or were permanently disabled while on Guard duty are also eligible. Applicants must be entering their first year of higher education as a full-time student or presently attending a college or vocational school in any state as a full-time student. Along with their application, they must submit an essay that outlines their military and civilian plans for the future. Selection is based on academic potential, military commitment, extracurricular activities, and Guard participation.

Financial data Stipends range from $400 to $1,000.

Duration 1 year.

Additional information The sponsoring organization includes the National Guard Association of Pennsylvania (NGAP) and the Pennsylvania National Guard Enlisted Association (PNGEA). This program, which began in 1977, includes the following named scholarships: the BG Richard E. Thorn Memorial Scholarship, the Murtha Memorial Scholarship, the BG Hugh S. Niles Memorial Scholarship, the PNGEA USAA Scholarship (sponsored by the USAA Insurance Corporation), and the 28th Infantry Division Scholarship.

Number awarded Varies each year; recently, 13 were awarded: 4 at $1,000, 2 at $500, and 7 at $400.

Deadline June of each year.

[776]
PENNSYLVANIA POSTSECONDARY EDUCATIONAL GRATUITY PROGRAM

Pennsylvania Higher Education Assistance Agency
Attn: Special Programs
1200 North Seventh Street
P.O. Box 8157
Harrisburg, PA 17105-8157
(717) 720-2800   Toll Free: (800) 692-7392
Fax: (717) 720-3786   TDD: (800) 654-5988
E-mail: pegp@pheaa.org
Web: www.pheaa.org

Summary To provide financial assistance for college to the children of Pennsylvania public service personnel who died in the line of service.

Eligibility This program is open to residents of Pennsylvania who are the children of 1) Pennsylvania police officers, firefighters, rescue and ambulance squad members, corrections facility employees, or National Guard members who died in the line of duty after January 1, 1976; or 2) Pennsylvania sheriffs, deputy sheriffs, National Guard members, and certain other individuals on federal or state active military duty who died after September 11, 2001 as a direct result of performing their official duties. Applicants must be 25 years of age or younger and enrolled or accepted at a Pennsylvania community college, state-owned institution, or state-related institution as a full-time student working on an associate or baccalaureate degree. They must have already applied for other scholarships, including state and federal grants and financial aid from the postsecondary institution to which they are applying.

Financial data Grants cover tuition, fees, room, and board charged by the institution, less awarded scholarships and federal and state grants.

Duration Up to 5 years.

Additional information This program began in the 1998-99 winter/spring term to cover service personnel who died after January 1, 1976. It was amended in 2004 to cover additional service personnel who died after September 11, 2001.

Number awarded Varies each year.

Deadline March of each year.

[777]
PETER CONNACHER MEMORIAL SCHOLARSHIPS

Oregon Student Access Commission
Attn: Grants and Scholarships Division
1500 Valley River Drive, Suite 100
Eugene, OR 97401-2146
(541) 687-7395   Toll Free: (800) 452-8807, ext. 7395
Fax: (541) 687-7414   TDD: (800) 735-2900
E-mail: awardinfo@osac.state.or.us
Web: www.oregonstudentaid.gov/scholarships.aspx

Summary To provide financial assistance for college or graduate school to ex-prisoners of war and their descendants.

Eligibility Applicants must be U.S. citizens who 1) were military or civilian prisoners of war; or 2) are the descendants of ex-prisoners of war. They must be full-time undergraduate or graduate students. A copy of the ex-prisoner of war's discharge papers from the U.S. armed forces must accompany the application. In addition, written proof of POW status must be submitted, along with a statement of the relationship between the applicant and the ex-prisoner of war (father, grandfather, etc.). Selection is based on academic record and financial need. Preference is given to Oregon residents or their dependents.

Financial data Stipends for scholarships offered by the Oregon Student Access Commission (OSAC) range from $200 to $10,000 but recently averaged $5,200.

Duration 1 year; may be renewed for up to 3 additional years for undergraduate students or 2 additional years for graduate students. Renewal is dependent on evidence of continued financial need and satisfactory academic progress.

Additional information This program is administered by the OSAC with funds provided by the Oregon Community Foundation and by the Columbia River Chapter of American Ex-prisoners of War, Inc.

Number awarded Varies each year; recently, 4 were awarded.

Deadline February of each year.

[778]
PHOEBE PEMBER MEMORIAL SCHOLARSHIP

United Daughters of the Confederacy
Attn: Second Vice President General
328 North Boulevard
Richmond, VA 23220-4008
(804) 355-1636   Fax: (804) 353-1396
E-mail: jamieretired@sbcglobal.net
Web: www.hqudc.org/Scholarships/index.htm

Summary To provide financial assistance to lineal descendants of Confederate veterans who are interested in studying nursing.

Eligibility Eligible to apply for these scholarships are lineal descendants of worthy Confederates or collateral descendants who are members of the Children of the Confederacy or the United Daughters of the Confederacy. Applicants must intend to study nursing and must submit a family financial report and certified proof of the Confederate record of 1 ancestor, with the company and regiment in which he served. They must have at least a 3.0 GPA in high school.

Financial data The amount of this scholarship depends on the availability of funds.

Duration 1 year; may be renewed for up to 3 additional years.

Number awarded 1 each year.

Deadline April of each year.

[779]
PHOENIX/EANGKY SCHOLARSHIP

Enlisted Association National Guard of Kentucky
Attn: Scholarship Committee
P.O. Box 4062
Frankfort, KY 40604-4062
Web: www.ngaky.org/scholarships

Summary To provide financial assistance to members of the Enlisted Association National Guard of Kentucky (EANGKY) and their families who are interested in attending college in any state.

Eligibility This program is open to EANGKY members and their dependent children and spouses; children of deceased members who were in good standing at the time of their death are also eligible. Applicants must be attending or planning to attend a college, university, or trade school in any state. Along with their application, they must submit transcripts, letters of recommendation, and a statement describing their long-range personal educational goals and explaining why they need the scholarship assistance.

Financial data The stipend is $1,000.

Duration 1 year.

Number awarded 1 or more each year.

Deadline December of each year.

[780]
PHS COMMISSIONED OFFICERS FOUNDATION DEPENDENT SCHOLARSHIP PROGRAM

Commissioned Officers Association of the U.S. Public Health Service
Attn: PHS Commissioned Officers Foundation for the Advancement of Public Health
8201 Corporate Drive, Suite 200
Landover, MD 20785
(301) 731-9080   Fax: (301) 731-9084
E-mail: jmcelligott@coausphs.org
Web: www.phscof.org/education/cof-scholarship-program

Summary To provide financial assistance to spouses and descendants of members of the Commissioned Officers Association of the U.S. Public Health Service (COA) who are interested in working on an undergraduate or graduate degree in any of the Public Health Service (PHS) categories.

Eligibility This program is open to high school seniors, undergraduates, and graduate students who are the spouse, child, or grandchild of an active-duty or retired COA member. Applicants must be preparing for a career in a PHS category (e.g., dentist, dietician, engineer, nurse, pharmacist, physician, clinical or rehabilitation therapist, veterinarian).

Financial data The stipend is approximately $1,000.

Duration 1 year.

Number awarded Varies each year; recently, 13 were awarded.

Deadline Deadline not specified.

[781]
PIKES PEAK POST SAME SCHOLARSHIP

Society of American Military Engineers-Pikes Peak Post
c/o Chuck Weiss, Education and Mentoring Chair
WHPacific, Inc.
1536 Cole Boulevard, Suite 150
Lakewood, CO 80401
(303) 810-6007   E-mail: cweiss@whpacific.com
Web: posts.same.org/pikespeak/scholarships.html

Summary To provide financial assistance to high school seniors in the Colorado Springs area of Colorado and students at colleges anywhere in the state who have a family connection to the Society of American Military Engineers (SAME) or the U.S. military and are interested in working on an undergraduate degree in engineering at a school in any state.

Eligibility This program is open to 1) seniors graduating from high schools in the Colorado Springs area of Colorado and planning to work full time on a degree in engineering at a college or university in any state; and 2) full-time undergraduate engineering students at 4-year colleges and universities throughout Colorado. Applicants must be preparing for a military career and have at least 1 family member (sibling, parent, grandparent) who is either 1) a member of the Pikes Peak Post of SAME; or 2) a current or retired military member. They must have a GPA of 3.0 or higher. Along with their application, they must submit a paragraph explaining why they chose engineering or an engineering-related field of study and why they should receive this scholarship. Selection is based on that essay, GPA, SAT and/or ACT score, extracurricular activities, professional activities and organizations, and honors or other recognition.

Financial data Stipends range from $1,000 to $2,000.

Duration 1 year.

Number awarded Varies each year; recently, 4 were awarded.

Deadline February of each year.

[782]
PISCATAQUA POST SAME SCHOLARSHIPS

Society of American Military Engineers-Piscataqua Post
c/o David Abrahamson, Post Secretary
Weston Solutions
45 Constitution Avenue, Suite 100
Concord, NH 03301
(603) 656-5400   Fax: (603) 656-5401
E-mail: samepiscataquapost@gmail.com
Web: same-piscataqua.org/index.php

Summary To provide financial assistance to high school seniors in Maine, Massachusetts, and New Hampshire (especially those interested in joining ROTC or with ties to the military) who are planning to attend college in any state to major in engineering or the physical sciences.

Eligibility This program is open to seniors graduating from high schools in Maine, Massachusetts, or New Hampshire and planning to attend a college or university in any state. Applicants must be interested in majoring in engineering or the physical sciences and enrolling in ROTC, especially if they do not receive an ROTC scholarship. They should be willing to attend meetings of the Society of American Military Engineers (SAME) to share their learning experiences. Preference is given to students who are related to members of the Piscataqua Post of SAME and those whose relatives have prior or current U.S. military service.

Financial data The stipend is $1,500.

Duration 1 year.

Number awarded Up to 2 each year.

Deadline March or June of each year.

[783]
PLANNING SYSTEMS INCORPORATED SCIENCE AND ENGINEERING SCHOLARSHIP

Navy League of the United States
Attn: Scholarships
2300 Wilson Boulevard, Suite 200
Arlington, VA 22201-5424
(703) 528-1775   Toll Free: (800) 356-5760
Fax: (703) 528-2333
E-mail: scholarships@navyleague.org
Web: www.navyleague.org/aboutus/scholarship.html

Summary To provide financial assistance to dependent children of sea service personnel or veterans who are interested in majoring in science or engineering in college.

Eligibility This program is open to U.S. citizens who are 1) dependents or direct descendants of an active, Reserve, retired, or honorably discharged member of the U.S. sea service (including the Navy, Marine Corps, Coast Guard, or Merchant Marine); or 2) currently an active member of the Naval Sea Cadet Corps. Applicants must be high school seniors entering their freshman year at an accredited college or university and planning to major in science or engineering. They must have a GPA of 3.0 or higher. Along with their application, they must submit transcripts, 2 letters of recommendation, SAT/ACT scores, documentation of financial need, proof of

qualifying sea service duty, and a 1-page personal statement on why they should be considered for this scholarship.

Financial data The stipend is $2,500 per year.

Duration 4 years, provided the recipient maintains a GPA of 3.0 or higher.

Number awarded 1 each year.

Deadline February of each year.

[784]
POPASMOKE SCHOLARSHIPS

USMC/Combat Helicopter Association
c/o Marine Corps Scholarship Foundation
909 North Washington Street, Suite 400
Alexandria, VA 22314
(703) 549-0060   Toll Free: (866) 496-5462
Fax: (703) 549-9474   E-mail: students@mcsf.org
Web: www.popasmoke.com/scholarships

Summary To provide financial assistance for college to the children and grandchildren of members of the USMC/Combat Helicopter Association.

Eligibility This program is open to children and grandchildren of members of the USMC/Combat Helicopter Association who are high school seniors, high school graduates, undergraduates enrolled at an accredited college or university, or students enrolled at an accredited postsecondary vocational/technical school. Applicants must be the child or grandchild of 1) a Marine on active duty, in the Reserve, retired, or deceased; or 2) a Marine or Marine Reservist who has received an honorable discharge, medical discharge, or was killed on active duty. Along with their application, they must submit academic transcripts, a copy of their parent's or grandparent's honorable discharge (if appropriate), and a 500-word essay on a topic that changes periodically. Only undergraduate study is supported. The family income of applicants must be less than $90,000 per year.

Financial data Stipends range from $500 to $1,000 per year.

Duration 1 year; may be renewed for up to 3 additional years.

Additional information This program includes the MGYSGT George T. Curtis Scholarship, established in 2006, the LTCOL Hubert "Black Bart" Bartels Scholarship, established in 2008, the PFC Mike Clausen Scholarship, established in 2010, the Captain Stephen W. Pless Scholarship, established in 2012, and the Corporal Ernesto "Gooie" Gomez Scholarship, established in 2014.

Number awarded 5 each year.

Deadline March of each year.

[785]
PRAIRIE MINUTEMAN SCHOLARSHIP

National Guard Association of Illinois
Attn: Executive Director
1301 North MacArthur Boulevard
Springfield, IL 62702-2317
(217) 836-5251   Fax: (217) 483-5469
E-mail: execdir@ngai.com
Web: www.ngai.com/services.aspx

Summary To provide financial assistance to dependents of members of the National Guard Association of Illinois (NGAI) who are interested in attending college in any state.

Eligibility This program is open to dependents (children and spouses) of NGAI members in good standing. Applicants may be high school seniors, high school graduates, or currently-enrolled students at a college or university in any state. They must submit a completed application form, official transcripts, 2 letters of recommendation, a verified copy of their ACT/SAT scores, and a 250-word essay on their scholastic and professional goals and aspirations. Financial need is also considered in the selection process.

Financial data The stipend is $2,000 or $700.

Duration 1 year.

Number awarded 3 each year: 1 at $2,000 to an Illinois Army National Guard dependent, 1 at $2,000 to an Illinois Air National Guard dependent, and 1 at $700 (sponsored by USAA Insurance Corporation) to an enlisted Illinois National Guard dependent who is also a member of NGAI.

Deadline Applications must be submitted at least 45 days prior to the sponsor's annual conference. The conference is usually in late April, so applications are due in mid-March.

[786]
PVA EDUCATIONAL SCHOLARSHIP PROGRAM

Paralyzed Veterans of America
Attn: Membership and Volunteer Department
801 18th Street, N.W.
Washington, DC 20006-3517
(202) 416-7776   Toll Free: (800) 424-8200, ext. 776
Fax: (202) 416-1250   TDD: (800) 795-HEAR
E-mail: christi@pva.org
Web: www.pva.org

Summary To provide financial assistance for college to members of the Paralyzed Veterans of America (PVA) and their families.

Eligibility This program is open to PVA members, spouses of members, and unmarried dependent children of members under 24 years of age. Applicants must be attending or planning to attend an accredited U.S. college or university as a full-time or part-time student. They must be U.S. citizens. Along with their application, they must submit a personal statement explaining why they wish to further their education, short- and long-term academic goals, how this will meet their career objectives, and how it will affect the PVA membership. Selection is based on that statement, academic records, letters of recommendation, and extracurricular and community activities.

Financial data The stipend is $1,000.

Duration 1 year.

Additional information This program began in 1986.

Number awarded Varies each year; recently 20 were awarded. Since this program was established, it has awarded more than $300,000 in scholarships.

Deadline May of each year.

[787]
RADM COURTNEY G. CLEGG AND MRS. MARGARET H. CLEGG SCHOLARSHIP

Navy-Marine Corps Relief Society
Attn: Education Division
875 North Randolph Street, Suite 225
Arlington, VA 22203-1757
(703) 696-4960   Fax: (703) 696-0144
E-mail: education@nmcrs.org
Web: www.nmcrs.org

Summary To provide financial assistance for college to the children and spouses of active-duty and retired Navy or Marine Corps personnel.

Eligibility This program is open to children under 23 years of age of active-duty and retired sailors and Marines and spouses of active-duty or retired sailors and Marines. Applicants must be enrolled or planning to enroll full time at a college, university, or vocational/technical school. They must have a GPA of 3.0 or higher and be able to demonstrate financial need.

Financial data Stipends range from $500 to $2,000 per year. Funds are disbursed directly to the financial institution.

Duration 1 year; recipients may reapply.

Number awarded Varies each year.

Deadline April of each year.

[788]
RANGER MEMORIAL SCHOLARSHIPS

National Ranger Memorial Foundation
Attn: Executive Secretary
P.O. Box 53369
Fort Benning, GA 31995
(706) 687-0906   E-mail: rangermemorial@gmail.com
Web: www.rangermemorial.com

Summary To provide financial assistance for college to U.S. Army Rangers and their descendants.

Eligibility This program is open to Rangers from any era and their descendants; some awards (those offered by the Ranger Battalions Association of WWII) are limited to descendants of Rangers who served during the World War II era. Applicants must be graduating high school seniors or students currently enrolled at an accredited 2- or 4-year educational or technical institution. They must have a GPA of 3.0 or higher. Along with their application, they must submit information on their leadership activities, future goals and how they plan to attain those, and honors and awards received to date. Financial need is not considered in the selection process.

Financial data The stipend is $1,000.

Duration 1 year.

Additional information The National Ranger Memorial Foundation began awarding scholarships in 1999. The Ranger Battalions Association of WWII became a partner in 2007 and offered additional scholarships to descendants of World War II era Rangers.

Number awarded 49 each year: 45 offered by the National Ranger Memorial Foundation and 4 by the Ranger Battalions Association of WWII.

Deadline May of each year.

[789]
RAYMOND T. WELLINGTON, JR. MEMORIAL SCHOLARSHIP

American Legion Auxiliary
Department of New York
112 State Street, Suite 1310
Albany, NY 12207
(518) 463-1162   Toll Free: (800) 421-6348
Fax: (518) 449-5406
E-mail: alanykathleen@nycap.rr.com
Web: www.deptny.org/scholarships

Summary To provide financial assistance to New York residents who are the descendants of veterans and interested in attending college in any state.

Eligibility This program is open to residents of New York who are high school seniors or graduates and attending or planning to attend an accredited college or university in any state. Applicants must be the children, grandchildren, or great-grandchildren of veterans who served during specified periods of wartime. Along with their application, they must submit a 700-word autobiography that includes their interests, experiences, long-range plans, and goals. Selection is based on character (15%), Americanism (15%), community involvement (15%), leadership (15%), scholarship (20%), and financial need (20%). U.S. citizenship is required.

Financial data The stipend is $1,000. Funds are paid directly to the recipient's school.

Duration 1 year.

Number awarded 1 each year.

Deadline February of each year.

[790]
RED RIVER VALLEY FIGHTER PILOTS ASSOCIATION KINSHIP SCHOLARSHIP GRANT PROGRAM

Red River Valley Association Foundation
Attn: Executive Director
P.O. Box 1553
Front Royal, VA 22630-0033
(540) 639-9798   Toll Free: (866) 401-7287
Fax: (540) 636-9776
E-mail: ExecutiveOffice@river-rats.org
Web: www.river-rats.org/about-us/scholarship-program.html

Summary To provide financial assistance for college or graduate school to the spouses and children of selected service personnel and members of the Red River Valley Fighter Pilots Association.

Eligibility This program is open to the spouses and children of 1) servicemembers missing in action (MIA) or killed in action (KIA) in combat situations involving U.S. military forces from August 1964 through the present; 2) U.S. military aircrew members killed in a non-combat aircraft accident in which they were performing aircrew duties; and 3) current members of the association and deceased members who were in good standing at the time of their death. Scholarships are also available to students in fields related to aviation and space, even if they have no kinship relationship to a deceased aviator or member of the association. Applicants must be enrolled or planning to enroll full or part time at an accredited college, university, vocational/technical institute, or career school to work on an undergraduate or graduate degree. They must be 30 years of age or younger, although the age limit is extended to 40 for current and former military personnel. Selection is based on demonstrated academic achievement, SAT or ACT scores, financial need, and accomplishments in school, church, civic, and social activities.

Financial data The amount awarded varies, depending upon the need of the recipient. Recently, undergraduate stipends have ranged from $500 to $3,500 and averaged $1,725; graduate stipends have ranged from $500 to $2,000 and averaged $1,670. Funds are paid directly to the recipient's institution and are to be used for tuition, fees, books, and room and board for full-time students.

Duration 1 year; may be renewed if the recipient maintains a GPA of 2.0 or higher.

Additional information This program began in 1970, out of concern for the families of aircrews (known as "River Rats") who were killed or missing in action in the Red River Valley of North Vietnam.

Number awarded Varies each year; since this program was established, it has awarded more than 1,000 scholarships worth more than $1,700,000.

Deadline June of each year.

[791]
REDUCED TUITION FOR CHILDREN AND SPOUSES OF SOUTH DAKOTA NATIONAL GUARDSMEN DISABLED OR DECEASED IN THE LINE OF DUTY

South Dakota Board of Regents
Attn: Scholarship Committee
306 East Capitol Avenue, Suite 200
Pierre, SD 57501-3159
(605) 773-3455   Fax: (605) 773-2422
E-mail: info@sdbor.edu
Web: www.sdbor.edu/students/redtuit_nationalguard.htm

Summary To provide reduced tuition at public universities in South Dakota to the children and spouses of disabled and deceased members of the National Guard.

Eligibility This program is open to the spouses and children (24 years of age or younger) of members of the South Dakota Army or Air National Guard who died or sustained a total and permanent disability while on state active duty, federal active duty, or any authorized duty training. Applicants must be proposing to work on an undergraduate degree at a public institution of higher education in South Dakota.

Financial data Qualifying applicants are granted a 100% tuition waiver at state-supported postsecondary institutions in South Dakota. The waiver applies only to tuition, not fees.

Duration 8 semesters or 12 quarters of either full- or part-time study.

Number awarded Varies each year.

Deadline Deadline not specified.

[792]
RENEE FELDMAN SCHOLARSHIPS

Blinded Veterans Association Auxiliary
c/o Hazel C. Compton, Scholarship Chair
P.O. Box 267
Richlands, VA 24641
(276) 963-3745
Web: www.bvaaux.org

Summary To provide financial assistance for college to spouses and children of blinded veterans.

Eligibility This program is open to children and spouses of blinded veterans who are enrolled or planning to enroll full time at a college, university, community college, or vocational school. Grandchildren are not eligible. The veteran's blindness may be service-connected or non-service connected. The veteran is not required to be a member of the Blinded Veterans Association. Applicants must submit a 300-word essay on their career goals and aspirations. Selection is based on that essay, academic achievement, and letters of reference.

Financial data Stipends are $2,000 or $1,000 per year. Funds are paid directly to the recipient's school to be applied to tuition, books, and general fees.

Duration 1 year; may be renewed up to 3 additional years.

Number awarded 3 each year: 2 at $2,000 and 1 at $1,000.

Deadline April of each year.

[793]
REOC CHARITABLE SCHOLARSHIP FUND

San Antonio Area Foundation
Attn: Scholarship Funds Program Officer
303 Pearl Parkway, Suite 114
San Antonio, TX 78215-1285
(210) 228-3759   Fax: (210) 225-1980
E-mail: buresti@ssafdn.org
Web: www.saafdn.org

Summary To provide financial assistance for college to the children of armed services members who were killed in action, lost limbs, or suffered a serious traumatic injury.

Eligibility This program is open to seniors graduating from high schools in any state who are the child of an American service man or woman who has been killed in action, lost limbs, or suffered a serious traumatic injury. Applicants must be planning to attend an accredited college, university, or vocational school in any state and major in any field. They must have a GPA of 2.5 or higher.

Financial data A stipend is awarded (amount not specified).

Duration 1 year; may be renewed.

Number awarded 1 or more each year.

Deadline February of each year.

[794]
RESTORED ENTITLEMENT PROGRAM FOR SURVIVORS (REPS)

Department of Veterans Affairs
Attn: Veterans Benefits Administration
810 Vermont Avenue, N.W.
Washington, DC 20420
(202) 418-4343   Toll Free: (800) 827-1000
Web: www.benefits.va.gov/WARMS/M21_1MR9.asp

Summary To provide benefits to survivors of certain deceased veterans.

Eligibility This program is open to survivors of members or former members of the armed forces who died while on active duty prior to August 13, 1981 or from a disability incurred or aggravated by active duty prior to that date. Spouses of veterans are eligible if they have children between 16 and 18 years of age. Children of veterans between 18 and 22 years of age are eligible if they are enrolled full-time in a college or university.

Financial data The benefits are similar to the benefits for students and surviving spouses with children that were eliminated from the Social Security Act. The exact amount of the benefits is based on information provided by the Social Security Administration.

Duration Benefits are paid to spouses during the period that their children are between 16 and 18 years of age and to children of veterans while they are enrolled full time in college and are younger than 22 years of age.

Additional information The benefits are payable in addition to any other benefits to which the family may be entitled.

Number awarded Varies each year.

Deadline Applications may be submitted at any time.

[795]
RICHARD T. NUSKE MEMORIAL SCHOLARSHIPS

Vietnam Veterans of America-Wisconsin State Council
c/o Virginia Nuske, Scholarship Committee Chair
N5448 Broder Road
Shawano, WI 54166
(715) 524-2587
Web: www.vvawi.org/scholarships

Summary To recognize and reward high school seniors in Wisconsin who submit outstanding essays based on an interview of a Vietnam veteran, especially if the veteran is a relative.

Eligibility This competition is open to seniors graduating from high schools in Wisconsin who plan to attend an accredited institution of higher education in any state. Applicants must submit an essay, from 3 to 5 pages in length, based on an interview of a veteran of any branch who served on active duty anywhere in the world during the Vietnam War (from January 1, 1959 to May 7, 1975). Essays are judged on originality, appearance, and elements of grammar; up to 35 points may be awarded, depending on the quality of the essay. An additional 10 points are awarded if the student is the child or grandchild of the veteran; an additional 5 points are awarded if the student is another relative (niece, cousin) of the veteran.

Financial data The award is a $1,500 scholarship that may be used at a college or university in any state.

Duration The awards are presented annually.

Number awarded 2 each year.

Deadline January of each year.

[796]
ROBERT H. CONNAL EDUCATION AWARDS

Enlisted Association of the New York National Guard, Inc.
Attn: Educational Award Chair
330 Old Niskayuna Road
Latham, NY 12110-2224
(518) 344-2670   E-mail: awards@eanyng.org
Web: www.eanyng.org/AwardsandScholarships.html

Summary To provide financial assistance to members of the Enlisted Association of the New York National Guard (EANYNG) and their families who are interested in attending college in any state.

Eligibility This program is open to EANYNG members and their spouses, children, and grandchildren. Applicants must be high school seniors or current undergraduates at a college or university in any state. The applicant or sponsor must have belonged to EANYNG for more than 1 year. Membership in

EANYNG is limited to enlisted personnel in the New York Air or Army National Guard. Selection is based on academic achievement, community service, extracurricular activities, and leadership abilities.

Financial data Stipends are $1,000, $700, or $500.

Duration 1 year; nonrenewable.

Additional information Funding for this program is provided by the production of the association's yearly journal, members' dues, and a donation from USAA Insurance Corporation.

Number awarded 5 each year: 2 at $1,000, 1 at $700, and 2 at $500.

Deadline March of each year.

[797]
ROSEDALE POST 346 SCHOLARSHIP FUND

American Legion
Department of Kansas
1314 S.W. Topeka Boulevard
Topeka, KS 66612-1886
(785) 232-9315   Fax: (785) 232-1399
Web: www.ksamlegion.org

Summary To provide financial assistance to the children of members of the Kansas American Legion or American Legion Auxiliary who are interested in attending college in any state.

Eligibility This program is open to high school seniors and college freshmen and sophomores who are attending or planning to attend an approved college, university, junior college, or trade school in any state. Applicants must have an average or better academic record. At least 1 of their parents must be a veteran and have been a member of an American Legion post or Auxiliary in Kansas for at least 3 consecutive years. Along with their application, they must submit an essay of 250 to 500 words on "Why I Want to Go to College." Financial need is also considered in the selection process.

Financial data The stipend is $1,500.

Duration 1 year; nonrenewable.

Number awarded 2 each year.

Deadline February of each year.

[798]
ROY C. AND DOROTHY JEAN OLSON MEMORIAL SCHOLARSHIP

International Military Community Executives' Association
Attn: Scholarship
P.O. Box 7946
Round Rock, TX 78683-7946
(940) 463-5145   Fax: (866) 369-2435
E-mail: imcea@imcea.org
Web: www.imcea.org/awards/scholarship-info

Summary To provide financial assistance to children of members of the International Military Community Executives' Association (IMCEA) who are interested in attending college.

Eligibility This program is open to dependent children of regular IMCEA members who are graduating from high school or already enrolled at a college or university. Along with their application, they must submit a 2-page essay on the appropriate role of the U.S. military in the world today. Selection is based on that essay, participation in extracurricular activities over the past 4 years, participation in community

activities over the past 4 year, and commendations and honors received during the past 4 years.

Financial data The stipend is $1,000.

Duration 1 year.

Additional information Regular membership in IMCEA is open to Army, Air Force, Navy, Marine Corps, and Coast Guard personnel who provide MWR services at military installations and bases worldwide.

Number awarded 1 each year.

Deadline May of each year.

[799]
RUBY LORRAINE PAUL SCHOLARSHIP FUND

American Legion Auxiliary
Department of Nebraska
P.O. Box 5227
Lincoln, NE 68505-0227
(402) 466-1808   Fax: (402) 466-0182
E-mail: neaux@windstream.net
Web: www.nebraskalegionaux.net

Summary To provide financial assistance to students in Nebraska who have a connection to the American Legion and plan to attend college in any state and study any field except nursing.

Eligibility Applicants must have been residents of Nebraska for at least 3 years and either 1) have been a member for at least 2 years of the American Legion, American Legion Auxiliary, or Sons of the American Legion; or 2) be the child, grandchild, or great-grandchild of an American Legion or American Legion Auxiliary member who has been a member for at least 2 years. They must be high school seniors or graduates who maintained a GPA of 3.0 or higher during the last 2 semesters of high school and have been accepted at an accredited college or university in any state to study any field except nursing. Along with their application, they must submit a brief essay describing their chosen field and how this scholarship will help them achieve their goals. Financial need is considered in the selection process.

Financial data A stipend is awarded (amount not specified).

Duration 1 year.

Number awarded 1 each year.

Deadline February of each year.

[800]
SAD SACKS NURSING SCHOLARSHIP

AMVETS-Department of Illinois
2200 South Sixth Street
Springfield, IL 62703
(217) 528-4713   Toll Free: (800) 638-VETS (within IL)
Fax: (217) 528-9896   E-mail: info@ilamvets.org
Web: www.ilamvets.org

Summary To provide financial assistance for nursing education to Illinois residents, especially descendants of disabled or deceased veterans.

Eligibility This program is open to seniors at high schools in Illinois who have been accepted to an approved nursing program and students already enrolled in an approved school of nursing in Illinois. Priority is given to dependents of deceased or disabled veterans. Selection is based on academic record, character, interest and activity record, and financial need. Preference is given to students in the following order: third-year students, second-year students, and first-year students.

Financial data A stipend is awarded (amount not specified).

Duration 1 year; nonrenewable.

Number awarded Varies each year; recently, 2 were awarded.

Deadline February of each year.

[801]
SAM ROSE MEMORIAL SCHOLARSHIP

Ladies Auxiliary of the Fleet Reserve Association
c/o Sandra Robbins, National Scholarship Chair
2712 Holly Ridge Road
Orange Park, FL 32073
(904) 269-2136   E-mail: slgr@bellsouth.net
Web: www.la-fra.org/scholarship.html

Summary To provide financial assistance for college to the children and grandchildren of deceased members of the Fleet Reserve Association (FRA).

Eligibility This program is open to children and grandchildren of deceased members of the association or those who were eligible to be members at the time of death. Applicants must submit an essay on their life experiences, career objectives, and what motivated them to select those objectives. Selection is based on academic record, financial need, extracurricular activities, leadership skills, and participation in community activities. U.S. citizenship is required.

Financial data The stipend is $2,500.

Duration 1 year.

Additional information Membership in the FRA is open to active-duty, retired, and Reserve members of the Navy, Marine Corps, and Coast Guard.

Number awarded 1 each year.

Deadline April of each year.

[802]
SAMSUNG AMERICAN LEGION SCHOLARSHIPS

American Legion
Attn: Americanism and Children & Youth Division
700 North Pennsylvania Street
P.O. Box 1055
Indianapolis, IN 46206-1055
(317) 630-1202   Fax: (317) 630-1223
E-mail: scholarships@legion.org
Web: www.legion.org/scholarships/samsung

Summary To provide financial assistance for college to descendants of veterans who participate in Girls State or Boys State.

Eligibility This program is open to students entering their senior year of high school who are selected to participate in Girls State or Boys State, sponsored by the American Legion Auxiliary or American Legion in their state. Applicants must be the child, grandchild, or great-grandchild of a veteran who saw active-duty service during specified periods of wartime. Finalists are chosen at each participating Girls and Boys State, and they are then nominated for the national awards. Selection is based on academic record, community service, involvement in school and community activities, and financial need. Special consideration is given to descendants of U.S. veterans of the Korean War.

Financial data Stipends are $20,000 or $1,100.

Duration 4 years.

Additional information These scholarships were first presented in 1996, following a gift in July 1995 to the American Legion from Samsung Corporation of Korea, as an act of appreciation for U.S. involvement in the Korean War.

Number awarded Varies each year; recently, 9 scholarships at $20,000 and 88 at $1,100 were awarded.

Deadline Deadline not specified.

[803]
SCHNEIDER-EMANUEL AMERICAN LEGION SCHOLARSHIPS

American Legion
Department of Wisconsin
2930 American Legion Drive
P.O. Box 388
Portage, WI 53901-0388
(608) 745-1090   Fax: (608) 745-0179
E-mail: info@wilegion.org
Web: www.wilegion.org

Summary To provide financial assistance to members of the American Legion in Wisconsin and their children or grandchildren who plan to attend college in any state.

Eligibility This program is open to seniors and graduates from accredited Wisconsin high schools. Applicants must be at least 1 of the following 1) a child whose father, mother, or legal guardian is a member of the Department of Wisconsin of the American Legion, American Legion Auxiliary, or Sons of the American Legion; 2) a grandchild whose grandfather, grandmother, or legal guardian is a member of the Department of Wisconsin of the American Legion, American Legion Auxiliary, or Sons of the American Legion; 3) a member of the Sons of the American Legion, American Legion Auxiliary, or Junior American Legion Auxiliary; or 4) a veteran and an American Legion member in Wisconsin. Applicants must have participated in Legion and Auxiliary youth programs. They must be planning to attend a college or university in any state to work on a baccalaureate degree. Selection is based on moral character; scholastic excellence (GPA of 3.0 or higher); participation and accomplishment in American Legion affiliated activities; and personality, leadership, and participation in general extracurricular activities.

Financial data The stipend is $1,000.

Duration 1 year.

Additional information This program began in 1968.

Number awarded 3 each year.

Deadline February of each year.

[804]
SCHOLARSHIPS FOR MILITARY CHILDREN

Fisher House Foundation
111 Rockville Pike, Suite 420
Rockville, MD 20850
Toll Free: (888) 294-8560
E-mail: JWeiskopf@fisherhouse.org
Web: www.militaryscholar.org/sfmc/index.html

Summary To provide financial assistance for college to the children of veterans and military personnel.

Eligibility This program is open to sons and daughters of U.S. military servicemembers (including active duty, retirees, Guard/Reserves, and survivors of deceased members) who are enrolled or accepted for enrollment as a full-time under-graduate at a college or university. Applicants must be younger than 23 years of age and enrolled in the Defense Enrollment Eligibility Reporting System (DEERS). They must have a GPA of 3.0 or higher. Along with their application, they must submit a 500-word essay on a topic that changes annually; recently, students were asked to identify the 4 persons whose faces they would place on a 21st century Mount Rushmore type of monument and why. Selection is based on merit.

Financial data The stipend is $2,000.

Duration 1 year; recipients may reapply.

Additional information This program, established in 2001, is administered by the Fisher House Foundation on behalf of the Defense Commissary Agency.

Number awarded At least 1 scholarship is allocated for each of the commissaries worldwide operated by the Defense Commissary Agency (DeCA); more than 1 scholarship per commissary may be available, depending on donations from suppliers and manufacturers whose products are sold at commissaries. Recently, the program awarded more than $1 million to 670 students.

Deadline February of each year.

[805]
SCOTT B. LUNDELL TUITION WAIVER FOR MILITARY MEMBERS' SURVIVING DEPENDENTS

Utah Department of Veterans and Military Affairs
Attn: Director
550 Foothill Boulevard, Room 202
P.O. Box 58897
Salt Lake City, UT 84158-0897
(801) 326-2372   Toll Free: (800) 894-9497 (within UT)
Fax: (801) 326-2369   E-mail: veterans@utah.gov
Web: www.veterans.utah.gov/state-benefits

Summary To provide a tuition waiver to residents of Utah who are dependents of deceased military personnel and attending a public institution in the state.

Eligibility This program is open to residents of Utah who are dependents of military members killed in the line of duty after September 11, 2001. Applicants must be working on an undergraduate degree at a public college or university in the state.

Financial data Tuition is waived for qualified dependents.

Duration Tuition is waived until completion of a bachelor's degree.

Additional information This program began in 2007.

Number awarded Varies each year.

Deadline Deadline not specified.

[806]
SEABEE MEMORIAL SCHOLARSHIP ASSOCIATION PROGRAM

Seabee Memorial Scholarship Association
P.O. Box 6574
Silver Spring, MD 20916
(301) 570-2850   Fax: (301) 570-2873
E-mail: smsa@erols.com
Web: www.seabee.org/apply-for-a-scholarship.html

Summary To provide financial assistance for college to the children or grandchildren of active or deceased members of the Naval Construction Battalion (Seabees) or Navy Civil Engineering Corps.

Eligibility This program is open to the children, stepchildren, and grandchildren of active, Reserve, retired, deceased, or honorably discharged officers and enlisted members who are now serving in or have served in the Naval Construction Force (Seabees) or Navy Civil Engineering Corps. Applicants may be high school seniors, high school graduates, or students currently enrolled full-time at a 4-year college or university. Selection is based on financial need, citizenship, leadership, and scholastic record.

Financial data The stipend recently was $1,900 per year.

Duration 1 year; may be renewed for 3 additional years.

Number awarded Varies each year; recently, 22 new scholarships were awarded through this program.

Deadline April of each year.

[807]
SECOND MARINE DIVISION ASSOCIATION MEMORIAL SCHOLARSHIP

Second Marine Division Association
Attn: Memorial Scholarship Fund
P.O. Box 8180
Camp Lejeune, NC 28547-8180
(910) 451-3167
Web: www.2dmardiv.com/Scholarship.html

Summary To provide financial assistance for college to the children and grandchildren of veterans or members of the Second Marine Division.

Eligibility This program is open to unmarried dependent children and grandchildren of individuals who are serving or have served in the Second Marine Division or in a unit attached to it (e.g., hospital corpsmen, aviation, logistics). Applicants must be high school seniors, high school graduates, or full-time undergraduate students in accredited colleges or vocational/technical schools. They must have a family income of less than $70,000.

Financial data The stipend is $1,200 per year.

Duration 1 year; may be renewed.

Number awarded Varies each year.

Deadline March of each year.

[808]
SERGEANT ANDREW EDMUND TOPHAM MEMORIAL SCHOLARSHIP

Army Scholarship Foundation
11700 Preston Road, Suite 660-301
Dallas, TX 75230
E-mail: ContactUs@armyscholarshipfoundation.org
Web: www.armyscholarshipfoundation.org

Summary To provide financial assistance for undergraduate study to the children and spouses of Army personnel, especially those who served in the Global War on Terrorism.

Eligibility This program is open to 1) children of regular active-duty, active-duty Reserve, and active-duty Army National Guard members in good standing; 2) spouses of serving enlisted regular active-duty, active-duty Reserve, and active-duty Army National Guard members in good standing; and 3) children of former U.S. Army members who received an honorable or medical discharge or were killed while serving in the U.S. Army. Preference is given to students who are family members of soldiers who served in either Afghanistan or Iraq as part of the Global War on Terrorism. Applicants must be high school seniors, high school graduates, or undergraduates enrolled at an accredited college, university, or vocational/technical institute. They must be U.S. citizens and have a GPA of 2.0 or higher; children must be younger than 24 years of age. Financial need is considered in the selection process.

Financial data The stipend ranges from $500 to $2,000 per year.

Duration 1 year; recipients may reapply.

Additional information The Army Scholarship Foundation was established in 2001.

Number awarded 1 each year.

Deadline April of each year.

[809]
SERGEANT FELIX M. DELGRECO, JR. SCHOLARSHIP FUND

Connecticut Community Foundation
43 Field Street
Waterbury, CT 06702-1906
(203) 753-1315   Fax: (203) 756-3054
E-mail: scholarships@conncf.org
Web: www.conncf.org/students/apply-scholarship

Summary To provide financial assistance to high school seniors and current college students whose parents are members of the Connecticut Army National Guard.

Eligibility This program is open to the children of members of the Connecticut Army National Guard who are attending or planning to attend college in any state. Applicants must have a grade average of "B-" or higher. Selection is based on merit; financial need is not considered. U.S. citizenship is required.

Financial data The stipend is $4,000 per year. Funds are paid directly to the recipient's school.

Duration 1 year; recipients may reapply up to the minimum number of years required to complete an undergraduate degree in their course of study, provided they maintain a grade average of "C+" or higher.

Additional information This program is supported by the Connecticut National Guard Foundation.

Number awarded Varies each year.

Deadline March of each year.

[810]
SERGEANT MAJOR DOUGLAS R. DRUM MEMORIAL SCHOLARSHIPS

American Military Retirees Association, Inc.
Attn: Scholarship Committee
5436 Peru Street, Suite 1
Plattsburgh, NY 12901
(518) 563-9479   Toll Free: (800) 424-2969
Fax: (518) 324-5204   E-mail: info@amra1973.org
Web: www.amra1973.org/Scholarship

Summary To provide financial assistance for college to members of the American Military Retirees Association (AMRA) and their dependents.

Eligibility This program is open to current members of AMRA and their spouses and dependent children and grandchildren. Applicants must be attending or planning to attend an accredited college or university. They may apply either as incoming freshmen or returning college students (including adult military retirees and spouses). Along with their application, they must submit a 750-word essay on why they deserve

this scholarship. Selection is based on academic achievement, leadership abilities, character, citizenship, and community service.

Financial data Stipends are $5,000, $2,500, or $1,000.

Duration 1 year.

Additional information Membership in AMRA is open to all retired members of the armed forces, regardless of rank.

Number awarded 24 of these scholarships are awarded each year: 12 to incoming freshmen (1 at $5,000, 1 at $2,500, and 10 at $1,000) and 12 to returning college students (1 at $5,000, 1 at $2,500, and 10 at $1,000).

Deadline February of each year.

[811]
SERGEANTS HENRY AND JEANNE ROSE SCHOLARSHIPS

Marines' Memorial Association
c/o Marines Memorial Club and Hotel
609 Sutter Street
San Francisco, CA 94102
(415) 673-6672, ext. 293   Fax: (415) 441-3649
E-mail: scholarship@marineclub.com
Web: www.marineclub.com/membership/scholarship.php

Summary To provide financial assistance for college to members of the Marines' Memorial Association from all branches of the armed forces and their descendants.

Eligibility This program is open to active members of the association and their children and grandchildren. Applicants must be high school seniors or students currently enrolled full time in an undergraduate degree program at a college or university. Along with their application, they must submit an essay of 250 to 500 words on why the United States has the highest rates of poverty and income inequality of any developed nation and what we can do to reduce the prevalence of those problems in our country. Graduating high school seniors must submit a high school transcript and SAT or ACT scores; continuing college students must submit a college transcript. Selection is based on the essay, academic merit, references, and financial need.

Financial data The stipend is $10,000 per year.

Duration 1 year; recipients may reapply for up to 3 additional years.

Additional information Membership in the association is open to veterans of the Marines, Army, Navy, Air Force, or Coast Guard and to personnel currently serving in a branch of the armed forces.

Number awarded 2 each year.

Deadline April of each year.

[812]
SFC CURTIS MANCINI MEMORIAL SCHOLARSHIPS

Association of the United States Army-Rhode Island
   Chapter
c/o CSM (Ret) Anthony Ferri, Secretary
47 Spokane Street
Providence, RI 02904
(401) 861-2997   E-mail: afnf458673755@aol.com
Web: www.ausari.org/index.html

Summary To provide financial assistance to members of the Rhode Island Chapter of the Association of the United States Army (AUSA) and their families who are interested in attending college or graduate school in any state.

Eligibility This program is open to members of the AUSA Rhode Island Chapter and their family members (spouses, children, and grandchildren). Applicants must be high school seniors or graduates accepted at an accredited college, university, or vocational/technical school in any state or current undergraduate or graduate students. Along with their application, they must submit a 250-word essay on why they feel their achievements should qualify them for this award. Selection is based on academic and individual achievements; financial need is not considered. Membership in AUSA is open to current and retired Army personnel (including Reserves and National Guard), ROTC cadets, or civilian employees of the Army.

Financial data The stipend is $1,000.

Duration 1 year.

Number awarded 2 each year.

Deadline March of each year.

[813]
SHIRO KASHINO MEMORIAL SCHOLARSHIPS

Nisei Veterans Committee
Attn: NVC Foundation
1212 South King Street
Seattle, WA 98144-2025
(206) 322-1122 E-mail: scholarship@nvcfoundation.org
Web: www.seattlenvc.org/education/scholarship

Summary To provide financial assistance to high school seniors and current college students who are related to a member of the Nisei Veterans Committee or the NVC Foundation.

Eligibility This program is open to college-bound high school seniors and students who are already enrolled in college and are relatives of members of the Nisei Veterans Committee (an organization of Japanese American veterans) or of the NVC Foundation. Applicants must submit essays on 1) what the Nisei veterans' legacy means to them; and 2) their future aspirations and life plans. Special consideration is given to students who have helped support the NVC organization. Financial need is considered in the selection process.

Financial data The stipend is $2,500.

Duration 1 year.

Number awarded 3 each year.

Deadline January of each year.

[814]
SIXTH MARINE DIVISION ASSOCIATION SCHOLARSHIP

Sixth Marine Division Association
c/o Marine Corps Scholarship Foundation
909 North Washington Street, Suite 400
Alexandria, VA 22314
(703) 549-0060 Toll Free: (866) 496-5462
Fax: (703) 549-9474 E-mail: students@mcsf.org
Web: www.mcsf.org/apply/eligibility

Summary To provide financial assistance for college to the grandchildren of veterans who served with the Sixth Marine Division during World War II.

Eligibility This program is open to grandchildren of veterans who served with the Sixth Marine Division during World War II and are or were members of the Sixth Marine Division Association. Applicants must be high school seniors, high school graduates, or current college students. Along with

their application, they must submit academic transcripts, a copy of their grandparent's honorable discharge, and a 500-word essay on a topic that changes periodically. Only undergraduate study is supported. The family income of applicants must be less than $93,000 per year.

Financial data Stipends depend on the need of the recipient and the availability of funds, but generally range from $500 to $2,500 per year.

Duration 1 year; may be renewed for up to 3 additional years.

Additional information The highest-ranked applicant receives an award that is designated the Peter Mucci Memorial Scholarship.

Number awarded Varies each year; recently, 4 were awarded.

Deadline February of each year.

[815]
SOCIETY OF THE 3RD INFANTRY DIVISION SCHOLARSHIPS

Society of the 3rd Infantry Division
Attn: Scholarship Foundation
2010 Worcester Lane
Garland, TX 75040-3331
(972) 495-1704 E-mail: ldball1@msn.com
Web: 3idscholarshipfoundation.org

Summary To provide financial assistance for college to descendants of members of the Society of the 3rd Infantry Division and spouses of deceased 3rd Infantry Division members.

Eligibility This program is open to 1) children, grandchildren, and great-grandchildren of members of the society; and 3) children, grandchildren, and unremarried spouses of 3rd Infantry Division soldiers killed in action or died of wounds while on active duty. Applicants must be enrolled or planning to enroll as an undergraduate student. Along with their application, they must submit an essay of 2 to 4 pages on the history of the 3rd Infantry Division, national pride, loyalty to the nation, patriotism, or a related subject. Selection is based on the essay, academic accomplishment, extracurricular activities, community service involvement, goals after graduation, and financial need.

Financial data The stipend is $1,000.

Duration 1 year; recipients may reapply.

Additional information This program began in 2005.

Number awarded Varies each year; recently, 9 were awarded.

Deadline April of each year.

[816]
SONS OF UNION VETERANS OF THE CIVIL WAR SCHOLARSHIPS

Sons of Union Veterans of the Civil War
1 Lincoln Circle at Reservoir Park, Suite 240
Harrisburg, PA 17103-2411
(717) 232-7000 Fax: (717) 412-7492
E-mail: execdir@suvcw.org
Web: www.suvcw.org/?page_id=807

Summary To provide financial assistance for college to descendants, males and females considered separately, of Union Civil War veterans.

Eligibility This program is open to high school seniors and students currently enrolled at a 4-year college or university. Applicants must 1) rank in the upper quarter of their high school graduating class (preferably in the upper tenth); 2) have a record of performance in school and community activities; 3) have an interest in and positive attitude toward college; 4) provide 3 letters of recommendation; and 5) submit an official grade transcript. Males must be a current member or associate of Sons of Union Veterans of the Civil War. Females must be the daughter or granddaughter of a current member or associate of Sons of Union Veterans of the Civil War and a current member of at least 1 of the following organizations: Woman's Relief Corps, Ladies of the Grand Army of the Republic, Daughters of Union Veterans of the Civil War 1861-1865, or Auxiliary to the Sons of Union Veterans of the Civil War. Financial need is not considered in the selection process.

Financial data The stipend is $1,000. Funds are to be used for tuition and books. Checks are mailed directly to the recipient's school.

Duration 1 year.

Number awarded 2 each year: 1 to a male and 1 to a female.

Deadline March of each year.

[817]
SOUTH CAROLINA TUITION ASSISTANCE FOR CERTAIN WAR VETERANS CHILDREN

South Carolina Division of Veterans' Affairs
c/o VA Regional Office Building
6437 Garners Ferry Road, Suite 1126
Columbia, SC 29209
(803) 647-2434   Fax: (803) 647-2312
E-mail: va@oepp.sc.gov
Web: www.govoepp.state.sc.us/va/benefits.html

Summary To provide free college tuition to the children of disabled and other South Carolina veterans.

Eligibility This program is open to the children of wartime veterans who were legal residents of South Carolina both at the time of entry into military or naval service and during service, or who have been residents of South Carolina for at least 1 year. Veteran parents must 1) be permanently and totally disabled as determined by the U.S. Department of Veterans Affairs; 2) have been a prisoner of war; 3) have been killed in action; 4) have died from other causes while in service; 5) have died of a disease or disability resulting from service; 6) be currently missing in action; 7) have received the Congressional Medal of Honor; 8) have received the Purple Heart Medal from wounds received in combat; or 9) now be deceased but qualified under categories 1 or 2 above. The veteran's child must be 26 years of age or younger and working on an undergraduate degree.

Financial data Children who qualify are eligible for free tuition at any South Carolina state-supported college, university, or postsecondary technical education institution. The waiver applies to tuition only. The costs of room and board, certain fees, and books are not covered.

Duration Students are eligible to receive this support as long as they are younger than 26 years of age and working on an undergraduate degree.

Number awarded Varies each year.

Deadline Deadline not specified.

[818]
SOUTH DAKOTA LEGION EDUCATIONAL LOAN

American Legion
Department of South Dakota
14 First Avenue S.E.
P.O. Box 67
Watertown, SD 57201-0067
(605) 886-3604   Fax: (605) 886-2870
E-mail: sdlegion@dailypost.com
Web: www.sdlegion.org/pdf%20page.htm

Summary To provide loans to children and grandchildren of South Dakota veterans who are interested in attending college in the state.

Eligibility This program is open to residents of South Dakota who are wartime veterans or their children or grandchildren; wartime veterans includes those eligible for membership in the American Legion (although Legion membership is not required). Applicants must be interested in attending a South Dakota college or technical school (unless no school in the state offers the professional or technical degree being sought).

Financial data Loans are available up to $1,500 per year. Repayment begins 90 days after the student leaves school, with interest at 3%.

Duration 1 year; the lifetime maximum that may be borrowed is $3,000.

Additional information This program began in 1956 for the children of veterans. It was expanded in 2002 to include veterans themselves and in 2006 to include grandchildren of veterans.

Number awarded Varies each year.

Deadline April of each year for fall semester; October of each year for spring semester.

[819]
SOUTH DAKOTA REDUCED TUITION FOR CHILDREN OF DECEASED SERVICEMEN/WOMEN

South Dakota Board of Regents
Attn: Scholarship Committee
306 East Capitol Avenue, Suite 200
Pierre, SD 57501-2545
(605) 773-3455   Fax: (605) 773-2422
E-mail: info@sdbor.edu
Web: www.sdbor.edu/students/redtuit_childservice.htm

Summary To provide free tuition at South Dakota public colleges and universities to children of military personnel who died while in service.

Eligibility This program is open to residents of South Dakota younger than 25 years of age. The applicant's parent must have been killed in action or died of other causes while on active duty and must have been a resident of South Dakota for at least 6 months immediately preceding entry into active service.

Financial data Qualifying applicants are granted a 100% tuition waiver at state-supported postsecondary institutions in South Dakota. The waiver applies only to tuition, not fees.

Duration 8 semesters or 12 quarters of either full- or part-time study.

Number awarded Varies each year.

Deadline Deadline not specified.

[820]
SOUTH DAKOTA REDUCED TUITION FOR DEPENDENTS OF PRISONERS OF WAR OR MISSING IN ACTION

South Dakota Board of Regents
Attn: Scholarship Committee
306 East Capitol Avenue, Suite 200
Pierre, SD 57501-2545
(605) 773-3455   Fax: (605) 773-2422
E-mail: info@sdbor.edu
Web: www.sdbor.edu/students/redtuit_deppowmia.htm

Summary   To provide free tuition at South Dakota public colleges and universities to dependents of prisoners of war (POWs) and persons missing in action (MIAs).

Eligibility   This program is open to residents of South Dakota who are the dependents of POWs or of MIAs who are officially listed as residents of the state. Dependents include 1) children born before or during the period of time when the parent was declared MIA or POW; 2) children legally adopted or in legal custody of the parent during the period of time when the parent was declared MIA or POW; and 3) the spouse (if not legally separated) of the individual who is MIA or POW. Applicants must be attending or planning to attend a state-supported school in South Dakota.

Financial data   For those who qualify, tuition and mandatory fees are waived.

Duration   8 semesters or 12 quarters of either full- or part-time study.

Number awarded   Varies each year.

Deadline   Deadline not specified.

[821]
SPECIAL OPERATIONS WARRIOR FOUNDATION SCHOLARSHIPS

Special Operations Warrior Foundation
1137 Marbella Plaza Drive
P.O. Box 89367
Tampa, FL 33689
(813) 805-9400   Toll Free: (877) 337-7693
Fax: (813) 805-0567   E-mail: warrior@specialops.org
Web: www.specialops.org/?page=collegescholarship

Summary   To provide financial assistance for college to the children of Special Operations personnel who died in training or operational missions.

Eligibility   This program is open to the children of parents who served in Special Operations and were killed in a training accident or an operational mission. This is an entitlement program; all eligible students receive support.

Financial data   A stipend is awarded (amount not specified). Funding is intended to cover all expenses not included in the Marine Gunnery Sergeant John David Fry Scholarship or for dependents whose Special Operations parent was killed prior to September 11, 2001.

Duration   4 years or more.

Additional information   This program began in 1980 because of the high casualty rates experienced by personnel of U.S. Special Operations Command.

Number awarded   Varies each year.

Deadline   Applications may be submitted at any time.

[822]
SPECIAL OPS SURVIVORS EDUCATION AND CAREER ADVANCEMENT GRANTS

Special Ops Survivors
Attn: Executive Director
P.O. Box 181097
Coronado, CA 92118
(619) 437-1137   Toll Free: (800) 804-UWSF
Fax: (413) 677-1143   E-mail: Elizabeth@uwsf.org
Web: specialopssurvivors.org

Summary   To provide financial assistance for college to the spouses of Special Operations military personnel killed in the line of duty after September 11, 2001.

Eligibility   This program is open to the surviving spouses of soldiers, sailors, airmen, and marines who were serving under a U.S. military Special Operations command or directly supporting a Special Operations mission and were killed after September 11, 2001. Applicants must be enrolled or planning to enroll at an accredited college or technical school or in a professional licensure or certification program. They must have a GPA of 3.0 or higher. Along with their application, they must submit a 500-word essay explaining why they have chosen their intended program of study and how that program of study will contribute to their immediate or long-range career plans. Selection is based on the essay, merit, academic potential, and financial need.

Financial data   The stipend is $2,500 per year. Funds are paid directly to the recipient to be used for payment of tuition, books, supplies, child care costs, and transportation expenses.

Duration   1 year; may be renewed up to 3 additional years.

Additional information   This sponsor began in 2002 as the United Warrior Survivor Foundation. It adopted its current name in 2012.

Number awarded   1 or more each year.

Deadline   July of each year.

[823]
SPIRIT OF YOUTH SCHOLARSHIP FOR JUNIOR MEMBERS

American Legion Auxiliary
8945 North Meridian Street
Indianapolis, IN 46260
(317) 569-4500   Fax: (317) 569-4502
E-mail: alahq@alaforveterans.org
Web: www.alaforveterans.org

Summary   To provide financial assistance for college to junior members of the American Legion Auxiliary.

Eligibility   Applicants for this scholarship must have been junior members of the Auxiliary for at least the past 3 years. They must be seniors at an accredited high school in the United States, have a GPA of 3.0 or higher, and be planning to enroll full time at an accredited 4-year institution of higher education. Along with their application, they must submit a 1,000-word essay on a topic that changes annually; recently, students were asked to write on "How I Can Help Children of Military Families." Selection is based on that essay (30%), character and leadership (30%), and academic record (40%). Each unit of the Auxiliary may select a candidate for application to the department level, and each department submits a candidate for the national award.

Financial data   The stipend is $1,250 per year.

Duration 4 years.

Additional information Applications are available from the president of the candidate's own unit or from the secretary or education chair of the department.

Number awarded 5 each year: 1 in each division of the American Legion Auxiliary.

Deadline Applications must be submitted to the unit president by February of each year.

[824]
SSGT. ROBERT V. MILNER MEMORIAL SCHOLARSHIP

American Academy of Physician Assistants-Veterans
  Caucus
Attn: Veterans Caucus
P.O. Box 362
Danville, PA 17821-0362
Fax: (302) 526-7154   E-mail: fbrace@veteranscaucus.org
Web: www.veteranscaucus.org

Summary To provide financial assistance to Air Force veterans and their dependents who are studying to become physician assistants.

Eligibility This program is open to U.S. citizens who are currently enrolled in a physician assistant program. The program must be approved by the Commission on Accreditation of Allied Health Education. Applicants must be honorably discharged members of the United States Air Force or the dependent of an Air Force veteran. Selection is based on military honors and awards received, civic and college honors and awards received, professional memberships and activities, and GPA. An electronic copy of the applicant's DD Form 214 must accompany the application.

Financial data The stipend is $2,000.

Duration 1 year.

Number awarded 1 each year.

Deadline February of each year.

[825]
STAND WATIE SCHOLARSHIP

Sons of Confederate Veterans
Attn: Executive Director
P.O. Box 59
Columbia, TN 38401-0059
(931) 380-1844   Toll Free: (800) MY-DIXIE
Fax: (931) 381-6712   E-mail: exedir@scv.org
Web: www.scv.org/services/documents.php

Summary To provide financial assistance for college to members of various Civil War veterans organizations.

Eligibility This program is open to members in good standing of the Sons of Confederate Veterans, Children of the Confederacy, or the United Daughters of the Confederacy. Applicants must be currently enrolled in a junior college, 4-year college, or university. They must have completed their freshman year and be classified as a college sophomore, junior, or senior.

Financial data The stipend is $1,000.

Duration 1 year; nonrenewable.

Additional information This program began in 1975.

Number awarded Varies each year; recently, 5 were awarded.

Deadline June of each year.

[826]
STANLEY A. DORAN MEMORIAL SCHOLARSHIPS

Fleet Reserve Association
Attn: FRA Education Foundation
125 North West Street
Alexandria, VA 22314-2754
(703) 683-1400   Toll Free: (800) FRA-1924
Fax: (703) 549-6610   E-mail: scholars@fra.org
Web: www.fra.org

Summary To provide financial assistance for college or graduate school to children of members of the Fleet Reserve Association (FRA).

Eligibility This program is open to the dependent children of FRA members who are in good standing (or were at the time of death, if deceased). Applicants must be working on or planning to work full time on an undergraduate or graduate degree. Along with their application, they must submit an essay on why they want to go to college and what they intend to accomplish with their degree. Selection is based on academic record, financial need, extracurricular activities, leadership skills, and participation in community activities. U.S. citizenship is required.

Financial data Stipends range up to $5,000 per year.

Duration 1 year; may be renewed.

Additional information Membership in the FRA is restricted to active-duty, retired, and Reserve members of the Navy, Marine Corps, and Coast Guard.

Number awarded 3 each year.

Deadline April of each year.

[827]
SURVIVING DEPENDENTS OF MONTANA NATIONAL GUARD MEMBER WAIVER

Office of the Commissioner of Higher Education
Attn: Montana University System
State Scholarship Coordinator
2500 Broadway
P.O. Box 203201
Helena, MT 59620-3201
(406) 444-6570   Toll Free: (800) 537-7508
Fax: (406) 444-1469   E-mail: snewlun@montana.edu
Web: www.mus.edu

Summary To provide financial assistance for undergraduate study to dependents of deceased National Guard members in Montana.

Eligibility Eligible for this benefit are residents of Montana who are surviving spouses or children of Montana National Guard members killed as a result of injury, disease, or other disability incurred in the line of duty while serving on state active duty. Financial need is considered.

Financial data Students eligible for this benefit are entitled to attend any unit of the Montana University System without payment of undergraduate registration or incidental fees.

Duration Undergraduate students are eligible for continued fee waiver as long as they maintain reasonable academic progress as full-time students.

Additional information The waiver does not apply if the recipient is eligible for educational benefits from any governmental or private program that provides comparable benefits.

Number awarded Varies each year.

Deadline Deadline not specified.

[828]
SURVIVORS' AND DEPENDENTS' EDUCATIONAL ASSISTANCE PROGRAM

Department of Veterans Affairs
Attn: Veterans Benefits Administration
810 Vermont Avenue, N.W.
Washington, DC 20420
(202) 418-4343   Toll Free: (888) GI-BILL1
Web: www.benefits.va.gov

Summary   To provide financial assistance for undergraduate or graduate study to children and spouses of deceased and disabled veterans, MIAs, and POWs.

Eligibility   Eligible for this assistance are spouses and children of 1) veterans who died or are permanently and totally disabled as the result of active service in the armed forces; 2) veterans who died from any cause while rated permanently and totally disabled from a service-connected disability; 3) servicemembers listed as missing in action or captured in the line of duty by a hostile force; 4) servicemembers listed as forcibly detained or interned by a foreign government or power; and 5) servicemembers who are hospitalized or receiving outpatient treatment for a service-connected permanent and total disability and are likely to be discharged for that disability. Children must be between 18 and 26 years of age, although extensions may be granted. Spouses and children over 14 years of age with physical or mental disabilities are also eligible.

Financial data   Monthly stipends for study at an academic institution are $1,018 for full time, $763 for three-quarter time, or $506 for half-time. Other rates apply for apprenticeship and on-the-job training, farm cooperative training, and special restorative training.

Duration   Benefits are provided for up to 45 months (or the equivalent in part-time training). Some beneficiaries who qualify for more than 1 education program may be eligible for up to 81 months. Spouses must complete their training within 10 years of the date they are first found eligible. For spouses of servicemembers who died on active duty, benefits end 20 years from the date of death.

Additional information   Benefits may be used to work on associate, bachelor's, or graduate degrees at colleges and universities, including independent study, cooperative training, and study abroad programs. Courses leading to a certificate or diploma from business, technical, or vocational schools may also be taken. Other eligible programs include apprenticeships, on-the-job training programs, farm cooperative courses, and correspondence courses (for spouses only). Remedial, deficiency, and refresher courses may be approved under certain circumstances.

Number awarded   Varies each year.

Deadline   Applications may be submitted at any time.

[829]
TAILHOOK EDUCATIONAL FOUNDATION SCHOLARSHIPS

Tailhook Educational Foundation
9696 Businesspark Avenue
P.O. Box 26626
San Diego, CA 92196-0626
(858) 689-9223   Toll Free: (800) 322-4665
E-mail: tag@tailhook.net
Web: www.tailhook.net/A_Foundation_Index.html

Summary   To provide financial assistance for college to personnel associated with naval aviation and their children.

Eligibility   This program is open to 1) the children (natural, step, and adopted) and grandchildren of current or former U.S. Navy, Coast Guard, or Marine Corps personnel who served as an aviator, flight officer, or air crewman; or 2) personnel and children and grandchildren of personnel who are serving or have served on board a U.S. Navy aircraft carrier as a member of the ship's company or air wing. Applicants must be enrolled or accepted for enrollment at an accredited college or university. Selection is based on educational and extracurricular achievements, merit, and citizenship.

Financial data   The stipend ranges from $1,500 to $23,000.

Duration   1 to 2 years.

Number awarded   Varies each year; recently, 80 were awarded.

Deadline   March of each year.

[830]
TENNESSEE EAGLE SCOUT OF THE YEAR SCHOLARSHIP

American Legion
Department of Tennessee
318 Donelson Pike
Nashville, TN 37214
(615) 391-5088   Fax: (615) 391-5099
E-mail: taltnia@comcast.net
Web: www.tennesseelegion.org/content.php?id=100

Summary   To recognize and reward, with scholarships for college in any state, Eagle Scouts who are members of a troop associated with the American Legion in Tennessee or a son or grandson of a member of the Legion in the state.

Eligibility   The Tennessee nominee for American Legion Scout of the Year receives this scholarship. Applicants must be 1) registered, active members of a Boy Scout Troop or Varsity Scout Team sponsored by an American Legion Post in Tennessee or Auxiliary Unit in Tennessee; or 2) registered, active members of a duly chartered Boy Scout Troop or Varsity Scout Team and the sons or grandsons of American Legion or Auxiliary members. Candidates must also 1) be active members of their religious institution and have received the appropriate religious emblem; 2) have demonstrated practical citizenship in church, school, Scouting, and community; and 3) be at least 15 years of age and enrolled in high school. They must be planning to attend college in any state.

Financial data   The award is a $3,000 scholarship.

Duration   The award is presented annually.

Number awarded   1 each year.

Deadline   February of each year.

[831]
TENTH MOUNTAIN DIVISION FOUNDATION SCHOLARSHIP PROGRAM

Tenth Mountain Division Foundation, Inc.
133 South Van Gordon Street, Suite 200
Lakewood, CO 80228
(303) 756-8486   Fax: (303) 987-9489
E-mail: admin@10thmdf.ort
Web: www.10thmdf.org/scholarship.htm

Summary To provide financial assistance for college or graduate school to descendants of former members of the Tenth Mountain Division.

Eligibility This program is open to the descendants of veterans who served in the Tenth Mountain Division during World War II. Applicants must have completed at least 2 years of undergraduate study at an accredited college, university, or other comparable institution or be enrolled in a graduate program. Along with their application, they must submit an essay on the military service of their ancestor during World War II. Selection is based on that essay and financial need.

Financial data The stipend is $5,000.

Duration 1 year; nonrenewable.

Number awarded Up to 5 each year.

Deadline April of each year.

[832]
TEXAS AMERICAN LEGION AUXILIARY PAST PRESIDENT'S PARLEY SCHOLARSHIPS

American Legion Auxiliary
Department of Texas
P.O. Box 140407
Austin, TX 78714-0407
(512) 476-7278   Fax: (512) 482-8391
E-mail: alatexas@txlegion.org
Web: www.alatexas.org/activity/scholarships

Summary To provide financial assistance to descendants of Texas veterans who wish to study a field related to medicine at a school in the state.

Eligibility This program is open to the children, grandchildren, and great-grandchildren of veterans who served during specified periods of wartime. Applicants must be residents of Texas studying or planning to study a medical field at a postsecondary institution in the state. Selection is based on need, goals, character, citizenship, and objectives.

Financial data The stipend is $1,000.

Duration 1 year.

Additional information Applications for these scholarships must be submitted through local units of the American Legion Auxiliary in Texas.

Number awarded 1 or more each year.

Deadline May of each year.

[833]
TEXAS B-ON-TIME LOAN PROGRAM

Texas Higher Education Coordinating Board
Attn: Hinson-Hazlewood College Student Loan Program
1200 East Anderson Lane
P.O. Box 12788
Austin, TX 78711-2788
(512) 427-6340   Toll Free: (800) 242-3062
Fax: (512) 427-6423   E-mail: loaninfo@thecb.state.tx.us
Web: www.hhloans.com

Summary To provide forgivable loans to students in Texas who are residents of the state or entitled to pay resident tuition as a dependent child of a member of the U.S. armed forces.

Eligibility This program is open to residents of Texas and residents of other states who are entitled to pay resident tuition as a dependent child of a member of the U.S. armed forces. Applicants must 1) have graduated from a public or accredited private high school in Texas or from a high school operated by the U.S. Department of Defense; or 2) earned an associate degree from an eligible Texas institution. They must be enrolled full time in an undergraduate degree or certificate program at an eligible college, university, junior college, or public technical college in Texas.

Financial data Eligible students may borrow up to $4,000 per semester ($8,000 per year) for a 4-year public or private institution, $1,350 per semester ($2,700 per year) for a 2-year public or private junior college, or $2,350 per semester ($4,700 per year) for a public technical college. A 3% origination fee is deducted from the loan proceeds. No interest is charged. Loans are forgiven if the students 1) graduate with a cumulative GPA of 3.0 or higher within 4 calendar years after they initially enroll; within 5 calendar years after they initially enroll in a degree program in architecture, engineering, or other field that normally requires more than 4 years for completion; or within 2 calendar years if they initially enroll in a public or private 2-year institution; or 2) graduate with a cumulative GPA of 3.0 or higher with a total number of credit hours that is no more than 6 hours beyond what is required to complete the degree or certificate.

Duration 1 year. May be renewed after the first year if the recipient makes satisfactory academic progress toward a degree or certificate. May be renewed after the second and subsequent years if the recipient completes at least 75% of the semester credit hours attempted and has a cumulative GPA of 2.5 or higher on all course work. Loans are available for a maximum of 150 credit hours.

Number awarded Varies each year; recently, 8,130 of these loans, worth $52,733,274, were awarded.

Deadline Deadline not specified.

[834]
TEXAS CHILDREN OF U.S. MILITARY WHO ARE MISSING IN ACTION OR PRISONERS OF WAR EXEMPTION PROGRAM

Texas Higher Education Coordinating Board
Attn: Grants and Special Programs
1200 East Anderson Lane
P.O. Box 12788
Austin, TX 78711-2788
(512) 427-6340   Toll Free: (800) 242-3062
Fax: (512) 427-6420   E-mail: grantinfo@thecb.state.tx.us
Web: www.collegeforalltexans.com

Summary To provide educational assistance to the children of Texas military personnel declared prisoners of war or missing in action.

Eligibility Eligible are dependent children of Texas residents who are either prisoners of war or missing in action. Applicants must be under 21 years of age, or under 25 if they receive the majority of support from their parent(s).

Financial data Eligible students are exempted from the payment of all dues, fees, and tuition charges at publicly-supported colleges and universities in Texas.

Duration Up to 8 semesters, provided recipients maintain a GPA specified by their institution.

Number awarded Varies each year; recently, 3 of these exemptions, worth $1,909, were granted.

Deadline Deadline not specified.

[835]
TEXAS WAIVERS OF NON-RESIDENT TUITION FOR MILITARY SURVIVORS

Texas Higher Education Coordinating Board
Attn: Grants and Special Programs
1200 East Anderson Lane
P.O. Box 12788
Austin, TX 78711-2788
(512) 427-6340　　　　　Toll Free: (800) 242-3062
Fax: (512) 427-6420　E-mail: grantinfo@thecb.state.tx.us
Web: www.collegeforalltexans.com

Summary To provide a partial tuition exemption to the surviving spouses and dependent children of deceased military personnel who move to Texas following the servicemember's death.

Eligibility Eligible for these waivers are the surviving spouses and dependent children of members of the U.S. armed forces and commissioned officers of the Public Health Service who died while in service. Applicants must move to Texas within 60 days of the date of the death of the servicemember. They must be attending or planning to attend a public college or university in the state. Children are eligible even if the surviving parent does not accompany them to Texas.

Financial data Although persons eligible under this program are still classified as non-residents, they are entitled to pay the resident tuition at Texas institutions of higher education on an immediate basis.

Duration 1 year.

Additional information This program became effective in 2003.

Number awarded Varies each year.

Deadline Deadline not specified.

[836]
THANKSUSA SCHOLARSHIPS

ThanksUSA
1390 Chain Bridge Road, Suite 260
McLean, VA 22101
(703) 641-3767　　　　　Toll Free: (877) 849-8720
E-mail: thanksusa@scholarshipamerica.org
Web: www.thanksusa.org/scholarship-program.html

Summary To provide financial assistance for college to children and spouses of military personnel who served after September 11, 2001.

Eligibility This program is open to dependent children 24 years of age or younger and spouses of active-duty military personnel. The parent or spouse must 1) have served on active duty for at least 180 days since September 11, 2001; 2) have been killed or wounded in action since that date; 3) be a member of the military Reserves activated to full-time duty; or 4) be a member of the National Guard who have been federalized. Children and spouses of retired or discharged service personnel are eligible if the parent or spouse served 180 days after September 11, 2011. Applicants must be entering or attending an accredited 2- or 4-year college, university, vocational school, or technical school as a full-time student. Spouses may use the award for non-degree licensure or certification programs and may enroll part time. All applicants must have a GPA of 2.0 or higher. Selection is based on financial need, academic record, a statement of goals, and demonstrated leadership and participation in school and community activities. Preference is given to children or spouses of service personnel killed or injured during active duty.

Financial data The stipend is $3,000.

Duration 1 year; recipients may reapply.

Additional information This program began in 2006. Selection of recipients is made by Scholarship Management Services, a division of Scholarship America.

Number awarded Approximately 500 each year. Since the program was established, it has awarded nearly 3,400 scholarships with a value of more than $10 million.

Deadline May of each year.

[837]
THIRD MARINE DIVISION ASSOCIATION MEMORIAL SCHOLARSHIP FUND

Third Marine Division Association, Inc.
P.O. Box 254
Chalfont, PA 18914-0254
(215) 822-9094　　　　　E-mail: GYGEE@aol.com
Web: www.caltrap.org/3rd_MarDivAssoc/scholarship.asp

Summary To provide financial assistance for college to children and some spouses of members of the Third Marine Division Association.

Eligibility This program is open to dependent unmarried children whose sponsoring parent has been a member of the association for at least 2 years. Associate members do not qualify, except for widows of deceased regular or life member who had qualifying Third Marine Division service and association membership. Dependent children of military personnel who served in any Third Marine Division unit and lost their lives as a result of combat actions while serving in the operations known as Desert Shield, Desert Storm, or any other southwest Asia operation after August 2, 1990, are also eligible. Applicants must be interested in attending a college or university in the United States or Canada. They must be between 16 and 23 years of age and able to demonstrate financial need. Grandchildren of members are not eligible.

Financial data Stipends range from $400 to $2,400, depending upon need.

Duration 1 year; may be renewed for up to 3 additional years for undergraduate study or until the recipient reaches 26 years of age, provided a "C" average is maintained.

Additional information This program began in 1969.

Number awarded 20 to 25 each year.

Deadline April of each year.

[838]
THOMAS H. MILLER SCHOLARSHIP

Blinded Veterans Association
477 H Street, N.W.
Washington, DC 20001-2694
(202) 371-8880　　　　　Toll Free: (800) 669-7079
Fax: (202) 371-8258　　　E-mail: temanuel@bva.org
Web: www.bva.org/services.html

Summary To provide financial assistance for undergraduate or graduate study, especially of music or the fine arts, to immediate family of blinded veterans and servicemembers.

Eligibility This program is open to dependent children, grandchildren, and spouses of blinded veterans and active-duty blinded servicemembers of the U.S. armed forces. The veteran or servicemember must be legally blind; the blindness may be either service-connected or nonservice-connected. Applicants must have been accepted or be currently enrolled as a full-time student in an undergraduate or graduate program at an accredited institution of higher learning. Preference is given to students of music or the fine arts. Along with their application, they must submit a 300-word essay on their career goals and aspirations. Financial need is not considered in the selection process.

Financial data The stipend is $1,000; funds are intended to be used to cover the student's expenses, including tuition, other academic fees, books, dormitory fees, and cafeteria fees. Funds are paid directly to the recipient's school.

Duration 1 year; recipients may reapply for up to 3 additional years.

Number awarded 1 each year.

Deadline April of each year.

[839]
TILLMAN MILITARY SCHOLARS PROGRAM

Pat Tillman Foundation
217 North Jefferson Street, Suite 602
Chicago, IL 60661
(773) 360-5277
E-mail: scholarships@pattillmanfoundation.org
Web: www.pattillmanfoundation.org/apply-to-be-a-scholar

Summary To provide financial assistance to active service-members, veterans, and their spouses who are interested in working on an undergraduate or graduate degree.

Eligibility This program is open to veterans and active servicemembers of all branches of the armed forces from both the pre- and post-September 11 era and their spouses; children are not eligible. Applicants must be enrolled or planning to enroll full time at a 4-year public or private college or university to work on an undergraduate, graduate, or postgraduate degree. Current and former servicemembers must submit 400-word essays on 1) their motivation and decision to serve in the U.S. military and how that decision and experience has changed their life and ambitions; and 2) their educational and career goals, how they will incorporate their military service experience into those goals, and how they intend to continue their service to others and the community. Spouses must submit 400-word essays on 1) their previous service to others and the community; and 2) their educational and career goals, how they will incorporate their service experiences and the impact of their spouse's military service into those goals, and how they intend to continue their service to others and the community. Selection is based on those essays, educational and career ambitions, record of military service, record of personal achievement, demonstration of service to others in the community, desire to continue such service, and leadership potential.

Financial data The stipend depends on the need of the recipient and the availability of funds; recently, stipends averaged approximately $15,000.

Duration 1 year; may be renewed, provided the recipient maintains a GPA of 3.0 or higher, remains enrolled full time, and documents participation in civic action or community service.

Additional information This program began in 2009.

Number awarded 60 each year. Since the program began, it has awarded more than $6 million to 348 scholars.

Deadline March of each year.

[840]
TONY LOPEZ SCHOLARSHIP PROGRAM

Louisiana National Guard Enlisted Association
c/o CMSgt John Harris
694 South Rue Marcel
Gretna, LA 70056
(504) 388-5423   E-mail: john.harris1@bellsouth.net
Web: www.langea.org

Summary To provide financial assistance to members of the Louisiana National Guard Enlisted Association (LANGEA) and their dependents who plan to attend college in any state.

Eligibility This program is open to members of the association, their spouses and unmarried dependent children, and the unremarried spouses and unmarried dependent children of deceased members who were in good standing at the time of their death. The qualifying LANGEA members must have at least 1 year remaining on their enlistment following completion of the school year for which the application is submitted or have served 20 years of more in the Louisiana National Guard. Applicants must be enrolled or planning to enroll full time at an accredited college, university, trade school, or business school in any state. Graduate students are not eligible. Selection is based on academic achievement, character, leadership, and financial need.

Financial data The stipend is $2,000.

Duration 1 year; nonrenewable.

Number awarded 2 each year.

Deadline April of each year.

[841]
TRANSFER OF POST-9/11 GI-BILL BENEFITS TO DEPENDENTS

Department of Veterans Affairs
Attn: Veterans Benefits Administration
810 Vermont Avenue, N.W.
Washington, DC 20420
(202) 418-4343   Toll Free: (888) GI-BILL1
Web: www.benefits.va.gov/gibill/post911_transfer.asp

Summary To provide financial assistance to dependents of military personnel who qualify for Post-9/11 GI Bill benefits and agree to transfer unused benefits to their spouse or child.

Eligibility This program is open to dependents of current military personnel whose parent or spouse 1) has at least 6 years of service in the armed forces (active duty and/or Selected Reserve) and agrees to serve 4 additional years; 2) has at least 10 years of service, is precluded by either standard policy or statute from committing to 4 additional years, but agrees to serve for the maximum amount of time allowed by such policy or statute; or 3) is or becomes retirement eligible during the period following August 1, 2012 and agrees to serve for an additional period up to 4 years, depending on the date of retirement eligibility. The military parent or spouse must agree to transfer unused months of educational benefits to a dependent while still serving on active duty. Dependents must be enrolled or planning to enroll in an educational program, including work on an undergraduate or graduate degree, vocational/technical training, on-the-job training, flight training, correspondence training, licensing and national testing programs, entrepreneurship training, and tutorial assistance.

Financial data Dependents working on an undergraduate or graduate degree at public institutions in their state receive full payment of tuition and fees. For dependents who attend private institutions in most states, tuition and fee reimbursement is capped at $20,235.02 per academic year. Benefits for other types of training programs depend on the amount for which the spouse or parent qualified under prior educational programs. Dependents also receive a monthly housing allowance that is 1) based on the Department of Defense Basic Allowance for Housing (BAH) for an E-5 with dependents (which depends on the location of the school but ranges from approximately $1,000 per month to approximately $2,500 per month); 2) $1,509 per month at schools in foreign countries; or 3) $754.50 per month for online training classes. They also receive an annual book allowance of $1,000 and (for participants who live in a rural county remote from an educational institution) a rural benefit payment of $500 per year.

Duration Military members may transfer all or a portion of their 36 months of entitlement to a dependent. Spouses may start to use the benefit immediately, but children may use the benefit only after they have completed high school (or equivalency certificate) or reached 18 years of age. They are not subject to the 15-year limit but may not use the benefit after reaching 26 years of age.

Additional information This supplement was added to the Post-9/11 GI Bill program as a result of legislation passed by Congress in 2010.

Number awarded Varies each year.

Deadline Deadline not specified.

[842]
TREA NATIONAL SCHOLARSHIPS

The Enlisted Association
Attn: National Scholarship Committee
1111 South Abilene Court
Aurora, CO 80012-4909
(303) 752-0660   Toll Free: (800) 338-9337
Fax: (303) 752-0835   E-mail: treahq@trea.org
Web: www.trea.org/scholarship-info.html

Summary To provide financial assistance for college to the dependents of members of The Enlisted Association.

Eligibility This program is open to dependent children and grandchildren of regular and associate members or deceased members who were in good standing at the time of their death. Applicants must be high school seniors or full-time college students and interested in attending a 2- or 4-year college or university. Along with their application, they must submit a 300-word essay on a topic that changes annually; recently, students were asked to give their opinion on whether government entitlement programs have a positive or negative impact on society. Special consideration is given to students who can demonstrate financial need.

Financial data The stipend is $1,000 per year.

Duration 1 year; recipients may reapply.

Additional information The Enlisted Association began as The Retired Enlisted Association (TREA) in 1963. In 2012, it changed its name and opened regular membership to all enlisted personnel—retired, active duty, National Guard, and Reserves. Associate membership is open to widows and widowers of members and of non-members who were eligible for membership at the time of their death.

Number awarded 40 each year.

Deadline April of each year.

[843]
TUITION WAIVER FOR DISABLED CHILDREN OF KENTUCKY VETERANS

Kentucky Department of Veterans Affairs
Attn: Tuition Waiver Coordinator
321 West Main Street, Suite 390
Louisville, KY 40202
(502) 595-4447   Toll Free: (800) 928-4012 (within KY)
Fax: (502) 595-3369
Web: www.veterans.ky.gov

Summary To provide financial assistance for college to the children of Kentucky veterans who have a disability related to their parent's military service.

Eligibility This program is open to the children of veterans who have acquired a disability as a direct result of their parent's military service. The disability must have been designated by the U.S. Department of Veterans Affairs as compensable (currently defined as spina bifida). The veteran parent must 1) have served on active duty with the U.S. armed forces or in the National Guard or Reserve component on state active duty, active duty for training, or inactive duty training; and 2) be (or if deceased have been) a resident of Kentucky. Applicants must have been admitted to a state-supported university, college, or vocational training institute in Kentucky.

Financial data Eligible children are exempt from payment of tuition at state-supported institutions of higher education in Kentucky.

Duration There are no age or time limits on the waiver.

Number awarded Varies each year.

Deadline Deadline not specified.

[844]
UDT-SEAL SCHOLARSHIP

Navy Seal Foundation
Attn: Chief Financial Officer
1619 D Street, Building 5326
Virginia Beach, VA 23459
(757) 363-7490   Fax: (757) 363-7491
E-mail: info@navysealfoundation.org
Web: www.navysealfoundation.org

Summary To provide financial assistance for college to children of members of the UDT-SEAL Association.

Eligibility This program is open to children of members who are single, under 24 years of age, and a dependent of a sponsoring member of the association. Sponsors must be serving or have served in the armed forces and the Naval Special Warfare Community, have been an association member for the last 4 consecutive years, and have paid their dues for the current year. Applicants may be high school seniors, high school graduates, or full-time undergraduate students. Selection is based on GPA, SAT scores, class ranking, extracurricular activities, volunteer community involvement, leadership positions held, military service record, and employment (as appropriate).

Financial data Stipends are $15,000 or $7,500 per year.

Duration 1 year; may be renewed.

Additional information Membership in the association is open to all officers and enlisted personnel of the armed forces (active, retired, discharged, or separated) who have served with a Navy Combat Demolition Unit (NCDU), Underwater Demolition Team (UDT), or SEAL Team.

Number awarded Varies each year; recently, the Navy Seal Foundation awarded 12 dependent scholarships for all of its programs: 3 for 4 years at $15,000 per year to high school seniors and graduates, 3 for 1 year at $7,500 to high school seniors and graduates, 3 for 1 year at $15,000 to current college students, and 3 for 1 year at $7,500 to current college students.

Deadline February of each year.

[845]
UNITED DAUGHTERS OF THE CONFEDERACY SCHOLARSHIPS

United Daughters of the Confederacy
Attn: Second Vice President General
328 North Boulevard
Richmond, VA 23220-4008
(804) 355-1636   Fax: (804) 353-1396
E-mail: jamieretired@sbcglobal.net
Web: www.hqudc.org/Scholarships/index.htm

Summary To provide financial assistance for college to lineal descendants of Confederate veterans.

Eligibility Eligible to apply for these scholarships are lineal descendants of worthy Confederates or collateral descendants who are members of the Children of the Confederacy or the United Daughters of the Confederacy. Applicants must be high school seniors or college students and submit a family financial report and certified proof of the Confederate record of 1 ancestor, with the company and regiment in which he served. They must have a high school GPA of 3.0 or higher.

Financial data The amount of the scholarships depends on the availability of funds.

Duration 1 year; may be renewed up to 3 additional years.

Additional information Applications must be submitted through the division or chapter of their home state. Each division or chapter may present only 1 candidate for any 1 scholarship. Unrestricted scholarships include the Admiral Raphael Semmes Memorial Scholarship, the Barbara Jackson Sichel Memorial Scholarship, the Cody Bachman Memorial Scholarship, the Cora Bell Wesley Memorial Scholarship, the Cornelia Branch Stone Scholarship, the David Stephen Wylie Scholarship, the Dorothy Williams Scholarship, the Frances Pauline Clark Keys Memorial Scholarship, the Hector W. Church Memorial Scholarship, the Henry Clay Darsey Memorial Scholarship, the Janet B. Seippel Scholarship, the Lucy Robinson Search Scholarship, the Major Madison Bell Scholarship, the Mary B. Poppenheim Memorial Scholarship, the Matthew Fontaine Maury Scholarship, the Mrs. Ella M. Franklin Memorial Scholarship, the Mrs. L.H. Raines Memorial Scholarship, the S.A. Cunningham Scholarship, the Schomburg Family Trust Scholarship, the Stonewall Jackson Scholarship, the Vicki K. Heilig Scholarship, and the William Dudley Roe Contingency Fund Scholarship. The unrestricted scholarships may be used at any institution approved by the Education Committee of the United Daughters of the Confederacy. Members of the same family may not hold scholarships simultaneously, and only 1 application per family will be accepted within a current year. All requests for applications must be accompanied by a self-addressed stamped envelope.

Number awarded 18 unrestricted scholarships are available; another 13 scholarships with varying restrictions are also offered.

Deadline April of each year.

[846]
UNITED STATES ARMY WARRANT OFFICERS ASSOCIATION SCHOLARSHIP PROGRAM

United States Army Warrant Officers Association
Attn: USAWOA Scholarship Foundation
462 Herndon Parkway, Suite 207
Herndon, VA 20170-5235
(703) 742-7727   Toll Free: (800) 5-USAWOA
Fax: (703) 742-7728   E-mail: usawoasf@cavetel.net
Web: www.usawoa.org/scholarship-overview

Summary To provide financial assistance for college to dependents of members of the United States Army Warrant Officers Association.

Eligibility This program is open to children, grandchildren, and dependent stepchildren, under 23 years of age, of regular members of the association. Spouses of members are also eligible. Applicants must be enrolled or planning to enroll full time at an accredited U.S. college, university, or vocational/technical institution. They must have a GPA of 3.0 or higher. Along with their application, they must submit transcripts, SAT/ACT scores, letters of recommendation, a list of extracurricular activities, information on any special circumstances that would impact their attending college, and an essay of 800 to 1,000 words describing their educational goals and how reaching those goals will benefit the world around them. Financial need is not considered in the selection process.

Financial data The stipend is at least $1,000.

Duration 1 year; may be renewed.

Additional information This program, which began in 2003, includes the CW4 (Ret) Allnatt Memorial Scholarships and the CW4 (Ret) Calabrese Memorial Scholarship.

Number awarded Varies each year; recently, 15 were awarded.

Deadline April of each year.

[847]
UNITED STATES FIELD ARTILLERY ASSOCIATION SCHOLARSHIPS

United States Field Artillery Association
Attn: Scholarship Committee
Building 758, McNair Avenue
P.O. Box 33027
Fort Sill, OK 73503-0027
(580) 355-4677   Toll Free: (866) 355-4677
Fax: (580) 355-8745   E-mail: suzette@fieldartillery.org
Web: www.fieldartillery.org/#!membership/c1ghi

Summary To provide financial assistance for college to members of the United States Field Artillery Association (USFAA) and their immediate family.

Eligibility This program is open to 3 categories of students: USFAA members (officer or enlisted), immediate family of enlisted members, and immediate family of officer members. Applicants must have been accepted for admission as an undergraduate at an accredited college, university, or vocational program. Along with their application, they must submit an essay explaining their educational goals and how this scholarship will help meet those goals. Financial need is also considered in the selection process. The highest-ranked applicant receives the GEN Donald R. Keith Scholarship.

Financial data Stipends range from $1,000 to $2,500.

Duration 1 year.

Additional information The USFAA services the field artillery branch of the military.

Number awarded Varies each year; recently, 11 were awarded: 1 at $2,500 (the GEN Donald R. Keith Scholarship), 4 at $1,500, and 6 at $1,000.

Deadline March of each year.

[848]
UNIVERSITY INTERSCHOLASTIC LEAGUE PATRIOT SCHOLARSHIP

University Interscholastic League
Attn: Texas Interscholastic League Foundation
1701 Manor Road
Austin, TX 78722
(512) 232-4937　　　　Fax: (512) 232-7311
E-mail: tilf@uiltexas.org
Web: tilf.uiltexas.org/scholarships/list

Summary To provide financial assistance to high school seniors who participate in programs of the Texas Interscholastic League Foundation (TILF), are children of veterans, and plan to attend college in the state.

Eligibility This program is open to seniors graduating from high schools in Texas who have competed in a University Interscholastic League (UIL) academic state meet (participation in athletic or music contests does not qualify). Applicants must be the child of a veteran, rank in the top 25% of their class, and have a GPA of 2.5 or higher. They must be planning to enroll full time at a college or university in the state and major in any field. Along with their application, they must submit high school transcripts that include SAT and/or ACT scores and documentation of financial need. Preference is given to children of injured veterans.

Financial data The stipend is $2,000.

Duration 1 year; nonrenewable.

Number awarded 1 or more each year.

Deadline May of each year.

[849]
U.S. ARMY RANGER ASSOCIATION LEGACY SCHOLARSHIPS

U.S. Army Ranger Association
Attn: Scholarship Fund
P.O. Box 52126
Fort Benning, GA 31995-2126
Web: www.ranger.org/page-986310

Summary To provide financial assistance for college to descendants of members of the U.S. Army Ranger Association (USARA).

Eligibility This program is open to the unmarried children, grandchildren, and great-grandchildren of USARA members who have been regular members of USARA for at least 1 year or are deceased members. Applicants must be younger than 23 years of age and attending or planning to attend an accredited college, university, or technical school.

Financial data The stipend ranges from $1,000 to $3,000; funds are disbursed directly to the recipient's institution.

Duration 1 year.

Additional information Regular membership in USARA is open to veterans who have been awarded the Ranger Tab by the Department of the Army, or who served in a combat arms capacity in a recognized U.S. Army Ranger unit for at least 1 year, or (if less) were awarded the Combat Infantryman Badge or the Combat Medical Badge while serving in that unit.

Number awarded Varies each year; recently, 5 were awarded.

Deadline Deadline not specified.

[850]
U.S. ARMY WOMEN'S FOUNDATION LEGACY SCHOLARSHIPS

U.S. Army Women's Foundation
Attn: Scholarship Committee
P.O. Box 5030
Fort Lee, VA 23801-0030
(804) 734-3078　　　　E-mail: info@awfdn.org
Web: www.awfdn.org/programs/legacyscholarships.shtml

Summary To provide financial assistance for college or graduate school to women who are serving or have served in the Army and their children.

Eligibility This program is open to 1) women who have served or are serving honorably in the U.S. Army, U.S. Army Reserve, or Army National Guard; and 2) children of women who served honorably in the U.S. Army, U.S. Army Reserve, or Army National Guard. Applicants must be 1) high school graduates or GED recipients enrolled at a community college or technical certificate program who have a GPA of 2.5 or higher; 2) sophomores or higher at an accredited college or university who have a GPA of 3.0 or higher; or 3) students enrolled in or accepted to a graduate program who have a GPA of 3.0 or higher. Along with their application, they must submit a 2-page essay on why they should be considered for this scholarship, their future plans as related to their program of study, and information about their community service, activities, and work experience. Selection is based on merit, academic potential, community service, and financial need.

Financial data The stipend is $2,500 for college and graduate students or $1,000 for community college and certificate students.

Duration 1 year.

Number awarded 5 to 10 each year.

Deadline January of each year.

[851]
U.S. "UDIE" GRANT SCHOLARSHIP FUND

Sons of the American Legion
Detachment of Kansas
c/o American Legion Department of Kansas
1314 S.W. Topeka Boulevard
Topeka, KS 66612-1886
(785) 232-9315　　　　Fax: (785) 232-1399
Web: www.kssal.org/pages/education-scholarships

Summary To provide financial assistance for college to members of the Kansas Sons of the American Legion and their children and grandchildren.

Eligibility This program is open to high school seniors, college undergraduates, and adults holding high school diplomas and/or college credits who are attending or planning to attend an approved Kansas college, university, junior college, or trade school. Applicants must be a member of the Sons of the American Legion of the Detachment of Kansas or the child or grandchild of a member for at least the past 3 consecutive years. Along with their application, they must submit an essay of up to 500 words on their goals in life and why they want to attend college. Financial need is also considered in the selection process.

Financial data   The stipend is $1,000.

Duration   1 year; nonrenewable.

Number awarded   1 each year.

Deadline   February of each year.

[852]
USMCCCA SCHOLARSHIPS

United States Marine Corps Combat Correspondents
   Association
Attn: Executive Director
110 Fox Court
Wildwood, FL 34785
(352) 748-4698   E-mail: usmccca@cfl.rr.com
Web: www.usmccca.org/archives/4941

Summary   To provide financial assistance to members of the U.S. Marine Corps Combat Correspondents Association (USMCCCA) or their dependents and Marines in designated occupational fields who are interested in studying communications in college.

Eligibility   This program is open to 1) members of USMCCCA, their dependents, and their spouses; and 2) active-duty Marines in Occupational Fields 4300 and 4600 and their dependents who are USMCCCA members or will agree to become members if awarded a scholarship. Applicants must be enrolled or planning to enroll in an undergraduate program in communications. Along with their application, they must submit 500-word essays on 1) their noteworthy achievements and long-range goals; and 2) "the United States I want to see in 15 years and my role in the transformation." Financial need is not considered in the selection process.

Financial data   Stipends range up to $3,000; funds are disbursed directly to the recipient's institution to be used exclusively for tuition, books, and/or fees.

Duration   1 year.

Number awarded   1 or more each year.

Deadline   May of each year.

[853]
USO DESERT STORM EDUCATION FUND

USO World Headquarters
Attn: Scholarship Program
Washington Navy Yard, Building 198
901 M Street, S.E.
Washington, DC 20374
(202) 610-5700   Fax: (202) 610-5699
Web: www.desert-storm.com/soldiers/uso.html

Summary   To provide financial assistance for academic or vocational education to spouses and children of military personnel who died in the Persian Gulf War.

Eligibility   This program is open to the spouses and children of armed service personnel killed, either through accidental causes or in combat, during Operations Desert Shield and Desert Storm. Department of Defense guidelines will be

used to determine those service personnel who were taking part in either of these operations at the time of their deaths. This is an entitlement program; neither financial need nor academic achievement are factors in allocating support from the fund. All eligible candidates are contacted directly.

Financial data   It is the purpose of the fund to provide as much financial support as possible to all eligible persons. To this end, USO will distribute all of the funds to the eligible persons in equal amounts.

Duration   There will be a 1-time distribution of these funds.

Number awarded   All eligible survivors will receive funding.

Deadline   Deadline not specified.

[854]
USS AMERICA CARRIER VETERANS ASSOCIATION MERIT SCHOLARSHIP

USS America Carrier CVA, Inc.
Attn: Scholarship Coordinator
P.O. Box 1239
Hopewell Junction, NY 12533
Toll Free: (888) 391-CV66
E-mail: daydream@irvineonline.net
Web: www.ussamerica.org/Default.aspx?pageId=1786790

Summary   To provide financial assistance for college to high school seniors who are descendants of members of the USS America Carrier Veterans Association.

Eligibility   This program is open to graduating high school seniors who are children or grandchildren of members of the association who served aboard the USS America. Applicants must have a high school GPA of 2.5 or higher. They must be planning to attend a 2- or 4-year college, university, or trade school. Along with their application, they must submit SAT and/or ACT results, transcripts, 3 personal references, and an essay of 150 to 250 words on a current event or a patriotic theme.

Financial data   The stipend is $1,000.

Duration   1 year.

Number awarded   1 each year.

Deadline   May of each year.

[855]
USS CORAL SEA REMEMBRANCE SCHOLARSHIPS

USS Coral Sea CVA-43 Association
c/o Jon Lickey, Scholarship Chair
2321 North Delaware Street
Peoria, IL 61603-2645
(309) 688-3939   E-mail: jjlickey47@yahoo.com
Web: www.usscoralsea.org/scholarship.php

Summary   To provide financial assistance for college to descendants of members of the USS Coral Sea CVA-43 Association.

Eligibility   This program is open to children, grandchildren, and great-grandchildren of 1) association members in good standing; 2) deceased members in good standing at the time of death; and 3) non-members who were killed in the line of duty while serving aboard the USS Coral Sea, or were captured as a prisoner of war, or were injured in the line of duty. Applicants must be high school seniors who have a GPA of 3.0 or higher and are planning to enroll at an accredited 2- or 4-year college, university, or vocational/technical school.

Along with their application, they must submit an essay of 800 to 1,000 words on their choice of 3 assigned topics.
Financial data Stipends are $2,000 or $500.
Duration 1 year.
Additional information This program began in 2002.
Number awarded 2 each year: 1 at $2,000 and 1 at $500.
Deadline March of each year.

[856]
USS ENTERPRISE (CVAN/CVN-65) ASSOCIATION SCHOLARSHIPS

USS Enterprise (CVAN/CVN-65) Association
c/o Donald Thiry, Scholarship Chair
26831 Coachlight
Woodhaven, MI 48183
E-mail: donthiry@gmail.com
Web: www.cvan-cvn-65.org

Summary To provide financial assistance for college to dependents of members of the USS Enterprise (CVAN/CVN-65) Association.
Eligibility This program is open to dependents of members of the association who are enrolled or planning to enroll at a college or university. Applicants must submit an essay of 100 to 250 words on why they feel they deserve this scholarship. Selection is based on that essay, SAT or ACT scores, transcripts, and recommendations.
Financial data The stipend is $1,000.
Duration 1 year.
Number awarded 2 each year.
Deadline Deadline not specified.

[857]
USS KITTY HAWK (CV/CVA-63) VETERAN'S ASSOCIATION SCHOLARSHIPS

USS Kitty Hawk (CV/CVA-63) Veteran's Association
c/o Richard Orth, Scholarship Committee Chair
300 Town Line Road
Eitzen, MN 55931
(507) 495-3291   E-mail: orth@acegroup.cc
Web: www.kittyhawkvets.com/SCHOLARSHIPS.html

Summary To provide financial assistance for college to the children and grandchildren of members of the USS Kitty Hawk (CV/CVA-63) Veteran's Association.
Eligibility This program is open to the children and grandchildren of members of the association or deceased members. Applicants must be graduating high school seniors or students currently enrolled full or part time at a college, university, or technical/trade school. Along with their application, they must submit an essay of 500 to 750 words on their obligation to the United States. Financial need is not considered in the selection process.
Financial data The stipend is $1,000.
Duration 1 year.
Number awarded 3 each year.
Deadline April of each year.

[858]
USS LITTLE ROCK ASSOCIATION NROTC SCHOLARSHIP PROGRAM

USS Little Rock Association
c/o LCDR Robert M. Baker, USN (Retired), Scholarship
   Committee Chair
18426 Mount Lock Hill Road
Sharpsburg, MD 21782-2029
(301) 799-9089   E-mail: rmbusnret@gmail.com
Web: www.usslittlerock.org/scholarship.html

Summary To provide financial assistance to Naval ROTC midshipmen in college who have a personal or family connection to the sea services or are members of the USS Little Rock Association.
Eligibility This program is open to students entering their third academic year of an NROTC program (scholarship, college program, Marine Enlisted Commissioning Program, or Seaman to Admiral). Applicants must 1) be the children or direct descendants of active, retired, or honorably discharged members of the sea services (U.S. Navy, U.S. Marine Corps, or U.S. Coast Guard) or their Reserve components; 2) themselves be serving or have served in any of the regular or Reserve sea services; or 3) have been Junior Associate members of the USS Little Rock Association for at least 2 years. They must have a GPA of 3.0 or higher and have demonstrated superior leadership qualities and aptitude for service in all of their NROTC activities. Along with their application, they must submit a 500-word letter describing why they consider themselves worthy of the award.
Financial data The stipend is $1,000 per year.
Duration 1 year; may be renewed 1 additional year.
Additional information This program began in 2001.
Number awarded 1 or 2 each year.
Deadline May of each year.

[859]
USS LITTLE ROCK ASSOCIATION SCHOLARSHIP PROGRAM FOR DESCENDANTS OF MEMBERS

USS Little Rock Association
c/o Frank E. Berglas, Secretary
63 Barnes Road
Stamford, CT 06902-1201
(203) 355-9314   E-mail: fberglas@optonline.net
Web: www.usslittlerock.org/ScholarshipCallForApps.html

Summary To provide financial assistance for college to descendants of members of the USS Little Rock Association.
Eligibility This program is open to full-time students who have completed the second year of an accredited 4-year program leading to a bachelor's degree. Applicants must be a direct descendant (child, grandchild, or great-grandchild) of a USS Little Rock veteran who is an active association member. They must have a GPA of 3.0 or higher. Along with their application, they must submit a 500-word letter describing why they consider themselves worthy of the award. Selection is based on academic achievement and motivation.
Financial data The stipend is $1,000 per year.
Duration 1 year; may be renewed 1 additional year.
Additional information This program began in 2007.
Number awarded 1 or 2 each year.
Deadline May of each year.

[860]
USS PITTSBURGH FUND

Pittsburgh Foundation
Attn: Scholarship Coordinator
Five PPG Place, Suite 250
Pittsburgh, PA 15222-5414
(412) 391-5122   Fax: (412) 391-7259
E-mail: turnerd@pghfdn.org
Web: www.pittsburghfoundation.org/node/1725

Summary   To provide financial assistance for college to students with ties to the USS Pittsburgh.

Eligibility   This program is open to past and present crewmembers and dependents of crewmembers of the USS Pittsburgh. Applicants must be attending or planning to attend an institution of higher education to major in engineering or other "hard" science. Along with their application, they must submit a resume, a statement of why the scholarship is desired, 2 letters of reference, and transcripts.

Financial data   The stipend is $2,500.

Duration   1 year.

Additional information   This program was established by the Pittsburgh Council of the Navy League of the United States.

Number awarded   3 each year.

Deadline   April of each year.

[861]
USS THEODORE ROOSEVELT SCHOLARSHIP

Wings Over America Scholarship Foundation
Attn: Scholarship Administrator
4966 Euclid Road, Suite 109
Virginia Beach, VA 23462
(757) 671-3200, ext. 117
E-mail: scholarship@wingsoveramerica.us
Web: wingsoveramerica.us

Summary   To provide financial assistance for college to dependents of Navy personnel who are serving or have served on the USS Theodore Roosevelt.

Eligibility   This program is open to 1) children of a military sponsor who are graduating high school seniors planning to enroll in college full time to work on a bachelor's degree or who are already enrolled in such a program; and 2) spouses of a military sponsor currently enrolled full or part time and working on an associate or bachelor's degree at an accredited college or university. Children must be unmarried and younger than 22 years of age. The military sponsor must have served or be currently serving aboard USS Theodore Roosevelt (ship's company, not air wing) and be currently on active duty, honorably discharged, retired, or deceased. Also eligible are children of members of the U.S. Navy who died while on active duty serving with a Naval air force unit, regardless of the length of service of the deceased parent. Selection is based on academic proficiency, extracurricular activities, community contributions, and life experience and character of the applicant.

Financial data   A stipend is awarded (amount not specified).

Duration   1 year.

Additional information   This program began in 2013.

Number awarded   1 each year.

Deadline   Pre-qualification forms must be submitted by January of each year.

[862]
**USS YORKTOWN CV-10 ASSOCIATION
SCHOLARSHIP PROGRAM**

USS Yorktown CV-10 Association
P.O. Box 1021
Mount Pleasant, SC 29465
(843) 881-5925
Web: www.ussyorktown.net

Summary   To provide financial assistance for college in any state to descendants of crew members of the USS Yorktown and to high school seniors in the tri-county area of Charleston, South Carolina.

Eligibility   This program is open to 1) direct descendants of crew members who served on the USS Yorktown CV-10, CVA-10, or CVS-10 from 1943 to 1970 who are high school seniors, graduates, or current undergraduates; and 2) seniors graduating from high schools in Berkeley, Charleston, or Dorchester counties in South Carolina. Applicants must be enrolled or planning to enroll full time at an accredited 2- or 4-year college, university, or vocational/technical school in any state. They must be U.S. citizens and have a GPA of 3.0 or higher. Selection is based on academic record, demonstrated leadership and participation in school and community activities, honors, work experience, a statement of goals and aspirations, unusual personal or family circumstances, an outside appraisal, and financial need.

Financial data   The stipend is $1,250 per year.

Duration   1 year; may be renewed up to 3 additional years, provided the recipient remains enrolled full time and maintains a cumulative GPA of 3.0 or higher.

Additional information   This program, which began in 2013, is administered by Scholarship Management Services, a division of Scholarship America.

Number awarded   2 each year: 1 to a descendant of a Yorktown crew member and 1 to a resident of South Carolina.

Deadline   February of each year.

[863]
USSVI SCHOLARSHIPS

United States Submarine Veterans, Inc.
Attn: National Scholarship Committee Chair
30 Surrey Lane
Norwich, CT 06360-6541
(860) 889-4750   E-mail: hogan343@aol.com
Web: www.ussvi.org/charitable.asp

Summary   To provide financial assistance for college to the children and grandchildren of members of the United States Submarine Veterans, Inc. (USSVI).

Eligibility   This program is open to children and grandchildren of USSVI members who are high school seniors planning to attend college or already enrolled as college students. Applicants must be unmarried and under 21 years of age (or 23 if currently enrolled in a full-time course of study). Along with their application, they must submit a 400-word essay on why they should be awarded a scholarship and how they would use it. Selection is based on that essay, academic achievement, extracurricular activities, personal recommendations, and financial need.

Financial data   Stipends vary; recently, they were $1,500, $1,250, or $950.

Duration   1 year.

Number awarded Varies each year; recently, 18 were awarded: 2 at $1,500, 6 at $1,250, and 10 at $950.

Deadline April of each year.

[864]
UTAH ASMC CHAPTER SCHOLARSHIPS

American Society of Military Comptrollers-Utah Chapter
c/o Donna Parada, Scholarship Chair
AFLCMC/LZPED
6020 Gum Lane, Building 1218
Hill AFB, UT 84056
(801) 586-4908   E-mail: Donna.Parada@us.af.mil
Web: chapters.asmconline.org/utah/category/scholarships

Summary To provide financial assistance to members of the Utah Chapter of the American Society of Military Comptrollers (ASMC) and their families who are interested in studying any field at a college in any state.

Eligibility This program is open to members of the ASMC Utah Chapter, their spouses, and their dependents. Applicants must be attending or planning to attend a college or university in any state and work on a degree in any field. Along with their application, they must submit 3 essays, up to 150 words each, on 1) their extracurricular activities; 2) their leadership skills, abilities, opportunities, and experiences; and 3) their involvement in and service to their neighborhood, community, church, or other organizations. Selection is based on the information in those essays (10 points each), GPA (30 points), ACT/SAT scores (10 points), difficulty of classes (20 points), a personal letter on their educational and career goals (5 points), and reference letters (5 points).

Financial data The stipend is $1,000.

Duration 1 year.

Additional information The ASMC is open to all financial management professionals employed by the U.S. Department of Defense and Coast Guard, both civilian and military.

Number awarded Varies each year; recently, 4 were awarded.

Deadline April of each year.

[865]
VADM ROBERT L. WALTERS SCHOLARSHIP

Surface Navy Association
Attn: Scholarship Coordinator
6551 Loisdale Court, Suite 222
Springfield, VA 22150
(703) 960-6800   Toll Free: (800) NAVY-SNA
Fax: (703) 960-6807   E-mail: navysna@aol.com
Web: www.navysna.org

Summary To provide financial assistance for college or graduate school to dependents of members of the Surface Navy Association (SNA).

Eligibility This program is open to the children, stepchildren, wards, and spouses of SNA members. The SNA member must 1) be in the second or subsequent consecutive year of membership; 2) be serving, retired, or honorably discharged; 3) be a Surface Warfare Officer or Enlisted Surface Warfare Specialist; and 4) have served for at least 3 years on a surface ship of the U.S. Navy or Coast Guard. Applicants must be enrolled or planning to enroll full time at an accredited undergraduate or graduate institution; the full-time requirement may be waived for spouses. Along with their application, they must submit a 500-word essay about them-

selves and why they should be selected to receive this scholarship. High school seniors should also include a transcript of high school grades and a copy of ACT or SAT scores. Current college students should also include a transcript of the grades from their most recent 4 semesters of school. Selection is based on academic proficiency, non-scholastic activities, scholastic and non-scholastic awards, character, and financial need.

Financial data The stipend is $2,000 per year.

Duration 4 years, provided the recipient maintains a GPA of 3.0 or higher.

Number awarded Varies each year.

Deadline February of each year.

[866]
VAW/VRC MERIT SCHOLARSHIPS

VAW/VRC Officers' Spouses' Association
Attn: VAW/VRC Memorial Scholarship Fund
P.O. Box 15322
Norfolk, VA 23511-0322
(757) 463-7604
E-mail: admin@vaw-vrc-memorialfund.org
Web: www.vaw-vrc-memorialfund.org/Scholarship.html

Summary To provide financial assistance for college to spouses and children of current and former members of the Navy VAR/VRC community.

Eligibility This program is open to students entering or continuing at a college or university who are the spouses or college-age children of current or former Navy personnel. The spouse or parent of the supplicant must be serving or have served in a Carrier Airborne Early Warning Squadron (VAW) or a Fleet Logistics Support Squadron (VRC). Selection is based entirely on merit.

Financial data Stipends are $7,000 or $3,000.

Duration 1 year; may be renewed 1 additional year.

Additional information This program includes the Captain Ed Caffrey Merit Scholarship and the First Command Merit Scholarship, sponsored by the First Command Educational Foundation.

Number awarded Varies each year; recently, 9 were awarded: 1 at $7,000 and 8 at $3,000.

Deadline April of each year.

[867]
VETERANS UNITED FOUNDATION SCHOLARSHIPS

Veterans United Home Loans
Attn: Veterans United Foundation
1400 Veterans United Drive
Columbia, MO 65203
(573) 445-7999   Toll Free: (800) 884-5560
E-mail: customer_service@vu.com
Web: www.enhancelives.com/scholarships

Summary To provide financial assistance for college or graduate school to students who have a tie to the military.

Eligibility This program is open to 1) active-duty military personnel with plans to attend college; 2) honorably-discharged veterans of the U.S. military; 3) spouses of military members or veterans; 4) surviving spouses and children of fallen servicemembers; and 5) children of veterans or active-duty military. Applicants must be attending or planning to attend college as a full-time undergraduate or graduate student. They must have a GPA of 2.5 or higher. Selection is based primarily on an essay.

Financial data   The stipend is $2,000.

Duration   1 year.

Additional information   This program began in 2007.

Number awarded   Up to 20 each year: 10 each term.

Deadline   April or October of each year.

[868]
VICE ADMIRAL E.P. TRAVERS LOAN PROGRAM

Navy-Marine Corps Relief Society
Attn: Education Division
875 North Randolph Street, Suite 225
Arlington, VA 22203-1757
(703) 696-4960   Fax: (703) 696-0144
E-mail: education@nmcrs.org
Web: www.nmcrs.org

Summary   To provide interest-free loans for college to the spouses and children of Navy and Marine Corps personnel.

Eligibility   This program is open to the dependent children of active-duty and retired Navy and Marine Corps personnel (including Reservists while on active duty over 90 days) and the spouses of active-duty Navy and Marine Corps personnel. Applicants must have a GPA of 2.0 or higher and be able to demonstrate financial need. They must be enrolled or planning to enroll as a full-time undergraduate student at an accredited college, university, or vocational/technical school.

Financial data   The loan amount is determined on the basis of need, from $500 to $3,000 per academic year. No interest is charged on the money borrowed. The loan must be repaid within 24 months by allotment of pay, at a monthly rate of at least $50.

Number awarded   Varies each year.

Deadline   April of each year.

[869]
VIETNAM VETERANS GROUP OF SAN QUENTIN SCHOLARSHIPS

Vietnam Veterans Group of San Quentin
c/o Lt. R. Luna, Chief Sponsor
San Quentin State Prison
1 Main Street
San Quentin, CA 94964
(415) 454-1460, ext. 5808   Fax: (415) 455-4113
Web: vvgsq.tripod.com

Summary   To provide financial assistance to high school seniors in California who are interested in attending college in any state and are children of current or former members of the U.S. armed forces.

Eligibility   This program is open to graduating high school seniors in California who plan to attend a college or university in any state. Applicants must have a parent or legal guardian who is currently serving in the armed forces or has been honorably discharged. Along with their application, they must submit an essay, up to 250 words in length, on the effect their parent's military service has had on their life. The Mary Manley Inspirational Award may be presented for an exceptionally inspiring essay. Financial need is not considered in the selection process.

Financial data   The scholarship stipend is $1,500. The Mary Manley Inspirational Award, if presented, is an additional $750.

Duration   1 year.

Additional information   Membership in the sponsoring organization consists of Vietnam veterans who are currently incarcerated at San Quentin State Prison. Awards are presented at the annual scholarship banquet at the prison. Winners are allowed to bring up to 6 guests to accompany them for the presentation of the scholarships.

Number awarded   Up to 3 each year.

Deadline   May of each year.

[870]
VII CORPS DESERT STORM VETERANS ASSOCIATION SCHOLARSHIP

VII Corps Desert Storm Veterans Association
Attn: Scholarship Committee
Army Historical Foundation
2425 Wilson Boulevard
Arlington, VA 22201
(703) 978-6867   E-mail: viicorpsdsva@aol.com
Web: www.desertstormvets.org/scholarships

Summary   To provide financial assistance for college to students who served, or are the spouses or other family members of individuals who served, with VII Corps in Operations Desert Shield, Desert Storm, or related activities.

Eligibility   Applicants must have served, or be a family member of those who served, with VII Corps in Operations Desert Shield/Desert Storm, Provide Comfort, or 1 of the support base activities. Scholarships are limited to students entering or enrolled in accredited technical institutions (trade or specialty), 2-year colleges, and 4-year colleges or universities. Awards will not be made to individuals receiving military academy appointments or full 4-year scholarships. Letters of recommendation and a transcript are required. Selection is not based solely on academic standing; consideration is also given to extracurricular activities and other self-development skills and abilities obtained through on-the-job training or correspondence courses. Priority is given to survivors of VII Corps soldiers who died during Operations Desert Shield/Desert Storm or Provide Comfort, veterans who are also members of the VII Corps Desert Storm Veterans Association, and family members of veterans who are also members of the VII Corps Desert Storm Veterans Association.

Financial data   The stipend ranges from $1,000 to $5,000 per year. Funds are paid to the recipients upon proof of admission or registration at an accredited institution, college, or university.

Duration   1 year; recipients may reapply.

Additional information   This program began in 1998.

Number awarded   Approximately 3 each year; since this program began, it has awarded more than $250,000 in scholarships.

Deadline   January of each year.

[871]
VIRGIN ISLAND NATIONAL GUARD GRANTS

Virgin Islands Board of Education
60B, 61, and 62 Dronningens Gade
P.O. Box 11900
St. Thomas, VI 00801
(340) 774-4546   Fax: (340) 774-3384
E-mail: stt@myviboe.com
Web: www.myviboe.com/Special-Legislative.html

Summary To provide financial assistance to the children of deceased or disabled members of the Virgin Islands National Guard who wish to attend a college in the territory or on the mainland.

Eligibility This program is open to children under 25 years of age of members of the National Guard of the Virgin Islands who have died or sustained permanent and total disability in the line of official duty while on territorial active military duty, federal active duty, or training duty. Applicants must have a GPA of 2.0 or higher and be attending or accepted for enrollment at an accredited institution of higher learning in the territory or on the mainland. They may be planning to major in any field. Financial need is considered in the selection process.

Financial data The stipend is $2,000 per year.

Duration 1 year; may be renewed up to 3 additional years.

Additional information This program is offered as part of the Special Legislative Grants of the Virgin Islands Board of Education.

Number awarded 1 or more each year.

Deadline April of each year.

[872]
VIRGINIA DIVISION GIFT SCHOLARSHIPS

United Daughters of the Confederacy-Virginia Division
c/o Patt Graves, Second Vice President
838 Crymes Road
Keysville, VA 23947-2815
(434) 696-2202   E-mail: thebargthree@aol.com
Web: www.vaudc.org

Summary To provide financial assistance to Confederate descendants from Virginia who are interested in attending college in the state.

Eligibility This program is open to residents of Virginia who are 1) lineal descendants of Confederates; or 2) collateral descendants and also members of the Children of the Confederacy or the United Daughters of the Confederacy. Applicants must submit proof of the Confederate military record of at least 1 ancestor, with the company and regiment in which he served. They must also submit a personal letter pledging to make the best possible use of the scholarship; describing their health, social, family, religious, and fraternal connections within the community; and reflecting on what a Southern heritage means to them (using the term "War Between the States" in lieu of "Civil War"). They must have a GPA of 3.0 or higher and be able to demonstrate financial need.

Financial data The amount of the stipend depends on the availability of funds. Payment is made directly to the college or university the recipient attends.

Duration 1 year; may be renewed up to 3 additional years if the recipient maintains a GPA of 3.0 or higher.

Additional information This program includes the following named scholarships: the Mary Custis Lee Memorial Scholarship, the Matthew Fontaine Maury Scholarship, the Catherine Custis Taylor Goffigan Scholarship, the Rives Cosby Ford Memorial Scholarship, the Margaret Hart Barnes Memorial Scholarship, the Martha Anthony Scholarship, and the Jennie Gunn Ball Scholarship.

Number awarded These scholarships are offered whenever a prior recipient graduates or is no longer eligible.

Deadline April of years in which any of the scholarships are available.

[873]
VIRGINIA MILITARY SURVIVORS AND DEPENDENTS EDUCATION PROGRAM

Virginia Department of Veterans Services
Attn: VMSDEP Administrator
900 East Main Street
Richmond, VA 23219
(804) 225-2083   Fax: (804) 786-0809
E-mail: melek.sanchez@dvs.virginia.gov
Web: www.dvs.virginia.gov/vmsdep.shtml

Summary To provide educational assistance to the children and spouses of disabled and other Virginia veterans or service personnel.

Eligibility This program is open to residents of Virginia whose parent or spouse served in the U.S. armed forces (including the Reserves, the Virginia National Guard, or the Virginia National Guard Reserves) during any armed conflict subsequent to December 6, 1941, as a result of a terrorist act, during military operations against terrorism, or on a peacekeeping mission. The veterans must have been killed, be missing in action, have been taken prisoner of war, or become at least 90% disabled as a result of such service. Applicants must have been accepted at a public college or university in Virginia as an undergraduate or graduate student. Children must be between 16 and 29 years of age; there are no age restrictions for spouses. The veteran must have been a resident of Virginia at the time of entry into active military service or for at least 5 consecutive years immediately prior to the date of application or death. Surviving spouses must have been residents of Virginia for at least 5 years prior to marrying the veteran or for at least 5 years immediately prior to the date on which the application was submitted.

Financial data The program provides 1) waiver of tuition and all required fees at public institutions of higher education in Virginia; and 2) a stipend (amount not specified) to offset the costs of room, board, books, and supplies at those institutions.

Duration Entitlement extends to a maximum of 36 months (4 years).

Additional information Individuals entitled to this benefit may use it to pursue any vocational, technical, undergraduate, or graduate program of instruction. Generally, programs listed in the academic catalogs of state-supported institutions are acceptable, provided they have a clearly-defined educational objective (such as a certificate, diploma, or degree). This program was formerly known as the Virginia War Orphans Education Program.

Number awarded Varies each year; recently, funding allowed for a total of 1,000 stipends.

Deadline Applications may be submitted at any time, but they must be received at least 30 days prior to the start of the term.

[874]
VIRGINIA NATIONAL GUARD ASSOCIATION SCHOLARSHIP

Virginia National Guard Association
Attn: Scholarship Committee
11518 Hardwood Drive
Midlothian, VA 23114
(804) 350-0175
Web: www.vnga.org/scholarship.shtml

Summary To provide financial assistance to members of the Virginia National Guard Association (VNGA) and their families who are interested in attending college in any state.

Eligibility Applicants must have been enrolled at a college or university in any state for 1 year and qualify under 1 of the following conditions: 1) an officer or warrant officer in the Virginia National Guard and a VNGA member; 2) the dependent child or spouse of an officer or warrant officer in the Virginia National Guard who is a VNGA member; 3) the dependent child or spouse of a retired officer or warrant officer who is a VNGA member; 4) the dependent child or spouse of a deceased retired officer or warrant officer; or 5) the dependent child or spouse of a Virginia National Guard officer or warrant officer who died while in the Virginia National Guard. Along with their application, they must submit a brief description of their educational and/or military objectives, a list of their leadership positions and honors, and a brief statement of their financial need.

Financial data A stipend is awarded; the amount is determined annually.

Duration 1 year; may be renewed for 2 additional years.

Additional information The association also offers a special scholarship in memory of CW4 William C. Singletary who, in rescuing 2 elderly women from drowning, gave his own life.

Number awarded Varies each year.

Deadline September of each year.

[875]
VIRGINIA PENINSULA POST SAME SCHOLARSHIPS

Society of American Military Engineers-Virginia Peninsula Post
c/o James H. King, Jr., Scholarship Chair
129 Andrews Street, Suite 217
Hampton, VA 23665
(757) 764-7570   Fax: (757) 764-3439
E-mail: james.king.45@us.af.mil

Summary To provide financial assistance to high school seniors, undergraduates, and graduate students entering or enrolled at universities in Virginia who have a tie to the Virginia Peninsula Post of the Society of American Military Engineers (SAME) and are majoring in engineering or architecture.

Eligibility This program is open to 1) high school seniors planning to enroll in an engineering or architecture program at an accredited college or university in Virginia; 2) students enrolled as freshmen through graduate students at an accredited college or university in Virginia and working on a bachelor's or higher degree in engineering or architecture; and 3) members and dependents of members of the SAME Virginia Peninsula Post. Applicants must have demonstrated commitment to future military service by enrolling in an ROTC program, a commissioning program, or an extended enlistment. Selection is based on academic standing and accom-

plishments (50%), involvement in university and community programs, including those with military involvement (30%), and financial need (20%).

Financial data The stipend is $1,500.

Duration 1 year.

Number awarded 4 each year: 1 to a high school senior, 1 to a college freshman or sophomore, 1 to a college junior or senior, and 1 to a graduate student.

Deadline February of each year.

[876]
WAIVERS OF NON-RESIDENT TUITION FOR DEPENDENTS OF MILITARY PERSONNEL MOVING TO TEXAS

Texas Higher Education Coordinating Board
Attn: Grants and Special Programs
1200 East Anderson Lane
P.O. Box 12788
Austin, TX 78711-2788
(512) 427-6340   Toll Free: (800) 242-3062
Fax: (512) 427-6420   E-mail: grantinfo@thecb.state.tx.us
Web: www.collegeforalltexans.com

Summary To exempt dependents of military personnel who move to Texas from the payment of non-resident tuition at public institutions of higher education in the state.

Eligibility Eligible for these waivers are the spouses and dependent children of members of the U.S. armed forces and commissioned officers of the Public Health Service who move to Texas while the servicemember remains assigned to another state. Applicants must be attending or planning to attend a public college or university in the state. They must indicate their intent to become a Texas resident. For dependent children to qualify, the spouse must also move to Texas.

Financial data Although persons eligible under this program are still classified as non-residents, they are entitled to pay the resident tuition at Texas institutions of higher education on an immediate basis.

Duration 1 year.

Additional information This program became effective in 2003.

Number awarded Varies each year.

Deadline Deadline not specified.

[877]
WAIVERS OF NON-RESIDENT TUITION FOR DEPENDENTS OF MILITARY PERSONNEL WHO PREVIOUSLY LIVED IN TEXAS

Texas Higher Education Coordinating Board
Attn: Grants and Special Programs
1200 East Anderson Lane
P.O. Box 12788
Austin, TX 78711-2788
(512) 427-6340   Toll Free: (800) 242-3062
Fax: (512) 427-6420   E-mail: grantinfo@thecb.state.tx.us
Web: www.collegeforalltexans.com

Summary To provide a partial tuition exemption to the spouses and dependent children of military personnel who are Texas residents but are not assigned to duty in the state.

Eligibility Eligible for these waivers are the spouses and dependent children of members of the U.S. armed forces who are not assigned to duty in Texas but have previously resided in the state for at least 6 months. Servicemembers must verify that they remain Texas residents by designating Texas as their place of legal residence for income tax purposes, registering to vote in the state, and doing 1 of the following: owning real property in Texas, registering an automobile in Texas, or executing a will indicating that they are a resident of the state. The spouse or dependent child must be attending or planning to attend a Texas public college or university.

Financial data Although persons eligible under this program are classified as non-residents, they are entitled to pay the resident tuition at Texas institutions of higher education, regardless of their length of residence in Texas.

Duration 1 year.

Number awarded Varies each year.

Deadline Deadline not specified.

[878]
WALTER BEALL SCHOLARSHIP

Walter Beall Scholarship Foundation
c/o W. Ralph Holcombe, Secretary/Treasurer
4911 Fennell Court
Suffolk, VA 23435
(757) 484-7403   Fax: (757) 686-5952
E-mail: info@walterbeallscholarship.org
Web: www.walterbeallscholarship.org

Summary To provide financial assistance to members of the Fleet Reserve Association (FRA) and their families who are interested in studying engineering, aeronautical engineering, or aviation in college.

Eligibility This program is open to FRA members who have been in good standing for at least the past 2 consecutive years and their spouses, children, and grandchildren. Students in a Reserve officer candidate program receiving aid or attending a military academy are not eligible. Applicants must be enrolled at an accredited college, university, or technical institution in the United States in a program related to general engineering, aviation, or aeronautical engineering. Selection is based on GPA, scholastic aptitude test scores, curriculum goals, interests, community activities, awards, and financial need. U.S. citizenship is required.

Financial data The amounts of the awards depend on the availability of funds and the need of the recipients; they range from $2,000 to $5,000.

Duration 1 year; recipients may reapply.

Additional information The Walter Beall Scholarship Foundation is sponsored by the Past Regional Presidents Club of the Fleet Reserve Association. Membership in the FRA is restricted to active-duty, retired, and Reserve members of the Navy, Marine Corps, and Coast Guard.

Number awarded 1 or more each year.

Deadline April of each year.

[879]
WALTER REED SMITH SCHOLARSHIP PROGRAM

United Daughters of the Confederacy
Attn: Second Vice President General
328 North Boulevard
Richmond, VA 23220-4008
(804) 355-1636   Fax: (804) 353-1396
E-mail: jamieretired@sbcglobal.net
Web: www.hqudc.org/Scholarships/index.htm

Summary To provide financial assistance to mature women who are lineal descendants of Confederate veterans and plan to major in selected fields in college.

Eligibility Eligible to apply for these scholarships are women over the age of 30 who are lineal descendants of worthy Confederates or collateral descendants and members of the Children of the Confederacy or the United Daughters of the Confederacy. Applicants must intend to study business administration, computer science, home economics, nutrition, or nursing. They must submit certified proof of the Confederate record of 1 ancestor, with the company and regiment in which he served, and must have had at least a 3.0 GPA in high school.

Financial data The amount of this scholarship depends on the availability of funds.

Duration 1 year; may be renewed.

Number awarded 1 each year.

Deadline April of each year.

[880]
WASHINGTON LEGION CHILDREN AND YOUTH SCHOLARSHIPS

American Legion
Department of Washington
3600 Ruddell Road S.E.
P.O. Box 3917
Lacey, WA 98509-3917
(360) 491-4373   Fax: (360) 491-7442
E-mail: administrator@walegion.org
Web: www.walegion.org/ChildrenandYouth.html

Summary To provide financial assistance to the children of members of the American Legion or American Legion Auxiliary in Washington who plan to attend college in the state.

Eligibility This program is open to sons and daughters of Washington Legionnaires or Auxiliary members, living or deceased, who are high school seniors. Applicants must be planning to attend an accredited institution of higher education, trade, or vocational school in the state of Washington. Selection is based on presentation, initiative, goals, commitment to goals, and financial need.

Financial data The stipend is $2,500 or $1,500, payable in equal amounts per semester.

Duration 1 year.

Number awarded 2 each year: 1 at $2,500 and 1 at $1,500.

Deadline March of each year.

[881]
WAVES NATIONAL COLLEGE SCHOLARSHIP

Women of the WAVES
c/o Betty Hand, Scholarship Contest Chair
5128 Sammy Street
Virginia Beach, VA 23455
(901) 568-0521   E-mail: hand.craftylady@gmail.com
Web: www.womenofthewaves.com

Summary To provide financial assistance for college or graduate school to relatives of women who served or are serving in the sea services.

Eligibility This program is open to male and female relatives (by birth, legal adoption, or marriage) of women who have served or are currently serving in the Navy, Coast Guard, or Marine Corps. Applicants must be enrolled or planning to enroll at a 2- or 4-year college, university, trade/technical school, or graduate school. They must have a GPA of 3.2 or higher. Along with their application, they must submit an essay of 1,000 to 1,500 words based on an interview with their female sea service relative on how their service changed the lives of others. Financial need is not considered in the selection process.

Financial data The stipend is $1,500.

Duration 1 year.

Number awarded 1 each year.

Deadline March of each year.

[882]
WEST VIRGINIA SONS OF THE AMERICAN LEGION SCHOLARSHIP

Sons of the American Legion
Detachment of West Virginia
2016 Kanawha Boulevard, East
P.O. Box 3191
Charleston, WV 25332-3191
(304) 343-7591   Toll Free: (888) 534-4667
Fax: (304) 343-7592
Web: www.wvsal.org

Summary To provide financial assistance to high school seniors in West Virginia who have a family link to the American Legion and are planning to attend college in the state.

Eligibility This program is open to seniors graduating from high schools in West Virginia who are the child or grandchild of a member of the American Legion, American Legion Auxiliary, or Sons of the American Legion. Applicants must be planning to attend a college or university in West Virginia. Along with their application, they must submit a 500-word essay on what democracy means to them.

Financial data The stipend is $1,000 or $500. Funds are paid directly to the students, but only after they have completed their first semester of college.

Duration 1 year; nonrenewable.

Number awarded 2 each year: 1 at $1,000 and 1 at $500.

Deadline May of each year.

[883]
WEST VIRGINIA STATE WAR ORPHANS EDUCATIONAL PROGRAM

West Virginia Department of Veteran's Assistance
Attn: Executive Secretary
1321 Plaza East, Suite 109
Charleston, WV 25301-1400
(304) 558-3661   Toll Free: (866) WV4-VETS (within WV)
Fax: (304) 558-3662 E-mail: Angela.S.Meadows@wv.gov
Web: www.veterans.wv.gov

Summary To provide financial assistance for college to the children of deceased West Virginia veterans.

Eligibility This program is open to residents of West Virginia who are children between 16 and 25 years of age of deceased veterans. The veteran must have entered service as a resident of West Virginia; served during specified periods of wartime; and died during that wartime period or, if subsequent to discharge, as a result of disability incurred in that wartime service. Applicants must be attending or planning to attend a college or university in West Virginia.

Financial data The state appropriates $5,000 per year for the educational expenses of each qualifying child or spouse.

That includes a waiver of tuition and fees at state-supported colleges and universities.

Duration 1 year; may be renewed upon reapplication if the student maintains a cumulative GPA of at least 2.0.

Number awarded Varies each year.

Deadline July of each year for the fall semester; November of each year for the spring semester.

[884]
WILLIAM BODDINGTON SCHOLARSHIP

Tenth Mountain Division Foundation, Inc.
133 South Van Gordon Street, Suite 200
Lakewood, CO 80228
(303) 756-8486   Fax: (303) 987-9489
E-mail: admin@10thmdf.ort
Web: www.10thmdf.org/scholarship.htm

Summary To provide financial assistance for college or graduate school to descendants of former members of the Tenth Mountain Division who demonstrate outstanding character.

Eligibility This program is open to the descendants of veterans who served in the Tenth Mountain Division during World War II. Applicants must have completed at least 2 years of undergraduate study at an accredited college, university, or other comparable institution or be enrolled in a graduate program. They must have a record of strong school and community service. Along with their application, they must submit an essay on how they emulate and put into practice the ideals and character traits valued by William Boddington, who served in the Division during World War II. Selection is based on that essay and financial need.

Financial data The stipend is $5,500.

Duration 1 year; nonrenewable.

Number awarded 1 each year.

Deadline April of each year.

[885]
WILLIAM P. O'CONNELL MEMORIAL VETERANS REHABILITATION SCHOLARSHIP

Sons of the American Legion
Detachment of New York
112 State Street, Suite 1300
Albany, NY 12207
(518) 463-2215   Fax: (518) 427-8443
E-mail: info@nylegion.org
Web: www.sonsdny.org

Summary To provide financial assistance to high school seniors and graduates in New York who are have been active in veterans rehabilitation activities of the Sons of the American Legion and plan to attend college in any state.

Eligibility This program is open to members of the Sons of the American Legion in New York who have been active in its veterans rehabilitation activities. Applicants must be high school seniors or graduates and planning to attend college or trade school in any state. Along with their application, they must submit a 200-word essay either on why a college education is important to them or why they want to continue their postsecondary education in a business trade school. Selection is based on academics (25%), character (25%), community service (25%), and participation in veterans rehabilitation activities (25%).

Financial data The stipend is $1,000.

Duration 1 year.
Number awarded 1 each year.
Deadline April of each year.

[886]
WILMA D. HOYAL/MAXINE CHILTON SCHOLARSHIPS

American Legion Auxiliary
Department of Arizona
4701 North 19th Avenue, Suite 100
Phoenix, AZ 85015-3727
(602) 241-1080   Fax: (602) 604-9640
E-mail: secretary@aladeptaz.org
Web: www.aladeptaz.org/Scholarships.html

Summary To provide financial assistance to veterans, the dependents of veterans, and other students who are majoring in selected subjects at Arizona public universities.

Eligibility This program is open to second-year or upper-division full-time students majoring in political science, public programs, or special education at public universities in Arizona (the University of Arizona, Northern Arizona University, or Arizona State University). Applicants must have been Arizona residents for at least 1 year. They must have a GPA of 3.0 or higher. U.S. citizenship is required. Honorably-discharged veterans and immediate family members of veterans receive preference. Selection is based on scholarship (25%), financial need (40%), character (20%), and leadership (15%).

Financial data The stipend is $1,000.

Duration 1 year; renewable.

Number awarded 3 each year: 1 to each of the 3 universities.

Deadline May of each year.

[887]
WINGS OVER AMERICA SCHOLARSHIPS

Wings Over America Scholarship Foundation
Attn: Scholarship Administrator
4966 Euclid Road, Suite 109
Virginia Beach, VA 23462
(757) 671-3200, ext. 117
E-mail: scholarship@wingsoveramerica.us
Web: www.wingsoveramerica.us/application

Summary To provide financial assistance for college to dependents of naval aviators.

Eligibility This program is open to 1) children of a military sponsor who are graduating high school seniors planning to enroll in college full time to work on a bachelor's degree or who are already enrolled in such a program; and 2) spouses of a military sponsor currently enrolled full or part time and working on an associate or bachelor's degree at an accredited college or university. Children must be unmarried and younger than 22 years of age. The military sponsor must have completed at least 8 years of active-duty service in a Naval air force or subordinate command and be currently on active duty, honorably discharged, retired, or deceased. Also eligible are children of members of the U.S. Navy who died while on active duty serving with a Naval air force unit, regardless of the length of service of the deceased parent. Selection is based on academic proficiency, extracurricular activities, community contributions, and life experience and character of the applicant. The highest ranked applicant receives the CAPT Neil Kinnear Scholarship.

Financial data The CAPT Neil Kinnear Scholarship is $3,000 per year. Other stipend amounts depend on the availability of funds.

Duration 1 year; may be renewed.

Additional information This program began in 1987.

Number awarded Varies each year; recently, 48 were awarded. Since the program was established, it has awarded more than $640,000 in scholarships.

Deadline Pre-qualification forms must be submitted by January of each year.

[888]
WINNIE C. DAVIS CHILDREN OF THE CONFEDERACY SCHOLARSHIP

United Daughters of the Confederacy
Attn: Second Vice President General
328 North Boulevard
Richmond, VA 23220-4008
(804) 355-1636   Fax: (804) 353-1396
E-mail: jamieretired@sbcglobal.net
Web: www.hqudc.org/Scholarships/index.htm

Summary To provide financial assistance for college to lineal descendants of Confederate veterans who are members of the Children of the Confederacy.

Eligibility Eligible to apply for these scholarships are lineal descendants of worthy Confederates or collateral descendants. Applicants must submit a family financial report and certified proof of the Confederate record of 1 ancestor, with the company and regiment in which he served. In addition, applicants themselves must be, or have been until age 18, participating members of the Children of the Confederacy. They must have at least a 3.0 GPA in high school.

Financial data The amount of this scholarship depends on the availability of funds.

Duration 1 year; may be renewed for up to 3 additional years.

Additional information Members of the same family may not hold scholarships simultaneously, and only 1 application per family will be accepted within any 1 year. All requests for applications must be accompanied by a self-addressed stamped envelope.

Number awarded 1 each year.

Deadline April of each year.

[889]
WISCONSIN EAGLE SCOUT OF THE YEAR SCHOLARSHIP

American Legion
Department of Wisconsin
2930 American Legion Drive
P.O. Box 388
Portage, WI 53901-0388
(608) 745-1090   Fax: (608) 745-0179
E-mail: info@wilegion.org
Web: www.wilegion.org

Summary To recognize and reward, with scholarships for college in any state, Eagle Scouts who are members of a troop associated with the American Legion in Wisconsin or a son or grandson of a member of the Legion in the state.

Eligibility The Wisconsin nominee for American Legion Scout of the Year receives this scholarship. Applicants must be 1) a registered, active members of a Boy Scout Troop, Varsity Scout Team, or Explorer Post chartered to an American Legion Post in Wisconsin or Auxiliary Unit in Wisconsin; or 2) a registered, active member of a Boy Scout Troop, Varsity Scout Team, or Venturing Crew and the son or grandson of an American Legion or Auxiliary member. They must have received the Eagle Scout award; be an active member of their religious institution and have received the appropriate Boy Scout religious emblem; have demonstrated practical citizenship in church, school, Scouting, and community; have reached their 15th birthday; be enrolled in high school; and be planning to attend college in any state.

Financial data The award is a $1,000 scholarship.

Duration The award is presented annually.

Number awarded 1 each year.

Deadline February of each year.

[890]
WISCONSIN G.I. BILL TUITION REMISSION PROGRAM

Wisconsin Department of Veterans Affairs
201 West Washington Avenue
P.O. Box 7843
Madison, WI 53707-7843
(608) 266-1311   Toll Free: (800) WIS-VETS
Fax: (608) 267-0403   E-mail: WDVAInfo@dva.state.wi.us
Web: www.dva.state.wi.us/Ben-Education.asp

Summary To provide financial assistance for college or graduate school to Wisconsin veterans and their dependents.

Eligibility This program is open to current residents of Wisconsin who 1) were residents of the state when they entered or reentered active duty in the U.S. armed forces; or 2) have moved to the state and have been residents for at least 5 consecutive years after entry or reentry into service. Applicants must have served on active duty for at least 2 continuous years or for at least 90 days during specified wartime periods. Also eligible are 1) qualifying children and unremarried surviving spouses of Wisconsin veterans who died in the line of duty or as the direct result of a service-connected disability; and 2) children and spouses of Wisconsin veterans who have a service-connected disability rated by the U.S. Department of Veterans Affairs as 30% or greater. Children must be between 17 and 25 years of age (regardless of the date of the veteran's death or initial disability rating) and be a Wisconsin resident for tuition purposes. Spouses remain eligible for 10 years following the date of the veteran's death or initial disability rating; they must be Wisconsin residents for tuition purposes but they may enroll full or part time. Students may attend any institution, center, or school within the University of Wisconsin (UW) System or the Wisconsin Technical College System (WCTS). There are no income limits, delimiting periods following military service during which the benefit must be used, or limits on the level of study (e.g., vocational, undergraduate, professional, or graduate).

Financial data Veterans who qualify as a Wisconsin resident for tuition purposes are eligible for a remission of 100% of standard academic fees and segregated fees at a UW campus or 100% of program and material fees at a WCTS institution. Veterans who qualify as a Wisconsin veteran for purposes of this program but for other reasons fail to meet the definition of a Wisconsin resident for tuition purposes at the UW system are eligible for a remission of 100% of non-resident fees. Spouses and children of deceased or disabled vet-

erans are entitled to a remission of 100% of tuition and fees at a UW or WCTS institution.

Duration Up to 8 semesters or 128 credits, whichever is greater.

Additional information This program began in 2005 as a replacement for Wisconsin Tuition and Fee Reimbursement Grants.

Number awarded Varies each year.

Deadline Applications must be submitted within 14 days from the office start of the academic term: in October for fall, March for spring, or June for summer.

[891]
WISCONSIN JOB RETRAINING GRANTS

Wisconsin Department of Veterans Affairs
201 West Washington Avenue
P.O. Box 7843
Madison, WI 53707-7843
(608) 266-1311   Toll Free: (800) WIS-VETS
Fax: (608) 267-0403   E-mail: WDVAInfo@dva.state.wi.us
Web: www.dva.state.wi.us/Ben-Retraininggrants.asp

Summary To provide funds to recently unemployed Wisconsin veterans or their families who need financial assistance while being retrained for employment.

Eligibility This program is open to current residents of Wisconsin who 1) were residents of the state when they entered or reentered active duty in the U.S. armed forces; or 2) have moved to the state and have been residents for any consecutive 12-month period after entry or reentry into service. Applicants must have served on active duty for at least 2 continuous years or for at least 90 days during specified wartime periods. Unremarried spouses and minor or dependent children of deceased veterans who would have been eligible for the grant if they were living today may also be eligible. The applicant must, within the year prior to the date of application, have become unemployed (involuntarily laid off or discharged, not due to willful misconduct) or underemployed (experienced an involuntary reduction of income). Underemployed applicants must have current annual income from employment that does not exceed federal poverty guidelines (currently $11,490 for a family of 1, rising to $39,630 for a family of 8). All applicants must be retraining at accredited schools in Wisconsin or in a structured on-the-job program. Course work toward a college degree does not qualify. Training does not have to be full time, but the program must be completed within 2 years and must reasonably be expected to lead to employment.

Financial data The maximum grant is $3,000 per year; the actual amount varies, depending upon the amount of the applicant's unmet need. In addition to books, fees, and tuition, the funds may be used for living expenses.

Duration 1 year; may be renewed 1 additional year.

Number awarded Varies each year.

Deadline Applications may be submitted at any time.

[892]
WISCONSIN LEGION AUXILIARY DEPARTMENT PRESIDENT'S SCHOLARSHIP

American Legion Auxiliary
Department of Wisconsin
Attn: Education Chair
2930 American Legion Drive
P.O. Box 140
Portage, WI 53901-0140
(608) 745-0124   Toll Free: (866) 664-3863
Fax: (608) 745-1947   E-mail: alawi@amlegionauxwi.org
Web: www.amlegionauxwi.org/Scholarships.htm

Summary To provide financial assistance to Wisconsin residents who are members or children of members of the American Legion Auxiliary and interested in attending college in any state.

Eligibility This program is open to members and children of members of the American Legion Auxiliary in Wisconsin. Applicants must be high school seniors or graduates and attending or planning to attend a college or university in any state. They must have a GPA of 3.5 or higher and be able to demonstrate financial need. Along with their application, they must submit a 300-word essay on "Education—An Investment in the Future."

Financial data The stipend is $1,000.

Duration 1 year.

Number awarded 3 each year.

Deadline March of each year.

[893]
WISCONSIN LEGION AUXILIARY MERIT AND MEMORIAL SCHOLARSHIPS

American Legion Auxiliary
Department of Wisconsin
Attn: Education Chair
2930 American Legion Drive
P.O. Box 140
Portage, WI 53901-0140
(608) 745-0124   Toll Free: (866) 664-3863
Fax: (608) 745-1947   E-mail: alawi@amlegionauxwi.org
Web: www.amlegionauxwi.org/Scholarships.htm

Summary To provide financial assistance to Wisconsin residents who are related to veterans or members of the American Legion Auxiliary and interested in working on an undergraduate degree at a school in any state.

Eligibility This program is open to the children, wives, and widow(er)s of veterans who are high school seniors or graduates and have a GPA of 3.5 or higher. Grandchildren and great-grandchildren of members of the American Legion Auxiliary are also eligible. Applicants must be residents of Wisconsin and interested in working on an undergraduate degree at a school in any state. Along with their application, they must submit a 300-word essay on "Education—An Investment in the Future." Financial need is considered in the selection process.

Financial data The stipend is $1,000.

Duration 1 year; nonrenewable.

Additional information This program includes the following named scholarships: the Harriet Hass Scholarship, the Adalin Macauley Scholarship, the Eleanor Smith Scholarship, the Pearl Behrend Scholarship, the Barbara Kranig Scholarship, and the Jan Pulvermacher-Ryan Scholarship.

Number awarded 7 each year.

Deadline March of each year.

[894]
WISCONSIN LEGION AUXILIARY PAST PRESIDENTS PARLEY HEALTH CAREER SCHOLARSHIPS

American Legion Auxiliary
Department of Wisconsin
Attn: Education Chair
2930 American Legion Drive
P.O. Box 140
Portage, WI 53901-0140
(608) 745-0124   Toll Free: (866) 664-3863
Fax: (608) 745-1947   E-mail: alawi@amlegionauxwi.org
Web: www.amlegionauxwi.org/Scholarships.htm

Summary To provide financial assistance for health-related education at a school in any state to the dependents and descendants of veterans in Wisconsin.

Eligibility This program is open to the children, wives, and widow(er)s of veterans who are attending or entering a hospital, university, or technical school in any state to prepare for a health-related career. Grandchildren and great-grandchildren of American Legion Auxiliary members are also eligible.. Applicants must be residents of Wisconsin and have a GPA of 3.5 or higher. Along with their application, they must submit a 300-word essay on "The Importance of Health Careers Today." Financial need is considered in the selection process.

Financial data The stipend is $1,000.

Duration 1 year; nonrenewable.

Number awarded 2 each year.

Deadline March of each year.

[895]
WISCONSIN LEGION AUXILIARY PAST PRESIDENTS PARLEY REGISTERED NURSE SCHOLARSHIPS

American Legion Auxiliary
Department of Wisconsin
Attn: Education Chair
2930 American Legion Drive
P.O. Box 140
Portage, WI 53901-0140
(608) 745-0124   Toll Free: (866) 664-3863
Fax: (608) 745-1947   E-mail: alawi@amlegionauxwi.org
Web: www.amlegionauxwi.org/Scholarships.htm

Summary To provide financial assistance to the dependents and descendants of Wisconsin veterans who are interested in studying nursing at a school in any state.

Eligibility This program is open to the wives, widow(er)s, and children of Wisconsin veterans who are enrolled or have been accepted in an accredited school of nursing in any state to prepare for a career as a registered nurse. Grandchildren and great-grandchildren of American Legion Auxiliary members are also eligible. Applicants must be Wisconsin residents and have a GPA of 3.5 or higher. Along with their application, they must submit a 300-word essay on "The Need for Trained Nurses Today." Financial need is considered in the selection process.

Financial data The stipend is $1,000.

Duration 1 year.

Number awarded 2 each year.
Deadline March of each year.

[896]
WISCONSIN NATIONAL GUARD ENLISTED ASSOCIATION AUXILIARY SCHOLARSHIP PROGRAM

Wisconsin National Guard Enlisted Association Auxiliary
c/o Barbara Sedgwick, WNGEA Auxiliary Chair
N63 W15393 Pontiac Drive
Menomonee Falls, WI 53051
Web: www.wngea.org/aboutus/abus-xsch.htm

Summary To provide financial assistance for college to members of the Wisconsin National Guard Enlisted Association (WNGEA) Auxiliary and to their spouses and children.
Eligibility This program is open to WNGEA Auxiliary members, the unmarried dependent children, stepchildren, grandchildren, and step-grandchildren of WNGEA Auxiliary members, and the spouses of WNGEA Auxiliary members. Dependents must be 25 years of age or younger. The sponsor must have been an Auxiliary member for at least 2 years. Applicants must be enrolled full time at a college, university, trade school, or business school in any state; graduate students are not eligible. Selection is based on academic achievement, financial need, leadership, and moral character.
Financial data A stipend is awarded (amount not specified).
Duration 1 year; nonrenewable.
Number awarded 1 each year.
Deadline August of each year.

[897]
WISCONSIN NATIONAL GUARD ENLISTED ASSOCIATION COLLEGE GRANT PROGRAM

Wisconsin National Guard Enlisted Association
Attn: Executive Director
2400 Wright Street
Madison, WI 53704-2572
(608) 242-3112   E-mail: WNGEA@yahoo.com
Web: www.wngea.org/extrasforyou/exfy-scho.htm

Summary To provide financial assistance to members of the Wisconsin National Guard Enlisted Association (WNGEA) and their spouses and children who are interested in attending college or graduate school in any state.
Eligibility This program is open to WNGEA members, the unmarried children and spouses of WNGEA members, and the unmarried children and spouses of deceased WNGEA members. WNGEA member applicants, as well as the parents or guardians of unmarried children who are applicants, must have at least 1 year remaining on their enlistment following completion of the school year for which application is submitted (or they must have 20 or more years of service). Applicants must be enrolled full or part time at a college, university, graduate school, trade school, or business school in any state. Selection is based on financial need, leadership, and moral character.
Financial data Stipends are $1,000 or $500 per year.
Duration 1 year; recipients may not reapply for 2 years.
Additional information This program includes 1 scholarship sponsored by the USAA Insurance Corporation.

Number awarded Varies each year; recently, 5 were awarded: the Raymond A. Matera Scholarship at $1,000 and 4 others (1 reserved for a graduate student) at $500 each.
Deadline April of each year.

[898]
WISCONSIN SONS OF THE AMERICAN LEGION SCHOLARSHIP

Sons of the American Legion
Detachment of Wisconsin
P.O. Box 388
Portage, WI 53901
(608) 745-1090   E-mail: adjutant@wisal.org
Web: www.wisal.org

Summary To provide financial assistance to members of the Wisconsin Detachment of the Sons of the American Legion (SAL) who plan to attend college in any state.
Eligibility This program is open to members of the SAL in Wisconsin who are seniors in high school or within 1 year of graduation from high school. Applicants must have at least 3 years of consecutive membership. They must be planning to attend a 4-year college or university or a 2-year technical school in any state. Along with their application, they must submit a 100-word essay on their educational objectives, the life's work for which they desire to prepare by attending college, and the value and contribution this scholarship would make toward the realization of those goals. Selection is based on that essay, academic record, contributions to school and community, SAL involvement, and financial need.
Financial data The stipend is $1,000, paid directly to the school.
Duration 1 year.
Number awarded 1 each year.
Deadline March of each year.

[899]
WOMEN MARINES ASSOCIATION SCHOLARSHIP PROGRAM

Women Marines Association
P.O. Box 377
Oaks, PA 19456-0377
Toll Free: (888) 525-1943
E-mail: scholarship@womenmarines.org
Web: www.womenmarines.org

Summary To provide financial assistance for college or graduate school to students with ties to the military who are sponsored by members of the Women Marines Association (WMA).
Eligibility Applicants must be sponsored by a WMA member and fall into 1 of the following categories: 1) have served or are serving in the U.S. Marine Corps, regular or Reserve; 2) are a direct descendant by blood or legal adoption or a stepchild of a Marine on active duty or who has served honorably in the U.S. Marine Corps, regular or Reserve; 3) are a sibling or a descendant of a sibling by blood or legal adoption or a stepchild of a Marine on active duty or who has served honorably in the U.S. Marine Corps, regular or Reserve; or 4) have completed 2 years in a Marine Corps JROTC program. WMA members may sponsor an unlimited number of applicants per year. High school seniors must submit transcripts (GPA of 3.0 or higher) and SAT or ACT scores. Undergraduate and graduate students must have a GPA of 3.0 or higher.

Financial data Stipends are $1,500 or $3,000 per year.

Duration 1 year; may be renewed 1 additional year.

Additional information This program includes the following named scholarships: the WMA Memorial Scholarships, the Lily H. Gridley Memorial Scholarship, the Ethyl and Armin Wiebke Memorial Scholarship, the Maj. Megan Malia McClung Memorial Scholarship, the Agnes Sopcak Memorial Scholarship, the Virginia Guveyan Memorial Scholarship, and the LaRue A. Ditmore Music Scholarships. Applicants must know a WMA member to serve as their sponsor; the WMA will not supply listings of the names or addresses of chapters or individual members.

Number awarded Varies each year.

Deadline January of each year.

[900]
WOMEN'S ARMY CORPS VETERANS' ASSOCIATION SCHOLARSHIP

Women's Army Corps Veterans' Association
P.O. Box 663
Weaver, AL 36277
(256) 820-6824　　　E-mail: info@armywomen.org
Web: www.armywomen.org/pdf/_10ScholarApp.pdf

Summary To provide financial assistance for college to the relatives of Army military women.

Eligibility This program is open to high school seniors who are the children, grandchildren, nieces, or nephews of Army service women. Applicants must have a cumulative GPA of 3.5 or higher and be planning to enroll full time at an accredited college or university in the United States. They must submit a 500-word biographical sketch that includes their future goals and how the scholarship would be used. Selection is based on academic achievement, leadership ability as expressed through co-curricular activities and community involvement, the biographical sketch, and recommendations. Financial need is not considered. U.S. citizenship is required.

Financial data The stipend is $1,500.

Duration 1 year.

Number awarded 1 or more each year.

Deadline April of each year.

[901]
WORLD WAR II ILLINOIS DESCENDANTS SCHOLARSHIP

Community Foundation for the Land of Lincoln
Attn: Scholarship Coordinator
205 South Fifth Street, Suite 930
Springfield, IL 62701
(217) 789-4431　　　Fax: (217) 789-4635
E-mail: scholarships@CFLL.org
Web: www.cfll.org

Summary To provide financial assistance to high school seniors in Illinois who are the direct descendant of a veteran of World War II and plan to attend college in any state.

Eligibility This program is open to seniors graduating from high schools in Illinois who are the direct descendant (i.e., grandchild or great-grandchild, but not a great niece or nephew) of an Illinois veteran of World War II. Applicants must be planning to enroll full time at an accredited community college or 4-year college or university in any state. They must have an unweighted GPA of 4.0 or be projected to be the valedictorian or salutatorian of their class.

Financial data The stipend is $2,000.

Duration 1 year.

Number awarded 2 each year.

Deadline February of each year.

[902]
WYOMING COMBAT VETERAN SURVIVING ORPHAN TUITION BENEFIT

Wyoming Community College Commission
Attn: Veterans Tuition Benefit
2300 Capitol Avenue, Fifth Floor, Suite B
Cheyenne, WY 82002
(307) 777-7763　　　Fax: (307) 777-6567
Web: www.communitycolleges.wy.edu

Summary To provide financial assistance to children of deceased, POW, or MIA Wyoming veterans who are interested in attending college in the state.

Eligibility This program is open to children of veterans whose parent had been a resident of Wyoming for at least 1 year at the time of entering service and received the armed forces expeditionary medal or a campaign medal for service in an armed conflict in a foreign country. The veteran parent must 1) have died during active service in an armed conflict in a foreign country; 2) be listed officially as being a POW or MIA as a result of active service with the military forces of the United States; or 3) have been honorably discharged from the military and subsequently died of an injury or disease incurred while in service and was a Wyoming resident at the time of death. Applicants must have been younger than 21 years of age when the veteran died or was listed as POW or MIA and must apply within 3 years of the graduation date of their high school class. They must be attending or planning to attend the University of Wyoming or a community college in the state while they are still younger than 22 years of age.

Financial data Qualifying veterans' children are eligible for free resident tuition at the University of Wyoming or at any of the state's community colleges.

Duration Up to 10 semesters, provided the recipient maintains a GPA of 2.0 or higher.

Additional information This program began in 2006. The Wyoming Community College Commission was tasked to implement the benefit and reimburse the University of Wyoming and the community colleges in the state.

Number awarded Varies each year.

Deadline Applications may be submitted at any time, but they should be received 2 or 3 weeks before the beginning of the semester.

[903]
WYOMING COMBAT VETERAN SURVIVING SPOUSE TUITION BENEFIT

Wyoming Community College Commission
Attn: Veterans Tuition Benefit
2300 Capitol Avenue, Fifth Floor, Suite B
Cheyenne, WY 82002
(307) 777-7763　　　Fax: (307) 777-6567
Web: www.communitycolleges.wy.edu

Summary To provide financial assistance to surviving spouses of deceased, POW, or MIA Wyoming veterans who are interested in attending college in the state.

Eligibility This program is open to spouses of veterans whose spouse had been a resident of Wyoming for at least 1 year at the time of entering service and received the armed forces expeditionary medal or a campaign medal for service in an armed conflict in a foreign country. The veteran spouse must 1) have died during active service during armed conflict in a foreign country; 2) be listed officially as being a POW or MIA as a result of active service with the military forces of the United States; or 3) have been honorably discharged from the military and subsequently died of an injury or disease incurred while in service and was a Wyoming resident at the time of death. Applicants must enroll at the University of Wyoming or a community college in the state within 10 years following the death of the combat veteran.

Financial data   Qualifying veterans' spouses are eligible for free resident tuition at the University of Wyoming or at any of the state's community colleges.

Duration   Up to 10 semesters, provided the recipient maintains a GPA of 2.0 or higher.

Additional information   This program began in 2006. The Wyoming Community College Commission was tasked to implement the benefit and reimburse the University of Wyoming and the community colleges in the state.

Number awarded   Varies each year.

Deadline   Applications may be submitted at any time, but they should be received 2 or 3 weeks before the beginning of the semester.

[904]
WYOMING NATIONAL GUARD ASSOCIATION SCHOLARSHIPS

Wyoming National Guard Association
c/o Laura Jeffrey
P.O. Box 2615
Cheyenne, WY 82003-2615
(307) 214-3114   E-mail: buckinhorses@gmail.com
Web: www.wynga.org/scholarships

Summary   To provide financial assistance to members of the Wyoming National Guard Association (WYNGA) and their families who are interested in attending college in any state.

Eligibility   This program is open to enlisted and officer members of the WYNGA and their spouses and unmarried children. Applicants must be attending or planning to attend an accredited institution of higher education in any state. Along with their application, they must submit a cover letter that includes information on their educational career goals, their need for this scholarship, their family involvement in WYNGA, and a list of awards, honors, extracurricular activities, and organizations in which they have participated.

Financial data   A stipend is awarded (amount not specified).

Duration   1 year.

Additional information   This program includes the following named scholarships: the MG Charles J. Wing Family Program Scholarship, the Mrs. Beverly Holmes Scholarship, the Wyoming Army National Guard Combined Club Scholarship, and the USAA Insurance Corporation Scholarship.

Number awarded   Varies each year; recently, 7 were awarded.

Deadline   February of each year.

[905]
WYOMING VIETNAM VETERAN SURVIVING CHILD TUITION BENEFIT

Wyoming Community College Commission
Attn: Veterans Tuition Benefit
2300 Capitol Avenue, Fifth Floor, Suite B
Cheyenne, WY 82002
(307) 777-7763   Fax: (307) 777-6567
Web: www.communitycolleges.wy.edu

Summary   To provide financial assistance to children of deceased, POW, or MIA Wyoming veterans of the Vietnam era who are interested in attending college in the state.

Eligibility   This program is open to children of veterans whose parent had been a resident of Wyoming for at least 1 year at the time of entering service, served between August 5, 1964 and May 7, 1975, and received the Vietnam service medal. The veteran parent must 1) have died as a result of service-connected causes; 2) be listed officially as being a POW or MIA as a result of active service with the military forces of the United States; or 3) have been honorably discharged from the military and subsequently died of an injury or disease incurred while in service and was a Wyoming resident at the time of death. Applicants must be attending or planning to attend the University of Wyoming or a community college in the state.

Financial data   Qualifying veterans' children are eligible for free resident tuition at the University of Wyoming or at any of the state's community colleges.

Duration   Up to 10 semesters, provided the recipient maintains a GPA of 2.0 or higher.

Additional information   This program began in 2006 and was amended in 2007 to include Vietnam veterans. The Wyoming Community College Commission was tasked to implement the benefit and reimburse the University of Wyoming and the community colleges in the state.

Number awarded   Varies each year.

Deadline   Applications may be submitted at any time, but they should be received 2 or 3 weeks before the beginning of the semester.

[906]
WYOMING VIETNAM VETERAN SURVIVING SPOUSE TUITION BENEFIT

Wyoming Community College Commission
Attn: Veterans Tuition Benefit
2300 Capitol Avenue, Fifth Floor, Suite B
Cheyenne, WY 82002
(307) 777-7763   Fax: (307) 777-6567
Web: www.communitycolleges.wy.edu

Summary   To provide financial assistance to surviving spouses of deceased, POW, or MIA Wyoming veterans of the Vietnam era who are interested in attending college in the state.

Eligibility   This program is open to spouses of veterans whose spouse had been a resident of Wyoming for at least 1 year at the time of entering service, served between August 5, 1964 and May 7, 1975, and received the Vietnam service medal. The veteran spouse must 1) have died as a result of service-connected causes; 2) be listed officially as being a POW or MIA as a result of active service with the military forces of the United States; or 3) have been honorably discharged from the military and subsequently died of an injury or disease incurred while in service and was a Wyoming resident at the time of death. Applicants must be attending or planning to attend the University of Wyoming or a community college in the state.

Financial data Qualifying veterans' surviving spouses are eligible for free resident tuition at the University of Wyoming or at any of the state's community colleges.

Duration Up to 10 semesters, provided the recipient maintains a GPA of 2.0 or higher.

Additional information This program began in 2006 and was amended in 2007 to include Vietnam veterans. The Wyoming Community College Commission was tasked to implement the benefit and reimburse the University of Wyoming and the community colleges in the state.

Number awarded Varies each year.

Deadline Applications may be submitted at any time, but they should be received 2 or 3 weeks before the beginning of the semester.

[907]
YELLOW RIBBON PROGRAM OF THE POST-9/11 GI BILL

Department of Veterans Affairs
Attn: Veterans Benefits Administration
810 Vermont Avenue, N.W.
Washington, DC 20420
(202) 418-4343   Toll Free: (888) GI-BILL1
Web: www.benefits.va.gov/gibill/yellow_ribbon.asp

Summary To provide financial assistance to veterans and their dependents who qualify for the Post-9/11 GI Bill and wish to attend a high cost private or out-of-state public institution.

Eligibility Maximum Post-9/11 GI Bill benefits are available to veterans who 1) served on active duty for at least 36 aggregate months after September 11, 2001; or 2) were honorably discharged for a service-connected disability and served at least 30 continuous days after September 11, 2001. Military personnel currently on active duty and their spouses may qualify for Post-9/11 GI Bill benefits but are not eligible for the Yellow Ribbon Program. This program is available to veterans who qualify for those benefits at the 100% rate, the children of those veterans to whom they wish to transfer their benefits, and the children and spouses of active-duty personnel who qualify for benefits at the 100% rate to whom they wish to transfer those benefits. Applicants must be working on or planning to work on an undergraduate or graduate degree at a private or out-of-state public institution that charges tuition in excess of the $20,235.02 cap imposed by the Post-9/11 GI Bill and that has agreed with the Department of Veterans Affairs (VA) to participate in this program.

Financial data Colleges and universities that charge more than $20,235.02 per academic year in tuition and fees agree to waive tuition (up to 50%) for qualifying veterans and dependents. The amount that the college or university waives is matched by VA.

Duration Most participants receive up to 36 months of entitlement under this program. Benefits are payable for up to 15 years following release from active duty.

Number awarded Varies each year.

Deadline Deadline not specified.

Graduate Studies

Military Personnel ●

ROTC Students ●

Military Family Members ●

Described here are 229 programs available to 1) military personnel, 2) ROTC students, and 3) military family members (spouses, children, grandchildren, parents, and other relatives with family ties to the military) who are or will be pursuing graduate study for a master's, doctoral, or other professional degree in the United States. Of these listings, 110 are available to military personnel, 10 to ROTC students, and 109 to military family members. If you are looking for a particular program and don't find it in this section, be sure to check the Program Title Index to see if it is covered elsewhere in the directory.

Military Personnel

[908]
ADVANCED CIVIL SCHOOLING PROGRAM

U.S. Army
Human Resources Command
Attn: OPCF ACS Program
1500 Spearhead Division Avenue
Fort Knox, KY 40122-5408
Toll Free: (800) 872-8272
E-mail: usarmy.knox.hrc.mbx.tagd-pdeei@mail.mil
Web: myarmybenefits.us.army.mil

Summary To provide financial assistance to Army officers interested in working on an advanced degree in selected fields.

Eligibility This program is open to Army officers who wish to work on an advanced degree at an approved civilian institution on a full-time basis. Applicants must have a regular Army commission or a United States Army Reserve (USAR) commission with Voluntary Indefinite Status (VI) and less than 17 years of active federal service. They must have completed a bachelor's degree with a GPA of 2.5 or higher and must have a GRE score of 153 or higher in verbal reasoning, 144 or higher in quantitative reasoning, and 4.0 or higher in the analytical category. Applicants for management-related degrees must have at least 500 on the GMAT.

Financial data The officer continues to receive regular Army salary and allowances. The fellowship pays tuition up to $14,500 per year, a 1-time payment of $600 for application fees, and a book allotment of $200 per year.

Duration 12 to 22 months, depending on the program.

Additional information Participants in this program incur an additional service obligation of 3 days of service for each day of educational leave. Further information and applications are available from the applicant's assignment officer.

Number awarded Approximately 412 each year.

Deadline September of each year.

[909]
AFCEA NOVA SCHOLARSHIPS

Armed Forces Communications and Electronics
  Association-Northern Virginia Chapter
Attn: Scholarship Chair
400 North Washington Street, Suite 300
Alexandria, VA 22314
(703) 778-4645   Fax: (703) 683-5480
E-mail: scholarships@afceanova.org
Web: www.afceanova.org/scholarships

Summary To provide financial assistance for undergraduate and graduate study in fields of science, technology, engineering, or mathematics (STEM) to military and civilian personnel affiliated with the Northern Virginia chapter of the Armed Forces Communications and Electronics Association (AFCEA NOVA).

Eligibility This program is open to residents of the greater Washington, D.C. area and to members of AFCEA NOVA and their children who live elsewhere. Applicants must be U.S. government service employees or military personnel (enlisted or junior grade officers) or their offspring; veterans are also given consideration. Applicants must be working on an undergraduate or graduate degree in a field of STEM (including information technology, computer science, and other technology fields supportive of national security). Selection is based on merit, although financial need and past and current military and government service may also be considered. U.S. citizenship is required.

Financial data The stipend is $2,000 for full-time students or $1,000 for part-time students.

Duration 1 year.

Additional information The greater Washington area is defined to include the District of Columbia; the Maryland counties of Calvert, Charles, Frederick, Montgomery, and Prince George's; the Virginia cities of Alexandria, Fairfax, Falls Church, Fredericksburg, Manassas, and Manassas Park; the Virginia counties of Arlington, Clarke, Culpeper, Fairfax, Fauquier, King George, Loudoun, Prince William, Spotsylvania, Stafford, and Warren; and the West Virginia counties of Berkeley and Jefferson.

Number awarded More than 30 each year.

Deadline February of each year.

[910]
AIR FORCE HEALTH PROFESSIONS SCHOLARSHIP PROGRAM

U.S. Air Force
Attn: Air Force Institute of Technology
2950 P Street, Building 642
Wright-Patterson AFB, OH 45433-7765
(937) 255-5824, ext. 3036   Toll Free: (800) 588-5260
Fax: (937) 656-7156   E-mail: afit.cimj3@afit.edu
Web: www.airforce.com/opportunities/healthcare/education

Summary To provide financial assistance for education in a medical or scientific field to future Air Force medical officers.

Eligibility This program is open to U.S. citizens who are accepted to or already enrolled in a health care professional program. They must be working on a degree that will prepare them for service in Air Force Biomedical Science Corps specialties (pharmacists, optometrists, clinical psychologists, or public health officers), Nurse Corps specialties, Medical Corps, or Dental Corps. Upon acceptance into the program, applicants are commissioned as officers in the U.S. Air Force; after completion of medical school, they must perform at least 3 years of active-duty service in the U.S. Air Force.

Financial data This program pays full tuition at any school of medicine or osteopathy located in the United States or Puerto Rico, and it also covers the cost of fees, books, and other required equipment. In addition, recipients are awarded a stipend of $2,157 per month for 10 1/2 months of the year; for the other 1 1/2 months of each year, they perform active-duty service, usually at an Air Force medical facility, and receive the normal pay of a Second Lieutenant.

Duration 1 or 2 years for Biomedical Service Corps specialties, 2 or 3 years for Nurse Corps specialties, 3 or 4 years for Medical Corps or Dental Corps.

Additional information Following receipt of the degree, students serve an internship and residency either in an Air Force hospital (in which case they receive Air Force active-duty pay) or, if not selected for Air Force graduate medical education, in a civilian hospital (where they receive only the regular salary paid by the civilian institution). Only after completion of the residency, in either an Air Force or a civilian hospital, do the students begin the active-duty service obligation. That obligation is equal to the number of years of support received plus 1 year.

Number awarded Approximately 325 each year.

Deadline Deadline not specified.

[911]
AIR FORCE JUDGE ADVOCATE GENERAL'S DEPARTMENT FUNDED LEGAL EDUCATION PROGRAM

U.S. Air Force
Attn: HQ USAF/JAX
1500 West Perimeter Road, Suite 3330
Joint Base Andrews, MD 20762
Toll Free: (800) JAG-USAF
E-mail: afsana.ahmed@pentagon.af.mil
Web: www.airforce.com

Summary To provide financial assistance to Air Force officers interested in attending law school.

Eligibility This program is open to commissioned officers in the U.S. Air Force who have at least 2 but no more than 6 years of active-duty military service (including both enlisted and commissioned time) and have graduated from an accredited college or university with a bachelor's degree. Applicants must be currently in the pay grade of O-3 or below. They must submit transcripts from undergraduate (and/or graduate) schools, their LSAT results, and proof of an application or acceptance to an ABA-accredited law school.

Financial data Selectees continue to receive their regular pay and allowances during participation in this program. They also receive payment of tuition (to a maximum of $12,000 per year) and a book allowance.

Duration Until completion of a law degree.

Additional information Selectees are required to perform legal internships each summer they are in law school. Following completion of law school and passage of a bar examination, they enter service as an Air Force judge advocate with an active-duty obligation of 2 years for each year of legal training supported by this program.

Number awarded Varies each year; recently, 8 officers received support from this program.

Deadline February of each year.

[912]
AIR FORCE RESERVE TUITION ASSISTANCE

U.S. Air Force Reserve
Attn: Air Reserve Personnel Center
Directorate of Personnel Services
18420 East Silver Creek Avenue, Building 390, MS68
Buckley AFB, CO 80011
(303) 676-7037   Toll Free: (800) 525-0102
Fax: (478) 327-2215
E-mail: arpc.contactcenter@arpc.denver.af.mil
Web: www.arpc.afrc.af.mil

Summary To provide financial assistance for college or graduate school to members of the Air Force Reserve.

Eligibility This program is open to Air Force Reserve members interested in working on an undergraduate or graduate degree either through distance learning or on-campus courses from an accredited postsecondary institution. Applicants must be actively participating (for pay and points) and in good standing (not have a UIF, not placed on a control roster,

not pending or issued an Article 15, and/or not pending court martial). They must submit a degree plan specifying all classes for which they are seeking assistance. Enlisted students must have retainability that extends beyond the last course approved for assistance or they must extend or re-enlist; commissioned officers must have a mandatory separation date of not less than 48 months of service commitment starting at the end of the last course completed.

Financial data Airmen receive 100% of tuition for undergraduate or graduate study, to a maximum of $250 per semester hour or $4,500 per year.

Duration 1 year; may be renewed.

Number awarded Varies each year.

Deadline Applications may be submitted at any time.

[913]
AIR FORCE SERVICES CLUB MEMBERSHIP SCHOLARSHIP PROGRAM

Air Force Services Agency
Attn: HQ AFPC/SVOFT
10100 Reunion Place, Suite 501
San Antonio, TX 78216-4138
(210) 395-7351   E-mail: clubs@myairforcelife.com
Web: www.myairforcelife.com/Clubs/Scholarship.aspx

Summary To recognize and reward, with funding for undergraduate or graduate studies, Air Force Club members and their families who submit outstanding essays.

Eligibility This program is open to Air Force Club members and their spouses, children, and stepchildren who have been accepted by or are enrolled at an accredited college or university. Grandchildren are eligible if they are the dependent of a club member. Applicants may be undergraduate or graduate students enrolled full or part time. They must submit an essay of up to 500 words on a topic that changes annually; a recent topic was "My Contribution to the Air Force." Applicants must also include a 1-page summary of their long-term career and life goals and previous accomplishments, including civic, athletic, and academic awards.

Financial data Awards are $1,000 scholarships. Each winner also receives a laptop computer.

Duration The competition is held annually.

Additional information This competition, first held in 1997, is sponsored by Chase Military Credit Card Services.

Number awarded 25 each year.

Deadline April of each year.

[914]
AIR FORCE TUITION ASSISTANCE PROGRAM

U.S. Air Force
Attn: Air Force Personnel Center
Headquarters USAF/DPPAT
550 C Street West, Suite 10
Randolph AFB, TX 78150-4712
Fax: (210) 565-2328
Web: www.airforce.com/opportunities/enlisted/education

Summary To provide financial assistance for college or graduate school to active-duty Air Force personnel.

Eligibility Eligible to apply for this program are active-duty Air Force personnel who have completed 2 years of their service obligation.

Financial data Air Force personnel chosen for participation in this program continue to receive their regular Air Force pay. The Air Force will pay 100% of the tuition costs in an approved program, to a maximum of $4,500 per year or $250 per semester hour, whichever is less. Funding is available only for tuition, not fees or other associated expenses.

Duration Up to 4 years. Undergraduates must complete all courses with a grade of "C" or better; graduate students must complete classes with a grade of "B" of better. If recipients fail to achieve those grades, they must reimburse the Air Force for all funds received.

Additional information Applications and further information about this program are available from counselors at the education centers on Air Force bases. Most Air Force personnel who receive tuition assistance participate in the Community College of the Air Force; there, participants earn a 2-year associate degree by combining on-the-job technical training or attendance at Air Force schools with enrollment in college courses at a civilian institution during off-duty hours. In addition, each Air Force base offers at least 4 subject areas in which selected Air Force personnel can receive tuition assistance for study leading to a bachelor's degree, and 2 disciplines in which they can pursue graduate study.

Number awarded Varies each year.

Deadline Deadline not specified.

[915]
AL PONTE GRADUATE SCHOLARSHIP AWARD

Association of Former Intelligence Officers
Attn: Scholarships Committee
7700 Leesburg Pike, Suite 324
Falls Church, VA 22043
(703) 790-0320   Fax: (703) 991-1278
E-mail: scholarships@afio.com
Web: www.afio.com/13_scholarships.htm

Summary To provide financial assistance to members or the children or grandchildren of members of the Association of Former Intelligence Officers (AFIO) who are interested in working on a graduate degree in international relations and/or intelligence.

Eligibility This program is open to college seniors who are interested in attending graduate school to work on a degree in international relations and/or intelligence. Applicants must be AFIO members, the children or grandchildren of members, or the children or grandchildren of personnel currently serving in military intelligence. Selection is based on merit, character, estimated future potential, background, and relevance of their studies to the full spectrum of national security interests and career ambitions. U.S. citizenship is required.

Financial data The stipend is $1,000.

Duration 1 year.

Number awarded 1 each year.

Deadline June of each year.

[916]
ALABAMA NATIONAL GUARD EDUCATIONAL ASSISTANCE PROGRAM

Alabama Commission on Higher Education
Attn: Grants Coordinator
100 North Union Street
P.O. Box 302000
Montgomery, AL 36130-2000
(334) 242-2273   Fax: (334) 242-0268
E-mail: cheryl.newton@ache.alabama.gov
Web: www.ache.alabama.gov

Summary To provide financial assistance to members of the Alabama National Guard interested in attending college or graduate school in the state.

Eligibility This program is open to Alabama residents who are enrolled in an associate, baccalaureate, master's, or doctoral program at a public college, university, community college, technical college, or junior college in the state; are making satisfactory academic progress as determined by the eligible institution; and are members in good standing of the Alabama National Guard who have completed basic training and advanced individual training. Applicants may be receiving federal veterans benefits, but they must show a cost less aid amount of at least $25.

Financial data Scholarships cover tuition, educational fees, books, and supplies, up to a maximum of $1,000 per year. All Alabama Student Grant program proceeds for which the student is eligible are deducted from this award.

Duration Up to 12 years after the date of the first grant payment to the student through this program.

Number awarded Varies each year; recently, 653 were awarded. Awards are determined on a first-in, first-out basis as long as funds are available.

Deadline July of each year.

[917]
ALASKA NATIONAL GUARD STATE TUITION REIMBURSEMENT PROGRAM

Alaska National Guard
Attn: Education Services Office
P.O. Box 5800
Joint Base Elmendorf-Richardson, AK 99505-5800
(907) 428-6477   Fax: (907) 428-6929
E-mail: ngak-eduservicesoffice@ng.army.mil
Web: guardedu.alaska.gov

Summary To provide financial assistance to current and former members of the Alaska National Guard who wish to attend a college or university in the state.

Eligibility This program is open to members of the Alaska National Guard (Air and Army) and Naval Militia who have a rating of E-1 through O-5, including warrant officers, and are attending a university program in Alaska. Eligibility extends to members who 1) have satisfactorily completed their service contract and who served honorably in federal active service or federally-funded state active service after September 11, 2001; or 2) have been separated or discharged from the Guard because of a service-connected injury, disease, or disability. First priority is given to undergraduates; if funding is available, students working on a second bachelor's degree or a master's degree may be supported. Non-prior servicemembers must complete Initial Active Duty for Training (IADT); prior servicemembers are eligible immediately.

Financial data Recipients are entitled to reimbursement equivalent to 100% of the cost of tuition and fees at the University of Alaska, to a maximum of $7,500 per fiscal year.

Duration 1 semester; may be renewed for a total of 144 semester credits.

Number awarded Varies each year.

Deadline Applications may be submitted at any time, but they must be received at least 90 days after the last official day of the class or term.

[918]
ALOHA CHAPTER ASMC MEMBERS' CONTINUING EDUCATION PROGRAM

American Society of Military Comptrollers-Aloha Chapter
Attn: Scholarship Chair
P.O. Box 29564
Honolulu, HI 96820
(808) 473-8000, ext. 6320E-mail: mary.c.garcia@navy.mil
Web: chapters.asmconline.org/aloha/awards-4

Summary To provide financial assistance to members of the American Society of Military Comptrollers (ASMC) in Hawaii who are interested in continuing education.

Eligibility This program is open to residents of Hawaii who have been ASMC members for at least 2 consecutive years. Applicants must be interested in continuing education activities in a field of study directly related to financial resource management, including business administration, economics, public administration, accounting, or finance. Selection is based primarily on the applicant's justification of desired educational outcome.

Financial data A stipend is awarded (amount not specified).

Duration 1 year.

Additional information The ASMC is open to all financial management professionals employed by the U.S. Department of Defense and Coast Guard, both civilian and military.

Number awarded Varies each year.

Deadline March of each year.

[919]
ARMY AVIATION ASSOCIATION OF AMERICA LOAN PROGRAM

Army Aviation Association of America
Attn: AAAA Scholarship Foundation
593 Main Street
Monroe, CT 06468-2806
(203) 268-2450   Fax: (203) 268-5870
E-mail: aaaa@quad-a.org
Web: www.quad-a.org

Summary To provide educational loans to members of the Army Aviation Association of America (AAAA) and their relatives.

Eligibility This program is open to AAAA members and their spouses, unmarried siblings, and unmarried children and grandchildren. Applicants must be enrolled or accepted for enrollment as an undergraduate or graduate student at an accredited college or university.

Financial data The maximum loan is $1,000 per year. All loans are interest free.

Duration Up to 4 years.

Number awarded Varies each year; recently, 1 of these loans was granted.

Deadline April of each year.

[920]
ARMY AVIATION ASSOCIATION OF AMERICA SCHOLARSHIPS

Army Aviation Association of America Scholarship
  Foundation
Attn: AAAA Scholarship Foundation
593 Main Street
Monroe, CT 06468-2806
(203) 268-2450   Fax: (203) 268-5870
E-mail: aaaa@quad-a.org
Web: www.quad-a.org

Summary To provide financial aid for undergraduate or graduate study to members of the Army Aviation Association of America (AAAA) and their relatives.

Eligibility This program is open to AAAA members (or deceased members) and their spouses, unmarried siblings, unmarried children, and unmarried grandchildren. Applicants must be enrolled or accepted for enrollment as an undergraduate or graduate student at an accredited college or university. Graduate students must include a 250-word essay on their life experiences, work history, and aspirations. Some scholarships are specifically reserved for enlisted, warrant officer, company grade, and Department of the Army civilian members. Selection is based on academic merit and personal achievement.

Financial data Stipends range from $1,000 to $2,500 per year.

Duration Scholarships may be for 1 year, 2 years, or 4 years.

Number awarded Varies each year; recently, $363,500 in scholarships was awarded to 236 students. Since the program began in 1963, the foundation has awarded more than $4.5 million to nearly 2,700 qualified applicants.

Deadline April of each year.

[921]
ARMY HEALTH PROFESSIONS SCHOLARSHIP PROGRAM

U.S. Army
Human Resources Command, Health Services Division
Attn: AHRC-OPH-AN
1500 Spearhead Division Avenue
Fort Knox, KY 40122-5408
Toll Free: (800) 872-8272
E-mail: usarmy.knox.hrc.mbx.tagd-pdeei@mail.mil
Web: www.goarmy.com/amedd/education/hpsp.html

Summary To provide financial assistance to future Army officers who are interested in preparing for a career in medically-related fields.

Eligibility This program is open to U.S. citizens under 35 years of age. Applicants must be enrolled in or accepted as a full-time student at an accredited professional school located in the United States or Puerto Rico in 1 of the following areas: allopathic or osteopathic medicine, dentistry, clinical or counseling psychology, optometry, veterinary science, or psychiatric nurse practitioner. Upon acceptance into the program, applicants are commissioned as officers in the U.S. Army Reserve; after completion of school, they must perform active-duty service in the U.S. Army Medical Corps, Dental Corps, Medical Service Corps (for clinical psychology and optometry), Nurse Corps, or Veterinary Corps.

Financial data This program pays full tuition at any school or college granting a doctoral or other relevant professional degree located in the United States or Puerto Rico and covers the cost of fees, books, and other required equipment. Recipients are also awarded a stipend of $2,157 per month for 10 1/2 months of the year. During the other 1 1/2 months of each year, they perform active-duty service, usually at an Army medical facility, and receive the normal pay of a Second Lieutenant.

Duration 1 to 4 years for the medical program; 1 to 4 years for the dental program; 2 or 3 years for the clinical or counseling psychology program; 2 to 4 years for the optometry program; and 1 to 3 years for the veterinary program.

Additional information Participants incur an active-duty obligation based on existing Department of Defense and Army Directives in effect at the time they sign their contract accepting support through this program. Recently, the obligation has been 1 year for each year of support and a minimum of 2 years for the medical program or 3 years for the dental, clinical or counseling psychology, optometry, or veterinary programs.

Number awarded Varies each year.

Deadline Applications may be submitted at any time.

[922]
ARMY JUDGE ADVOCATE GENERAL CORPS FUNDED LEGAL EDUCATION PROGRAM

U.S. Army
Attn: Office of the Judge Advocate General
Personnel, Plans and Training Office
2200 Army Pentagon, Room 2B517
Washington, DC 20310
(703) 545-2843   Toll Free: (866) ARMY-JAG
E-mail: Yvonne.Caron@us.army.mil
Web: www.jagcnet.army.mil

Summary To provide financial assistance to Army officers interested in obtaining a law degree.

Eligibility This program is open to commissioned active-duty Army officers who have graduated from an accredited college or university with a baccalaureate (or equivalent) degree. Applicants must have completed at least 2 but not more than 6 years of active duty (including warrant officer and enlisted service) and currently hold a rank of O-1 through O-3. They must be interested in attending a regular course of instruction leading to a J.D. or LL.B. degree at an approved civilian law school. U.S. citizenship is required. Selection is based on the "total person concept," including an evaluation of undergraduate and graduate school transcripts, LSAT score, ORB, OERs, SJA interview letter, and statement of motivation to attend law school.

Financial data While participating in this program, officers continue to receive their regular Army salary. The program also covers tuition, fees, and all other educational costs.

Duration 3 years.

Additional information Participants normally are expected to attend a state-supported law school where they qualify for in-state tuition or where military members are granted in-state tuition rates. Following completion of their law degree and admission to the bar, they incur a 2-year active-duty service obligation as an attorney in the Judge Advocate General's Corps (JAGC) for each academic year spent in law school. If they fail to pass the bar examination or are not assigned to the JAGC for any other reason, they are returned to their basic branch of assignment for completion of their service obligation. If they refuse to accept appointment in or assignment to the JAGC, they are returned to their basic branch of assignment for completion of their service obligation; they must also reimburse the government for all costs of their advanced education.

Number awarded Up to 25 each year.

Deadline October of each year.

[923]
ARMY MEDICAL AND DENTAL SCHOOL STIPEND PROGRAM (MDSSP)

U.S. Army
Human Resources Command, Health Services Division
Attn: AHRC-OPH-AN
1500 Spearhead Division Avenue
Fort Knox, KY 40122-5408
Toll Free: (800) 872-8272
E-mail: usarmy.knox.hrc.mbx.tagd-pdeei@mail.mil
Web: www.goarmy.com

Summary To provide financial assistance to students in designated medically-related fields who are interested in serving in the U.S. Army Reserve after graduation.

Eligibility This program is open to U.S. citizens under 35 years of age. Applicants must be enrolled in or accepted as a full-time student at an accredited professional school located in the United States or Puerto Rico in 1 of the following areas: allopathic or osteopathic medicine, dentistry, psychology (doctoral level only), optometry, or psychiatric nurse practitioner. Upon acceptance into the program, applicants are commissioned as officers in the U.S. Army Reserve; after completion of school, they must train as part of an Army Reserve unit and serve when needed.

Financial data This program pays a stipend of $2,157 per month.

Duration Until completion of a degree.

Additional information Participants incur an obligation to serve 1 year in the Selected Reserve for each 6 months of support received, including 12 days of annual training or active duty for training.

Number awarded Varies each year.

Deadline Applications may be submitted at any time.

[924]
ARMY NATIONAL GUARD FEDERAL TUITION ASSISTANCE

U.S. Army National Guard
Education Support Center
Camp J.T. Robinson
Box 46
North Little Rock, AR 72199-9600
Toll Free: (866) 628-5999   E-mail: esc@ng.army.mil
Web: www.nationalguard.com

Summary To provide financial assistance for college or graduate school to members of the Army National Guard in each state.

Eligibility This program is open to members of the Army National Guard in every state who are interested in attending a college, community college, or university within the state. Applicants must have sufficient time to complete the course before their Expiration Time of Service (ETS) date. They must be interested in working on a high school diploma or equivalent (GED), certificate, associate degree, bachelor's degree, master's degree, or first professional degree, including those in architecture, Certified Public Accountant (C.P.A.), podiatry, dentistry (D.D.S. or D.M.D.), medicine (M.D.), optometry, osteopathic medicine, pharmacy (Pharm.D.), or theology (M.Div. or M.H.L.). Commissioned officers must agree to remain in the Guard for at least 4 years following completion of the course for which assistance is provided, unless they are involuntarily separated from the service.

Financial data Assistance provides up to 100% of tuition (to a maximum of $250 per semester hour or $4,500 per person per fiscal year).

Duration Participants in Officer Candidate School (OCS), Warrant Officer Candidate School (WOCS), and ROTC Simultaneous Membership Program (SMP) may enroll in up to 15 semester hours per year until completion of a baccalaureate degree. Warrant Officers are funded to complete an associate degree.

Additional information Tuition assistance may be used along with federal Pell Grants but not with Montgomery GI Bill benefits. State tuition assistance programs can be used concurrently with this program, but not to exceed 100% of tuition costs.

Number awarded Varies each year; recently, more than 22,000 Guard members received tuition assistance.

Deadline Deadline not specified.

[925]
ARMY NURSE CORPS ASSOCIATION SCHOLARSHIPS

Army Nurse Corps Association
Attn: Education Committee
P.O. Box 39235
San Antonio, TX 78218-1235
(210) 650-3534   Fax: (210) 650-3494
E-mail: education@e-anca.org
Web: e-anca.org/ANCAEduc.htm

Summary To provide financial assistance to students who have a connection to the Army and are interested in working on an undergraduate or graduate degree in nursing.

Eligibility This program is open to U.S. citizens attending colleges or universities that have accredited programs offering associate, bachelor's, master's, or doctoral degrees in nursing. Applicants must be 1) students currently enrolled in an accredited baccalaureate or advanced nursing or nurse anesthesia program who are serving or have served (and received an honorable discharge) in any branch and at any rank of a component of the U.S. Army; or 2) nursing or anesthesia students whose parent(s) or spouse are serving or have served in a component of the U.S. Army. Along with their application, they must submit a personal statement on their professional career objectives, reasons for applying for this scholarship, financial need, special considerations, personal and academic interests, and why they are preparing for a nursing career. Students who are receiving any support from any branch of the military, including ROTC scholarships, are not eligible.

Financial data The stipend is $3,000. Funds are sent directly to the recipient's school.

Duration 1 year.

Additional information Although the sponsoring organization is made up of current, retired, and honorably discharged officers of the Army Nurse Corps, it does not have an official affiliation with the Army. Therefore, students who receive these scholarships do not incur any military service obligation.

Number awarded 1 or more each year.

Deadline April of each year.

[926]
ARMY RESERVE TUITION ASSISTANCE

U.S. Army Reserve
Attn: Director, USAR Education
ARPC-PS
1 Reserve Way
St. Louis, MO 63132-5200
Toll Free: (800) 452-0201
Web: www.goarmyed.com

Summary To provide financial assistance for college or graduate school to specified members of the U.S. Army Reserve (USAR).

Eligibility This program is open to drilling USAR soldiers in good standing. Applicants must be working on their first bachelor's or master's degree and be able to declare an educational goal after completing 15 credit hours. Enlisted members and warrant officers must be able to complete the program under their current term of service or reenlist. Commissioned officers must have at last 4 years of remaining service obligation from the date or course completion.

Financial data Assistance is provided at the rate of $250 per credit hour, to a maximum of $4,500 per fiscal year.

Duration 1 year; may be renewed.

Number awarded Varies each year.

Deadline Applications may be submitted at any time.

[927]
ARMY SPECIALIZED TRAINING ASSISTANCE PROGRAM (STRAP)

U.S. Army National Guard
Education Support Center
Camp J.T. Robinson
Box 46
North Little Rock, AR 72199-9600
Toll Free: (866) 628-5999   E-mail: esc@ng.army.mil
Web: www.nationalguard.com

Summary To provide funding for service to members of the United States Army Reserve (USAR) or Army National Guard (ARNG) who are interested in obtaining additional training in designated health care fields that are considered critical for wartime medical needs.

Eligibility This program is open to members of the USAR or ARNG who are 1) medical residents (currently in orthopedic surgery, family practice, emergency medicine, general surgery, obstetrics/gynecology, or internal medicine); 2) dental residents (currently in general dentistry, oral surgery, prosthodontics, or comprehensive dentistry); 3) nursing students working on a master's degree (currently in community health, psychiatric nurse practitioner, or nurse anesthesia; or 4) associate degree or diploma nurses working on a bachelor's degree. Applicants must agree to a service obligation of 1 year for every 6 months of support received.

Financial data This program pays a stipend of $2,122 per month.

Duration 1 year; may be renewed.

Additional information During their obligated period of service, participants must attend Extended Combat Training (ECT) at least 12 days each year and complete the Officer Basic Leadership Course (OBLC) within the first year.

Number awarded Varies each year.

Deadline Applications may be submitted at any time.

[928]
ARMY TUITION ASSISTANCE BENEFITS

U.S. Army
Human Resources Command
AHRC-PDE-EI
Attn: Education Incentives and Counseling Branch
1500 Spearhead Division Avenue
Fort Knox, KY 40122-5408
Toll Free: (800) 872-8272
E-mail: usarmy.knox.hrc.mbx.tagd-pdeei@mail.mil
Web: www.goarmyed.com

Summary To provide financial assistance to Army personnel interested in working on an undergraduate or master's degree.

Eligibility This program is open to active-duty Army personnel, including members of the Army National Guard and Army Reserve on active duty, who have completed at least 1 year of service after graduation from AIT, OCS, or BOLC; graduate students must have completed 10 years of service. Applicants must first visit an education counselor to declare an educational goal and establish an educational plan. They may enroll in up to 16 semester hours of academic courses. Support is not provided for a second equivalent degree or for first professional degrees (e.g., Ph.D., M.D., or J.D.).

Financial data Those selected for participation in this program receive their regular Army pay and 100% of tuition at the postsecondary educational institution of their choice, but capped at $4,500 per year or $250 per semester hour, whichever is less. Funding is available only for tuition, not fees or other associated expenses.

Duration Up to 130 semester hours for completion of a bachelor's degree or up to 39 semester hours for completion of a master's degree. Undergraduates must complete all courses with a grade of "C" or better; graduate students must complete classes with a grade of "B" of better. If recipients fail to achieve those grades, they must reimburse the Army for all funds received.

Additional information This program is part of the Army Continuing Education System (ACES). Further information is available from counselors at the education centers at all Army installations with a troop strength of 750 or more. Officers incur a service obligation of 2 years for active duty or 4 years for Reserve and National Guard.

Number awarded Varies each year; recently, this program funded completion of 8,525 degree for active soldier, 1,359 for Guard soldiers, and 1,469 for Reserve soldiers.

Deadline Deadline not specified.

[929]
ASMC MEMBERS' CONTINUING EDUCATION GRANTS

American Society of Military Comptrollers
Attn: National Awards Committee
415 North Alfred Street
Alexandria, VA 22314
(703) 549-0360   Toll Free: (800) 462-5637
Fax: (703) 549-3181   E-mail: awards@asmconline.org
Web: asmc.nonprofitcms.org/a

Summary To provide financial assistance for continuing education to members of the American Society of Military Comptrollers (ASMC).

Eligibility Applicants for this assistance must have been members of the society for at least 2 full years and must have been active in the local chapter at some level (e.g., board member, committee chair or member, volunteer for chapter events), They must be enrolled or planning to enroll at an academic institution in a field of study directly related to military comptrollership, including business administration, economics, public administration, accounting, or finance. Selection is based on individual merit.

Financial data Stipends are $3,000 or $1,250.

Duration 1 year.

Additional information The ASMC is open to all financial management professionals employed by the U.S. Department of Defense and Coast Guard, both civilian and military. The applicant whose service to the society is judged the most exceptional is designated the Dick Vincent Scholarship winner.

Number awarded 11 each year: 1 at $3,000 (the Dick Vincent Scholarship) and 10 at $1,250.

Deadline March of each year.

[930]
BART LONGO MEMORIAL SCHOLARSHIPS

National Chief Petty Officers' Association
c/o Marjorie Hays, Treasurer
1014 Ronald Drive
Corpus Christi, TX 78412-3548
Web: www.goatlocker.org/ncpoa/scholarship.htm

Summary To provide financial assistance for college or graduate school to members of the National Chief Petty Officers' Association (NCPOA) and their families.

Eligibility This program is open to members of the NCPOA and the children, stepchildren, and grandchildren of living or deceased members. Applicants may be high school seniors or graduates entering a college or university or students currently enrolled full time as undergraduate or graduate students. Selection is based on academic achievement and participation in extracurricular activities; financial need is not considered.

Financial data The stipend is $1,000.

Duration 1 year.

Additional information Membership in the NCPOA is limited to men and women who served or are serving as Chief Petty Officers in the U.S. Navy, U.S. Coast Guard, or their Reserve components for at least 30 days.

Number awarded 2 each year: 1 to a high school senior or graduate and 1 to an undergraduate or graduate student.

Deadline May of each year.

[931]
BG BENJAMIN B. TALLEY SCHOLARSHIP

Society of American Military Engineers-Anchorage Post
Attn: BG B.B. Talley Scholarship Endowment Fund
P.O. Box 6409
Anchorage, AK 99506-6409
(907) 244-8063   E-mail: cturletes@gci.net
Web: www.sameanchorage.org/h_about/scholinfo.html

Summary   To provide financial assistance to student members of the Society of American Military Engineers (SAME) from Alaska who are working on a bachelor's or master's degree in designated fields of engineering or the natural sciences.

Eligibility   This program is open to members of the Anchorage Post of SAME who are residents of Alaska, attending college in Alaska, an active-duty military member stationed in Alaska, or a dependent of an active-duty military member stationed in Alaska. Applicants must be 1) sophomores, juniors, or seniors majoring in engineering, architecture, construction or project management, natural sciences, physical sciences, applied sciences, or mathematics at an accredited college or university; or 2) students working on a master's degree in those fields. They must have a GPA of 2.5 or higher. U.S. citizenship is required. Along with their application, they must submit an essay of 250 to 500 words on their career goals. Selection is based on that essay, academic achievement, participation in school and community activities, and work/family activities; financial need is not considered.

Financial data   Stipends range up to $3,000.

Duration   1 year.

Additional information   This program began in 1997.

Number awarded   Several each year; at least 1 scholarship is reserved for a master's degree students.

Deadline   December of each year.

[932]
BRAXTON BRAGG CHAPTER AUSA SCHOLARSHIPS

Association of the United States Army-Braxton Bragg
   Chapter
Attn: Vice President for Scholarships
P.O. Box 70036
Fort Bragg, NC 28307
(910) 396-3755   E-mail: hbraxtonbraggc@nc.rr.com
Web: www.braggausa.org/?page_id=1425

Summary   To provide financial assistance to members of the Braxton Bragg Chapter of the Association of the United States Army (AUSA) in North Carolina and their dependents who are interested in attending college or graduate school in any state.

Eligibility   This program is open to chapter members and their families in North Carolina who are working on or planning to work on an undergraduate, graduate, or technical degree at a college or technical school in any state. Applicants must submit a 500-word essay on how the Army and Army values have influenced their life; letters of recommendation; a list of personal accomplishments; and a transcript that includes their ACT or SAT score. Selection is based on academic achievement, participation in extracurricular activities at school, and participation in community service activities. Membership in AUSA is open to current and retired Army personnel (including Reserves and National Guard), ROTC cadets, or civilian employees of the Army. Active-duty soldiers are especially encouraged to apply.

Financial data   The stipend is $1,000.

Duration   1 year; recipients may reapply.

Additional information   Membership in the Braxton Bragg Chapter is open to all Army active, National Guard, and Reserve members in North Carolina, along with Department of the Army civilians, retirees, concerned citizens, and family members.

Number awarded   Varies each year; recently, 26 were awarded.

Deadline   April of each year.

[933]
CALIFORNIA NATIONAL GUARD EDUCATION ASSISTANCE AWARD PROGRAM

California State Military Department
Joint Force Headquarters
Attn: EEAP Coordinator
9800 Goethe Road, Box 37
Sacramento, CA 95826
(916) 854-4255   Fax: (916) 854-3739
E-mail: katrina.beck2@us.army.mil
Web: www.calguard.ca.gov/education/Pages/default.aspx

Summary   To provide financial assistance to members of the California National Guard who are interested in attending college or graduate school in the state.

Eligibility   This program is open to residents of California who have served at least 2 years as active members of the California National Guard (CNG) or the State Military Reserve (SMR). Applicants must be planning to attend a college, university, community college, or vocational/technical institute in the state to obtain a certificate, degree (associate, bachelor's, master's, or doctoral) or diploma that they do not currently hold. They must agree to remain an active member of the Guard, Reserve, or Militia as long as they participate in the program.

Financial data   The maximum stipends are equal to those provided by Cal Grants A and B; recently, those were $12,192 at branches of the University of California or non-public institutions, $5,472 at branches of the California State University system, or $1,473 at community colleges. Graduate students receive an additional stipend of $500 for books and supplies.

Duration   1 year; may be renewed, provided the recipient maintains a GPA of 2.0 or higher.

Additional information   This program operates in partnership with the California Student Aid Commission.

Number awarded   Up to 1,000 each year.

Deadline   The priority deadline for new applications is April of each year.

[934]
CALIFORNIA NON-RESIDENT COLLEGE FEE WAIVER PROGRAM FOR MILITARY PERSONNEL AND DEPENDENTS

California Department of Veterans Affairs
Attn: Division of Veterans Services
1227 O Street, Room 101
P.O. Box 942895
Sacramento, CA 94295
(916) 653-2573   Toll Free: (877) 741-8532
Fax: (916) 653-2563   TDD: (800) 324-5966
Web: www.calvet.ca.gov

Summary To waive non-resident fees at public institutions in California for undergraduate or graduate students from other states who are active-duty military personnel, recently-discharged veterans, or dependents of active-duty military personnel.

Eligibility This program is open to residents of states outside California who are 1) veterans of the U.S. armed forces who spent more than 1 year on active duty in California immediately prior to being discharged; 2) members of the U.S. armed forces stationed in California on active duty; or 3) the natural or adopted child, stepchild, or spouse of a member of the U.S. armed forces stationed in California on active duty. Applicants must be attending or planning to attend a community college, branch of the California State University system, or campus of the University of California as an undergraduate or graduate student.

Financial data This program waives non-resident fees of qualifying military personnel, veterans, and families who attend publicly-supported community or state colleges or universities in California.

Duration 1 year; may be renewed until completion of an undergraduate degree or for 1 additional year for military personnel working on a graduate degree; nonrenewable for graduate students who are children or spouses.

Number awarded Varies each year.

Deadline Deadline not specified.

[935]
CANNON ENDOWMENT SCHOLARSHIP

United Church of Christ
Attn: Minister for Grants and Scholarships
700 Prospect Avenue East
Cleveland, OH 44115-1100
(216) 736-3839   Toll Free: (866) 822-8224, ext. 3839
Fax: (216) 736-3783   E-mail: jeffersv@ucc.org
Web: www.ucc.org/scholarships

Summary To provide financial assistance to seminary students who are interested in becoming a military chaplain.

Eligibility This program is open to students at accredited seminaries who are affiliated with the Christian Church (Disciples of Christ), Presbyterian Church (USA), United Church of Christ, or United Methodist Church. Applicants must be planning to become military chaplains. They must have a GPA of 3.0 or higher and be able to demonstrate financial need.

Financial data The stipend is approximately $2,500.

Duration 1 year.

Additional information This program began in 1992.

Number awarded Varies each year; recently, 5 were awarded.

Deadline March of each year.

[936]
CAPTAIN JODI CALLAHAN MEMORIAL SCHOLARSHIP

Air Force Association
Attn: Manager, Awards and Scholarships
1501 Lee Highway
Arlington, VA 22209-1198
(703) 247-5800, ext. 4807
Toll Free: (800) 727-3337, ext. 4807
Fax: (703) 247-5853   E-mail: awards@afa.org
Web: www.afa.org/CallahanScholarship

Summary To provide financial assistance for graduate education to Air Force personnel who are members of the Air Force Association.

Eligibility This program is open to active-duty Air Force members and full-time Guard and Reserve personnel (officer or enlisted) who are also members of the association. Applicants must be working on a master's degree in a non-technical field during off-duty time and have a GPA of 3.0 or higher. Along with their application, they must submit a 2-page essay describing their academic goals and how they expect their degree to enhance their service to the Air Force.

Financial data The stipend is $1,000. Funds may be used for any reasonable expenses related to working on a degree, including tuition, lab fees, and books.

Duration 1 year; nonrenewable.

Number awarded 1 each year.

Deadline June of each year.

[937]
CAPTAIN SEAN P. GRIMES PHYSICIAN ASSISTANT EDUCATIONAL SCHOLARSHIP AWARD

Society of Army Physician Assistants
c/o Harold Slusher
6762 Candlewood Drive
P.O. Box 07490
Fort Myers, FL 33919
(239) 482-2162   Fax: (239) 482-2162
E-mail: hal.shusher@juno.com
Web: www.sapa.org/SeanScholarshipPage.htm

Summary To provide financial assistance to current and former Army personnel interested in seeking training as a physician assistant.

Eligibility This program is open to Army veterans, Army active-duty soldiers, Army National Guard soldiers, and Army Reservists. Soldiers may be of any enlisted or officer rank from E-5 through O-4. Applicants may be seeking initial training as a physician assistant or current physician assistants working on a baccalaureate, master's, or doctoral degree. They must have a GPA of 2.5 or higher. Candidates for initial training must be enrolled in an ARC-PA approved program. Other candidates must be enrolled at an accredited college or university. Financial need is considered in the selection process.

Financial data The stipend is $6,000.

Duration 1 year.

Additional information This program began in 2006.

Number awarded 1 each year.

Deadline January of each year.

[938]
CGMA EDUCATION LOAN PROGRAM

Coast Guard Mutual Assistance
4200 Wilson Boulevard, Suite 610
Arlington, VA 20598-7180
(202) 872-6716   Toll Free: (800) 881-2462
E-mail: ARL-DG-CGMA@uscg.mil
Web: www.cgmahq.org

Summary To provide loans to members of Coast Guard Mutual Assistance (CGMA) and their families who are working on an undergraduate or graduate degree.

Eligibility This program is open to 1) active-duty or retired Coast Guard personnel; 2) members of the Coast Guard Selected Reserve and retirement-eligible members of the IRR; 3) Coast Guard permanent and term civilian employees; 4) Coast Guard Auxiliary members; 5) U.S. Public Health Service officers serving with the Coast Guard; 6) unremarried widowed spouses of any of those; and 7) unmarried dependent children under 23 years of age and not enrolled in any military service of any of those. Applicants must be enrolled in an associate, bachelor's, or graduate degree program or an approved vocational/technical training program.

Financial data The maximum loan is $2,000.

Duration Loans must be repaid by the end of the month in which the course is completed.

Number awarded Varies each year.

Deadline Applications must be submitted no later than 30 days after the course begins.

[939]
CHAPLAIN SAMUEL GROVER POWELL SCHOLARSHIP

United Methodist Higher Education Foundation
Attn: Scholarships Administrator
60 Music Square East, Suite 350
P.O. Box 340005
Nashville, TN 37203-0005
(615) 649-3990   Toll Free: (800) 811-8110
Fax: (615) 649-3980
E-mail: umhefscholarships@gbhem.org
Web: www.umhef.org

Summary To provide funding to students interested in preparing for a career as a military chaplain.

Eligibility This program is open to middlers and seniors at accredited theological seminaries who are either involved in the chaplain candidate (seminarian) program or serving in a military Reserve component after having completed an active-duty tour in 1 of the armed forces. Preference is given to students in their senior year who plan to serve in the U.S. Air Force. However, students preparing for chaplaincy in any branch of the military are considered. Applicants must submit a letter that includes a brief personal history and a statement about their decision to choose military chaplaincy as a career, a recent photograph, undergraduate and graduate transcripts, a financial statement, and a report on their ministry in the chaplain candidate (seminarian) program.

Financial data A stipend is awarded (amount not specified). Funds must be used to pay for tuition. Checks are mailed to the recipient's school.

Duration 1 year; recipients may reapply for 1 additional year (but new applicants are given priority each year).

Additional information This program began in 1980. Recipients are expected to serve in the U.S. Military Chaplaincy upon completion of seminary and ordination. If this does not happen (due to factors within the recipient's control), the recipient may be asked to repay the scholarship.

Number awarded 1 or more each year.

Deadline June of each year.

[940]
CHURCH, STATE AND INDUSTRY FOUNDATION SEMINARY OR GRADUATE SCHOOL GRANT/LOAN

Church, State and Industry Foundation
P.O. Box 384
West Branch, IA 52358-0384
E-mail: info@chaplain-csif.com
Web: www.chaplain-csif.com/Apply.html

Summary To provide forgivable loans to chaplain candidates of the armed forces who are interested in attending a seminary or graduate school.

Eligibility This program is open to members of the Army, Navy, and Air Force (active duty, National Guard or Reserve) who are "experiencing a Call from God" to serve as qualified clergy (e.g., ministers, priests, imams, rabbis). Applicants must be enrolled or planning to enroll full time at a seminary or graduate school to enroll in a course of study that is required for pre-ordination and/or endorsement. They must have been granted chaplain candidate status and have a GPA of 2.8 or higher.

Financial data Support is provided in the form of a loan of $5,000 per year. If the recipient proceeds to commissioning as a military chaplain, the loan converts to a grant and is forgiven. Otherwise, the loan must be repaid with an interest rate specified at the time of the award.

Duration Up to 3 years. Recipients whose faith requires further study for ordination and endorsement may apply for additional support.

Additional information This program began in 2014.

Number awarded Varies each year.

Deadline February of each year.

[941]
CIVIL ENGINEER CORPS COLLEGIATE PROGRAM

U.S. Navy
Bureau of Navy Personnel
BUPERS-314E
5720 Integrity Drive
Millington, TN 38055-4630
(901) 874-4034   Toll Free: (866) CEC-NAVY
Fax: (901) 874-2681   E-mail: p4413d@persnet.navy.mil
Web: www.navycs.com/officer/civilengineerofficer.html

Summary To provide financial assistance to undergraduate and graduate students in architecture and engineering who are interested in serving in the Navy's Civil Engineer Corps (CEC) following graduation.

Eligibility This program is open to bachelor's and master's degree students who are U.S. citizens between 19 and 35 years of age. Applicants must be enrolled in an engineering program accredited by the Accreditation Board for Engineering and Technology (ABET) or an architecture program accredited by the National Architectural Accrediting Board

(NAAB) and have a GPA of 2.7 or higher overall and 3.0 or higher in science and technical courses. They may be civilians, enlisted personnel of the regular Navy and the Naval Reserve, or enlisted personnel of other branches of the armed services with a conditional release from their respective service. Eligible majors include civil engineering, construction engineering, electrical engineering, environmental engineering, industrial engineering, mechanical engineering, ocean engineering, or architecture. Preference is given to applicants who have engineering or architecture work experience and registration as a Professional Engineer (P.E.) or Engineer-in-Training (EIT). Applicants must also be able to meet the Navy's physical fitness requirements.

Financial data While attending classes, students are assigned to the Naval Reserve and receive the standard pay at E-3 level (approximately $2,575 per month) as an undergraduate or E-5 (approximately $4,700 per month) as a graduate student.

Duration Up to 24 months.

Additional information While in college, selectees have no uniforms, drills, or military duties. After graduation with a bachelor's or master's degree, they enter the Navy and attend 13 weeks at Officer Candidate School (OCS) in Pensacola, Florida, followed by 15 weeks at Civil Engineer Corps Officers School (CECOS) in Port Hueneme, California. They then serve 4 years in the CEC, rotating among public works, contract management, and the Naval Construction Force (Seabees).

Number awarded Varies each year.

Deadline Deadline not specified.

[942]
COAST GUARD FOUNDATION ENLISTED RESERVE SCHOLARSHIPS

U.S. Coast Guard
Attn: COMDT (CG-1311)
2703 Martin Luther King, Jr. Avenue, S.E., Stop 7907
Washington, DC 20593-7907
(202) 475-5459   E-mail: travis.p.thornell@uscg.mil
Web: www.uscg.mil/reserve/awards

Summary To provide financial assistance for college or graduate school to members of the Coast Guard Reserves and their dependents.

Eligibility This program is open to Coast Guard enlisted reservists (Selected Reserve or Individual Ready Reserve) and their dependents who are registered in the Defense Enrollment Eligibility Reporting System (DEERS). Applicants must be enrolled or accepted for enrollment at 1) an accredited institution in a program leading to an associate, bachelor's, master's, or doctoral degree; or 2) a 2- or 4-year course of study at an accredited technical or vocational training school. Along with their application, they must submit a 1-page essay on how the participation of themselves, their spouse, or their parent in the Coast Guard Reserve has contributed to their success. Selection is based on that essay and academic achievement.

Financial data The stipend is $1,000.

Duration 1 year.

Additional information This program is sponsored by the United States Automobile Association (USAA) Insurance Corporation.

Number awarded 6 each year.

Deadline July of each year.

[943]
COLONEL JERRY W. ROSS SCHOLARSHIP

American Pharmacists Association
Attn: APhA Foundation
2215 Constitution Avenue, N.W.
Washington, DC 20037-2985
(202) 429-7565   Toll Free: (800) 237-APhA
Fax: (202) 638-3793   E-mail: bwall@aphanet.org
Web: www.aphafoundation.org

Summary To provide financial assistance for work on a degree in pharmacy to Air Force pharmacy technicians who are members of the Academy of Student Pharmacists of the American Pharmacists Association (APhA-ASP) and their families.

Eligibility This program is open to full-time pharmacy students who are either 1) Air Force pharmacy technicians working on a degree in pharmacy; or 2) family members of an Air Force pharmacist or technician who is enrolled in an accredited college of pharmacy. Applicants must have been actively involved in their school's APhA-ASP chapter. They must have completed at least 1 year in the professional sequence of courses with a GPA of 2.75 or higher. Along with their application, they must submit a 500-word essay on a topic that changes annually but relates to the future of the pharmacy profession, 2 letters of recommendation, a current resume or curriculum vitae, and a list of pharmacy and non-pharmacy related activities. Preference is given to applicants who indicate further Air Force service.

Financial data The stipend is $1,000.

Duration 1 year; recipients may reapply.

Number awarded 1 each year.

Deadline November of each year.

[944]
COLONEL LOREN J. AND MRS. LAWONA R. SPENCER SCHOLARSHIP

Air Force Association
Attn: Manager, Awards and Scholarships
1501 Lee Highway
Arlington, VA 22209-1198
(703) 247-5800, ext. 4807
Toll Free: (800) 727-3337, ext. 4807
Fax: (703) 247-5853   E-mail: awards@afa.org
Web: www.afa.org

Summary To provide financial assistance to Air Force personnel interested in working on a master's degree in a field of management or administration.

Eligibility This program is open to active-duty Air Force members (officer or enlisted), Air Force civilians, and full-time Guard and Reserve personnel. Applicants must be interested in working on a master's degree in a management or administration field in preparation for senior level leadership roles and have a GPA of 3.0 or higher. Along with their application, they must submit a 2-page essay describing their academic goals and how they expect their degree to enhance their service to the Air Force. Selection is based on academic achievement and job performance.

Financial data The stipend is $5,000. Funds are sent directly to the recipient's education office.

Duration 1 year; nonrenewable.
Number awarded 1 or more each year.
Deadline June of each year.

[945]
CONNECTICUT TUITION WAIVER FOR VETERANS

Connecticut Board of Regents for Higher Education
39 Woodland Street
Hartford, CT 06105
(860) 723-0013   E-mail: fitzgerald2@ct.edu
Web: www.ct.edu/admission/veterans

Summary To provide financial assistance for college or graduate school to certain Connecticut military servicemembers, veterans, and their dependents.

Eligibility This program is open to 1) honorably-discharged Connecticut veterans who served at least 90 days during specified periods of wartime; 2) active members of the Connecticut Army or Air National Guard; 3) Connecticut residents who are a dependent child or surviving spouse of a member of the armed forces killed in action on or after September 11, 2001 who was also a Connecticut resident; and 4) Connecticut residents who are a dependent child or surviving spouse of a person officially declared missing in action or a prisoner of war while serving in the armed forces after January 1, 1960. Applicants must be attending or planning to attend a public college or university in the state.

Financial data The program provides a waiver of 100% of tuition for students working on an undergraduate or graduate degree at the University of Connecticut (including summer sessions and winter intersession), 100% of tuition for general fund courses at campuses of Connecticut State University, 50% of tuition for extension and summer courses at campuses of Connecticut State University, 100% of tuition at all Connecticut community colleges, and 50% or fees at Charter Oak State College.

Duration Up to 4 years.

Additional information This is an entitlement program; applications are available at the respective college financial aid offices.

Number awarded Varies each year.
Deadline Deadline not specified.

[946]
CSM ROBERT W. ELKEY AWARD

Army Engineer Association
Attn: Program Coordinator
P.O. Box 30260
Alexandria, VA 22310-8260
(703) 428-7084   Fax: (703) 428-6043
E-mail: execasst@armyengineer.com
Web: www.armyengineer.com/scholarships.htm

Summary To provide financial assistance for college or graduate school to enlisted members of the Army Engineer Association (AEA).

Eligibility This program is open to AEA members serving in an active, Reserve, or National Guard component Army Engineer unit, school, or organization within the Corps of Engineers of the United States Army. Applicants must be enlisted personnel (PVT, PFC, SPC, CPL, SGT, or SSG). They must be working on or planning to work on an associate, bachelor's, or master's degree at an accredited college or university. Selection is based primarily on financial need,

although potential for academic success and standards of conduct as supported by personal references are also considered.

Financial data The stipend is $1,000.
Duration 1 year.
Number awarded 3 each year.
Deadline June of each year.

[947]
DISTRICT OF COLUMBIA NATIONAL GUARD TUITION ASSISTANCE

District of Columbia National Guard
Attn: Education Services Office
2001 East Capitol Street, S.E.
Washington, DC 20003-1719
(202) 685-9825   Fax: (202) 685-9815
E-mail: joanne.thweatt@dc.ngb.army.mil
Web: states.ng.mil/sites/DC/education/Pages/tuition.aspx

Summary To provide financial assistance for college or graduate school to current members of the District of Columbia National Guard.

Eligibility This program is open to traditional, technician, and AGR members of the District of Columbia Air and Army National Guard. Applicants must have a high school diploma or equivalency and currently be working on an associate, bachelor's, or master's degree at an accredited postsecondary education institution. In some instances, support may also be available for an M.D., D.O., P.A., or J.D. degree.

Financial data Army National Guard members are eligible for up to $4,500 per year in federal tuition assistance; they may supplement that with up to $1,500 per year in District tuition assistance. Air National Guard members do not have access to federal tuition assistance, so they may receive up to $6,000 in District tuition assistance. Funds must be used to pay for tuition, fees, and/or books.

Duration 1 semester; recipients may reapply.
Number awarded Varies each year.
Deadline July of each year for the fall session, October of each year for the spring session, or April of each year for the summer session.

[948]
DONALDSON D. FRIZZELL MEMORIAL SCHOLARSHIPS

First Command Educational Foundation
Attn: Scholarship Programs Manager
1 FirstComm Plaza
Fort Worth, TX 76109-4999
(817) 569-2634   Toll Free: (877) 872-8289
Fax: (817) 569-2970   E-mail: Scholarships@fcef.com
Web: www.fcef.com

Summary To provide financial assistance to students, especially those with ties to the military (including ROTC), who are entering or attending college or graduate school.

Eligibility This program is open to 1) members of a U.S. uniformed service and their spouses and dependents; 2) clients of First Command Financial Services and their family members; 3) dependent family members of First Command Advisors or field office staff members; or 4) non-contractual ROTC students. Applicants may be traditional students (high school seniors and students already enrolled at a college, university, or accredited trade school) or nontraditional students (those defined by their institution as nontraditional and adult students planning to return to a college, university, or accredited trade school. They must have a GPA of 3.0 or higher and be working on a trade school certification or associate, undergraduate, or graduate degree. Applicants must submit 1-page essays on 1) their active involvement in community service programs; 2) the impact of financial literacy on their future; and 3) why they need this scholarship. Selection is based primarily on the essays, academic merit, and financial need.

Financial data Stipends are $5,000 or $2,500. Funds are disbursed directly to the recipient's college, university, or trade school.

Duration 1 year.

Additional information The sponsoring organization was formerly known as the USPA & IRA Educational Foundation, founded in 1983 to provide scholarships to the children of active, retired, or deceased military personnel. In addition to these scholarships, for which students may apply directly, it supports scholarships offered by a number of partner organizations. Since its establishment, it has awarded scholarships worth nearly $4 million.

Number awarded 6 each year: 2 at $5,000 and 4 at $2,500. Awards are split evenly between the 2 categories.

Deadline The online application process begins in February of each year and continues until 200 applications have been received in each category.

[949]
EDUCATION FOUNDATION FOR THE COLORADO NATIONAL GUARD GRANTS

National Guard Association of Colorado
Attn: Education Foundation, Inc.
P.O. Box 440889
Aurora, CO 80044-0889
(303) 909-6369   Fax: (720) 535-5925
E-mail: BernieRogoff@comcast.net
Web: www.efcong.org/Grants

Summary To provide financial assistance to members of the Colorado National Guard and their families who are interested in attending college or graduate school in any state.

Eligibility This program is open to current and retired members of the Colorado National Guard and their dependent unmarried children and spouses. Applicants must be enrolled or planning to enroll full or part time at a college, university, trade school, business school, or graduate school in any state. Along with their application, they must submit an essay, up to 2 pages in length, on their desire to continue their education, what motivates them, their financial need, their commitment to academic excellence, and their current situation. Selection is based on academic achievement, community involvement, and financial need.

Financial data Stipends are generally at least $1,000 per year.

Duration 1 year; may be renewed.

Number awarded Normally, 15 to 25 of these grants are awarded each semester.

Deadline August of each year for fall semester; January of each year for spring semester.

[950]
FLEET RESERVE ASSOCIATION GRADUATE SCHOLARSHIPS

Fleet Reserve Association
Attn: FRA Education Foundation
125 North West Street
Alexandria, VA 22314-2754
(703) 683-1400   Toll Free: (800) FRA-1924
Fax: (703) 549-6610   E-mail: scholars@fra.org
Web: www.fra.org

Summary To provide financial assistance for graduate school to members of the Fleet Reserve Association (FRA) and their families.

Eligibility This program is open to members of the FRA and the dependent children, grandchildren, and spouses of living or deceased members. Applicants must be enrolled as full-time graduate students. Along with their application, they must submit an essay on why they want to go to college and what they intend to accomplish with their degree. Selection is based on academic record, financial need, extracurricular activities, leadership skills, and participation in community activities. U.S. citizenship is required.

Financial data The stipend is $5,000 per year.

Duration 1 year; may be renewed.

Additional information Membership in the FRA is restricted to active-duty, retired, and Reserve members of the Navy, Marine Corps, and Coast Guard. This program, established in 2001, includes the Glenn F. Glezen Scholarship, the Joseph R. Baranski Scholarship, and the Robert W. Nolan Scholarship.

Number awarded At least 3 each year.

Deadline April of each year.

[951]
FLEET RESERVE ASSOCIATION MEMBER SCHOLARSHIPS

Fleet Reserve Association
Attn: FRA Education Foundation
125 North West Street
Alexandria, VA 22314-2754
(703) 683-1400   Toll Free: (800) FRA-1924
Fax: (703) 549-6610   E-mail: scholars@fra.org
Web: www.fra.org

Summary To provide financial assistance for college or graduate school to members of the Fleet Reserve Association (FRA) and their families.

Eligibility This program is open to members of the FRA and the dependent children, grandchildren, and spouses of living or deceased members. Applicants must be enrolled as full-time undergraduate or graduate students. Along with their application, they must submit an essay on why they want to go to college and what they intend to accomplish with their degree. Selection is based on academic record, financial need, extracurricular activities, leadership skills, and participation in community activities. U.S. citizenship is required.

Financial data The stipend is $5,000 per year.

Duration 1 year; may be renewed.

Additional information Membership in the FRA is restricted to active-duty, retired, and reserve members of the Navy, Marines, and Coast Guard. This program includes awards designated as the Robert M. Treadwell Annual Scholarship and the Donald Bruce Pringle Family Scholarship.

Number awarded 6 each year.
Deadline April of each year.

[952]
FLEET RESERVE ASSOCIATION NON-MEMBER SCHOLARSHIPS

Fleet Reserve Association
Attn: FRA Education Foundation
125 North West Street
Alexandria, VA 22314-2754
(703) 683-1400   Toll Free: (800) FRA-1924
Fax: (703) 549-6610   E-mail: scholars@fra.org
Web: www.fra.org

Summary To provide financial assistance for college or graduate school to sea service personnel and their families.
Eligibility This program is open to 1) active-duty, Reserve, honorably-discharged veterans, and retired members of the U.S. Navy, Marine Corps, and Coast Guard; and 2) their spouses, children, and grandchildren. Applicants must be enrolled as full-time undergraduate or graduate students, but neither they nor their family member are required to be members of the sponsoring organization. Along with their application, they must submit an essay on why they want to go to college and what they intend to accomplish with their degree. Selection is based on academic record, financial need, extracurricular activities, leadership skills, and participation in community activities. U.S. citizenship is required.
Financial data Stipends range up to $5,000 per year.
Duration 1 year; may be renewed.
Number awarded 1 or more each year.
Deadline April of each year.

[953]
FLORIDA NATIONAL GUARD EDUCATIONAL DOLLARS FOR DUTY (EDD) PROGRAM

Department of Military Affairs
Attn: DCSPER-EDD
82 Marine Street
P.O. Box 1008
St. Augustine, FL 32085-1008
(904) 823-0417   Toll Free: (800) 342-6528
Web: dma.myflorida.com

Summary To provide financial assistance for college or graduate school to members of the Florida National Guard.
Eligibility This program is open to current members of the Florida National Guard. Applicants must be attending or planning to attend a college or university in Florida to work on an undergraduate or master's degree. College preparatory and vocational/technical programs also qualify. Guard members who already have a master's degree are not eligible.
Financial data The program provides for payment of 100% of tuition and fees at a public college or university or an equivalent amount at a private institution.
Duration 1 year; may be renewed.
Number awarded Varies each year; recently, approximately 765 Florida National Guard members utilized this program.
Deadline Applications may be submitted at any time, but they must be received at least 90 days prior to the start of the class.

[954]
FLORIDA NAVY NURSE CORPS ASSOCIATION SCHOLARSHIPS

Florida Navy Nurse Corps Association
c/o Margaret Holder, Scholarship Committee
1033 Inverness Drive
St. Augustine, FL 32092
E-mail: maholder@me.com

Summary To provide financial assistance to undergraduate and graduate nursing students, especially residents of Florida with ties to the military.
Eligibility This program is open to students, including registered nursing continuing their studies, who are working on an undergraduate or graduate degree in nursing. Applicants must have completed at least 1 clinical nursing course and have a GPA of 3.0 or higher. They may be full- or part-time students. Preference is given to current active-duty and Reserve service members, veterans of military service, family members of current or former military service personnel, civil service employees, and residents of Florida. Financial need is considered in the selection process.
Financial data The stipend is $1,000. Funds are paid directly to the student.
Duration 1 year.
Additional information This program includes the Captain Miki Iwata Memorial Scholarship.
Number awarded Approximately 3 each year.
Deadline October of each year.

[955]
HARDY WOLF & DOWNING SCHOLARSHIP AWARDS

Hardy Wolf & Downing
Attn: Scholarship Awards
477 Congress Street, 15th Floor
Portland, ME 04101
Toll Free: (800) 992-7333   E-mail: stepler@hwdlaw.com
Web: www.hardywolf.com/scholarships

Summary To provide financial assistance for college or law school to students who have a connection to the U.S. military or to law enforcement.
Eligibility This program is open to 1) high school seniors who plan to attend an accredited U.S. college; 2) college students attending an accredited U.S. college; and 3) law students currently entering or enrolled at an ABA-accredited law school. Applicants must be active, retired, or immediate family members of any branch of the U.S. military or any branch of law enforcement. They must have a GPA of 3.0 or higher. Along with their application, they must submit essays of 1,500 to 2,000 words on the following topics: for members and family members of the military, the greatest challenges facing veterans when they return home from serving their country; for members and family members of law enforcement, the greatest challenges facing law enforcement personnel today; for all law students, the area of law they intend to practice and why.
Financial data Stipends range from $100 to $2,500.
Duration 1 year.
Number awarded 13 each year: 1 at $2,500, 1 at $1,000, 1 at $500, and 10 at $100.
Deadline December of each year.

[956]
ILLINOIS NATIONAL GUARD GRANT PROGRAM

Illinois Student Assistance Commission
Attn: Scholarship and Grant Services
1755 Lake Cook Road
Deerfield, IL 60015-5209
(847) 948-8550 Toll Free: (800) 899-ISAC
Fax: (847) 831-8549 TDD: (800) 526-0844
E-mail: isac.studentservices@isac.illinois.gov
Web: www.isac.org

Summary To provide financial assistance to current or former members of the Illinois National Guard who are interested in attending college or graduate school in the state.

Eligibility This program is open to members of the Illinois National Guard who 1) are currently active and have completed at least 1 full year of service; or 2) have been active for at least 5 consecutive years, have had their studies interrupted by being called to federal active duty for at least 6 months, and are within 12 months after their discharge date. Applicants must also be enrolled at an Illinois public 2- or 4-year college or university.

Financial data Recipients are eligible for payment of tuition and some fees for either undergraduate or graduate study at an Illinois state-supported college or university.

Duration This assistance extends for 4 academic years of full-time study (or the equivalent in part-time study) for Guard members with less than 10 years of active duty service. For Guard members with 10 years or more of active duty service, assistance is available for up to the equivalent of 6 academic years of full-time study.

Number awarded Varies each year.

Deadline September of each year for the academic year; February of each year for spring semester, winter quarter, or spring quarter; June of each year for summer term.

[957]
JAMES MONTAG, JR. SCHOLARSHIP

Tennessee Academy of Physician Assistants
Attn: Tennessee Physician Assistant Foundation
P.O. Box 150785
Nashville, TN 37215-0785
(615) 463-0026 Fax: (615) 463-0036
E-mail: info@tnpa.com
Web: www.tnpa.com/content/scholarship-applications

Summary To provide financial assistance to physician assistant students from Tennessee who are serving or have served in the military.

Eligibility This program is open to students in the first or second year of a physician assistant program who are either 1) enrolled at an approved program in Tennessee; or 2) residents of Tennessee enrolled at an approved school in another state. Applicants must be serving on active or Reserve duty in any branch of the military or the National Guard or have an honorable discharge; Air Force medics are particularly encouraged to apply. Along with their application, they must submit an essay of 2 to 3 pages on their professional career and lifetime goals. Financial need is not considered in the selection process.

Financial data The stipend is $1,000.

Duration 1 year.

Number awarded 1 each year.

Deadline August of each year.

[958]
JOE KING SCHOLARSHIPS

Council of College and Military Educators
c/o Kenneth D. McRae, Scholarship Committee Chair
Mississippi State University
G.V. "Sonny" Montgomery Center for America's Veterans
126 Magruder Street
P. O. Drawer 6283
Mississippi State, MS 39762
(662) 325-6719 Fax: (662) 325-6723
E-mail: scholarship@ccmeonline.aspx
Web: www.ccmeonline.org/scholarships

Summary To provide financial assistance to members of the armed services who are interested in working on an undergraduate or master's degree.

Eligibility This program is open to members of the uniformed services currently on active duty. Applicants must be currently enrolled full time at an accredited institution that is a member of the Council of College and Military Educators (CCME) and working on an associate, bachelor's, or master's degree. Undergraduates must have a GPA of 2.5 or higher and graduate students must have a GPA of 3.0 or higher. Along with their application, they must submit an essay of 400 to 750 words on how they would describe military leadership. Financial need is not considered in the selection process.

Financial data The stipend is $1,000. Funds are paid directly to the student.

Duration 1 year; nonrenewable.

Number awarded 5 each year.

Deadline September of each year.

[959]
JOHN CORNELIUS/MAX ENGLISH MEMORIAL SCHOLARSHIP AWARD

Marine Corps Tankers Association
c/o Stephen Chambers, Scholarship Chair
1922 Freeman Street
Oceanside, CA 92054
Web: www.usmarinetankers.org/scholarship-program

Summary To provide financial assistance for college or graduate school to children and grandchildren of members of the Marine Corps Tankers Association and to Marine and Navy personnel currently serving in tank units.

Eligibility This program is open to high school seniors and graduates who are children, grandchildren, or under the guardianship of an active, Reserve, retired, or honorably discharged Marine who served in a tank unit. Marine or Navy Corpsmen currently assigned to tank units are also eligible. Applicants must be enrolled or planning to enroll full time at a college or graduate school. Their parent or grandparent must be a member of the Marine Corps Tankers Association or, if not a member, must join if the application is accepted. Along with their application, they must submit an essay on their educational goals, future aspirations, and concern for the future of our society and for the peoples of the world. Selection is based on that essay, academic record, school activities, leadership potential, and community service.

Financial data The stipend is at least $2,000 per year.

Duration 1 year; recipients may reapply.

Number awarded Varies each year; recently, 15 were awarded.

Deadline March of each year.

[960]
KATZ & PHILLIPS LAW SCHOLARSHIP FOR VETERANS

Katz & Phillips, P.A.
509 West Colonial Drive
Orlando, FL 32804
(321) 420-1284   Toll Free: (866) 464-0782
Fax: (407) 898-6125
Web: www.thetixteam.com/veterans-law-scholarship

Summary To provide financial assistance to active military personnel and veterans who are interested in attending law school.

Eligibility This program is open to active military personnel and veterans who are currently enrolled at or accepted to attend an accredited law school in the United States. Applicants must have a GPA of 2.8 or higher. They must submit an essay on 1 of the following questions: 1) how their military service has inspired them to a career in the law; 2) how their military service has affected their outlook on our legal system; or 3) what has been their greatest challenge in balancing their military career and their pursuit of a legal education.

Financial data The stipend is $1,000.

Duration 1 year.

Additional information This program began in 2014.

Number awarded 1 each year.

Deadline September of each year.

[961]
KENTUCKY NATIONAL GUARD TUITION AWARD PROGRAM

Kentucky Higher Education Assistance Authority
Attn: Student Aid Branch
100 Airport Road
P.O. Box 798
Frankfort, KY 40602-0798
(502) 696-7392   Toll Free: (800) 928-8926, ext. 7392
Fax: (502) 696-7373   TDD: (800) 855-2880
E-mail: studentaid@kheaa.com
Web: www.kheaa.com/website/kheaa/military_ky?main=7

Summary To provide financial assistance for college or graduate school to members of the Kentucky National Guard.

Eligibility This program is open to active enlisted members of the Kentucky National Guard who are interested in working full or part time on an undergraduate or graduate degree. Applicants must have maintained standards of satisfactory membership in the Guard, including passing the most recent physical fitness test, meeting the height-weight standard, meeting attendance standards, having no unsatisfactory performance or absence-without-leave records, and having no other restrictions on their personnel file. Preference is given to applicants working on their first undergraduate degree.

Financial data The program provides payment of full tuition and fees at any state-supported university, community college, or vocational or technical school in Kentucky.

Duration 1 semester; may be renewed.

Number awarded Varies each year.

Deadline March of each year for summer or fall terms; September of each year for spring term.

[962]
LIFE'S CHOICES FOUNDATION GRADUATE SCHOLARSHIP AWARDS

Association of Former Intelligence Officers
Attn: Scholarships Committee
7700 Leesburg Pike, Suite 324
Falls Church, VA 22043
(703) 790-0320   Fax: (703) 991-1278
E-mail: scholarships@afio.com
Web: www.afio.com/13_scholarships.htm

Summary To provide financial assistance to graduate students who are members or descendants of members of the U.S. intelligence community and interested in working on a degree in a field related to national security.

Eligibility This program is open to graduate students who apply in their senior undergraduate year or first graduate year. Applicants must be personnel serving in government agencies comprising the U.S. intelligence community or their children or grandchildren. They must be working on a degree in a field related to national security or intelligence studies and be, or planning to be, serving in the U.S. government. Along with their application, they must submit a cover letter that explains their need for assistance, their career goals and dreams, and their views of U.S. world standing and its intelligence community. Selection is based on merit, character, estimated future potential, background, and relevance of their studies to the full spectrum of national security interests and career ambitions. U.S. citizenship is required.

Financial data The stipend is $3,500.

Duration 1 year.

Additional information This program is sponsored by the Morris Family Charitable Corporation.

Number awarded 2 each year.

Deadline June of each year.

[963]
LOUISIANA NATIONAL GUARD STATE TUITION EXEMPTION PROGRAM

Louisiana National Guard
Attn: Education Service Officer
Military Development (DMP-XD)
Jackson Barracks
New Orleans, LA 70146-0330
(504) 278-8532   Toll Free: (800) 899-6355
E-mail: alfred.e.horridge.mil@mail.mil
Web: www.geauxguard.com

Summary To provide financial assistance to members of the Louisiana National Guard who are interested in attending college or graduate school in the state.

Eligibility This program is open to active drilling members of the Louisiana Army National Guard or Air National Guard. Guard members are ineligible if they have been disqualified by their unit commander for any adverse action, have already obtained a bachelor's degree, are placed on academic probation or suspension, test positive on a drug/alcohol test or declare themselves as a self-referral, are separated or transfer to the Inactive National Guard, or have 9 or more AWOLs. Applicants must have been accepted for admission or be enrolled in a Louisiana public institution of higher learning, either part time or full time, to work on an associate, bachelor's, or master's degree.

Financial data Recipients are exempt from all tuition charges at Louisiana state-funded colleges, universities, or community colleges.

Duration The exemption may be claimed for 5 separate academic years or until the receipt of a degree, whichever occurs first.

Additional information The state legislature established this program in 1974.

Number awarded Varies each year.

Deadline Deadline not specified.

[964]
MARINE CORPS FUNDED LAW EDUCATION PROGRAM

U.S. Marine Corps
Manpower and Reserve Affairs
Attn: Graduate Education (MMOA-5)
3280 Russell Road
Quantico, VA 22134-5103
(703) 784-9286   Fax: (703) 784-9844
E-mail: Diane.Rodgers@usmc.mil
Web: www.marines.com

Summary To allow selected commissioned Marine Corps officers to earn a law degree by providing financial assistance for full-time study.

Eligibility Eligible to participate in this program are commissioned Marine Corps officers at the rank of captain or below. Applicants must have at least 2 but no more than 6 years of total active service and be able to complete 20 years of active service before their 55th birthday. They must have graduated from an accredited college or university with a bachelor's degree, have taken the LSAT at their own arrangement and expense, and have been accepted at an accredited law school in the United States.

Financial data Commissioned officers selected to participate in this program receive their regular Marine Corps pay and allowances while attending a college or university on a full-time basis, as well as payment for the cost of tuition (to a maximum of $10,000 per year).

Duration Up to the equivalent of 2 academic years.

Number awarded Varies each year; recently, 2 Marines were selected to participate in this program.

Deadline October of each year.

[965]
MARINE CORPS TUITION ASSISTANCE PROGRAM

U.S. Marine Corps
c/o Naval Education and Training Professional
   Development and Technology Command
Code N814
6490 Saufley Field Road
Pensacola, FL 32509-5241
(850) 452-1001   Toll Free: (877) 838-1659
Fax: (850) 473-6401   E-mail: SFLY_TA.Marine@navy.mil
Web: www.marines.mil

Summary To provide financial assistance for undergraduate or graduate study to Marine Corps personnel.

Eligibility Eligible for assistance under this program are active-duty Marines who wish to take college courses for academic credit during off-duty time. Funding is available for vocational/technical, undergraduate, graduate, undergraduate development, independent study, and distance learning

programs. Applicants must have completed at least 2 years of service, be eligible for promotion, and have completed designated military training courses. Commissioned officers must agree to remain on active duty for 2 years after the completion of any funded courses. Enlisted Marines must have an end of active duty status (EAS) of at least 60 days beyond the completion date of the course. All students must successfully complete their courses with a satisfactory grade.

Financial data Those selected for participation in this program receive their regular Marine Corps pay and 100% of tuition at the postsecondary educational institution of their choice, but capped at $4,500 per year or $250 per semester hour, whichever is less. Funding is available only for tuition, not fees or other associated expenses.

Duration Until completion of a bachelor's or graduate degree. Undergraduates must complete all courses with a grade of "C" or better; graduate students must complete classes with a grade of "B" of better. If recipients fail to achieve those grades, they must reimburse the Marine Corps for all funds received.

Number awarded Varies each year; in recent years, approximately 20,000 Marines availed themselves of this funding.

Deadline Applications must be submitted within 30 days of the start date of the class.

[966]
MARYLAND NATIONAL GUARD STATE TUITION WAIVER (STW)

Maryland National Guard
Attn: Education Services Office
Fifth Regiment Armory
29th Division Street, Room B-23
Baltimore, MD 21201-2288
(410) 576-1499   Toll Free: (800) 492-2526
Fax: (410) 576-6082
E-mail: mdng_education@md.ngb.army.mil
Web: www.md.ngb.army.mil

Summary To waive tuition for members of the Maryland National Guard at colleges and universities in the state.

Eligibility This program is open to members of the Maryland National Guard who wish to attend designated "Partners in Education" institutions in the state. That includes all 5 branches of the University of Maryland, 8 other public colleges and universities, 13 community colleges, 5 private universities, and 4 private career education institutions that have agreed to waive part of the tuition charges for National Guard members. Applicants must have a 2-year obligation remaining from the course start date.

Financial data The amount of the waiver ranges from 25% to 50%. Most 4-year colleges waive 50% of tuition for up to 6 credits per semester.

Duration 1 semester; recipients may reapply.

Additional information Some schools also limit the number of credits for which a Guard member can receive waivers during any semester.

Number awarded Varies each year.

Deadline Deadline not specified.

[967]
MASSACHUSETTS NATIONAL GUARD TUITION WAIVER PROGRAM

Massachusetts National Guard
Attn: Education Services Officer
50 Maple Street
Milford, MA 01757-3604
(508) 968-5889   Fax: (508) 968-5906
E-mail: ma-education@ng.army.mil
Web: states.ng.mil

Summary To provide financial assistance to members of the Massachusetts National Guard interested in working on an undergraduate or graduate degree at a college in the state.

Eligibility This program is open to actively participating members of the Army or Air National Guard in Massachusetts. Applicants must have less than 9 AWOLs (Absence Without Leave) at all times and must not ETS (Expiration of Term of Service) during the period enrolled. They must be accepted for admission or enrolled at 1 of 28 Massachusetts public colleges, universities, or community colleges and working on an associate, bachelor's, master's, or doctoral degree. The institution must have a vacancy after all tuition-paying students and all students who are enrolled under any scholarship or tuition waiver provisions have enrolled.

Financial data Eligible Guard members are exempt from any tuition payments at colleges or universities operated by the Commonwealth of Massachusetts and funded by the Massachusetts Board of Higher Education.

Duration Up to a total of 130 semester hours.

Additional information Recipients may enroll either part or full time in a Massachusetts state-supported institution. This program is funded through the Massachusetts Board of Higher Education.

Number awarded Varies each year.

Deadline Deadline not specified.

[968]
MCA CHAPLAIN CANDIDATE SCHOLARSHIPS

Military Chaplains Association of the United States of
  America
Attn: Executive Director
3776 Loch Highland Parkway N.E.
Roswell, GA 30075-2018
Fax: (770) 649-1972   E-mail: rgcertain@icloud.com
Web: www.mca-usa.org/scholarships

Summary To provide financial assistance to seminary students who are serving as chaplain candidates for the U.S. armed forces.

Eligibility This program is open to full-time students in accredited seminaries who are currently approved as and serving as chaplain candidates in the armed forces (Army, Air Force, or Navy). Applicants must be able to demonstrate financial need. Along with their application, they must submit an essay, up to 1,500 words in length on their sense of call to ministry with particular emphasis on 1) their call to provide pastoral care for military personnel and their families; and 2) their understanding thus far of ministry in a religiously diverse environment (such as the armed forces of the United States).

Financial data The stipend is $2,000.

Duration 1 year.

Additional information This program began in 1992.

Number awarded Several each year. Since the program was established, it has awarded 65 scholarships.

Deadline March of each year.

[969]
MEDICAL CORPS OPTION OF THE SEAMAN TO ADMIRAL-21 PROGRAM

U.S. Navy
Attn: Commander, Naval Service Training Command
250 Dallas Street, Suite A
Pensacola, FL 32508-5268
(850) 452-9563   Fax: (850) 452-2486
E-mail: PNSC_STA21@navy.mil
Web: www.sta-21.navy.mil/program_options.asp

Summary To allow outstanding enlisted Navy personnel to work on a bachelor's degree, affiliate with an ROTC unit, be accepted to medical school, earn an M.D. or D.O. degree, and be commissioned in the Navy Medical Corps.

Eligibility This program is open to U.S. citizens who are currently serving on active duty in the U.S. Navy or Naval Reserve, including Full Time Support (FTS), Selected Reserves (SELRES), and Navy Reservists on active duty, except for those on active duty for training (ACDUTRA). Applicants must be high school graduates (or GED recipients) who are able to 1) complete requirements for a baccalaureate degree within 36 months; 2) complete a medical degree through the Uniformed Services University of Health Services (USUHS) or the Health Professions Scholarship Program (HPSP); and 3) complete 20 years of active commissioned service as a physician by age 62. Within the past 3 years, they must have taken the SAT (and achieved scores of at least 500 on the mathematics section and 500 on the critical reading section) or the ACT (and achieved a score of at least 21 on the mathematics portion and 20 on the English portion).

Financial data Awardees continue to receive their regular Navy pay and allowances while they attend college on a full-time basis. They also receive reimbursement for tuition, fees, and books up to $10,000 per year. If base housing is available, they are eligible to live there. Participants are not eligible to receive benefits under the Navy's Tuition Assistance Program (TA), the Montgomery GI Bill (MGIB), the Navy College Fund, or the Veterans Educational Assistance Program (VEAP).

Duration Selectees are supported for up to 36 months of full-time, year-round study or completion of a bachelor's degree, as long as they maintain a GPA of 3.0 or higher. They are then supported until completion of a medical degree.

Additional information Upon acceptance into the program, selectees attend the Naval Science Institute (NSI) in Newport, Rhode Island for an 8-week program in the fundamental core concepts of being a naval officer (navigation, engineering, weapons, military history and justice, etc.). They then enter an NROTC affiliated college or university with a pre-medical program that confers an accredited B.S. degree to pursue full-time study. They become members of and drill with the NROTC unit. After they complete their bachelor's degree, they are commissioned as an ensign in the Naval Reserve. They must apply to and be accepted at medical school, either the USUSH or a civilian medical school through the HPSP. Following completion of medical school, they are promoted to lieutenant and assigned to active duty in the

Medical Corps. Selectees incur a service obligation of 5 years for their baccalaureate degree support plus whatever obligation they incur for medical degree support (usually 7 years if they attend USUSH or 4 years if they attend a civilian institution through HPSP).

Number awarded Varies each year.

Deadline June of each year.

[970]
MEDICAL SERVICE CORPS INSERVICE PROCUREMENT PROGRAM (MSC-IPP)

U.S. Navy
Attn: Navy Medicine Professional Development Center
8955 Wood Road, 16th Floor, Rooms 16141, 16148
Bethesda, MD 20889-5611
(301) 319-4520   Fax: (301) 295-1783
E-mail: mscipp@med.navy.mil
Web: www.med.navy.mil

Summary To provide funding to Navy and Marine enlisted personnel who wish to earn an undergraduate or graduate degree in selected health care specialties while continuing to receive their regular pay and allowances.

Eligibility This program is open to enlisted personnel who are serving on active duty in any rating in pay grade E-5 through E-9 of the U.S. Navy, U.S. Marine Corps, or the Marine Corps Reserve serving on active duty (including Full Time Support of the Reserve). Applicants must be interested in working on a degree to become commissioned in the following medical specialties: environmental health, health care administration, industrial hygiene, occupational therapy, pharmacy, physician assistant, radiation health, or social work. If they plan to work on a graduate degree, they must have scores of at least 1000 on the GRE or 500 on the GMAT; if they plan to work on a bachelor's or physician assistant degree, they must have scores of at least 1000 on the SAT (including 460 on the mathematics portion) or 42 on the ACT (21 on the English portion, 21 on the mathematics portion). They must be U.S. citizens who can be commissioned before they reach their 42nd birthday.

Financial data Participants receive payment of tuition, mandatory fees, a book allowance, and full pay and allowances for their enlisted pay grade. They are eligible for advancement while in college.

Duration 24 to 48 months of full-time, year-round study, until completion of a relevant degree.

Additional information Following graduation, participants are commissioned in the Medical Service Corps and attend Officer Indoctrination School. They incur an 8-year military service obligation, including at least 3 years served on active duty.

Number awarded Varies each year; recently, 36 were awarded: 2 in environmental health, 14 in health care administration, 1 in occupational therapy, 1 in pharmacy, 15 in physician assistant, 2 in radiation health, and 1 in social work.

Deadline August of each year.

[971]
MG LEIF J. SVERDRUP AWARD

Army Engineer Association
Attn: Program Coordinator
P.O. Box 30260
Alexandria, VA 22310-8260
(703) 428-7084   Fax: (703) 428-6043
E-mail: execasst@armyengineer.com
Web: www.armyengineer.com/scholarships.htm

Summary To provide financial assistance for college or graduate school to officers who are members of the Army Engineer Association (AEA).

Eligibility This program is open to AEA members serving in an active, Reserve, or National Guard component Army Engineer unit, school, or organization within the Corps of Engineers of the United States Army. Applicants must be commissioned officers (2LT, 1LT, or CPT) or warrant officers (WO1 or WO2). They must be working on or planning to work on an associate, bachelor's, or master's degree at an accredited college or university. Selection is based primarily on financial need, although potential for academic success and standards of conduct as supported by personal references are also considered.

Financial data The stipend is $1,000.

Duration 1 year.

Number awarded 2 each year: 1 to a commissioned officer and 1 to a warrant officer.

Deadline June of each year.

[972]
MINNESOTA G.I. BILL PROGRAM

Minnesota Department of Veterans Affairs
Attn: Programs and Services Division
20 West 12th Street, Room 206
St. Paul, MN 55155
(651) 296-2562   Toll Free: (888) LINK-VET
TDD: (800) 627-3529   E-mail: MNGIBill@state.mn.us
Web: mn.gov/mdva/resources/education/minnesotagibill.jsp

Summary To provide financial assistance for college or graduate school in Minnesota to residents who 1) served in the military after September 11, 2001 or 2) are the family members of deceased or disabled military personnel.

Eligibility This program is open to residents of Minnesota enrolled at colleges and universities in the state as undergraduate or graduate students. Applicants must be 1) a veteran who is serving or has served honorably in a branch of the U.S. armed forces at any time; 2) a non-veteran who has served honorably for a total of 5 years or more cumulatively as a member of the Minnesota National Guard or other active or Reserve component of the U.S. armed forces, and any part of that service occurred on or after September 11, 2001; or 3) a surviving child or spouse of a person who has served in the military at any time on or after September 11, 2001 and who has died or has a total and permanent disability as a result of that military service. Financial need is also considered in the selection process.

Financial data The stipend is $1,000 per semester for full-time study or $500 per semester for part-time study. The maximum award is $3,000 per academic year or $10,000 per lifetime.

Duration 1 year; may be renewed, provided the recipient continues to make satisfactory academic progress.

Additional information This program was established by the Minnesota Legislature in 2007.

Number awarded Varies each year.

Deadline Deadline not specified.

[973]
MINNESOTA NATIONAL GUARD MEDICAL PROFESSIONAL STUDENT STATE TUITION REIMBURSEMENT PROGRAM

Department of Military Affairs
Attn: Education Services Officer
JFMN-J1-ARED
20 West 12th Street
St. Paul, MN 55155-2098
(651) 282-4589   Toll Free: (800) 657-3848
Fax: (651) 282-4694
E-mail: ng.mn.mnarng.mbx.assets-education@mail.mil
Web: www.minnesotanationalguard.org

Summary To provide partial tuition reimbursement to medical, dental, and physician assistant students who are interested in serving in the Minnesota National Guard.

Eligibility This program is open to Minnesota Army and Air National Guard members who initially appoint as medical or dental student officers or are already commissioned officers and attain civilian physician assistant master's student status. Applicants must agree to accept a Medical Corps commission in the Guard after graduation.

Financial data This program provides reimbursement of the tuition charged, not to exceed 100% of the tuition costs at the University of Minnesota Twin Cities campus medical or dental schools. Upon graduation from medical, dental, or physician assistant school, officers must serve 2 years in the Minnesota National Guard for each year that they participated in the program. Failure to fulfill that service obligation will result in recoupment of a prorated portion of the tuition reimbursed.

Duration The program provides funding for up to 144 semester or 208 quarter credits.

Number awarded The number of participants at any given time is limited to 15 Army Guard officers and 4 Air Guard officers.

Deadline Participants must request reimbursement within 60 days of the last official day of the term.

[974]
MINNESOTA NATIONAL GUARD STATE TUITION REIMBURSEMENT

Department of Military Affairs
Attn: Education Services Officer
JFMN-J1-ARED
20 West 12th Street
St. Paul, MN 55155-2098
(651) 282-4589   Toll Free: (800) 657-3848
Fax: (651) 282-4694
E-mail: ng.mn.mnarng.mbx.assets-education@mail.mil
Web: www.minnesotanationalguard.org

Summary To provide financial assistance for college or graduate school to current members of the Minnesota National Guard.

Eligibility Eligible for this program are members of the Minnesota Army or Air National Guard who are currently serving in grades E-1 through O-5 (including warrant officers) and are

enrolled as undergraduate or graduate students at colleges or universities in Minnesota. Reimbursement is provided only for undergraduate courses completed with a grade of "C" or better or for graduate courses completed with a grade of "B" or better. Applicants must be serving satisfactorily according to National Guard standards.

Financial data The maximum reimbursement rate is 100% of the tuition rate at the University of Minnesota Twin Cities campus, with a maximum benefit of $13,000 per fiscal year for undergraduate course work or $22,000 per fiscal year for graduate course work.

Duration 1 semester, to a maximum of 18 credits per semester; may be renewed until completion of an associate, bachelor's, master's, or doctoral degree or 144 semester credits, whichever comes first.

Number awarded Varies each year.

Deadline Deadline not specified.

[975]
MONTGOMERY GI BILL (SELECTED RESERVE)

Department of Veterans Affairs
Attn: Veterans Benefits Administration
810 Vermont Avenue, N.W.
Washington, DC 20420
(202) 418-4343   Toll Free: (888) GI-BILL1
Web: www.benefits.va.gov/gibill/mgib_sr.asp

Summary To provide financial assistance for college or graduate school to members of the Reserves or National Guard.

Eligibility Eligible to apply are members of the Reserve elements of the Army, Navy, Air Force, Marine Corps, and Coast Guard, as well as the Army National Guard and the Air National Guard. To be eligible, a Reservist must 1) have a 6-year obligation to serve in the Selected Reserves signed after June 30, 1985 (or, if an officer, to agree to serve 6 years in addition to the original obligation); 2) complete Initial Active Duty for Training (IADT); 3) meet the requirements for a high school diploma or equivalent certificate before completing IADT; and 4) remain in good standing in a drilling Selected Reserve unit. Reservists who enlisted after June 30, 1985 can receive benefits for undergraduate degrees, graduate training, or technical courses leading to certificates at colleges and universities. Reservists whose 6-year commitment began after September 30, 1990 may also use these benefits for a certificate or diploma from business, technical, or vocational schools; cooperative training; apprenticeship or on-the-job training; correspondence courses; independent study programs; tutorial assistance; remedial, deficiency, or refresher training; flight training; or state-approved alternative teacher certification programs.

Financial data The current monthly rate is $367 for full-time study, $274 for three-quarter time study, $182 for half-time study, or $91.75 for less than half-time study. For apprenticeship and on-the-job training, the monthly stipend is $275.25 for the first 6 months, $201.85 for the second 6 months, and $128.45 for the remainder of the program. Other rates apply for cooperative education, correspondence courses, and flight training.

Duration Up to 36 months for full-time study, 48 months for three-quarter study, 72 months for half-time study, or 144 months for less than half-time study. Benefits end 10 years from the date the Reservist became eligible for the program.

Additional information This program is frequently referred to as Chapter 1606 (formerly Chapter 106).

Number awarded Varies each year.

Deadline Applications may be submitted at any time.

[976]
NATIONAL GUARD ASSOCIATION OF MINNESOTA SCHOLARSHIPS

National Guard Association of Minnesota
Attn: Executive Director
P.O. Box 47132
Plymouth, MN 55442
(763) 202-2151   E-mail: director@ngamn.org
Web: www.ngamn.org/node/56

Summary To provide financial assistance to current and retired members of the National Guard Association of Minnesota (NGAMN) and their families who are working on an undergraduate or graduate degree at a school in any state.

Eligibility This program is open to active members and retired life members of NGAMN and their spouses, children, and grandchildren. Applicants must be currently enrolled at least half time at an accredited institution of higher learning in any state and working on a 4-year bachelor's or graduate degree. They must have a GPA of 2.75 or higher. Along with their application, they must submit an essay on a topic that describes a value of the Army or Air Force, rotating among loyalty, duty, respect, selfless service, honor, integrity, personal courage, commitment, and excellence. Financial need is not considered in the selection process.

Financial data Stipends are $1,000 or $500. Funds are paid directly to the recipient.

Duration 1 year. Recipients may reapply after 3 years.

Additional information The $1,000 scholarship is sponsored by HiWay Federal Credit Union. This program began in 2008.

Number awarded 3 each year: 1 at $1,000 and 2 at $500 (1 to a member or retired member and 1 to a spouse, child, or grandchild).

Deadline July of each year.

[977]
NATIONAL GUARD ASSOCIATION OF NEW HAMPSHIRE SCHOLARSHIPS

National Guard Association of New Hampshire
Attn: Scholarship Committee
P.O. Box 22031
Portsmouth, NH 03802-2031
(603) 227-1597   E-mail: nganhscholarship@gmail.com
Web: www.nganh.org/Archive/Scholarship

Summary To provide financial assistance to members of the National Guard Association of New Hampshire and their dependents who are interested in attending college or graduate school in any state.

Eligibility This program is open to current members of the National Guard Association of New Hampshire (officer, enlisted, or retired), their spouses, and their dependent children. Applicants must be enrolled or planning to enroll full or part time in an associate, bachelor's, graduate, professional, or doctoral degree program at an accredited college or university in any state. Along with their application, they must submit a 1-page essay on a topic that changes annually;

recently, they were asked to describe what citizen service means to them.

Financial data The stipend is $1,000.

Duration 1 year.

Number awarded 1 each year.

Deadline April of each year.

[978]
NATIONAL GUARD ASSOCIATION OF NEW JERSEY SCHOLARSHIP PROGRAM

National Guard Association of New Jersey
Attn: Scholarship Committee
P.O. Box 266
Wrightstown, NJ 08562
(973) 541-6776   Fax: (973) 541-6909
E-mail: scholarship@nganj.org
Web: www.nganj.org/benefits.htm

Summary To provide financial assistance to members of the National Guard Association of New Jersey (NGANJ) or their dependents who are interested in attending college or graduate school in any state.

Eligibility This program is open to 1) active members of the NGANJ currently enrolled full time at an approved community college, school of nursing, or 4-year college in any state; and 2) the spouses, children, and grandchildren of active, retired, or deceased members entering or attending a 4-year college or university in any state. Applicants must submit transcripts, information on the civic and academic activities in which they have participated, and a list of offices, honors, awards, and special recognitions they have received. Selection is based on academic accomplishment, leadership, and citizenship.

Financial data Stipends up to $1,000 are available.

Duration 1 year; nonrenewable.

Number awarded Varies each year; recently, 10 were awarded.

Deadline April of each year.

[979]
NATIONAL GUARD ASSOCIATION OF SOUTH CAROLINA SCHOLARSHIPS

National Guard Association of South Carolina
Attn: NGASC Scholarship Foundation
132 Pickens Street
Columbia, SC 29205
(803) 254-8456   Toll Free: (800) 822-3235
Fax: (803) 254-3869   E-mail: nginfo@ngasc.org
Web: www.ngasc.org/services-view/scholorships

Summary To provide financial assistance to current and former South Carolina National Guard members and their dependents who are interested in attending college or graduate school in any state.

Eligibility This program is open to undergraduate students who are 1) current, retired, or deceased members of the South Carolina National Guard; 2) their dependents; and 3) members of the National Guard Association of South Carolina (NGASC). Graduate students are also eligible if they are members of the South Carolina National Guard. Applicants must be attending or interested in attending a college or university in any state as a full-time student. Several of the scholarships include additional restrictions on school or academic major; some are granted only for academic excellence, but most are based on both academics and financial need.

Financial data   The stipend is $1,500 or $1,000.

Duration   1 year; may be renewed up to 3 additional years.

Number awarded   Varies each year; recently, 55 were awarded.

Deadline   January of each year.

[980]
NATIONAL GUARD ASSOCIATION OF TEXAS SCHOLARSHIP PROGRAM

National Guard Association of Texas
Attn: Education Committee
3706 Crawford Avenue
Austin, TX 78731-6803
(512) 454-7300   Toll Free: (800) 252-NGAT
Fax: (512) 467-6803   E-mail: rlindner@ngat.org
Web: www.ngat.org/educate.php

Summary   To provide financial assistance to members and dependents of members of the National Guard Association of Texas who are interested in attending college or graduate school in any state.

Eligibility   This program is open to annual and life members of the association and their spouses and children (associate members and their dependents are not eligible). Applicants may be high school seniors, undergraduate students, or graduate students, either enrolled or planning to enroll at an institution of higher education in any state. Along with their application, they must submit an essay on their desire to continue their education. Selection is based on scholarship, citizenship, and leadership.

Financial data   Stipends range from $700 to $5,000.

Duration   1 year (nonrenewable).

Additional information   This program includes 1 scholarship sponsored by USAA Insurance Corporation.

Number awarded   Varies each year; recently, 9 were awarded: 1 at $5,000, 2 at $2,000, 1 at $1,500, 1 at $1,250, 3 at $1,000, and 1 at $750.

Deadline   February of each year.

[981]
NATIONAL GUARD ASSOCIATION OF VERMONT SCHOLARSHIPS

National Guard Association of Vermont
Attn: Scholarships
P.O. Box 694
Essex Junction, VT 05453
(802) 338-3185   E-mail: timothy.gariboldi@us.army.mil
Web: www.ngavt.org/scholarInfo.shtml

Summary   To provide financial assistance to members of the Vermont National Guard (VTNG) or the National Guard Association of Vermont (NGA-VT) and their children or spouses who are interested in attending college or graduate school in any state.

Eligibility   This program is open to current members of the VTNG or the NGA-VT, their spouses, and their unmarried children. Applicants must be working, or planning to work, on an associate, undergraduate, technical, or graduate degree as a full-time student at a school in any state. Along with their application, they must submit an essay on their commitment to selfless public service or their plan for pursuing it in the future. In the selection process, first priority is given to appli-

cants in grades E-1 through E-6, W-1 and W-2, and O-1 through O-3; second to E-7, E-8, and W3; third to E-9, W-4 and W-5, and O-4 and above. Other factors considered include the essay, academic performance, and community service. The program includes the COL James D. Kneeland Memorial Scholarship Award, reserved for a member of the Vermont Army National Guard Aviation Community.

Financial data   Stipends range from $500 to $1,500. Funds are sent directly to the recipient.

Duration   1 year; recipients may reapply.

Number awarded   4 each year: 1 at $1,500 (the COL James D. Kneeland Memorial Scholarship Award), 1 at $1,000, and 2 at $500 (1 for a student affiliated with the Vermont Army National Guard and 1 for a student affiliated with the Vermont Air National Guard).

Deadline   June of each year.

[982]
NAVAL HELICOPTER ASSOCIATION ACTIVE DUTY SCHOLARSHIPS

Naval Helicopter Association
Attn: Scholarship Fund
P.O. Box 180578
Coronado, CA 92178-0578
(619) 435-7139   Fax: (619) 435-7354
Web: nhascholarshipfund.org/scholarships-available.html

Summary   To provide financial assistance for college or graduate school to active-duty personnel who are working or have worked in rotary wing activities of the sea services.

Eligibility   This program is open to active-duty Navy, Marine Corps, or Coast Guard rotary wing aviators, aircrewmen, or support personnel. Applicants must be working on or planning to work on an undergraduate or graduate degree in any field. Along with their application, they must submit a personal statement on their academic and career aspirations. Selection is based on that statement, academic proficiency, scholastic achievements and awards, extracurricular activities, employment history, and letters of recommendation.

Financial data   Stipends are approximately $2,000.

Duration   1 year.

Number awarded   4 each year: 2 to undergraduates and 2 to graduate students.

Deadline   January of each year.

[983]
NAVAL HELICOPTER ASSOCIATION MEMORIAL SCHOLARSHIPS

Naval Helicopter Association
Attn: Scholarship Fund
P.O. Box 180578
Coronado, CA 92178-0578
(619) 435-7139   Fax: (619) 435-7354
Web: nhascholarshipfund.org/scholarships-available.html

Summary   To provide financial assistance for college or graduate school to 1) active-duty personnel who are working or have worked in rotary wing activities of the sea services and 2) members of their families.

Eligibility   This program is open to 1) active-duty Navy, Marine Corps, or Coast Guard rotary wing aviators, aircrewmen, or support personnel; and 2) the children and spouses of those personnel. Applicants must be working on or planning to work on an undergraduate or graduate degree in any field. Along with their application, they must submit a personal statement on their academic and career aspirations. Selection is based on that statement, academic proficiency, scholastic achievements and awards, extracurricular activities, employment history, and letters of recommendation.

Financial data Stipends are approximately $2,000.

Duration 1 year.

Additional information This program includes the following named awards: the Edward and Veronica Ream Memorial Scholarship, the CDR Mort McCarthy Memorial Scholarship, the Charles Karman Memorial Scholarship, the LT Christian "Horse" Hescock Memorial Scholarship, and the Captain Mark Starr Memorial Scholarship.

Number awarded Varies each year; recently, 4 were awarded.

Deadline January of each year.

[984]
NAVY ADVANCED EDUCATION VOUCHER PROGRAM

U.S. Navy
Naval Education and Training Command (N523)
Professional Development and Technology Center
Attn: AEV Program Office
250 Dallas Street
Pensacola, FL 32508-5220
(850) 452-7268   Fax: (850) 452-1272
E-mail: jason.szot@navy.mil
Web: www.navycollege.navy.mil/aev/aev_stu.aspx

Summary To provide financial assistance to senior Navy enlisted personnel who are interested in earning an undergraduate or graduate degree during off-duty hours.

Eligibility This program is open to senior enlisted Navy personnel in ranks E-7 through E-9. Applicants should be transferring to, or currently on, shore duty with sufficient time ashore to complete a bachelor's or master's degree. Personnel at rank E-7 may have no more than 17 years in service, E-8 no more than 19 years, and E-9 no more than 22 years. The area of study must be certified by the Naval Postgraduate School as Navy-relevant.

Financial data This program covers education costs (tuition, books, and fees), to a maximum of $6,700 per year or a total of $20,000 per participant for a bachelor's degree or $20,000 per year or a total of $40,000 per participant for a master's degree.

Duration Up to 36 months from the time of enrollment for a bachelor's degree; up to 24 months from the time of enrollment for a master's degree.

Additional information Recently approved majors for bachelor's degrees included human resources, construction management, information technology, emergency and disaster management, paralegal, engineering, business administration, leadership and management, nursing, strategic foreign languages, and electrical/electronic technology. Approved fields of study for master's degrees included business administration, education and training management, emergency and disaster management, engineering and technology, homeland defense and security, human resources, information technology, leadership and management, project management, and systems analysis. Recipients of this assistance incur an obligation to remain on active duty following completion of the program for a period equal to 3 times the

number of months of education completed, to a maximum obligation of 36 months.

Number awarded Varies each year; recently, 20 of these vouchers were awarded: 15 for bachelor's degrees and 5 for master's degrees.

Deadline May of each year.

[985]
NAVY GRADUATE EDUCATION VOUCHER PROGRAM

U.S. Navy
Naval Education and Training Command
Center for Personal and Professional Development
Attn: GEV Program Office
6490 Saufley Field Road
Pensacola, FL 32509-5204
(850) 452-1001, ext. 2247   Fax: (850) 452-1272
E-mail: marjoriette.dilworth@navy.mil
Web: www.navycollege.navy.mil/gev/gev_home.aspx

Summary To provide financial assistance to Navy officers who are interested in earning a graduate degree in selected fields during off-duty hours.

Eligibility This program is open to active-duty unrestricted line (URL) Navy officers in ranks O-3 through O-5. Applicants should be transferring to, or currently on, shore duty with sufficient time ashore to complete a master's degree program. Officers who already have a graduate degree funded through Department of Defense assistance or veteran's education benefits are not eligible. Officers currently enrolled in a qualifying master's degree program using the Navy Tuition Assistance Program, using any other financial assistance program, or paying privately are eligible to apply for this program, but they are not eligible for reimbursement of any previously-paid educational expenses. The area of study must be certified by the Naval Postgraduate School as Navy-relevant.

Financial data This program covers graduate education costs (tuition, books, and fees), up to a maximum of $20,000 per year.

Duration Up to 24 months from the time of enrollment, provided the student maintains a GPA of 3.0 or higher.

Additional information This program began in 1999. Recently, support was provided for graduate study in chemistry, computer science, engineering, English, financial management, history, mathematics, operations analysis, operations research, and regional studies. Recipients of this assistance incur an obligation to remain on active duty following completion of the program for a period equal to 3 times the number of months of education completed, to a maximum obligation of 36 months.

Number awarded Varies each year; recently, 115 of these positions were available (40 for aviation officers, 30 for submarine officers, 40 for surface warfare officers, and 5 for special warfare and special operations officers).

Deadline Deadline not specified.

[986]
NAVY HEALTH PROFESSIONS SCHOLARSHIP PROGRAM

U.S. Navy
Attn: Navy Bureau of Medicine and Surgery
Accessions Department
8955 Wood Road, Suite 13132
Bethesda, MD 20889-5628
(301) 295-1217   Toll Free: (800) USA-NAVY
Fax: (301) 295-1811   E-mail: OH@med.navy.mil
Web: www.med.navy.mil

Summary To provide financial assistance for a graduate degree in a medical field to future Navy medical officers.

Eligibility Applicants for this assistance must be U.S. citizens, under 36 years of age, who are enrolled in or accepted at an accredited medical, osteopathic, dental, or optometry school or in their first year of a Ph.D. or Psy.D. program in clinical psychology located in the United States or Puerto Rico. Upon acceptance into the program, applicants are commissioned as officers in the U.S. Navy Medical Corps Reserve; after completion of medical school, they must perform at least 3 years of active-duty service in the U.S. Navy.

Financial data This program pays full tuition at any school of medicine, osteopathy, dentistry, or optometry or a course leading to a doctoral degree as a clinical psychologist located in the United States or Puerto Rico, and also covers the cost of fees, books, and required equipment. In addition, recipients are awarded a stipend of $2,157 per month for 10 1/2 months of the year; for the other 1 1/2 months of each year, they perform active-duty service, usually at a Navy medical facility, and receive the normal pay of an Ensign.

Duration Assistance under this program continues until the student completes work for a doctorate degree in medicine, osteopathy, dentistry, or optometry or a master's degree as a physician assistant.

Additional information Following receipt of the doctorate degree, recipients serve an internship and residency either in a naval hospital (in which case they receive Navy active-duty pay) or, if not selected for naval graduate medical education, in a civilian hospital (where they receive only the regular salary of the civilian institution). After completion of the residency, the students must begin the active-duty service obligation. That obligation is 1 year for each year of participation in the program, with a minimum service obligation of 3 years.

Number awarded Varies each year.

Deadline August of each year.

[987]
NAVY LAW EDUCATION PROGRAM

U.S. Navy
Attn: Naval Education and Training Command
Center for Personal and Professional Development
Code N2A2LEP
6490 Saufley Field Road
Pensacola, FL 32509-5204
(850) 452-1001, ext. 2219 E-mail: billie.colonna@navy.mil
Web: www.jag.navy.mil

Summary To provide financial assistance to Navy and Marine Corps officers who are interested in working on a law degree on a full-time basis.

Eligibility This program is open to active-duty Navy and Marine Corps commissioned officers in pay grade O-1 through O-3. Applicants must have served at least 2 but not more than 6 years on active duty and be able to complete 20 years of active service as a commissioned officer before their 62nd birthday. They must have a baccalaureate degree from an accredited institution and be interested in working on a degree at an ABA-accredited law school. U.S. citizenship is required.

Financial data This program provides payment of mandatory tuition and fees, up to $500 per year for required textbooks, and a 1-time payment of $1,500 for a bar examination review course. Recipients continue to earn full pay and benefits while attending law school.

Duration Participants must complete their law degree within 36 months.

Additional information Following completion of their law degree, participants serve as career judge advocates in the Navy for 2 years for each year of legal training from this program.

Number awarded 7 each year.

Deadline September of each year.

[988]
NAVY SEAL FOUNDATION SCHOLARSHIPS

Navy Seal Foundation
Attn: Chief Financial Officer
1619 D Street, Building 5326
Virginia Beach, VA 23459
(757) 363-7490   Fax: (757) 363-7491
E-mail: info@navysealfoundation.org
Web: www.navysealfoundation.org

Summary To provide financial assistance for college or graduate school to Naval Special Warfare (NSW) personnel and their families.

Eligibility This program is open to active-duty Navy SEALS, Special Warfare Combatant-craft Crewmen (SWCC), and military personnel assigned to other NSW commands. Their dependent children and spouses are also eligible. Applicants must be entering or continuing full or part-time students working on an associate or bachelor's degree. Active-duty and spouses, but not dependent children, may also work on a graduate degree. Selection is based on GPA, SAT scores, class ranking, extracurricular activities, volunteer community involvement, leadership positions held, military service record, and employment (as appropriate).

Financial data Stipends are $15,000, $7,500, or $5,000 per year.

Duration 1 year; may be renewed.

Number awarded Varies each year; recently, the Navy Seal Foundation awarded 16 scholarships for all of its programs: 3 for 4 years at $15,000 per year to high school seniors and graduates, 3 for 1 year at $7,500 to high school seniors and graduates, 3 for 1 year at $15,000 to current college students, 3 for 1 year at $7,500 to current college students, and 4 for 1 year at $5,000 to spouses.

Deadline February of each year.

[989]
NAVY TUITION ASSISTANCE PROGRAM

U.S. Navy
Attn: Naval Education and Training Professional
  Development and Technology Command
Code N814
6490 Saufley Field Road
Pensacola, FL 32509-5241
(850) 452-1001   Toll Free: (877) 838-1659
Fax: (850) 473-6401   E-mail: SFLY_TA.Navy@navy.mil
Web: www.navycollege.navy.mil/ta_info.aspx

Summary To provide financial assistance for high school, vocational, undergraduate, or graduate studies to Navy personnel.

Eligibility This program is open to active-duty Navy officers and enlisted personnel, including Naval Reservists on continuous active duty, enlisted Naval Reservists ordered to active duty for 120 days or more, and Naval Reservist officers ordered to active duty for 2 years or more. Applicants must register to take courses at accredited civilian schools during off-duty time. They must be working on their first associate, bachelor's, master's, doctoral, or professional degree. Tuition assistance is provided for courses taken at accredited colleges, universities, vocational/technical schools, private schools, and through independent study/distance learning (but not for flight training).

Financial data Those selected for participation in this program receive their regular Navy pay and 100% of tuition at the postsecondary educational institution of their choice, but capped at $250 per semester hour and 16 semester hours per fiscal year, or a total of $4,500 per fiscal year. Funding is available only for tuition, not fees or other associated expenses.

Duration Until completion of a bachelor's or graduate degree. Undergraduates must complete all courses with a grade of "C" or better; graduate students must complete classes with a grade of "B" of better. If recipients fail to achieve those grades, they must reimburse the Navy for all funds received.

Additional information Officers must agree to remain on active duty for at least 2 years after completion of courses funded by this program.

Number awarded Varies each year.

Deadline Deadline not specified.

[990]
NBCC FOUNDATION MILITARY SCHOLARSHIPS

National Board for Certified Counselors
Attn: NBCC Foundation
3 Terrace Way
Greensboro, NC 27403
(336) 232-0376   Fax: (336) 232-0010
E-mail: foundation@nbcc.org
Web: www.nbccf.applicantstack.com/x/detail/a2ei42lhwwzc

Summary To provide financial assistance to 1) current and former military personnel and 2) spouses of servicemembers who are interested in working on a master's degree in counseling.

Eligibility This program is open to students enrolled in an accredited master's degree counseling program who have completed at least 18 credit hours and are enrolled in at least 6 credit hours during the current semester. Applicants must be prior or current active-duty U.S. military service personnel or the spouse of a servicemember. Veterans must have served in the military within the past 5 years and have received an honorable discharge. Applicants must be able to demonstrate a commitment to apply for the National Certified Counselor credential prior to graduation and to provide counseling services to servicemembers and/or veterans for at least 2 years after graduation.

Financial data The stipend is $5,000.

Duration 1 year.

Additional information This program began in 2010.

Number awarded 5 each year.

Deadline October of each year.

[991]
NEVADA NATIONAL GUARD STATE TUITION WAIVER PROGRAM

Nevada National Guard
Attn: Education Officer
2460 Fairview Drive
Carson City, NV 89701-6807
(775) 887-7326   Fax: (775) 887-7279
E-mail: NV-TSC@ng.army.mil
Web: www.nv.ngb.army.mil

Summary To provide financial assistance to Nevada National Guard members who are interested in attending college or graduate school in the state.

Eligibility This program is open to active members of the Nevada National Guard who are interested in attending a public community college, 4-year college, or university in the state. Applicants must be residents of Nevada. Independent study, correspondence courses, and study at the William S. Boyd School of Law, the University of Nevada School of Medicine, and the UNLV School of Dental Medicine are not eligible.

Financial data This program provides a waiver of 100% of tuition at state-supported community colleges, colleges, or universities in Nevada.

Duration 1 year; may be renewed.

Additional information This program was established on a pilot basis in 2003 and became permanent in 2005. Recipients must attain a GPA of at least 2.0 or refund all tuition received.

Number awarded Varies each year.

Deadline Applications must be received at least 3 weeks prior to the start of classes.

[992]
NEW HAMPSHIRE NATIONAL GUARD TUITION WAIVER PROGRAM

Office of the Adjutant General
Attn: Education Office
State Military Reservation
4 Pembroke Road
Concord, NH 03301-5652
(603) 225-1312   Fax: (603) 225-1257
TDD: (800) 735-2964
E-mail: education@nharmyguard.com
Web: www.nh.ngb.army.mil/members/education

Summary To provide financial assistance to members of the New Hampshire National Guard who are interested in attending college or graduate school in the state.

Eligibility This program is open to active members of the New Hampshire National Guard who have completed advanced individual training or commissioning and have at least a 90% attendance rate at annual training and drill assemblies. Applicants may be working on any type of academic degree at public institutions in New Hampshire. They must apply for financial aid from their school, for the New Hampshire National Guard Scholarship Program, and for federal tuition assistance.

Financial data The program provides full payment of tuition.

Duration 1 year; may be renewed.

Additional information This program began in 1996.

Number awarded Varies each year, depending on availability of space.

Deadline Deadline not specified.

[993]
NEW JERSEY NATIONAL GUARD TUITION PROGRAM

New Jersey Department of Military and Veterans Affairs
Attn: New Jersey Army National Guard Education Center
3650 Saylors Pond Road
Fort Dix, NJ 08640-7600
(609) 562-0654   Toll Free: (888) 859-0352
Fax: (609) 562-0201
Web: www.state.nj.us/military/education/NJNGTP.htm

Summary To provide financial assistance for college or graduate school to New Jersey National Guard members and the surviving spouses and children of deceased members.

Eligibility This program is open to active members of the New Jersey National Guard who have completed Initial Active Duty for Training (IADT). Applicants must be New Jersey residents who have been accepted into a program of undergraduate or graduate study at any of 31 public institutions of higher education in the state. The surviving spouses and children of deceased members of the Guard who had completed IADT and were killed in the performance of their duties while a member of the Guard are also eligible if the school has classroom space available.

Financial data Tuition for up to 15 credits per semester is waived for full-time recipients in state-supported colleges or community colleges in New Jersey.

Duration 1 semester; may be renewed.

Number awarded Varies each year.

Deadline Deadline not specified.

[994]
NORTH CAROLINA NATIONAL GUARD TUITION ASSISTANCE PROGRAM

North Carolina National Guard
Attn: Education and Employment Center
1636 Gold Star Drive
Raleigh, NC 27607
(919) 664-6649   Toll Free: (800) 621-4136
Fax: (919) 664-6520
E-mail: stacy.m.steinmetz.nfg@mail.mil
Web: www.nc.ngb.army.mil/Services/Pages/Edu.aspx

Summary To provide financial assistance to members of the North Carolina National Guard who plan to attend college or graduate school in the state.

Eligibility This program is open to active members of the North Carolina National Guard (officer, warrant officer, or enlisted) who have at least 2 years of enlistment remaining after the end of the academic period for which tuition assistance is provided. Applicants must be enrolled in an eligible business or trade school, private institution, or public college/university in North Carolina. They may be working on a vocational, undergraduate, graduate, or doctoral degree.

Financial data The maximum stipend is currently $4,515 per academic year.

Duration 1 year; may be renewed.

Additional information This program is administered by the North Carolina State Education Assistance Authority.

Number awarded Varies each year; recently, 614 of these grants, with a value of $1,808,032, were awarded.

Deadline Deadline not specified.

[995]
NORTH DAKOTA NATIONAL GUARD TUITION ASSISTANCE PROGRAM

North Dakota National Guard
Attn: Education Services Office
P.O. Box 5511
Bismarck, ND 58506-5511
(701) 333-3064   E-mail: ngndj1esos@ng.army.mil
Web: www.ndguard.ngb.army.mil

Summary To provide financial assistance to members of the North Dakota National Guard who plan to attend college or graduate school in the state.

Eligibility This program is open to members of the North Dakota National Guard who have a record of satisfactory participation (no more than 9 unexcused absences in the past 12 months) and service remaining after completion of the class for which they are requesting assistance. Applicants must be seeking support for trade or vocational training or work on an associate, baccalaureate, or graduate degree. They must be attending or planning to attend a North Dakota higher education public institution or a participating private institution (currently, Jamestown College, University of Mary in Bismarck, MedCenter One College of Nursing, Rasmussen College, or Trinity Bible College). Full-time AGR personnel do not qualify for this program. This is an entitlement program, provided all requirements are met.

Financial data Participating colleges and universities waive 25% of tuition for eligible courses (undergraduate only), up to 25% of the tuition at the University of North Dakota. Through this program, the National Guard provides reimbursement of the remaining 75% of tuition for eligible courses (undergraduate and graduate), or up to 75% of the tuition at the University of North Dakota. The program also reimburses 100% of all regular fees, not to exceed 100% of the regular fees charged by the University of North Dakota. State reimbursements are paid directly to the student in the form of a check, based upon the number of credit hours successfully completed.

Duration Benefits are available for up to 144 semester credit hours or the completion of an undergraduate or graduate degree, provided the recipient earns a grade of "C" or higher in each undergraduate course or "B" or higher in each graduate course.

Number awarded Varies each year.

Deadline Applications should be submitted at least 30 days before the semester begins.

[996]
PENNSYLVANIA NATIONAL GUARD EDUCATIONAL ASSISTANCE PROGRAM

Pennsylvania Higher Education Assistance Agency
Attn: Special Programs
1200 North Seventh Street
P.O. Box 8157
Harrisburg, PA 17105-8157
(717) 720-2800   Toll Free: (800) 692-7392
Fax: (717) 720-3786   TDD: (800) 654-5988
Web: www.pheaa.org

Summary To provide scholarship/loans for college or graduate school to Pennsylvania National Guard members.

Eligibility This program is open to active members of the Pennsylvania National Guard who are Pennsylvania residents and serving as enlisted personnel, warrant officers, or commissioned officers of any grade. Applicants must accept an obligation to serve in the Pennsylvania National Guard for a period of 6 years from the date of entry into the program. Students who do not possess a baccalaureate degree must be enrolled full or part time in an approved program of education at an approved institution of higher learning in Pennsylvania. Master's degree students are supported on a part-time basis only. Guard members receiving an ROTC scholarship of any type are not eligible.

Financial data Full-time undergraduate students receive payment of 100% of tuition at a state-owned university. Part-time students receive either actual tuition charged or two-thirds of the full-time tuition charged to a Pennsylvania resident at a state-owned university, whichever is less. Graduate students receive either half the actual tuition charged or one-third of the full-time tuition charged to a Pennsylvania resident at a state-owned university, whichever is less. Recipients who fail to fulfill the service obligation must repay all funds received within 10 years, including interest at 7%.

Duration Up to 5 years.

Additional information This program, first offered in 1997, is jointly administered by the Pennsylvania Department of Military and Veterans Affairs and the Pennsylvania Higher Education Assistance Agency. Support for summer and graduate school is available only if funding permits.

Number awarded Varies each year; recently, 1,789 members of the Pennsylvania National Guard were enrolled in this program.

Deadline April of each year for students at colleges, universities, and transferable programs at community colleges; July of each year for students at business schools, trade/technical schools, hospital schools of nursing, and non-transferable programs at community colleges.

[997]
PLATOON LEADERS CLASS MARINE CORPS TUITION ASSISTANCE PROGRAM

U.S. Marine Corps
Attn: Marine Corps Recruiting Command
3280 Russell Road
Quantico, VA 22134-5103
(703) 784-9449   Fax: (703) 784-9859
E-mail: wendelrf@mcrc.usmc.mil
Web: www.marines.com

Summary To provide financial assistance to undergraduate and law students interested in participating in summer Marine Corps training programs and becoming an officer.

Eligibility This program is open to members of the Marine Corps Reserves enrolled full time in a bachelor's or law (J.D. or equivalent) degree program. Applicants must participate in the Marine Corps Platoon Leader Class (PLC) Program for 2 summers (if they enter the program as freshmen or sophomores) or for 1 summer (if they enter the program as juniors, seniors, or law students). They must agree to accept a commission in the active-duty Marine Corps and serve 5 years following completion of their degree. Undergraduates must have a score of at least 1000 on the critical reading and mathematics sections of the SAT, a combined score of at least 45 on the verbal and mathematics section of the ACT, or at least 120 on the Armed Forces Vocational Aptitude Battery. Law students must have an LSAT score of 150 or higher.

Financial data This program provides reimbursement of tuition, books, and required fees, up to a maximum of $5,200 per academic year.

Duration Up to 3 consecutive years, or completion of a bachelor's or law degree.

Additional information Participants who successfully obtain a bachelor's or law degree and complete officer candidate training are commissioned as second lieutenants in the Regular Marine Corps. This program was established in 1999.

Number awarded Up to 1,200 each year.

Deadline December of each year.

[998]
POST-9/11 GI BILL

Department of Veterans Affairs
Attn: Veterans Benefits Administration
810 Vermont Avenue, N.W.
Washington, DC 20420
(202) 418-4343   Toll Free: (888) GI-BILL1
Web: www.benefits.va.gov/gibill/post911_gibill.asp

Summary To provide financial assistance to military personnel and veterans who entered service on or after September 11, 2001.

Eligibility This program is open to current and former military personnel who 1) served on active duty for at least 90 aggregate days after September 11, 2001; or 2) were discharged with a service-connected disability after 30 days. Applicants must be planning to enroll in an educational program, including work on an undergraduate or graduate degree, vocational/technical training, on-the-job training, flight training, correspondence training, licensing and national testing programs, entrepreneurship training, and tutorial assistance.

Financial data Participants working on an undergraduate or graduate degree at public institutions in their state receive full payment of tuition and fees. For participants who attend private institutions in most states, tuition and fee reimbursement is capped at $20,235.02 per academic year. Benefits for other types of training programs depend on the amount for which the veteran qualified under prior educational programs. Veterans also receive a monthly housing allowance that is 1) based on the Department of Defense Basic Allowance for Housing (BAH) for an E-5 with dependents (which depends on the location of the school but ranges from approximately $1,000 per month to approximately $2,500 per month); 2) $1,509 per month at schools in foreign countries; or 3) $754.50 per month for online training classes. They also receive an annual book allowance of $1,000 and (for participants who live in a rural county remote from an educational institution) a rural benefit payment of $500 per year.

Duration Most participants receive up to 36 months of entitlement under this program. Benefits are payable for up to 15 years following release from active duty.

Additional information This program, referred to as Chapter 33, began in 2009 as a replacement for previous educational programs for veterans and military personnel (e.g., Montgomery GI Bill, REAP). Current participants in those programs may be able to transfer benefits from those programs to this new plan. To qualify for 100% of Post 9/11-GI Bill benefits, transferees must have at least 36 months of active-duty service. Transferees with less service are entitled to smaller percentages of benefits, ranging down to 40% for those with only 90 days of service.

Number awarded Varies each year; since the program began, it has awarded approximately $30 billion in benefits to nearly 1 million veterans.

Deadline Deadline not specified.

[999]
REDUCED TUITION FOR SOUTH DAKOTA NATIONAL GUARD MEMBERS

South Dakota Board of Regents
Attn: Scholarship Committee
306 East Capitol Avenue, Suite 200
Pierre, SD 57501-2545
(605) 773-3455   Fax: (605) 773-2422
E-mail: info@sdbor.edu
Web: www.sdbor.edu

Summary To provide financial assistance for college or graduate school to members of the South Dakota National Guard.

Eligibility Eligible to apply for this assistance are members of the South Dakota Army or Air National Guard who are South Dakota residents, have satisfactorily completed Initial Active Duty for Training (IADT), meet the entrance requirements at 1 of the 6 state educational institutions or 4 state vocational/technical schools, maintain sustained membership in their National Guard unit, and maintain satisfactory academic progress.

Financial data Qualifying Guard members are eligible for a 50% reduction in tuition at any state-supported postsecondary institution in South Dakota.

Duration This assistance is available for up to 128 credit hours at the undergraduate level and up to 32 credit hours at the graduate level.

Additional information Students participating in the Army Continuing Education Systems (ACES) or the Montgomery GI Bill are not authorized to use this program.

Number awarded Varies each year.

Deadline Deadline not specified.

[1000]
RESERVE EDUCATIONAL ASSISTANCE PROGRAM

Department of Veterans Affairs
Attn: Veterans Benefits Administration
810 Vermont Avenue, N.W.
Washington, DC 20420
(202) 418-4343   Toll Free: (888) GI-BILL1
Web: www.benefits.va.gov/gibill/reap.asp

Summary To provide financial assistance for college or graduate school to members of the Reserves or National Guard who are called to active duty during a period of national emergency.

Eligibility This program is open to members of the Selected Reserve and Individual Ready Reserve (including Reserve elements of the Army, Navy, Air Force, Marine Corps, and Coast Guard, as well as the Army National Guard and the Air National Guard) who have served on active duty on or after September 11, 2001 for at least 90 consecutive days. Applicants must be interested in working on an undergraduate or graduate degree, vocational or technical training, on-the-job or apprenticeship training, correspondence training, tests for licenses or certificates, or flight training.

Financial data For full-time study at a college or university, the current monthly rate is $686.80 for personnel with consecutive service of 90 days but less than 1 year, $1030.20 for personnel with consecutive service of more than 1 year but less than 2 years, or $1,373.60 for those with consecutive service of 2 years or more. Reduced rates apply for part-time college or university study, apprenticeship and on-the-job training, licensing and certification training, cooperative education, correspondence courses, and flight training.

Duration Up to 36 months for full-time study. There is no fixed time for persons eligible for this program to utilize its benefits (except in the case of a member separated from the Ready Reserve for a disability, who are entitled to benefits for 10 years after the date of eligibility).

Additional information This program, established in 2005, is frequently referred to as Chapter 1607.

Number awarded Varies each year.

Deadline Applications may be submitted at any time.

[1001]
RHODE ISLAND NATIONAL GUARD STATE TUITION ASSISTANCE PROGRAM

Rhode Island National Guard
Joint Force Headquarters
Attn: Education Service Office
645 New London Avenue
Cranston, RI 02920-3097
(401) 275-4039   Fax: (401) 275-4014
E-mail: dean.l.mansfield.mil@mail.mil
Web: states.ng.mil

Summary To provide financial support to members of the National Guard in Rhode Island interested in attending college or graduate school in the state.

Eligibility This program is open to active members of the Rhode Island National Guard in good standing who are currently satisfactorily participating in all unit training assemblies and annual training periods. Applicants must have at least 1 year of service remaining. They must be enrolled in or planning to enroll in an associate, bachelor's, or master's degree program at a public institution in the state.

Financial data Qualified Guard members are exempt from payment of tuition for up to 5 courses per semester.

Duration 1 semester; may be renewed.

Additional information This program began in 1999. The designated institutions are the University of Rhode Island, Rhode Island College, and the Community College of Rhode Island.

Number awarded Varies each year.

Deadline Deadline not specified.

[1002]
ROBERT W. BRUNSMAN MEMORIAL SCHOLARSHIP

International Military Community Executives' Association
Attn: Scholarship
P.O. Box 7946
Round Rock, TX 78683-7946
(940) 463-5145   Fax: (866) 369-2435
E-mail: imcea@imcea.org
Web: www.imcea.org/awards/scholarship-info

Summary To provide financial assistance to members of the International Military Community Executives' Association (IMCEA) who are working in the field of military morale, welfare, and recreation (MWR) and currently enrolled in college or graduate school.

Eligibility This program is open to regular IMCEA members who are currently employed in the field of military MWR. Applicants must be already enrolled at a college or university, either on-campus or online, and taking undergraduate or graduate courses related to MWR. Along with their application, they must submit a 2-page essay on how all MWR services (e.g., clubs, bowling, golf, child care, libraries) might work together to create synergy and enhance the mission of IMCEA. Selection is based on that essay, participation in IMCEA activities, and involvement in military MWR services.

Financial data The stipend is $1,000.

Duration 1 year.

Additional information Regular membership in IMCEA is open to Army, Air Force, Navy, Marine Corps, and Coast Guard personnel who provide MWR services at military installations and bases worldwide.

Number awarded 1 each year.

Deadline May of each year.

[1003]
SAMUEL ELIOT MORISON NAVAL HISTORY SCHOLARSHIP

Naval History and Heritage Command
Attn: Senior Historian
Washington Navy Yard
805 Kidder Breese Street, S.E.
Washington Navy Yard, DC 20374-5060
(202) 433-3940   Fax: (202) 433-3593
Web: www.history.navy.mil/prizes/prize3.htm

Summary To provide financial assistance to Navy and Marine Corps officers who are working on a graduate degree in a field related to naval history.

Eligibility This program is open to active-duty commissioned officers of the U.S. Navy or U.S. Marine Corps who are working on a graduate degree in history, international relations, or a related field. Applications must be submitted through and endorsed by applicants' commanding officers. Selection is based on the relevance of the chosen area of study to U.S. naval history; demonstrated professional performance with particular emphasis on the officer's specialty; academic ability, including baccalaureate record; career needs of the officer; and potential for professional growth.

Financial data The stipend is $5,000; funds are to be used for expenses related to research, travel, and the purchase of books or other educational materials.

Duration 1 year.

Number awarded 1 each year.

Deadline March of each year.

[1004]
SFC CURTIS MANCINI MEMORIAL SCHOLARSHIPS

Association of the United States Army-Rhode Island
   Chapter
c/o CSM (Ret) Anthony Ferri, Secretary
47 Spokane Street
Providence, RI 02904
(401) 861-2997   E-mail: afnf458673755@aol.com
Web: www.ausari.org/index.html

Summary To provide financial assistance to members of the Rhode Island Chapter of the Association of the United States Army (AUSA) and their families who are interested in attending college or graduate school in any state.

Eligibility This program is open to members of the AUSA Rhode Island Chapter and their family members (spouses, children, and grandchildren). Applicants must be high school seniors or graduates accepted at an accredited college, university, or vocational/technical school in any state or current undergraduate or graduate students. Along with their application, they must submit a 250-word essay on why they feel their achievements should qualify them for this award. Selection is based on academic and individual achievements; financial need is not considered. Membership in AUSA is open to current and retired Army personnel (including Reserves and National Guard), ROTC cadets, or civilian employees of the Army.

Financial data The stipend is $1,000.

Duration 1 year.

Number awarded 2 each year.

Deadline March of each year.

[1005]
SIGMA CHI MILITARY SERVICE SCHOLARSHIPS

Sigma Chi Foundation
Attn: Scholarship Committee
1714 Hinman Avenue
Evanston, IL 60201
(847) 869-3655, ext. 270   Fax: (847) 869-4906
E-mail: heidi.holley@sigmachi.org
Web: foundation.sigmachi.org

Summary To provide financial assistance to undergraduate and graduate student members of Sigma Chi who are serving or have served in the military.
Eligibility This program is open to undergraduate and graduate brothers of the fraternity who are currently serving or have served in the military (Army, Navy, Air Force, Marines, Coast Guard, or National Guard). They must have earned a GPA of 2.5 or higher and have completed at least 2 semesters of undergraduate study.
Financial data The stipend is $1,000. Funds are to be used for tuition/fees only and are paid directly to the recipient's school.
Duration 1 year.
Number awarded Varies each year.
Deadline May of each year.

[1006]
TILLMAN MILITARY SCHOLARS PROGRAM

Pat Tillman Foundation
217 North Jefferson Street, Suite 602
Chicago, IL 60661
(773) 360-5277
E-mail: scholarships@pattillmanfoundation.org
Web: www.pattillmanfoundation.org/apply-to-be-a-scholar

Summary To provide financial assistance to active service-members, veterans, and their spouses who are interested in working on an undergraduate or graduate degree.
Eligibility This program is open to veterans and active servicemembers of all branches of the armed forces from both the pre- and post-September 11 era and their spouses; children are not eligible. Applicants must be enrolled or planning to enroll full time at a 4-year public or private college or university to work on an undergraduate, graduate, or postgraduate degree. Current and former servicemembers must submit 400-word essays on 1) their motivation and decision to serve in the U.S. military and how that decision and experience has changed their life and ambitions; and 2) their educational and career goals, how they will incorporate their military service experience into those goals, and how they intend to continue their service to others and the community. Spouses must submit 400-word essays on 1) their previous service to others and the community; and 2) their educational and career goals, how they will incorporate their service experiences and the impact of their spouse's military service into those goals, and how they intend to continue their service to others and the community. Selection is based on those essays, educational and career ambitions, record of military service, record of personal achievement, demonstration of service to others in the community, desire to continue such service, and leadership potential.
Financial data The stipend depends on the need of the recipient and the availability of funds; recently, stipends averaged approximately $15,000.
Duration 1 year; may be renewed, provided the recipient maintains a GPA of 3.0 or higher, remains enrolled full time, and documents participation in civic action or community service.
Additional information This program began in 2009.
Number awarded 60 each year. Since the program began, it has awarded more than $6 million to 348 scholars.
Deadline March of each year.

[1007]
TROOPS-TO-TEACHERS PROGRAM

Defense Activity for Non-Traditional Education Support
Attn: Troops to Teachers
6490 Saufley Field Road
Pensacola, FL 32509-5243
Toll Free: (800) 231-6242   Fax: (850) 452-1096
E-mail: ttt@navy.mil
Web: www.troopstoteachers.net/Home.aspx

Summary To provide funding 1) to earn a teaching certificate or 2) for a bonus to military personnel and veterans interested in a second career as a public school teacher.
Eligibility This program is open to 1) active-duty military personnel who are retired or currently serving and have an approved date of retirement within 1 year; 2) members of a Reserve component who are retired or currently serving in the Selected Reserve with 10 or more years of credible service and commit to serving an additional 3 years or until eligible for retirement; 3) military personnel with at least 6 years on continuous active duty, will transfer to the Selected Reserve within 4 years, and are willing to commit to at least 3 years in the Selected Reserve or until eligible for retirement; and 4) active-duty or Selected Reserve personnel who separated on or after January 8, 2002 for a service-connected physical disability and who register for this program within 4 years of separation. Applicants must have a baccalaureate or advanced degree, the equivalent of 1 year of college with 6 years of work experience in a vocational or technical field, or meet state requirements for vocational/technical teacher referral. A bonus is available to applicants who are willing to accept employment as a teacher in 1) a school district that has at least 10% of the students from families living below the poverty level; and 2) at a specific school within the district where at least 50% of the students are eligible for the free or reduced cost lunch program or where at least 13.5% of the students have disabilities. A stipend is available to applicants who are willing to accept employment as a teacher at 1) any school within a "high need" district that has at least 20% of the students from families living below the poverty level; or 2) at a specific school where at least 50% of the students are eligible for the free or reduced cost lunch program or at least 13.5% of the students have disabilities, as long as that school is in a district that has between 10% and 20% of students who come from poverty-level families. Preference is given to applicants interested in teaching mathematics, science, or special education.
Financial data A bonus of $10,000 is awarded to recipients who agree to teach for 3 years in a school that serves a high percentage of students from low-income families. A stipend of $5,000 is awarded to recipients who agree to teach for 3 years in a school located in a "high-need" district; stipend funds are also intended to help pay for teacher certification costs.
Duration The bonuses are intended as 1-time grants.
Additional information This program began in 1994 by the Department of Defense (DoD). In 2000, program oversight and funding were transferred to the U.S. Department of Education, but DoD continues to operate the program. The No Child Left Behind Act of 2001 provided for continuation of the program.
Number awarded Varies each year.
Deadline Deadline not specified.

[1008]
U.S. ARMY WOMEN'S FOUNDATION LEGACY SCHOLARSHIPS

U.S. Army Women's Foundation
Attn: Scholarship Committee
P.O. Box 5030
Fort Lee, VA 23801-0030
(804) 734-3078   E-mail: info@awfdn.org
Web: www.awfdn.org/programs/legacyscholarships.shtml

Summary To provide financial assistance for college or graduate school to women who are serving or have served in the Army and their children.

Eligibility This program is open to 1) women who have served or are serving honorably in the U.S. Army, U.S. Army Reserve, or Army National Guard; and 2) children of women who served honorably in the U.S. Army, U.S. Army Reserve, or Army National Guard. Applicants must be 1) high school graduates or GED recipients enrolled at a community college or technical certificate program who have a GPA of 2.5 or higher; 2) sophomores or higher at an accredited college or university who have a GPA of 3.0 or higher; or 3) students enrolled in or accepted to a graduate program who have a GPA of 3.0 or higher. Along with their application, they must submit a 2-page essay on why they should be considered for this scholarship, their future plans as related to their program of study, and information about their community service, activities, and work experience. Selection is based on merit, academic potential, community service, and financial need.

Financial data The stipend is $2,500 for college and graduate students or $1,000 for community college and certificate students.

Duration 1 year.

Number awarded 5 to 10 each year.

Deadline January of each year.

[1009]
UTAH NATIONAL GUARD STATE TUITION ASSISTANCE PROGRAM

Utah Army National Guard
Attn: UT-G1-ESO
12953 South Minuteman Drive
P.O. Box 1776
Draper, UT 84020-1776
(801) 432-4354
E-mail: ng.ut.utarng.list.education-office@mail.mil
Web: www.ut.ngb.army.mil/education2/statetuition.htm

Summary To provide tuition assistance to currently-enrolled members of the Utah National Guard interested in working on an undergraduate or graduate degree.

Eligibility This program is open to Utah residents who are MOS/AFSC qualified members of the Utah National Guard. Applicants must be seeking funding to obtain a 1) high school diploma or GED certification; 2) undergraduate, graduate, vocational, technical, or licensure certificate; 3) associate degree; 4) baccalaureate degree; or 5) master's degree. Support is not provided for doctoral or first professional degrees, such as architecture, certified public accountant, podiatry (D.P.M.), dentistry (D.D.S. or D.M.D.), medicine (M.D.), optometry (O.D.), osteopathic medicine (D.O.), pharmacy (Pharm.D.), law (J.D.), or theology (M.Div. or M.H.L.). Enlisted personnel must have remaining obligation on their existing enlistment contract that will extend to or beyond the last date

of course enrollment for these funds. Officers must have at least 4 years of Selected Reserve service remaining from the date of completion of the course for which this funding is provided.

Financial data Support is provided for 100% of the cost of tuition, to a maximum of $250 per hour or a maximum of $4,500 per year.

Duration 1 semester; recipients may renew.

Additional information Recipients of this funding may continue to receive any GI Bill funding to which they are entitled, but they may not simultaneously apply for this and federal Tuition Assistance benefits.

Number awarded Varies each year; recently, a total of $750,000 was available for this program.

Deadline Applications must be received at least 3 weeks prior to the course start date. They are processed on a first-come, first-served basis.

[1010]
VETERANS UNITED FOUNDATION SCHOLARSHIPS

Veterans United Home Loans
Attn: Veterans United Foundation
1400 Veterans United Drive
Columbia, MO 65203
(573) 445-7999   Toll Free: (800) 884-5560
E-mail: customer_service@vu.com
Web: www.enhancelives.com/scholarships

Summary To provide financial assistance for college or graduate school to students who have a tie to the military.

Eligibility This program is open to 1) active-duty military personnel with plans to attend college; 2) honorably-discharged veterans of the U.S. military; 3) spouses of military members or veterans; 4) surviving spouses and children of fallen servicemembers; and 5) children of veterans or active-duty military. Applicants must be attending or planning to attend college as a full-time undergraduate or graduate student. They must have a GPA of 2.5 or higher. Selection is based primarily on an essay.

Financial data The stipend is $2,000.

Duration 1 year.

Additional information This program began in 2007.

Number awarded Up to 20 each year: 10 each term.

Deadline April or October of each year.

[1011]
VIRGINIA NATIONAL GUARD TUITION ASSISTANCE PROGRAM

Virginia National Guard
Attn: Educational Services Officer
Fort Pickett, Building 316
Blackstone, VA 23824-6316
(434) 298-3020   Toll Free: (888) 483-2682
Fax: (434) 298-6296
E-mail: ng.va.vaarng.mbx.ngva-education@mail.mil
Web: vko.va.ngb.army.mil

Summary To provide financial assistance to members of the Virginia National Guard who are interested in attending college or graduate school in the state.

Eligibility This program is open to active members of the Virginia National Guard who are residents of Virginia and interested in attending college or graduate school in the state.

Awards are presented in the following priority order: 1) enlisted personnel who have previously received assistance through this program; 2) officers who need to complete a bachelor's degree in order to be eligible for promotion to captain; 3) warrant officers working on an associate or bachelor's degree; 4) any member working on an undergraduate degree; and 4) any member working on a graduate degree.

Financial data The program provides reimbursement of tuition at approved colleges, universities, and vocational/technical schools in Virginia, to a maximum of $2,000 per semester or $6,000 per year. Bookstore grants up to $350 per semester are also provided.

Duration 1 semester; may be renewed.

Additional information This program began in 1983. Recipients must remain in the Guard for at least 2 years after being funded.

Number awarded Varies each year.

Deadline June of each year for fall semester; October of each year for spring semester; March of each year for summer session.

[1012]
VIRGINIA PENINSULA POST SAME SCHOLARSHIPS

Society of American Military Engineers-Virginia Peninsula
  Post
c/o James H. King, Jr., Scholarship Chair
129 Andrews Street, Suite 217
Hampton, VA 23665
(757) 764-7570   Fax: (757) 764-3439
E-mail: james.king.45@us.af.mil

Summary To provide financial assistance to high school seniors, undergraduates, and graduate students entering or enrolled at universities in Virginia who have a tie to the Virginia Peninsula Post of the Society of American Military Engineers (SAME) and are majoring in engineering or architecture.

Eligibility This program is open to 1) high school seniors planning to enroll in an engineering or architecture program at an accredited college or university in Virginia; 2) students enrolled as freshmen through graduate students at an accredited college or university in Virginia and working on a bachelor's or higher degree in engineering or architecture; and 3) members and dependents of members of the SAME Virginia Peninsula Post. Applicants must have demonstrated commitment to future military service by enrolling in an ROTC program, a commissioning program, or an extended enlistment. Selection is based on academic standing and accomplishments (50%), involvement in university and community programs, including those with military involvement (30%), and financial need (20%).

Financial data The stipend is $1,500.

Duration 1 year.

Number awarded 4 each year: 1 to a high school senior, 1 to a college freshman or sophomore, 1 to a college junior or senior, and 1 to a graduate student.

Deadline February of each year.

[1013]
WASHINGTON NATIONAL GUARD SCHOLARSHIP PROGRAM

Washington National Guard
Attn: Education Services Office
41st Division Drive, Building 15
Camp Murray, WA 98430
(253) 512-8435   Toll Free: (800) 606-9843 (within WA)
Fax: (253) 512-8941
E-mail: education@washingtonguard.org
Web: washingtonguard.org/edu

Summary To provide forgivable loans to members of the Washington National Guard who wish to attend college or graduate school in the state.

Eligibility This program is open to members of the Washington National Guard who have already served for at least 1 year and have at least 2 years remaining on their current contract. Applicants must have a rank between E1 and O3. They must be attending an accredited college as a resident of Washington state and must already have utilized all available federal educational benefits. Army Guard members must have completed BCT/AIT and awarded initial MOS; Air Guard members must have completed BMT/initial tech school and been awarded "3-Level" AFSC. Graduate students are eligible, but undergraduates receive preference as long as they are making satisfactory progress toward a baccalaureate degree. The minimum GPA requirement is 2.5 for undergraduates or 3.0 for graduate students.

Financial data This program provides a stipend that is based on the number of credits completed but does not exceed the amount required for tuition, books, and fees at the University of Washington. Recipients incur a service obligation of 1 additional year in the Guard for the initial scholarship award and 1 additional year for each full year of academic credit completed with this assistance. The grant serves as a loan which is forgiven if the recipient completes the contracted service time in the Washington National Guard. Failure to meet the service obligation requires the recipient to repay the loan plus 8% interest.

Duration 1 year; may be renewed.

Number awarded Varies each year. A total of $100,000 is available for this program annually; scholarships are awarded on a first-come, first-served basis as long as funds are available.

Deadline June of each year.

[1014]
WEST VIRGINIA NATIONAL GUARD EDUCATIONAL ENCOURAGEMENT PROGRAM

Office of the Adjutant General
Attn: Education Officer
1703 Coonskin Drive
Charleston, WV 25311-1085
(304) 561-6306   Toll Free: (866) 986-4326
Fax: (304) 561-6307   E-mail: kathy.kidd@us.army.mil
Web: www.wv.ngb.army.mil/education/benefits/default.aspx

Summary To provide financial assistance to members of the National Guard in West Virginia who are interested in attending college or graduate school in the state.

Eligibility This program is open to active members of the West Virginia National Guard who are residents of West Virginia and interested in attending a public or private college in the state. Applicants must have maintained satisfactory participation (90% attendance) in the Guard. They must be interested in working on a vocational, associate, bachelor's, or master's degree. In some instances, support may also be available to Guard members who are interested in working on an M.D., D.O., P.A., or J.D. degree.

Financial data The program provides payment of 100% of the tuition and fees at participating colleges and universities in West Virginia, to a maximum of $6,500 per year.

Duration 1 academic year; may be renewed.

Number awarded Varies each year.

Deadline Deadline not specified.

[1015]
WISCONSIN NATIONAL GUARD ENLISTED ASSOCIATION COLLEGE GRANT PROGRAM

Wisconsin National Guard Enlisted Association
Attn: Executive Director
2400 Wright Street
Madison, WI 53704-2572
(608) 242-3112   E-mail: WNGEA@yahoo.com
Web: www.wngea.org/extrasforyou/exfy-scho.htm

Summary To provide financial assistance to members of the Wisconsin National Guard Enlisted Association (WNGEA) and their spouses and children who are interested in attending college or graduate school in any state.

Eligibility This program is open to WNGEA members, the unmarried children and spouses of WNGEA members, and the unmarried children and spouses of deceased WNGEA members. WNGEA member applicants, as well as the parents or guardians of unmarried children who are applicants, must have at least 1 year remaining on their enlistment following completion of the school year for which application is submitted (or they must have 20 or more years of service). Applicants must be enrolled full or part time at a college, university, graduate school, trade school, or business school in any state. Selection is based on financial need, leadership, and moral character.

Financial data Stipends are $1,000 or $500 per year.

Duration 1 year; recipients may not reapply for 2 years.

Additional information This program includes 1 scholarship sponsored by the USAA Insurance Corporation.

Number awarded Varies each year; recently, 5 were awarded: the Raymond A. Matera Scholarship at $1,000 and 4 others (1 reserved for a graduate student) at $500 each.

Deadline April of each year.

[1016]
WOMEN MARINES ASSOCIATION SCHOLARSHIP PROGRAM

Women Marines Association
P.O. Box 377
Oaks, PA 19456-0377
Toll Free: (888) 525-1943
E-mail: scholarship@womenmarines.org
Web: www.womenmarines.org

Summary To provide financial assistance for college or graduate school to students with ties to the military who are sponsored by members of the Women Marines Association (WMA).

Eligibility Applicants must be sponsored by a WMA member and fall into 1 of the following categories: 1) have served

or are serving in the U.S. Marine Corps, regular or Reserve; 2) are a direct descendant by blood or legal adoption or a stepchild of a Marine on active duty or who has served honorably in the U.S. Marine Corps, regular or Reserve; 3) are a sibling or a descendant of a sibling by blood or legal adoption or a stepchild of a Marine on active duty or who has served honorably in the U.S. Marine Corps, regular or Reserve; or 4) have completed 2 years in a Marine Corps JROTC program. WMA members may sponsor an unlimited number of applicants per year. High school seniors must submit transcripts (GPA of 3.0 or higher) and SAT or ACT scores. Undergraduate and graduate students must have a GPA of 3.0 or higher.

Financial data Stipends are $1,500 or $3,000 per year.

Duration 1 year; may be renewed 1 additional year.

Additional information This program includes the following named scholarships: the WMA Memorial Scholarships, the Lily H. Gridley Memorial Scholarship, the Ethyl and Armin Wiebke Memorial Scholarship, the Maj. Megan Malia McClung Memorial Scholarship, the Agnes Sopcak Memorial Scholarship, the Virginia Guveyan Memorial Scholarship, and the LaRue A. Ditmore Music Scholarships. Applicants must know a WMA member to serve as their sponsor; the WMA will not supply listings of the names or addresses of chapters or individual members.

Number awarded Varies each year.

Deadline January of each year.

[1017]
WYOMING NATIONAL GUARD EDUCATIONAL ASSISTANCE PLAN

Wyoming National Guard
Attn: Education Services Officer
5410 Bishop Boulevard
Cheyenne, WY 82009
(307) 777-8160   Fax: (307) 777-8105
E-mail: philip.oconnor@wyo.gov
Web: wyomilitary.wyo.gov

Summary To provide financial assistance to members of the Wyoming National Guard who are interested in attending college or graduate school in the state.

Eligibility This program is open to members of the Wyoming Army National Guard and the Wyoming Air National Guard who have spent at least 6 years in the Guard or are currently serving under their initial 6-year enlistment period. New enlistees who commit to serving 6 years are also eligible. Applicants may be pursuing, or planning to pursue, a degree at any level at the University of Wyoming, a Wyoming community college, or an approved technical institution in Wyoming.

Financial data The program provides full payment of tuition at eligible institutions.

Duration Guard members may continue to receive these benefits as long as they maintain a GPA of 2.0 or higher, keep up with Guard standards for drill attendance, and remain in good standing with the Guard.

Additional information The Wyoming legislature created this program in 2001. Recipients must agree to serve in the Guard for at least 2 years after they graduate or stop using the plan.

Number awarded Varies each year.

Deadline Deadline not specified.

ROTC Students

[1018]
AIR FORCE GRADUATE LAW PROGRAM

U.S. Air Force
Attn: HQ USAF/JAX
1500 West Perimeter Road, Suite 3330
Joint Base Andrews, MD 20762
Toll Free: (800) JAG-USAF
E-mail: afsana.ahmed@pentagon.af.mil
Web: www.airforce.com

Summary To provide financial assistance to first-year law students who are willing to join Air Force ROTC and serve as Air Force Judge Advocates following completion of their studies.

Eligibility This program is open to students in their first year at an ABA-approved law school that has, or is located near, an AFROTC detachment. Applicants must be in good academic standing and able to meet AFROTC entry standards (U.S. citizenship, weight and medical qualifications, and Air Force Officer Qualification Test minimum score). They must be younger than 35 years of age upon commissioning and entering active duty. Eligible students include veterans, current military personnel, and first-year law students without military experience. Selection is based on academic performance, extracurricular activities, community service, prior military record (if any), work experience, and a recommendation by a staff judge advocate following an interview.

Financial data Participants receive a stipend for 10 months of the year at $400 per month and a salary at pay grade E-5 during summer field training. No other scholarship assistance is available.

Duration 2 years.

Additional information Selectees with no prior military experience attend field training encampment during the summer prior to entering the AFROTC program as contract cadets. Upon completion of their degree, participants are commissioned as inactive second lieutenants in the Air Force Reserves. After passing legal licensing requirements, they enter active duty as first lieutenants in the U.S. Air Force Judge Advocate General's Department. The initial required active-duty service obligation is 4 years.

Number awarded Varies each year.

Deadline January of each year.

[1019]
AIR FORCE ONE-YEAR COLLEGE PROGRAM (OYCP)

U.S. Air Force
Attn: HQ USAF/JAX
1500 West Perimeter Road, Suite 3330
Joint Base Andrews, MD 20762
Toll Free: (800) JAG-USAF
E-mail: afsana.ahmed@pentagon.af.mil
Web: www.airforce.com

Summary To provide financial assistance to second-year law students who are willing to join Air Force ROTC and serve as Air Force Judge Advocates following completion of their studies.

Eligibility This program is open to students in their second year at an ABA-approved law school that has, or is located near, an AFROTC detachment. Applicants must be in good academic standing and able to meet AFROTC entry standards (U.S. citizenship, weight and medical qualifications, and Air Force Officer Qualification Test minimum score). They must be younger than 35 years of age upon commissioning and entering active duty. Selection is based on academic performance, extracurricular activities, community service, prior military record (if any), work experience, and a recommendation by a staff judge advocate following an interview.

Financial data Participants receive a stipend for 10 months of the year at $400 per month and a salary at pay grade E-5 during summer field training. No other scholarship assistance is available.

Duration 1 year.

Additional information Selectees with no prior military experience attend field training encampment during the summer prior to entering the AFROTC program as contract cadets. Upon completion of their degree, participants are commissioned as inactive second lieutenants in the Air Force Reserves. After passing legal licensing requirements, they enter active duty as first lieutenants in the U.S. Air Force Judge Advocate General's Department. The initial required active-duty service obligation is 4 years.

Number awarded Varies each year.

Deadline January of each year.

[1020]
AIR FORCE ROTC PROFESSIONAL OFFICER CORPS INCENTIVE

U.S. Air Force
Attn: Headquarters AFROTC/RRUC
551 East Maxwell Boulevard
Maxwell AFB, AL 36112-5917
(334) 953-2091   Toll Free: (866) 4-AFROTC
Fax: (334) 953-6167   E-mail: afrotc1@maxwell.af.mil
Web: www.afrotc.com/scholarships

Summary To provide financial assistance for undergraduate and graduate studies to individuals who have completed 2 years of college and who are willing to join Air Force ROTC and serve as Air Force officers following completion of their degree.

Eligibility Applicants must be U.S. citizens who have completed 2 years of the general military course at a college or university with an Air Force ROTC unit on campus or a college with a cross-enrollment agreement with such a college. They must be full-time students, have a GPA of 2.0 or higher both cumulatively and for the prior term, be enrolled in both Aerospace Studies class and Leadership Laboratory, pass the Air Force Officer Qualifying Test, meet Air Force physical fitness and weight requirements, and be able to be commissioned before they become 31 years of age. They must agree to serve for at least 4 years as active-duty Air Force officers following graduation from college with either a bachelor's or graduate degree.

Financial data This scholarship provides a monthly subsistence allowance of $350 as a junior or $400 as a senior.

Duration Until completion of a graduate degree.

Additional information Scholarship recipients must complete 4 years of aerospace studies courses at 1 of the 143 colleges and universities that have an Air Force ROTC unit on campus; students may also attend 850 other colleges that have cross-enrollment agreements with the institutions that have an Air Force ROTC unit on campus. Recipients must also attend a 4-week summer training camp at an Air Force base between their junior and senior year.

Number awarded Varies each year.

Deadline Deadline not specified.

[1021]
BRAXTON BRAGG CHAPTER AUSA SCHOLARSHIPS

Association of the United States Army-Braxton Bragg Chapter
Attn: Vice President for Scholarships
P.O. Box 70036
Fort Bragg, NC 28307
(910) 396-3755   E-mail: hbraxtonbraggc@nc.rr.com
Web: www.braggausa.org/?page_id=1425

Summary To provide financial assistance to members of the Braxton Bragg Chapter of the Association of the United States Army (AUSA) in North Carolina and their dependents who are interested in attending college or graduate school in any state.

Eligibility This program is open to chapter members and their families in North Carolina who are working on or planning to work on an undergraduate, graduate, or technical degree at a college or technical school in any state. Applicants must submit a 500-word essay on how the Army and Army values have influenced their life; letters of recommendation; a list of personal accomplishments; and a transcript that includes their ACT or SAT score. Selection is based on academic achievement, participation in extracurricular activities at school, and participation in community service activities. Membership in AUSA is open to current and retired Army personnel (including Reserves and National Guard), ROTC cadets, or civilian employees of the Army. Active-duty soldiers are especially encouraged to apply.

Financial data The stipend is $1,000.

Duration 1 year; recipients may reapply.

Additional information Membership in the Braxton Bragg Chapter is open to all Army active, National Guard, and Reserve members in North Carolina, along with Department of the Army civilians, retirees, concerned citizens, and family members.

Number awarded Varies each year; recently, 26 were awarded.

Deadline April of each year.

[1022]
DEDICATED ARMY NATIONAL GUARD (DEDARNG) SCHOLARSHIPS

U.S. Army National Guard
Education Support Center
Camp J.T. Robinson
Box 46
North Little Rock, AR 72199-9600
Toll Free: (866) 628-5999   E-mail: esc@ng.army.mil
Web: www.nationalguard.com/tools/guard-scholarships

Summary To provide financial assistance to college and graduate students who are interested in enrolling in Army ROTC and serving in the Army National Guard following graduation.

Eligibility This program is open to full-time students entering their sophomore or junior year of college with a GPA of 2.5 or higher. Applicants must have a GPA of 2.5 or higher and scores of at least 19 on the ACT or 920 on the combined mathematics and critical reading SAT. Graduate students may also be eligible if they have only 2 years remaining for completion of their degree. Students who have been awarded an ROTC campus-based scholarship may apply to convert to this program during their freshman year. Applicants must meet all medical and moral character requirements for enrollment in Army ROTC. They must be willing to enroll in the Simultaneous Membership Program (SMP) of an ROTC unit on their campus; the SMP requires simultaneous membership in Army ROTC and the Army National Guard.

Financial data Participants receive full reimbursement of tuition, a grant of $1,200 per year for books, plus an ROTC stipend for 10 months of the year at $350 per month during their sophomore year, $450 per month during their junior year, and $500 per month during their senior year. As a member of the Army National Guard, they also receive weekend drill pay at the pay grade of a sergeant (approximately $225 per month) while participating in the SMP.

Duration 2 or 3 years.

Additional information After graduation, participants serve 3 to 6 months on active duty in the Officer Basic Course (OBC). Following completion of OBC, they are released from active duty and are obligated to serve 8 years in the Army National Guard.

Number awarded Approximately 600 each year.

Deadline Deadline not specified.

[1023]
DONALDSON D. FRIZZELL MEMORIAL SCHOLARSHIPS

First Command Educational Foundation
Attn: Scholarship Programs Manager
1 FirstComm Plaza
Fort Worth, TX 76109-4999
(817) 569-2634   Toll Free: (877) 872-8289
Fax: (817) 569-2970   E-mail: Scholarships@fcef.com
Web: www.fcef.com

Summary To provide financial assistance to students, especially those with ties to the military (including ROTC), who are entering or attending college or graduate school.

Eligibility This program is open to 1) members of a U.S. uniformed service and their spouses and dependents; 2) clients of First Command Financial Services and their family members; 3) dependent family members of First Command Advisors or field office staff members; or 4) non-contractual ROTC students. Applicants may be traditional students (high school seniors and students already enrolled at a college, university, or accredited trade school) or nontraditional students (those defined by their institution as nontraditional and adult students planning to return to a college, university, or accredited trade school. They must have a GPA of 3.0 or higher and be working on a trade school certification or associate, undergraduate, or graduate degree. Applicants must submit 1-page essays on 1) their active involvement in community service programs; 2) the impact of financial literacy on their future; and 3) why they need this scholarship. Selection is based primarily on the essays, academic merit, and financial need.

Financial data Stipends are $5,000 or $2,500. Funds are disbursed directly to the recipient's college, university, or trade school.

Duration 1 year.

Additional information The sponsoring organization was formerly known as the USPA & IRA Educational Foundation, founded in 1983 to provide scholarships to the children of active, retired, or deceased military personnel. In addition to these scholarships, for which students may apply directly, it supports scholarships offered by a number of partner organizations. Since its establishment, it has awarded scholarships worth nearly $4 million.

Number awarded 6 each year: 2 at $5,000 and 4 at $2,500. Awards are split evenly between the 2 categories.

Deadline The online application process begins in February of each year and continues until 200 applications have been received in each category.

[1024]
HONOLULU POST SAME SCHOLARSHIPS

Society of American Military Engineers-Honolulu Post
P.O. Box 201445
Honolulu, HI 96820
Web: www.samehonolulu.org

Summary To provide financial assistance to residents of Hawaii (particularly military servicemembers, military dependents, and ROTC students) who are interested in attending college or graduate school in any state to work on a degree in engineering or architecture.

Eligibility This program is open to residents of Hawaii who are graduating high school seniors or current undergraduates enrolled or planning to enroll full time at an accredited college or university in any state. Applicants must be planning to work on an undergraduate or graduate degree in engineering or architecture. They must be U.S. citizens and have a GPA of 3.0 or higher. Military affiliation or experience (i.e., ROTC, member or dependent of a member of the Society of Military Engineers (SAME), military dependent, Junior ROTC) is not required but is given preference. Along with their application, they must submit a transcript; a resume of work experience, academic activities, and extracurricular accomplishments; and a 1-page essay on how their engineering or architecture degree will impact our nation.

Financial data The stipend is $2,000 or $1,500 per year.

Duration 1 year for the $2,000 scholarships; 4 years for the $1,500 scholarships.

Number awarded Varies each year; recently, 6 were awarded: 2 at $2,000 for 1 year and 4 at $1,500 per year for 4 years.

Deadline March of each year.

[1025]
MEDICAL CORPS OPTION OF THE SEAMAN TO ADMIRAL-21 PROGRAM

U.S. Navy
Attn: Commander, Naval Service Training Command
250 Dallas Street, Suite A
Pensacola, FL 32508-5268
(850) 452-9563   Fax: (850) 452-2486
E-mail: PNSC_STA21@navy.mil
Web: www.sta-21.navy.mil/program_options.asp

Summary To allow outstanding enlisted Navy personnel to work on a bachelor's degree, affiliate with an ROTC unit, be accepted to medical school, earn an M.D. or D.O. degree, and be commissioned in the Navy Medical Corps.

Eligibility This program is open to U.S. citizens who are currently serving on active duty in the U.S. Navy or Naval Reserve, including Full Time Support (FTS), Selected Reserves (SELRES), and Navy Reservists on active duty, except for those on active duty for training (ACDUTRA). Applicants must be high school graduates (or GED recipients) who are able to 1) complete requirements for a baccalaureate degree within 36 months; 2) complete a medical degree through the Uniformed Services University of Health Services (USUHS) or the Health Professions Scholarship Program (HPSP); and 3) complete 20 years of active commissioned service as a physician by age 62. Within the past 3 years, they must have taken the SAT (and achieved scores of at least 500 on the mathematics section and 500 on the critical reading section) or the ACT (and achieved a score of at least 21 on the mathematics portion and 20 on the English portion).

Financial data Awardees continue to receive their regular Navy pay and allowances while they attend college on a full-time basis. They also receive reimbursement for tuition, fees, and books up to $10,000 per year. If base housing is available, they are eligible to live there. Participants are not eligible to receive benefits under the Navy's Tuition Assistance Program (TA), the Montgomery GI Bill (MGIB), the Navy College Fund, or the Veterans Educational Assistance Program (VEAP).

Duration Selectees are supported for up to 36 months of full-time, year-round study or completion of a bachelor's degree, as long as they maintain a GPA of 3.0 or higher. They are then supported until completion of a medical degree.

Additional information Upon acceptance into the program, selectees attend the Naval Science Institute (NSI) in Newport, Rhode Island for an 8-week program in the fundamental core concepts of being a naval officer (navigation, engineering, weapons, military history and justice, etc.). They then enter an NROTC affiliated college or university with a pre-medical program that confers an accredited B.S. degree to pursue full-time study. They become members of and drill with the NROTC unit. After they complete their bachelor's degree, they are commissioned as an ensign in the Naval Reserve. They must apply to and be accepted at medical school, either the USUSH or a civilian medical school through the HPSP. Following completion of medical school, they are promoted to lieutenant and assigned to active duty in the Medical Corps. Selectees incur a service obligation of 5 years for their baccalaureate degree support plus whatever obligation they incur for medical degree support (usually 7 years if they attend USUSH or 4 years if they attend a civilian institution through HPSP).

Number awarded Varies each year.

Deadline June of each year.

[1026]
SFC CURTIS MANCINI MEMORIAL SCHOLARSHIPS

Association of the United States Army-Rhode Island
  Chapter
c/o CSM (Ret) Anthony Ferri, Secretary
47 Spokane Street
Providence, RI 02904
(401) 861-2997   E-mail: afnf458673755@aol.com
Web: www.ausari.org/index.html

Summary To provide financial assistance to members of the Rhode Island Chapter of the Association of the United States Army (AUSA) and their families who are interested in attending college or graduate school in any state.

Eligibility This program is open to members of the AUSA Rhode Island Chapter and their family members (spouses, children, and grandchildren). Applicants must be high school seniors or graduates accepted at an accredited college, university, or vocational/technical school in any state or current undergraduate or graduate students. Along with their application, they must submit a 250-word essay on why they feel their achievements should qualify them for this award. Selection is based on academic and individual achievements; financial need is not considered. Membership in AUSA is open to current and retired Army personnel (including Reserves and National Guard), ROTC cadets, or civilian employees of the Army.

Financial data The stipend is $1,000.

Duration 1 year.

Number awarded 2 each year.

Deadline March of each year.

[1027]
VIRGINIA PENINSULA POST SAME SCHOLARSHIPS

Society of American Military Engineers-Virginia Peninsula
  Post
c/o James H. King, Jr., Scholarship Chair
129 Andrews Street, Suite 217
Hampton, VA 23665
(757) 764-7570   Fax: (757) 764-3439
E-mail: james.king.45@us.af.mil

Summary To provide financial assistance to high school seniors, undergraduates, and graduate students entering or enrolled at universities in Virginia who have a tie to the Virginia Peninsula Post of the Society of American Military Engineers (SAME) and are majoring in engineering or architecture.

Eligibility This program is open to 1) high school seniors planning to enroll in an engineering or architecture program at an accredited college or university in Virginia; 2) students enrolled as freshmen through graduate students at an accredited college or university in Virginia and working on a bachelor's or higher degree in engineering or architecture; and 3) members and dependents of members of the SAME Virginia Peninsula Post. Applicants must have demonstrated commitment to future military service by enrolling in an ROTC program, a commissioning program, or an extended enlistment. Selection is based on academic standing and accomplishments (50%), involvement in university and community programs, including those with military involvement (30%), and financial need (20%).

Financial data The stipend is $1,500.

Duration 1 year.

Number awarded 4 each year: 1 to a high school senior, 1 to a college freshman or sophomore, 1 to a college junior or senior, and 1 to a graduate student.

Deadline February of each year.

Military Family Members

[1028]
100TH INFANTRY BATTALION MEMORIAL SCHOLARSHIP FUND

Hawai'i Community Foundation
Attn: Scholarship Department
827 Fort Street Mall
Honolulu, HI 96813
(808) 566-5570   Toll Free: (888) 731-3863
Fax: (808) 521-6286
E-mail: scholarships@hcf-hawaii.org
Web: www.hawaiicommunityfoundation.org/scholarships

Summary To provide financial assistance for college or graduate school to descendants of 100th Infantry Battalion World War II veterans.

Eligibility This program is open to entering and continuing full-time undergraduate and graduate students at 2- and 4-year colleges and universities. Applicants must be a direct descendant of a World War II veteran of the 100th Infantry Battalion (which was comprised of Americans of Japanese descent). They must be able to demonstrate academic achievement (GPA of 3.5 or higher), an active record of extracurricular activities and community service, a willingness to promote the legacy of the 100th Infantry Battalion of World War II, and financial need. Along with their application, they must submit a short statement indicating their reasons for attending college, their planned course of study, their career goals, and what community service means to them. They must also submit a separate essay on the legacy of the 100th Infantry Battalion and how they will contribute to forwarding that legacy. Current residency in Hawaii is not required.

Financial data The amounts of the awards depend on the availability of funds and the need of the recipient. Recently, the average value of each of the scholarships awarded by the foundation was $2,200.

Duration 1 year.

Number awarded Varies each year; recently, 2 were awarded.

Deadline February of each year.

[1029]
11TH ARMORED CAVALRY VETERANS OF VIETNAM AND CAMBODIA SCHOLARSHIP

11th Armored Cavalry Veterans of Vietnam and
  Cambodia
Attn: National Headquarters
P.O. Box 956
Coffeyville, TX 76034-0956
Web: www.11thcavnam.com/scholarship/scholar.html

Summary To provide financial assistance for college or graduate school to members of the 11th Armored Cavalry

Veterans of Vietnam and Cambodia (11ACVVC) and to their children.

Eligibility This program is open to 1) current members of the 11ACVVC; 2) children and stepchildren of current members of the 11ACVVC; 3) children whose legal guardian is a current member of the 11ACVVC; 4) children of 11th Armored Cavalry troopers who were killed in action, died of wounds, or died as a result of service in Vietnam or Cambodia; and 5) children and stepchildren of 11th Armored Cavalry Regiment veterans who served in Vietnam or Cambodia but are not members of the 11ACVVC. There is no age limit. Applicants must be enrolled or planning to enroll as an undergraduate or graduate student. Along with their application, they must submit brief essays on 1) the field of study they plan to enter and why; and 2) why they would be a worthy recipient of this scholarship. Selection is based on those essays (15 points), completeness and legibility of the application (7 points), and grades (8 points); financial need is not considered.

Financial data The stipend is $4,000; funds are paid directly to the recipient's school, in 2 equal installments.

Duration 1 year; nonrenewable.

Additional information This program began in 1997. Recipients must use the awarded money within 44 months of being notified.

Number awarded Up to 24 each year. Since the program was established, it has awarded more than $1 million in scholarships.

Deadline May of each year.

[1030]
506TH AIRBORNE INFANTRY REGIMENT ASSOCIATION SCHOLARSHIP

506th Airborne Infantry Regiment Association
c/o Alfred May, Scholarship Committee
30 Sweetman Lane
West Milford, NJ 07480-2933
(973) 728-1458   E-mail: alfredmay@aol.com
Web: www.506infantry.org

Summary To provide financial assistance for college or graduate school to former members of the 506th Airborne Infantry Regiment and their families.

Eligibility This program is open to veterans who served with the 506th Airborne Infantry Regiment and their children, grandchildren, spouses, and siblings. Applicants must be entering or attending an undergraduate or graduate program at a college or university in the United States. They must submit a statement describing their personal achievements and career objectives. Selection is based on academic excellence, quality of the institution the applicant has chosen to attend, and financial need.

Financial data The stipend is $1,000.

Duration 1 year; nonrenewable.

Additional information This program includes the Marilyn and Eugene Overton Scholarship Award.

Number awarded 4 each year.

Deadline April of each year.

[1031]
ACADEMY SPOUSES CLUB MERIT SCHOLARSHIPS FOR SPOUSES

Academy Spouses Club
Attn: Sally Mueh, Scholarship Chair
P.O. Box 78
USAF Academy, CO 80840-0078
(719) 599-0694   E-mail: usafascholarships@live.com
Web: www.usafasc.org/scholarships.html

Summary To provide financial assistance to spouses of personnel affiliated with the Air Force Academy who are working on an undergraduate or graduate degree at a school in any state.

Eligibility This program is open to non-military spouses who are entering or continuing work on a degree at an accredited vocational school, junior college, 4-year college or university, or graduate school in any state. Military spouses at the rank of O-3 or below are also eligible. Applicants must be the spouse of 1) an active-duty military member stationed at the Air Force Academy; 2) a retiree who is eligible for membership in the sponsoring organization and resides in the Colorado Springs area; 3) an active-duty military member whose last assignment was the Air Force Academy and is on a remote tour and whose dependents remain in the area for the purpose of completing a high school education; 4) a POW/MIA or a deceased military member (applicant must reside in the area and have a military ID); 5) an Air Force National Guard or Reserve member currently assigned to the Air Force Academy; 6) a Department of Defense civilian employed at the Air Force Academy; or 7) an AFAAA employee. Selection is based on a statement of academic and personal goals, academic achievement, and community activities.

Financial data Stipends range from $500 to $1,000. Funds are sent directly to the recipient's school.

Duration 1 year; nonrenewable.

Number awarded Varies each year.

Deadline March of each year.

[1032]
AFCEA NOVA SCHOLARSHIPS

Armed Forces Communications and Electronics
    Association-Northern Virginia Chapter
Attn: Scholarship Chair
400 North Washington Street, Suite 300
Alexandria, VA 22314
(703) 778-4645   Fax: (703) 683-5480
E-mail: scholarships@afceanova.org
Web: www.afceanova.org/scholarships

Summary To provide financial assistance for undergraduate and graduate study in fields of science, technology, engineering, or mathematics (STEM) to military and civilian personnel affiliated with the Northern Virginia chapter of the Armed Forces Communications and Electronics Association (AFCEA NOVA).

Eligibility This program is open to residents of the greater Washington, D.C. area and to members of AFCEA NOVA and their children who live elsewhere. Applicants must be U.S. government service employees or military personnel (enlisted or junior grade officers) or their offspring; veterans are also given consideration. Applicants must be working on an undergraduate or graduate degree in a field of STEM (including information technology, computer science, and other technology fields supportive of national security). Selection is based on merit, although financial need and past and current military and government service may also be considered. U.S. citizenship is required.

Financial data The stipend is $2,000 for full-time students or $1,000 for part-time students.

Duration 1 year.

Additional information The greater Washington area is defined to include the District of Columbia; the Maryland counties of Calvert, Charles, Frederick, Montgomery, and Prince George's; the Virginia cities of Alexandria, Fairfax, Falls Church, Fredericksburg, Manassas, and Manassas Park; the Virginia counties of Arlington, Clarke, Culpeper, Fairfax, Fauquier, King George, Loudoun, Prince William, Spotsylvania, Stafford, and Warren; and the West Virginia counties of Berkeley and Jefferson.

Number awarded More than 30 each year.

Deadline February of each year.

[1033]
AIR FORCE SERVICES CLUB MEMBERSHIP SCHOLARSHIP PROGRAM

Air Force Services Agency
Attn: HQ AFPC/SVOFT
10100 Reunion Place, Suite 501
San Antonio, TX 78216-4138
(210) 395-7351   E-mail: clubs@myairforcelife.com
Web: www.myairforcelife.com/Clubs/Scholarship.aspx

Summary To recognize and reward, with funding for undergraduate or graduate studies, Air Force Club members and their families who submit outstanding essays.

Eligibility This program is open to Air Force Club members and their spouses, children, and stepchildren who have been accepted by or are enrolled at an accredited college or university. Grandchildren are eligible if they are the dependent of a club member. Applicants may be undergraduate or graduate students enrolled full or part time. They must submit an essay of up to 500 words on a topic that changes annually; a recent topic was "My Contribution to the Air Force." Applicants must also include a 1-page summary of their long-term career and life goals and previous accomplishments, including civic, athletic, and academic awards.

Financial data Awards are $1,000 scholarships. Each winner also receives a laptop computer.

Duration The competition is held annually.

Additional information This competition, first held in 1997, is sponsored by Chase Military Credit Card Services.

Number awarded 25 each year.

Deadline April of each year.

[1034]
AL AND WILLAMARY VISTE SCHOLARSHIP PROGRAM

101st Airborne Division Association
32 Screaming Eagle Boulevard
P.O. Box 929
Fort Campbell, KY 42223-0929
(931) 431-0199   Fax: (931) 431-0195
E-mail: 101stairbornedivisionassociation@comcast.net
Web: www.screamingeaglefoundation.org

Summary To provide financial assistance to the spouses, children, and grandchildren of members of the 101st Airborne Division Association who are upper-division or graduate students working on a degree in science.

Eligibility This program is open to college juniors, seniors, and graduate students who maintained a GPA of 3.75 or higher during the preceding school year and whose parent, grandparent, or spouse is (or, if deceased, was) a regular or life (not associate) member of the 101st Airborne Division. Preference is given to students working on a degree in a physical science, medical science, or other scientific research field. Applicants must submit a 500-word essay on what it means to be an American and a letter on their course of study, community service, hobbies, interests, personal achievements, and how a higher education for them in their chosen field can benefit our nation. Selection is based on the letter, career objectives, academic record, and letters of recommendation.

Financial data A stipend is awarded (amount not specified).

Duration 1 year; may be renewed.

Number awarded At least 1 each year.

Deadline May of each year.

[1035]
AL PONTE GRADUATE SCHOLARSHIP AWARD

Association of Former Intelligence Officers
Attn: Scholarships Committee
7700 Leesburg Pike, Suite 324
Falls Church, VA 22043
(703) 790-0320   Fax: (703) 991-1278
E-mail: scholarships@afio.com
Web: www.afio.com/13_scholarships.htm

Summary To provide financial assistance to members or the children or grandchildren of members of the Association of Former Intelligence Officers (AFIO) who are interested in working on a graduate degree in international relations and/or intelligence.

Eligibility This program is open to college seniors who are interested in attending graduate school to work on a degree in international relations and/or intelligence. Applicants must be AFIO members, the children or grandchildren of members, or the children or grandchildren of personnel currently serving in military intelligence. Selection is based on merit, character, estimated future potential, background, and relevance of their studies to the full spectrum of national security interests and career ambitions. U.S. citizenship is required.

Financial data The stipend is $1,000.

Duration 1 year.

Number awarded 1 each year.

Deadline June of each year.

[1036]
ALABAMA G.I. DEPENDENTS' SCHOLARSHIP PROGRAM

Alabama Department of Veterans Affairs
770 Washington Avenue, Suite 470
Montgomery, AL 36102-1509
(334) 242-5077   Fax: (334) 242-5102
Web: www.va.state.al.us/gi_dep_scholarship.aspx

Summary To provide educational benefits to the dependents of disabled, deceased, and other Alabama veterans.

Eligibility This program is open to children, spouses, and unremarried widow(er)s of veterans who are currently rated as 20% or more service-connected disabled or were so rated at time of death, were a former prisoner of war, have been declared missing in action, died as the result of a service-connected disability, or died while on active military duty in the line of duty. The veteran must have been a permanent civilian resident of Alabama for at least 1 year prior to entering active military service and served honorably for at least 90 days during wartime (or less, in case of death or service-connected disability). Veterans who were not Alabama residents at the time of entering active military service may also qualify if they have a 100% disability and were permanent residents of Alabama for at least 5 years prior to filing the application for this program or prior to death, if deceased. Children and step-children must be under the age of 26, but spouses and widow(er)s may be of any age. Spouses cease to be eligible if they become divorced from the qualifying veteran. Widow(er)s cease to be eligible if they remarry.

Financial data Eligible dependents may attend any state-supported Alabama institution of higher learning or enroll in a prescribed course of study at any Alabama state-supported trade school without payment of any tuition, book fees, or laboratory charges.

Duration This is an entitlement program for 5 years of full-time undergraduate or graduate study or part-time equivalent for all qualifying children and for spouses and unremarried widow(er)s who veteran spouse is or was rated 100% disabled or meets other qualifying requirements. Spouses and unremarried widow(er)s whose veteran spouse is or was rated between 20% and 90% disabled may attend only 3 standard academic years.

Additional information Benefits for children, spouses, and unremarried widow(er)s are available in addition to federal government benefits. Assistance is not provided for noncredit courses, placement testing, GED preparation, continuing educational courses, pre-technical courses, or state board examinations.

Number awarded Varies each year.

Deadline Applications may be submitted at any time.

[1037]
ARMY AVIATION ASSOCIATION OF AMERICA LOAN PROGRAM

Army Aviation Association of America
Attn: AAAA Scholarship Foundation
593 Main Street
Monroe, CT 06468-2806
(203) 268-2450   Fax: (203) 268-5870
E-mail: aaaa@quad-a.org
Web: www.quad-a.org

Summary To provide educational loans to members of the Army Aviation Association of America (AAAA) and their relatives.

Eligibility This program is open to AAAA members and their spouses, unmarried siblings, and unmarried children and grandchildren. Applicants must be enrolled or accepted for enrollment as an undergraduate or graduate student at an accredited college or university.

Financial data The maximum loan is $1,000 per year. All loans are interest free.

Duration Up to 4 years.

Number awarded Varies each year; recently, 1 of these loans was granted.

Deadline April of each year.

[1038]
ARMY AVIATION ASSOCIATION OF AMERICA SCHOLARSHIPS

Army Aviation Association of America Scholarship Foundation
Attn: AAAA Scholarship Foundation
593 Main Street
Monroe, CT 06468-2806
(203) 268-2450   Fax: (203) 268-5870
E-mail: aaaa@quad-a.org
Web: www.quad-a.org

Summary To provide financial aid for undergraduate or graduate study to members of the Army Aviation Association of America (AAAA) and their relatives.

Eligibility This program is open to AAAA members (or deceased members) and their spouses, unmarried siblings, unmarried children, and unmarried grandchildren. Applicants must be enrolled or accepted for enrollment as an undergraduate or graduate student at an accredited college or university. Graduate students must include a 250-word essay on their life experiences, work history, and aspirations. Some scholarships are specifically reserved for enlisted, warrant officer, company grade, and Department of the Army civilian members. Selection is based on academic merit and personal achievement.

Financial data Stipends range from $1,000 to $2,500 per year.

Duration Scholarships may be for 1 year, 2 years, or 4 years.

Number awarded Varies each year; recently, $363,500 in scholarships was awarded to 236 students. Since the program began in 1963, the foundation has awarded more than $4.5 million to nearly 2,700 qualified applicants.

Deadline April of each year.

[1039]
ARMY NURSE CORPS ASSOCIATION SCHOLARSHIPS

Army Nurse Corps Association
Attn: Education Committee
P.O. Box 39235
San Antonio, TX 78218-1235
(210) 650-3534   Fax: (210) 650-3494
E-mail: education@e-anca.org
Web: e-anca.org/ANCAEduc.htm

Summary To provide financial assistance to students who have a connection to the Army and are interested in working on an undergraduate or graduate degree in nursing.

Eligibility This program is open to U.S. citizens attending colleges or universities that have accredited programs offering associate, bachelor's, master's, or doctoral degrees in nursing. Applicants must be 1) students currently enrolled in an accredited baccalaureate or advanced nursing or nurse anesthesia program who are serving or have served (and received an honorable discharge) in any branch and at any rank of a component of the U.S. Army; or 2) nursing or anesthesia students whose parent(s) or spouse are serving or have served in a component of the U.S. Army. Along with their application, they must submit a personal statement on their professional career objectives, reasons for applying for this scholarship, financial need, special considerations, personal and academic interests, and why they are preparing for a nursing career. Students who are receiving any support from any branch of the military, including ROTC scholarships, are not eligible.

Financial data The stipend is $3,000. Funds are sent directly to the recipient's school.

Duration 1 year.

Additional information Although the sponsoring organization is made up of current, retired, and honorably discharged officers of the Army Nurse Corps, it does not have an official affiliation with the Army. Therefore, students who receive these scholarships do not incur any military service obligation.

Number awarded 1 or more each year.

Deadline April of each year.

[1040]
BART LONGO MEMORIAL SCHOLARSHIPS

National Chief Petty Officers' Association
c/o Marjorie Hays, Treasurer
1014 Ronald Drive
Corpus Christi, TX 78412-3548
Web: www.goatlocker.org/ncpoa/scholarship.htm

Summary To provide financial assistance for college or graduate school to members of the National Chief Petty Officers' Association (NCPOA) and their families.

Eligibility This program is open to members of the NCPOA and the children, stepchildren, and grandchildren of living or deceased members. Applicants may be high school seniors or graduates entering a college or university or students currently enrolled full time as undergraduate or graduate students. Selection is based on academic achievement and participation in extracurricular activities; financial need is not considered.

Financial data The stipend is $1,000.

Duration 1 year.

Additional information Membership in the NCPOA is limited to men and women who served or are serving as Chief Petty Officers in the U.S. Navy, U.S. Coast Guard, or their Reserve components for at least 30 days.

Number awarded 2 each year: 1 to a high school senior or graduate and 1 to an undergraduate or graduate student.

Deadline May of each year.

[1041]
BG BENJAMIN B. TALLEY SCHOLARSHIP

Society of American Military Engineers-Anchorage Post
Attn: BG B.B. Talley Scholarship Endowment Fund
P.O. Box 6409
Anchorage, AK 99506-6409
(907) 244-8063   E-mail: cturletes@gci.net
Web: www.sameanchorage.org/h_about/scholinfo.html

Summary To provide financial assistance to student members of the Society of American Military Engineers (SAME) from Alaska who are working on a bachelor's or master's degree in designated fields of engineering or the natural sciences.

Eligibility This program is open to members of the Anchorage Post of SAME who are residents of Alaska, attending college in Alaska, an active-duty military member stationed in Alaska, or a dependent of an active-duty military member stationed in Alaska. Applicants must be 1) sophomores, juniors, or seniors majoring in engineering, architecture, construction or project management, natural sciences, physical sciences, applied sciences, or mathematics at an accredited college or university; or 2) students working on a master's degree in those fields. They must have a GPA of 2.5 or higher. U.S. citizenship is required. Along with their application, they must submit an essay of 250 to 500 words on their career goals. Selection is based on that essay, academic achievement, participation in school and community activities, and work/family activities; financial need is not considered.

Financial data Stipends range up to $3,000.

Duration 1 year.

Additional information This program began in 1997.

Number awarded Several each year; at least 1 scholarship is reserved for a master's degree students.

Deadline December of each year.

[1042]
BRAXTON BRAGG CHAPTER AUSA SCHOLARSHIPS

Association of the United States Army-Braxton Bragg Chapter
Attn: Vice President for Scholarships
P.O. Box 70036
Fort Bragg, NC 28307
(910) 396-3755   E-mail: hbraxtonbraggc@nc.rr.com
Web: www.braggausa.org/?page_id=1425

Summary To provide financial assistance to members of the Braxton Bragg Chapter of the Association of the United States Army (AUSA) in North Carolina and their dependents who are interested in attending college or graduate school in any state.

Eligibility This program is open to chapter members and their families in North Carolina who are working on or planning to work on an undergraduate, graduate, or technical degree at a college or technical school in any state. Applicants must submit a 500-word essay on how the Army and Army values have influenced their life; letters of recommendation; a list of personal accomplishments; and a transcript that includes their ACT or SAT score. Selection is based on academic achievement, participation in extracurricular activities at school, and participation in community service activities. Membership in AUSA is open to current and retired Army personnel (including Reserves and National Guard), ROTC cadets, or civilian employees of the Army. Active-duty soldiers are especially encouraged to apply.

Financial data The stipend is $1,000.

Duration 1 year; recipients may reapply.

Additional information Membership in the Braxton Bragg Chapter is open to all Army active, National Guard, and Reserve members in North Carolina, along with Department of the Army civilians, retirees, concerned citizens, and family members.

Number awarded Varies each year; recently, 26 were awarded.

Deadline April of each year.

[1043]
BUCKINGHAM MEMORIAL SCHOLARSHIPS

Air Traffic Control Association
Attn: Scholarship Fund
1101 King Street, Suite 300
Alexandria, VA 22314
(703) 299-2430   Fax: (703) 299-2437
E-mail: info@atca.org
Web: www.atca.org/ATCA-Scholarship

Summary To provide financial assistance for college or graduate school to children of current or former air traffic control specialists.

Eligibility This program is open to U.S. citizens who are the children, natural or adopted, of a person currently or formerly serving as an air traffic control specialist with the U.S. government, with the U.S. military, or in a private facility in the United States. Applicants must be enrolled or planning to enroll at least half time in a baccalaureate or graduate program at an accredited college or university and have at least 30 semester hours to be completed before graduation. Along with their application, they must submit a 500-word essay on how they will blend their career with community service in their adult life. Financial need is considered in the selection process.

Financial data A stipend is awarded; recently, scholarships awarded by this sponsor averaged more than $5,000.

Duration 1 year; may be renewed.

Additional information This program was formerly known as the Children of Air Traffic Control Specialists Scholarship Program.

Number awarded Varies each year; recently, 4 were awarded.

Deadline April of each year.

[1044]
CALIFORNIA NON-RESIDENT COLLEGE FEE WAIVER PROGRAM FOR MILITARY PERSONNEL AND DEPENDENTS

California Department of Veterans Affairs
Attn: Division of Veterans Services
1227 O Street, Room 101
P.O. Box 942895
Sacramento, CA 94295
(916) 653-2573   Toll Free: (877) 741-8532
Fax: (916) 653-2563   TDD: (800) 324-5966
Web: www.calvet.ca.gov

Summary To waive non-resident fees at public institutions in California for undergraduate or graduate students from other states who are active-duty military personnel, recently-discharged veterans, or dependents of active-duty military personnel.

Eligibility This program is open to residents of states outside California who are 1) veterans of the U.S. armed forces who spent more than 1 year on active duty in California immediately prior to being discharged; 2) members of the U.S. armed forces stationed in California on active duty; or 3) the natural or adopted child, stepchild, or spouse of a member of the U.S. armed forces stationed in California on active duty. Applicants must be attending or planning to attend a community college, branch of the California State University system, or campus of the University of California as an undergraduate or graduate student.

Financial data This program waives non-resident fees of qualifying military personnel, veterans, and families who attend publicly-supported community or state colleges or universities in California.

Duration 1 year; may be renewed until completion of an undergraduate degree or for 1 additional year for military personnel working on a graduate degree; nonrenewable for graduate students who are children or spouses.

Number awarded Varies each year.

Deadline Deadline not specified.

[1045]
CGMA EDUCATION LOAN PROGRAM

Coast Guard Mutual Assistance
4200 Wilson Boulevard, Suite 610
Arlington, VA 20598-7180
(202) 872-6716   Toll Free: (800) 881-2462
E-mail: ARL-DG-CGMA@uscg.mil
Web: www.cgmahq.org

Summary To provide loans to members of Coast Guard Mutual Assistance (CGMA) and their families who are working on an undergraduate or graduate degree.

Eligibility This program is open to 1) active-duty or retired Coast Guard personnel; 2) members of the Coast Guard Selected Reserve and retirement-eligible members of the IRR; 3) Coast Guard permanent and term civilian employees; 4) Coast Guard Auxiliary members; 5) U.S. Public Health Service officers serving with the Coast Guard; 6) unremarried widowed spouses of any of those; and 7) unmarried dependent children under 23 years of age and not enrolled in any military service of any of those. Applicants must be enrolled in an associate, bachelor's, or graduate degree program or an approved vocational/technical training program.

Financial data The maximum loan is $2,000.

Duration Loans must be repaid by the end of the month in which the course is completed.

Number awarded Varies each year.

Deadline Applications must be submitted no later than 30 days after the course begins.

[1046]
CHAN-PADGETT SPECIAL FORCES MEMORIAL SCHOLARSHIP

American Academy of Physician Assistants-Veterans Caucus
Attn: Veterans Caucus
P.O. Box 362
Danville, PA 17821-0362
Fax: (302) 526-7154 E-mail: fbrace@veteranscaucus.org
Web: www.veteranscaucus.org

Summary To provide financial assistance to children and spouses of veterans of the Army Special Forces who are studying to become physician assistants.

Eligibility This program is open to U.S. citizens who are currently enrolled in a physician assistant program. The program must be approved by the Commission on Accreditation of Allied Health Education. Applicants must be children or surviving spouses of honorably discharged members of the Army Special Forces. Selection is based on military honors and awards received, civic and college honors and awards received, professional memberships and activities, and GPA.

An electronic copy of the sponsor's DD Form 214 must accompany the application.

Financial data The stipend is $2,000.

Duration 1 year.

Additional information This program began in 2002.

Number awarded 1 each year.

Deadline February of each year.

[1047]
CHILDREN AND SPOUSES OF INDIANA NATIONAL GUARD PROGRAM

Indiana Commission for Higher Education
Attn: Division of Student Financial Aid
W462 Indiana Government Center South
402 West Washington Street
Indianapolis, IN 46204
(317) 232-2355   Toll Free: (888) 528-4719 (within IN)
Fax: (317) 232-3260   E-mail: awards@sfa.che.in.gov
Web: www.in.gov/sfa/2528.htm

Summary To provide financial assistance to residents of Indiana who are children or spouses of deceased members of the National Guard and interested in attending college or graduate school in the state.

Eligibility This program is open to residents of Indiana whose father, mother, or spouse was a member of the Indiana National Guard and suffered a service-connected death while serving on state active duty. Applicants must be interested in working on an undergraduate, graduate, or professional degree at an eligible institution in Indiana.

Financial data Qualified applicants receive a 100% remission of tuition and all mandatory fees for undergraduate, graduate, or professional degrees at eligible postsecondary schools and universities in Indiana. Support is not provided for such fees as room and board.

Duration Up to 124 semester hours of study.

Number awarded Varies each year.

Deadline Applications must be submitted at least 30 days before the start of the college term.

[1048]
COAST GUARD FOUNDATION ENLISTED RESERVE SCHOLARSHIPS

U.S. Coast Guard
Attn: COMDT (CG-1311)
2703 Martin Luther King, Jr. Avenue, S.E., Stop 7907
Washington, DC 20593-7907
(202) 475-5459   E-mail: travis.p.thornell@uscg.mil
Web: www.uscg.mil/reserve/awards

Summary To provide financial assistance for college or graduate school to members of the Coast Guard Reserves and their dependents.

Eligibility This program is open to Coast Guard enlisted reservists (Selected Reserve or Individual Ready Reserve) and their dependents who are registered in the Defense Enrollment Eligibility Reporting System (DEERS). Applicants must be enrolled or accepted for enrollment at 1) an accredited institution in a program leading to an associate, bachelor's, master's, or doctoral degree; or 2) a 2- or 4-year course of study at an accredited technical or vocational training school. Along with their application, they must submit a 1-page essay on how the participation of themselves, their spouse, or their parent in the Coast Guard Reserve has con-

tributed to their success. Selection is based on that essay and academic achievement.

Financial data The stipend is $1,000.

Duration 1 year.

Additional information This program is sponsored by the United States Automobile Association (USAA) Insurance Corporation.

Number awarded 6 each year.

Deadline July of each year.

[1049]
COL CARL F. BASWELL FALLEN ENGINEER MEMORIAL SCHOLARSHIP

Army Engineer Association
Attn: Program Coordinator
P.O. Box 30260
Alexandria, VA 22310-8260
(703) 428-7084   Fax: (703) 428-6043
E-mail: execasst@armyengineer.com
Web: www.armyengineer.com/scholarships.htm

Summary To provide financial assistance for college to children and spouses of U.S. Army Engineers who were killed in Iraq or Afghanistan.

Eligibility This program is open to the children and spouses of U.S. Army Engineers who were killed in combat during Operation Iraqi Freedom or Operation Enduring Freedom. Applicants must be working on or planning to work on an associate, bachelor's, or master's degree at an accredited college or university. Selection is based primarily on financial need, although potential for academic success and personal references are also considered.

Financial data The stipend is $2,500.

Duration 1 year.

Additional information This program began in 2010.

Number awarded 1 each year.

Deadline June of each year.

[1050]
COLONEL JERRY W. ROSS SCHOLARSHIP

American Pharmacists Association
Attn: APhA Foundation
2215 Constitution Avenue, N.W.
Washington, DC 20037-2985
(202) 429-7565   Toll Free: (800) 237-APhA
Fax: (202) 638-3793   E-mail: bwall@aphanet.org
Web: www.aphafoundation.org

Summary To provide financial assistance for work on a degree in pharmacy to Air Force pharmacy technicians who are members of the Academy of Student Pharmacists of the American Pharmacists Association (APhA-ASP) and their families.

Eligibility This program is open to full-time pharmacy students who are either 1) Air Force pharmacy technicians working on a degree in pharmacy; or 2) family members of an Air Force pharmacist or technician who is enrolled in an accredited college of pharmacy. Applicants must have been actively involved in their school's APhA-ASP chapter. They must have completed at least 1 year in the professional sequence of courses with a GPA of 2.75 or higher. Along with their application, they must submit a 500-word essay on a topic that changes annually but relates to the future of the pharmacy profession, 2 letters of recommendation, a current resume or curriculum vitae, and a list of pharmacy and non-pharmacy related activities. Preference is given to applicants who indicate further Air Force service.

Financial data The stipend is $1,000.

Duration 1 year; recipients may reapply.

Number awarded 1 each year.

Deadline November of each year.

[1051]
CONNECTICUT TUITION WAIVER FOR VETERANS

Connecticut Board of Regents for Higher Education
39 Woodland Street
Hartford, CT 06105
(860) 723-0013   E-mail: fitzgerald2@ct.edu
Web: www.ct.edu/admission/veterans

Summary To provide financial assistance for college or graduate school to certain Connecticut military servicemembers, veterans, and their dependents.

Eligibility This program is open to 1) honorably-discharged Connecticut veterans who served at least 90 days during specified periods of wartime; 2) active members of the Connecticut Army or Air National Guard; 3) Connecticut residents who are a dependent child or surviving spouse of a member of the armed forces killed in action on or after September 11, 2001 who was also a Connecticut resident; and 4) Connecticut residents who are a dependent child or surviving spouse of a person officially declared missing in action or a prisoner of war while serving in the armed forces after January 1, 1960. Applicants must be attending or planning to attend a public college or university in the state.

Financial data The program provides a waiver of 100% of tuition for students working on an undergraduate or graduate degree at the University of Connecticut (including summer sessions and winter intersession), 100% of tuition for general fund courses at campuses of Connecticut State University, 50% of tuition for extension and summer courses at campuses of Connecticut State University, 100% of tuition at all Connecticut community colleges, and 50% or fees at Charter Oak State College.

Duration Up to 4 years.

Additional information This is an entitlement program; applications are available at the respective college financial aid offices.

Number awarded Varies each year.

Deadline Deadline not specified.

[1052]
CONNIE SETTLES SCHOLARSHIP

American Legion Auxiliary
Department of California
205 13th Street, Suite 3300
San Francisco, CA 94103-2461
(415) 861-5092   Fax: (415) 861-8365
E-mail: calegionaux@calegionaux.org
Web: www.calegionaux.org/scholarships.htm

Summary To provide financial assistance to members of the American Legion Auxiliary in California who are attending college or graduate school in the state.

Eligibility This program is open to residents of California who are currently working on an undergraduate or graduate degree at a college or university in the state. Applicants must

have been members of the American Legion Auxiliary for at least the 2 preceding years and be current members. Each unit of the Auxiliary may nominate only 1 member. Selection is based on transcripts, 2 letters of recommendation, a letter from the applicant about themselves and their goals, and financial need. Support is not provided for programs of study deemed to be nonessential (e.g., sewing classes, aerobics, sculpting).

Financial data The stipend is $5,000. Funds are paid directly to the recipient's college or university.

Duration 1 year.

Number awarded 1 each year.

Deadline Applications must be submitted to Auxiliary units by February of each year.

[1053]
DAEDALIAN FOUNDATION DESCENDANTS' SCHOLARSHIP PROGRAM

Daedalian Foundation
Attn: Scholarship Committee
55 Main Circle (Building 676)
P.O. Box 249
Randolph AFB, TX 78148-0249
(210) 945-2113   Fax: (210) 945-2112
E-mail: daedalus@daedalians.org
Web: www.daedalians.org/scholarships.htm

Summary To provide financial assistance to descendants of members of the Order of Daedalians who wish to prepare for a career in military aviation or space.

Eligibility This program is open to descendants of members of the order who are working on or planning to work on a baccalaureate or higher degree. Applicants must be interested in and willing to commit to a career as a commissioned military pilot, flight crew member, astronaut, or commissioned officer in 1 of the armed forces of the United States in a discipline directly supporting aeronautics or astronautics. They must be physically and mentally qualified for flight and/or space; if they intend to pursue a non-flying career as a commissioned officer in a scientific or engineering discipline supporting aviation or space, they must pass a physical examination qualifying for active commissioned duty in the U.S. armed forces. Nominations must be submitted by a local chapter (Flight) of Daedalian. Selection is based on academic achievement and recognition, extracurricular activities, honors, and employment experience. Financial need may be considered if all other factors are equal.

Financial data The stipend is $2,000.

Duration 1 year.

Additional information The Order of Daedalians was founded in 1934 as an organization of the nearly 14,000 aviators who served as military pilots during World War I and are still listed and designated as Founder Members. In the 1950s, the organization expanded eligibility to include 1) on a sponsorship basis, current and former commissioned military pilots from all services; and 2) on a hereditary basis, descendants of Founder Members.

Number awarded Up to 3 each year.

Deadline July of each year.

[1054]
DISABLED AMERICAN VETERANS AUXILIARY NATIONAL EDUCATION SCHOLARSHIP FUND

Disabled American Veterans Auxiliary
Attn: National Education Scholarship Fund
3725 Alexandria Pike
Cold Spring, KY 41076
(859) 441-7300   Toll Free: (877) 426-2838, ext. 4020
Fax: (859) 442-2095   E-mail: dava@davmail.org
Web: www.davauxiliary.org/membership/Programs.aspx

Summary To provide financial assistance to members of the Disabled American Veterans (DAV) Auxiliary who are interested in attending college or graduate school.

Eligibility This program is open to paid life members of the auxiliary who are attending or planning to attend a college, university, or vocational school as a full- or part-time undergraduate or graduate student. Applicants must be at least seniors in high school, but there is no maximum age limit. Selection is based on academic achievement; participation in DAV activities; participation in other activities for veterans in their school, community, or elsewhere; volunteer work; membership in clubs or organizations; honors and awards; a statement of academic goals; and financial need.

Financial data Stipends are $1,500 per year for full-time students or $750 per year for part-time students.

Duration 1 year; may be renewed for up to 4 additional years, provided the recipient maintains a GPA of 2.5 or higher.

Additional information Membership in the DAV Auxiliary is available to extended family members of veterans eligible for membership in Disabled American Veterans (i.e., any man or woman who served in the armed forces during a period of war or under conditions simulating war and was wounded, disabled to any degree, or left with long-term illness as a result of military service and was discharged or retired from military service under honorable conditions). This program was established in September 2010 as a replacement for the educational loan program that the DAV Auxiliary operated from 1931 until August 2010.

Number awarded Varies each year.

Deadline March of each year.

[1055]
DONALDSON D. FRIZZELL MEMORIAL SCHOLARSHIPS

First Command Educational Foundation
Attn: Scholarship Programs Manager
1 FirstComm Plaza
Fort Worth, TX 76109-4999
(817) 569-2634   Toll Free: (877) 872-8289
Fax: (817) 569-2970   E-mail: Scholarships@fcef.com
Web: www.fcef.com

Summary To provide financial assistance to students, especially those with ties to the military (including ROTC), who are entering or attending college or graduate school.

Eligibility This program is open to 1) members of a U.S. uniformed service and their spouses and dependents; 2) clients of First Command Financial Services and their family members; 3) dependent family members of First Command Advisors or field office staff members; or 4) non-contractual ROTC students. Applicants may be traditional students (high school seniors and students already enrolled at a college,

university, or accredited trade school) or nontraditional students (those defined by their institution as nontraditional and adult students planning to return to a college, university, or accredited trade school. They must have a GPA of 3.0 or higher and be working on a trade school certification or associate, undergraduate, or graduate degree. Applicants must submit 1-page essays on 1) their active involvement in community service programs; 2) the impact of financial literacy on their future; and 3) why they need this scholarship. Selection is based primarily on the essays, academic merit, and financial need.

Financial data Stipends are $5,000 or $2,500. Funds are disbursed directly to the recipient's college, university, or trade school.

Duration 1 year.

Additional information The sponsoring organization was formerly known as the USPA & IRA Educational Foundation, founded in 1983 to provide scholarships to the children of active, retired, or deceased military personnel. In addition to these scholarships, for which students may apply directly, it supports scholarships offered by a number of partner organizations. Since its establishment, it has awarded scholarships worth nearly $4 million.

Number awarded 6 each year: 2 at $5,000 and 4 at $2,500. Awards are split evenly between the 2 categories.

Deadline The online application process begins in February of each year and continues until 200 applications have been received in each category.

[1056]
EDUCATION FOUNDATION FOR THE COLORADO NATIONAL GUARD GRANTS

National Guard Association of Colorado
Attn: Education Foundation, Inc.
P.O. Box 440889
Aurora, CO 80044-0889
(303) 909-6369   Fax: (720) 535-5925
E-mail: BernieRogoff@comcast.net
Web: www.efcong.org/Grants

Summary To provide financial assistance to members of the Colorado National Guard and their families who are interested in attending college or graduate school in any state.

Eligibility This program is open to current and retired members of the Colorado National Guard and their dependent unmarried children and spouses. Applicants must be enrolled or planning to enroll full or part time at a college, university, trade school, business school, or graduate school in any state. Along with their application, they must submit an essay, up to 2 pages in length, on their desire to continue their education, what motivates them, their financial need, their commitment to academic excellence, and their current situation. Selection is based on academic achievement, community involvement, and financial need.

Financial data Stipends are generally at least $1,000 per year.

Duration 1 year; may be renewed.

Number awarded Normally, 15 to 25 of these grants are awarded each semester.

Deadline August of each year for fall semester; January of each year for spring semester.

[1057]
EDUCATIONAL GRANTS FOR SPOUSES OF ACTIVE-DUTY SERVICE MEMBERS

Corvias Foundation
1405 South County Trail, Suite 539
East Greenwich, RI 02818
(401) 228-2836　　　　　　　　　Fax: (401) 336-2523
E-mail: info@CorviasFoundation.org
Web: www.corviasfoundation.org

Summary　To provide financial assistance for college or graduate school to spouses of active-duty military personnel assigned to specified Army or Air Force installations throughout the United States.

Eligibility　This program is open to spouses of active-duty service members stationed at 1 of 13 designated Air Force or Army installations. Applicants must be enrolled or planning to enroll at a university, community college, or technical college in any state. Selection is based on academic performance, community involvement, plan for use of the grant, and financial need.

Financial data　The stipend is $5,000.

Duration　1 year; nonrenewable.

Additional information　The designated installations are Aberdeen Proving Ground (Maryland), Edwards AFB (California), Eglin AFB (Florida), Eielson AFB (Alaska), Fort Bragg (North Carolina), Fort Meade (Maryland), Fort Polk (Louisiana), Fort Riley (Kansas), Fort Rucker (Alabama), Fort Sill (Oklahoma), Hurlburt Field (Florida), McConnell AFB (Kansas), or Seymour Johnson AFB (North Carolina).

Number awarded　Up to 20 each year.

Deadline　May of each year.

[1058]
EDWARD T. CONROY MEMORIAL SCHOLARSHIP PROGRAM

Maryland Higher Education Commission
Attn: Office of Student Financial Assistance
6 North Liberty Street, Ground Suite
Baltimore, MD 21201
(410) 767-3301　　　　　　　Toll Free: (800) 974-0203
Fax: (410) 332-0250　　　　　TDD: (800) 735-2258
E-mail: osfamail@mhec.state.md.us
Web: www.mhec.state.md.us

Summary　To provide financial assistance for college or graduate school in Maryland to children and spouses of victims of the September 11, 2001 terrorist attacks and specified categories of veterans, public safety employees, and their children or spouses.

Eligibility　This program is open to entering and continuing undergraduate and graduate students in the following categories: 1) children and surviving spouses of victims of the September 11, 2001 terrorist attacks who died in the World Trade Center in New York City, in the Pentagon in Virginia, or on United Airlines Flight 93 in Pennsylvania; 2) veterans who have, as a direct result of military service, a disability of 25% or greater and have exhausted or are no longer eligible for federal veterans' educational benefits; 3) children of armed forces members whose death or 100% disability was directly caused by military service; 4) POW/MIA veterans of the Vietnam Conflict and their children; 5) state or local public safety officers or volunteers who became 100% disabled in the line of duty; and 6) children and unremarried surviving spouses of

state or local public safety employees or volunteers who died or became 100% disabled in the line of duty. The parent, spouse, veteran, POW, or public safety officer or volunteer must have been a resident of Maryland at the time of death or when declared disabled. Applicants must be planning to enroll at a 2- or 4-year Maryland college or university as a full-time or part-time degree-seeking undergraduate or graduate student or attend a private career school. Financial need is not considered.

Financial data　The amount of the award is equal to tuition and fees at a Maryland postsecondary institution, to a maximum of $10,085. The total amount of all Maryland scholarship awards from all sources may not exceed the cost of attendance or $19,000, whichever is less.

Duration　Up to 5 years of full-time study or 8 years of part-time study.

Number awarded　Varies each year.

Deadline　July of each year.

[1059]
EXEMPTION FROM TUITION FEES FOR DEPENDENTS OF KENTUCKY VETERANS

Kentucky Department of Veterans Affairs
Attn: Tuition Waiver Coordinator
321 West Main Street, Suite 390
Louisville, KY 40202
(502) 595-4447　　　　　Toll Free: (800) 928-4012 (within KY)
Fax: (502) 595-3369
Web: www.veterans.ky.gov

Summary　To provide financial assistance for undergraduate or graduate studies to the children or unremarried widow(er)s of deceased Kentucky veterans.

Eligibility　This program is open to the children, stepchildren, adopted children, and unremarried widow(er)s of veterans who were residents of Kentucky when they entered military service or joined the Kentucky National Guard. The qualifying veteran must have been killed in action during a wartime period or died as a result of a service-connected disability incurred during a wartime period. Applicants must be attending or planning to attend a state-supported college or university in Kentucky to work on an undergraduate or graduate degree.

Financial data　Eligible dependents and survivors are exempt from tuition and matriculation fees at any state-supported institution of higher education in Kentucky.

Duration　The exemption continues until completion of an undergraduate or graduate degree. There are no age or time limits.

Number awarded　Varies each year.

Deadline　Deadline not specified.

[1060]
FLEET RESERVE ASSOCIATION GRADUATE SCHOLARSHIPS

Fleet Reserve Association
Attn: FRA Education Foundation
125 North West Street
Alexandria, VA 22314-2754
(703) 683-1400　　　　　　Toll Free: (800) FRA-1924
Fax: (703) 549-6610　　　　E-mail: scholars@fra.org
Web: www.fra.org

Summary To provide financial assistance for graduate school to members of the Fleet Reserve Association (FRA) and their families.

Eligibility This program is open to members of the FRA and the dependent children, grandchildren, and spouses of living or deceased members. Applicants must be enrolled as full-time graduate students. Along with their application, they must submit an essay on why they want to go to college and what they intend to accomplish with their degree. Selection is based on academic record, financial need, extracurricular activities, leadership skills, and participation in community activities. U.S. citizenship is required.

Financial data The stipend is $5,000 per year.

Duration 1 year; may be renewed.

Additional information Membership in the FRA is restricted to active-duty, retired, and Reserve members of the Navy, Marine Corps, and Coast Guard. This program, established in 2001, includes the Glenn F. Glezen Scholarship, the Joseph R. Baranski Scholarship, and the Robert W. Nolan Scholarship.

Number awarded At least 3 each year.

Deadline April of each year.

[1061]
FLEET RESERVE ASSOCIATION MEMBER SCHOLARSHIPS

Fleet Reserve Association
Attn: FRA Education Foundation
125 North West Street
Alexandria, VA 22314-2754
(703) 683-1400   Toll Free: (800) FRA-1924
Fax: (703) 549-6610   E-mail: scholars@fra.org
Web: www.fra.org

Summary To provide financial assistance for college or graduate school to members of the Fleet Reserve Association (FRA) and their families.

Eligibility This program is open to members of the FRA and the dependent children, grandchildren, and spouses of living or deceased members. Applicants must be enrolled as full-time undergraduate or graduate students. Along with their application, they must submit an essay on why they want to go to college and what they intend to accomplish with their degree. Selection is based on academic record, financial need, extracurricular activities, leadership skills, and participation in community activities. U.S. citizenship is required.

Financial data The stipend is $5,000 per year.

Duration 1 year; may be renewed.

Additional information Membership in the FRA is restricted to active-duty, retired, and reserve members of the Navy, Marines, and Coast Guard. This program includes awards designated as the Robert M. Treadwell Annual Scholarship and the Donald Bruce Pringle Family Scholarship.

Number awarded 6 each year.

Deadline April of each year.

[1062]
FLEET RESERVE ASSOCIATION NON-MEMBER SCHOLARSHIPS

Fleet Reserve Association
Attn: FRA Education Foundation
125 North West Street
Alexandria, VA 22314-2754
(703) 683-1400   Toll Free: (800) FRA-1924
Fax: (703) 549-6610   E-mail: scholars@fra.org
Web: www.fra.org

Summary To provide financial assistance for college or graduate school to sea service personnel and their families.

Eligibility This program is open to 1) active-duty, Reserve, honorably-discharged veterans, and retired members of the U.S. Navy, Marine Corps, and Coast Guard; and 2) their spouses, children, and grandchildren. Applicants must be enrolled as full-time undergraduate or graduate students, but neither they nor their family member are required to be members of the sponsoring organization. Along with their application, they must submit an essay on why they want to go to college and what they intend to accomplish with their degree. Selection is based on academic record, financial need, extracurricular activities, leadership skills, and participation in community activities. U.S. citizenship is required.

Financial data Stipends range up to $5,000 per year.

Duration 1 year; may be renewed.

Number awarded 1 or more each year.

Deadline April of each year.

[1063]
FLORIDA LEGION AUXILIARY MASTER'S PROGRAM GRANT

American Legion Auxiliary
Department of Florida
1912A Lee Road
P.O. Box 547917
Orlando, FL 32854-7917
(407) 293-7411   Toll Free: (866) 710-4192
Fax: (407) 299-6522   E-mail: contact@alafl.org
Web: www.alafl.org

Summary To provide financial assistance to members of the Florida American Legion Auxiliary who are interested in working on a master's degree in any field at a university in any state.

Eligibility This program is open to residents of Florida who have been members of the American Legion Auxiliary for at least 5 consecutive years. Applicants must be planning to enroll in an accredited master's degree program in any field at a college or university in any state. They must be sponsored by the local American Legion Auxiliary unit. Selection is based on academic record and financial need.

Financial data The stipend is $2,500 per year. All funds are paid directly to the institution.

Duration 1 year; may be renewed 1 additional year if the recipient needs further financial assistance and has maintained at least a 2.5 GPA.

Number awarded 1 each year.

Deadline January of each year.

[1064]
FLORIDA NAVY NURSE CORPS ASSOCIATION SCHOLARSHIPS

Florida Navy Nurse Corps Association
c/o Margaret Holder, Scholarship Committee
1033 Inverness Drive
St. Augustine, FL 32092
E-mail: maholder@me.com

Summary To provide financial assistance to undergraduate and graduate nursing students, especially residents of Florida with ties to the military.

Eligibility This program is open to students, including registered nursing continuing their studies, who are working on an undergraduate or graduate degree in nursing. Applicants must have completed at least 1 clinical nursing course and have a GPA of 3.0 or higher. They may be full- or part-time students. Preference is given to current active-duty and Reserve service members, veterans of military service, family members of current or former military service personnel, civil service employees, and residents of Florida. Financial need is considered in the selection process.

Financial data The stipend is $1,000. Funds are paid directly to the student.

Duration 1 year.

Additional information This program includes the Captain Miki Iwata Memorial Scholarship.

Number awarded Approximately 3 each year.

Deadline October of each year.

[1065]
GROGAN MEMORIAL SCHOLARSHIP

American Academy of Physician Assistants-Veterans
 Caucus
Attn: Veterans Caucus
P.O. Box 362
Danville, PA 17821-0362
Fax: (302) 526-7154 E-mail: fbrace@veteranscaucus.org
Web: www.veteranscaucus.org

Summary To provide financial assistance to veterans and their dependents who are studying to become physician assistants.

Eligibility This program is open to U.S. citizens who are currently enrolled in a physician assistant program. The program must be approved by the Commission on Accreditation of Allied Health Education. Applicants must be honorably discharged members of any branch of the military or the dependents of those members. Selection is based on military honors and awards received, civic and college honors and awards received, professional memberships and activities, and GPA. An electronic copy of the applicant's DD Form 214 must accompany the application.

Financial data The stipend is $2,000.

Duration 1 year.

Number awarded 1 each year.

Deadline February of each year.

[1066]
HARDY WOLF & DOWNING SCHOLARSHIP AWARDS

Hardy Wolf & Downing
Attn: Scholarship Awards
477 Congress Street, 15th Floor
Portland, ME 04101
Toll Free: (800) 992-7333 E-mail: stepler@hwdlaw.com
Web: www.hardywolf.com/scholarships

Summary To provide financial assistance for college or law school to students who have a connection to the U.S. military or to law enforcement.

Eligibility This program is open to 1) high school seniors who plan to attend an accredited U.S. college; 2) college students attending an accredited U.S. college; and 3) law students currently entering or enrolled at an ABA-accredited law school. Applicants must be active, retired, or immediate family members of any branch of the U.S. military or any branch of law enforcement. They must have a GPA of 3.0 or higher. Along with their application, they must submit essays of 1,500 to 2,000 words on the following topics: for members and family members of the military, the greatest challenges facing veterans when they return home from serving their country; for members and family members of law enforcement, the greatest challenges facing law enforcement personnel today; for all law students, the area of law they intend to practice and why.

Financial data Stipends range from $100 to $2,500.

Duration 1 year.

Number awarded 13 each year: 1 at $2,500, 1 at $1,000, 1 at $500, and 10 at $100.

Deadline December of each year.

[1067]
HAZLEWOOD LEGACY ACT EXEMPTIONS FOR VETERANS' CHILDREN

Texas Veterans Commission
1700 North Congress Avenue, Suite 800
P.O. Box 12277
Austin, TX 78711-2277
(512) 463-5538 Toll Free: (800) 252-VETS (within TX)
Fax: (512) 475-2395 E-mail: VetsEd@tvc.texas.gov
Web: www.tvc.texas.gov/Hazlewood-Act.aspx

Summary To exempt the children of certain Texas veterans from payment of tuition for undergraduate or graduate study at public universities in the state.

Eligibility This program is open to the dependent children under 25 years of age of veterans who are current residents of Texas and were legal residents of the state at the time they entered the U.S. armed forces and served for at least 181 days of active military duty, excluding basic training, during specified periods of wartime. The veteran parent must have received an honorable discharge or separation or a general discharge under honorable conditions. They must have unused hours of exemption from tuition under the Hazlewood Act that they can assign to a dependent child. The dependent children must be enrolled or planning to enroll at a public college or university in Texas and all their other federal veterans education benefits (not including Pell and SEOG grants) may not exceed the value of this exemption.

Financial data Dependent children who are eligible for this benefit are entitled to free tuition and fees at state-supported colleges and universities in Texas.

Duration The combined exemptions for veteran and child may be claimed up to a cumulative total of 150 credit hours, including undergraduate and graduate study.

Additional information This program was previously administered by the Texas Higher Education Coordinating Board but was transferred to the Texas Veterans Commission in 2013.

Number awarded Varies each year; recently, 8,885 were granted.

Deadline Deadline not specified.

[1068]
HICKAM OFFICERS' SPOUSES' CLUB SCHOLARSHIPS

Hickam Officers' Spouses' Club
Attn: Scholarship Coordinator
PMB 168
P.O. Box 30800
Honolulu, HI 96820-0800
E-mail: scholarships@hickamosc.com
Web: www.hickamosc.com/page-1313406

Summary To provide financial assistance to dependents of current and former military personnel in Hawaii who are interested in attending college or graduate school in any state.

Eligibility This program is open to dependents of 1 of the following: 1) active-duty military members permanently stationed in Hawaii; 2) active-duty military members on a remote assignment from Hawaii; 3) retired military members resident in Hawaii; 4) full-time Hawaii National Guard and U.S. military Reserve members residing in Hawaii; and 5) survivors of deceased military members residing in Hawaii. Applicants must be seniors graduating from a Hawaii high school or accredited home school program based in Hawaii and planning to enroll at an accredited 2- or 4-year college, university, or vocational/technical school in any state; dependent children currently working on an undergraduate or graduate degree at a college or university in any state; or spouses currently working on an undergraduate or graduate degree at a college or university in any state. Selection is based on an essay, educational information, employment information, volunteer service and club activities, school activities, leadership roles, awards and honors, and a letter of recommendation.

Financial data A stipend is awarded (amount not specified).

Duration 1 year.

Number awarded 1 or more each year.

Deadline March of each year.

[1069]
HONOLULU POST SAME SCHOLARSHIPS

Society of American Military Engineers-Honolulu Post
P.O. Box 201445
Honolulu, HI 96820
Web: www.samehonolulu.org

Summary To provide financial assistance to residents of Hawaii (particularly military servicemembers, military dependents, and ROTC students) who are interested in attending college or graduate school in any state to work on a degree in engineering or architecture.

Eligibility This program is open to residents of Hawaii who are graduating high school seniors or current undergraduates enrolled or planning to enroll full time at an accredited college

or university in any state. Applicants must be planning to work on an undergraduate or graduate degree in engineering or architecture. They must be U.S. citizens and have a GPA of 3.0 or higher. Military affiliation or experience (i.e., ROTC, member or dependent of a member of the Society of Military Engineers (SAME), military dependent, Junior ROTC) is not required but is given preference. Along with their application, they must submit a transcript; a resume of work experience, academic activities, and extracurricular accomplishments; and a 1-page essay on how their engineering or architecture degree will impact our nation.

Financial data The stipend is $2,000 or $1,500 per year.

Duration 1 year for the $2,000 scholarships; 4 years for the $1,500 scholarships.

Number awarded Varies each year; recently, 6 were awarded: 2 at $2,000 for 1 year and 4 at $1,500 per year for 4 years.

Deadline March of each year.

[1070]
HOPE FOR THE WARRIORS SPOUSE/CAREGIVER SCHOLARSHIPS

Hope for the Warriors
Attn: Spouse/Caregiver Scholarships Director
5101C Backlick Road
Annandale, VA 22003
Toll Free: (877) 246-7349
E-mail: scholarships@hopeforthewarriors.org
Web: www.hopeforthewarriors.org

Summary To provide financial assistance for college or graduate school to the spouses and caregivers of wounded or deceased military personnel or veterans.

Eligibility This program is open to spouses and caregivers of current and former servicemembers who were wounded or killed in the line of duty while serving in support of Operation Enduring Freedom, Operation Iraqi Freedom, or Operation New Dawn. Applicants must be enrolled or planning to enroll full or part time at an accredited college, university, or trade school to work on a bachelor's degree, master's degree, or vocational certification. They must have a high school GPA of 2.6 or higher or a GED score of 650 or higher. Along with their application, they must submit a 500-word essay on how this scholarship will impact their ability to complete their degree. Selection is based on that essay, academic achievement, personal goals, and letters of recommendation.

Financial data The stipend is $1,000 per year.

Duration 1 year; may be renewed up to 3 additional years.

Number awarded 1 or more each year.

Deadline March of each year for fall; October of each year for spring.

[1071]
H.S. AND ANGELINE LEWIS SCHOLARSHIPS

American Legion Auxiliary
Department of Wisconsin
Attn: Education Chair
2930 American Legion Drive
P.O. Box 140
Portage, WI 53901-0140
(608) 745-0124   Toll Free: (866) 664-3863
Fax: (608) 745-1947   E-mail: alawi@amlegionauxwi.org
Web: www.amlegionauxwi.org/Scholarships.htm

Summary To provide financial assistance to Wisconsin residents who are related to veterans or members of the American Legion Auxiliary and interested in working on an undergraduate or graduate degree at a school in any state.
Eligibility This program is open to the children, wives, and widow(er)s of veterans who are high school seniors or graduates and have a GPA of 3.5 or higher. Grandchildren and great-grandchildren of members of the American Legion Auxiliary are also eligible. Applicants must be residents of Wisconsin and interested in working on an undergraduate or graduate degree at a school in any state. Along with their application, they must submit a 300-word essay on "Education—An Investment in the Future." Financial need is considered in the selection process.
Financial data The stipend is $1,000.
Duration 1 year; nonrenewable.
Number awarded 6 each year: 1 to a graduate student and 5 to undergraduates.
Deadline March of each year.

[1072]
HUI O'WAHINE MERIT SCHOLARSHIP FOR TRADITIONAL STUDENTS

Hui O'Wahine Fort Shafter Spouses Club
Attn: Scholarships
4285 Lawehana Street
PMB A-8
Honolulu, HI 96818-3128
E-mail: huiowahinescholarships@gmail.com
Web: www.huispirit.com/scholarshipwelfare.html

Summary To provide financial assistance to children of members of Hui O'Wahine (the Fort Shafter Spouses Club) in Hawaii who are interested in attending college or graduate school in any state.
Eligibility This program is open to children of members of Hui O'Wahine who are graduating high school seniors or currently enrolled as full- or part-time undergraduate or graduate students at a qualifying college, university, or vocational school in any state. Applicants must be younger than 23 years of age and have at least 1 parent who is an active-duty, Reserve, or retired military member or Department of Defense civilian residing in or assigned to Hawaii. They must submit transcripts that, for high school seniors, include ACT and/or SAT scores. Selection is based on academic merit and community involvement.
Financial data A stipend is awarded (amount not specified).
Duration 1 year.
Number awarded Several each year.
Deadline March of each year.

[1073]
JAPANESE AMERICAN VETERANS ASSOCIATION MEMORIAL SCHOLARSHIPS

Japanese American Veterans Association
c/o Terry Shima, Outreach and Education Committee Chair
415 Russell Avenue, Number 1005
Gaithersburg, MD 20877
(301) 987-6746   E-mail: ttshima@comcast.net
Web: www.javadc.org

Summary To provide financial assistance for college or graduate school to relatives of Japanese American veterans and military personnel.
Eligibility This program is open to graduating high school seniors and students currently working on an undergraduate or graduate degree at a college, university, or school of specialized study. Applicants must be related, by blood or marriage, to 1) a person who served with the 442nd Regimental Combat Team, the 100th Infantry Battalion, or other unit associated with those; 2) a person who served in the U.S. Military Intelligence Service during or after World War II; 3) a person of Japanese ancestry who is serving or has served in the U.S. armed forces and been honorable discharged; or 4) a member of the Japanese American Veterans Association (JAVA) whose membership extends back at least 1 year.
Financial data The stipend is $1,500.
Duration 1 year; recipients may reapply.
Additional information These scholarships, first awarded in 2008, include the following named awards: the Orville C. Shirey Memorial Scholarship, the Joseph Ichiuji Memorial Scholarship, the Phil and Douglas Ishio Scholarship, the Kiyoko Tsuboi Taubkin Scholarship, the Ranger Grant Hirabayashi Memorial Scholarship, the Victor and Teru Matsui Scholarship, the Betty Shima Scholarship, the Mitsugi Kasai Scholarship, and the U.S. Senator Daniel K. Inouye Scholarship.
Number awarded 10 each year.
Deadline April of each year.

[1074]
JOANNE HOLBROOK PATTON MILITARY SPOUSE SCHOLARSHIP PROGRAM

National Military Family Association, Inc.
Attn: Spouse Scholarship Program
2500 North Van Dorn Street, Suite 102
Alexandria, VA 22302-1601
(703) 931-NMFA   Toll Free: (800) 260-0218
Fax: (703) 931-4600
E-mail: scholarships@militaryfamily.org
Web: www.militaryfamily.org

Summary To provide financial assistance for undergraduate or graduate study to spouses of active and retired military personnel.
Eligibility This program is open to the spouses of military personnel (active, retired, Reserve, Guard, or survivor). Applicants must be attending or planning to attend an accredited postsecondary institution to work on an undergraduate or graduate degree, professional certification, vocational training, GED or ESL, or other postsecondary training. They may enroll part or full time and on-campus or online. Along with their application, they must submit an essay on a question that changes annually; recently, applicants were asked to write about what they like most about the health care they are receiving as a military family member, what they like the least, and what they would recommend to change it. Selection is based on that essay, community involvement, and academic achievement.
Financial data The stipend is $1,000. Funds are paid directly to the educational institution to be used for tuition, fees, and school room and board. Support is not provided for books, rent, or previous education loans.
Duration 1 year; recipients may reapply.

Additional information This program began in 2004.

Number awarded Varies each year; recently, 254 were awarded.

Deadline January of each year.

[1075]
JOHN CORNELIUS/MAX ENGLISH MEMORIAL SCHOLARSHIP AWARD

Marine Corps Tankers Association
c/o Stephen Chambers, Scholarship Chair
1922 Freeman Street
Oceanside, CA 92054
Web: www.usmarinetankers.org/scholarship-program

Summary To provide financial assistance for college or graduate school to children and grandchildren of members of the Marine Corps Tankers Association and to Marine and Navy personnel currently serving in tank units.

Eligibility This program is open to high school seniors and graduates who are children, grandchildren, or under the guardianship of an active, Reserve, retired, or honorably discharged Marine who served in a tank unit. Marine or Navy Corpsmen currently assigned to tank units are also eligible. Applicants must be enrolled or planning to enroll full time at a college or graduate school. Their parent or grandparent must be a member of the Marine Corps Tankers Association or, if not a member, must join if the application is accepted. Along with their application, they must submit an essay on their educational goals, future aspirations, and concern for the future of our society and for the peoples of the world. Selection is based on that essay, academic record, school activities, leadership potential, and community service.

Financial data The stipend is at least $2,000 per year.

Duration 1 year; recipients may reapply.

Number awarded Varies each year; recently, 15 were awarded.

Deadline March of each year.

[1076]
JUDGE WILLIAM M. BEARD SCHOLARSHIP

United Daughters of the Confederacy
Attn: Second Vice President General
328 North Boulevard
Richmond, VA 23220-4008
(804) 355-1636   Fax: (804) 353-1396
E-mail: jamieretired@sbcglobal.net
Web: www.hqudc.org/Scholarships/index.htm

Summary To provide financial assistance for a graduate degree in history or medicine to lineal descendants of Confederate veterans.

Eligibility Eligible to apply for these scholarships are lineal descendants of worthy Confederates or collateral descendants who are members of the Children of the Confederacy or the United Daughters of the Confederacy. Applicants must intend to work on a graduate degree in history or medicine and must submit certified proof of the Confederate record of 1 ancestor, with the company and regiment in which he served. They must have a GPA of 3.0 or higher.

Financial data The amount of the scholarship depends on the availability of funds.

Duration 1 year; may be renewed.

Number awarded 1 each year.

Deadline April of each year.

[1077]
KATHERN F. GRUBER SCHOLARSHIPS

Blinded Veterans Association
477 H Street, N.W.
Washington, DC 20001-2694
(202) 371-8880   Toll Free: (800) 669-7079
Fax: (202) 371-8258   E-mail: temanuel@bva.org
Web: www.bva.org/services.html

Summary To provide financial assistance for undergraduate or graduate study to immediate family members of blinded veterans and servicemembers.

Eligibility This program is open to dependent children, grandchildren, and spouses of blinded veterans and active-duty blinded servicemembers of the U.S. armed forces. The veteran or servicemember must be legally blind; the blindness may be either service-connected or nonservice-connected. Applicants must have been accepted or be currently enrolled as a full-time student in an undergraduate or graduate program at an accredited institution of higher learning. Along with their application, they must submit a 300-word essay on their career goals and aspirations. Financial need is not considered in the selection process.

Financial data The stipend is $2,000; funds are intended to be used to cover the student's expenses, including tuition, other academic fees, books, dormitory fees, and cafeteria fees. Funds are paid directly to the recipient's school.

Duration 1 year; recipients may reapply for up to 3 additional years.

Number awarded 6 each year.

Deadline April of each year.

[1078]
KOREAN WAR VETERAN DESCENDANT SCHOLARSHIPS

Korean American Scholarship Foundation
Eastern Region
1952 Gallows Road, Suite 310
Vienna, VA 22182
(703) 748-5935   Fax: (703) 748-1874
E-mail: erc.scholarship@kasf.org
Web: www.kasf.org/eastern

Summary To provide financial assistance to the descendants of the Korean War from any state who are working on an undergraduate or graduate degree in any field at a school in eastern states.

Eligibility This program is open to direct descendants of veterans who served in Korea from June 25, 1950 to January 31, 1955. Applicants may reside in any state but they must be enrolled as full-time undergraduate or graduate students at a college or university in Delaware, District of Columbia, Kentucky, Maryland, North Carolina, Pennsylvania, Virginia, or West Virginia. Selection is based on academic achievement (40%), an essay (40%), and recommendations (20%).

Financial data The stipend is $2,000.

Duration 1 year.

Additional information This program began in 2013.

Number awarded Varies each year.

Deadline July of each year.

[1079]
LIFE'S CHOICES FOUNDATION GRADUATE SCHOLARSHIP AWARDS

Association of Former Intelligence Officers
Attn: Scholarships Committee
7700 Leesburg Pike, Suite 324
Falls Church, VA 22043
(703) 790-0320   Fax: (703) 991-1278
E-mail: scholarships@afio.com
Web: www.afio.com/13_scholarships.htm

Summary To provide financial assistance to graduate students who are members or descendants of members of the U.S. intelligence community and interested in working on a degree in a field related to national security.

Eligibility This program is open to graduate students who apply in their senior undergraduate year or first graduate year. Applicants must be personnel serving in government agencies comprising the U.S. intelligence community or their children or grandchildren. They must be working on a degree in a field related to national security or intelligence studies and be, or planning to be, serving in the U.S. government. Along with their application, they must submit a cover letter that explains their need for assistance, their career goals and dreams, and their views of U.S. world standing and its intelligence community. Selection is based on merit, character, estimated future potential, background, and relevance of their studies to the full spectrum of national security interests and career ambitions. U.S. citizenship is required.

Financial data The stipend is $3,500.

Duration 1 year.

Additional information This program is sponsored by the Morris Family Charitable Corporation.

Number awarded 2 each year.

Deadline June of each year.

[1080]
LILLIAN CAMPBELL MEDICAL SCHOLARSHIP

Veterans of Foreign Wars of the United States-
  Department of Wisconsin
P.O. Box 6128
Monona, WI 53716-0128
(608) 221-5276   Fax: (608) 221-5277
E-mail: wivfw@att.net
Web: www.vfwofwi.com/downloadable-forms

Summary To provide financial assistance to students working on a degree in a medical field in Wisconsin who served in the military or are related to a person who did.

Eligibility This program is open to students who have completed at least 1 year of study in Wisconsin in a program in nursing, pharmacy, physician assistant, medical or surgical technology, physical or occupational therapy, dental assisting, radiology, or other related medical profession. Applicants or a member of their immediate family (parent, sibling, child, spouse, or grandparent) must have served in the military. They must have a high school diploma or GED but may be of any age. Along with their application, they must submit a 200-word essay on why they are studying this medical profession. Financial need is considered in the selection process.

Financial data The stipend is $1,000.

Duration 1 year.

Number awarded 1 or more each year.

Deadline April of each year.

[1081]
LORETTA CORNETT-HUFF SCHOLARSHIPS

Council of College and Military Educators
c/o Kenneth D. McRae, Scholarship Committee Chair
Mississippi State University
G.V. "Sonny" Montgomery Center for America's Veterans
126 Magruder Street
P. O. Drawer 6283
Mississippi State, MS 39762
(662) 325-6719   Fax: (662) 325-6723
E-mail: scholarship@ccmeonline.aspx
Web: www.ccmeonline.org/scholarships

Summary To provide financial assistance to spouses of members of the armed services who are interested in working on an undergraduate or master's degree.

Eligibility This program is open to spouses of members of the uniformed services, including active, National Guard, and Reserves. Applicants must be currently enrolled full time at an accredited institution that is a member of the Council of College and Military Educators (CCME) and working on an associate, bachelor's, or master's degree. Undergraduates must have a GPA of 2.5 or higher and graduate students must have a GPA of 3.0 or higher. Along with their application, they must submit an essay of 400 to 750 words on their most meaningful achievements and how those relate to their field of study and their future goals. Financial need is not considered in the selection process.

Financial data The stipend is $1,000.

Duration 1 year.

Number awarded 5 each year.

Deadline September of each year.

[1082]
LT. JOHN J. GRIFFIN/USS EMMONS MEMORIAL SCHOLARSHIP

USS Emmons Association
c/o Thomas Hoffman, Scholarship Committee Chair
3136 Northampton Street
Bethlehem, PA 18020
E-mail: ussemmons@gmail.com
Web: www.ussemmons.org/scholarship

Summary To provide financial assistance for college or graduate school to descendants of crewmembers of the USS Emmons who were killed during World War II.

Eligibility This program is open to 1) direct lineal descendants of crewmembers aboard the USS Emmons when it was destroyed on April 6, 1945 during the battle of Okinawa; and 2) direct lineal descendants of siblings of childless crewmembers of the USS Emmons when it was lost. Applicants must be enrolled or planning to enroll as full-time undergraduate or graduate students. Along with their application, they must submit an essay of 500 to 750 words on a topic that changes annually but relates to the history of the USS Emmons.

Financial data Stipends are $2,000 or $500.

Duration 1 year.

Number awarded 2 each year: 1 at $2,000 and 1 at $500.

Deadline May of each year.

[1083]
MAINE VETERANS DEPENDENTS EDUCATIONAL BENEFITS

Bureau of Veterans' Services
117 State House Station
Augusta, ME 04333-0117
(207) 430-6035   Toll Free: (800) 345-0116 (within ME)
Fax: (207) 626-4471   E-mail: mainebvs@maine.gov
Web: www.maine.gov/dvem/bvs/educational_benefits.htm

Summary To provide financial assistance for undergraduate or graduate education to dependents of disabled and other Maine veterans.

Eligibility Applicants for these benefits must be children (high school seniors or graduates under 22 years of age), non-divorced spouses, or unremarried widow(er)s of veterans who meet 1 or more of the following requirements: 1) living and determined to have a total permanent disability resulting from a service-connected cause; 2) killed in action; 3) died from a service-connected disability; 4) died while totally and permanently disabled due to a service-connected disability but whose death was not related to the service-connected disability; or 5) a member of the armed forces on active duty who has been listed for more than 90 days as missing in action, captured, forcibly detained, or interned in the line of duty by a foreign government or power. The veteran parent must have been a resident of Maine at the time of entry into service or a resident of Maine for 5 years preceding application for these benefits. Children may be working on an associate or bachelor's degree. Spouses, widows, and widowers may work on an associate, bachelor's, or master's degree.

Financial data Recipients are entitled to free tuition at institutions of higher education supported by the state of Maine.

Duration Children may receive up to 8 semesters of support; they have 6 years from the date of first entrance to complete those 8 semesters. Continuation in the program is based on their earning a GPA of 2.0 or higher each semester. Spouses are entitled to receive up to 120 credit hours of educational benefits and have 10 years from the date of first entrance to complete their program.

Additional information College preparatory schooling and correspondence courses are not supported under this program.

Number awarded Varies each year.

Deadline Deadline not specified.

[1084]
MAINE VIETNAM VETERANS SCHOLARSHIP FUND

Maine Community Foundation
Attn: Program Director
245 Main Street
Ellsworth, ME 04605
(207) 667-9735   Toll Free: (877) 700-6800
Fax: (207) 667-0447   E-mail: info@mainecf.org
Web: www.mainecf.org/statewidescholars.aspx

Summary To provide financial assistance for college or graduate school to Vietnam veterans or the dependents of Vietnam or other veterans in Maine.

Eligibility This program is open to residents of Maine who are Vietnam veterans or the descendants of veterans who served in the Vietnam Theater. As a second priority, children

of veterans from other time periods are also considered. Graduating high school seniors, nontraditional students, undergraduates, and graduate students are eligible to apply. Selection is based on financial need, extracurricular activities, work experience, academic achievement, and a personal statement of career goals and how the applicant's educational plans relate to them.

Financial data The stipend is $1,000 per year.

Duration 1 year.

Additional information This program began in 1985. There is a $3 processing fee.

Number awarded 3 to 6 each year.

Deadline April of each year.

[1085]
MALCOLM M. BERGLUND SCHOLARSHIP

United Daughters of the Confederacy
Attn: Second Vice President General
328 North Boulevard
Richmond, VA 23220-4008
(804) 355-1636   Fax: (804) 353-1396
E-mail: jamieretired@sbcglobal.net
Web: www.hqudc.org/Scholarships/index.htm

Summary To provide financial assistance for graduate school to lineal descendants of Confederate veterans.

Eligibility Eligible to apply for these scholarships are lineal descendants of worthy Confederates or collateral descendants who are members of the Children of the Confederacy or the United Daughters of the Confederacy. Applicants must intend to study at the graduate level and must submit certified proof of the Confederate record of 1 ancestor, with the company and regiment in which he served. They must have a GPA of 3.0 or higher.

Financial data The amount of this scholarship depends on the availability of funds.

Duration 1 year; may be renewed up to 2 additional years.

Number awarded 1 each year.

Deadline April of each year.

[1086]
MARGUERITE MC'ALPIN MEMORIAL SCHOLARSHIP

American Legion Auxiliary
Department of Washington
Attn: Education Chair
3600 Ruddell Road S.E.
P.O. Box 5867
Lacey, WA 98509-5867
(360) 456-5995   Fax: (360) 491-7442
E-mail: secretary@walegion-aux.org
Web: www.walegion-aux.org/EducationScholarships.html

Summary To provide financial assistance to Washington veterans or their descendants who are interested in working on an undergraduate or graduate degree in nursing at a school in any state.

Eligibility This program is open to Washington veterans and their children, grandchildren, and great-grandchildren. Applicants must be interested in studying nursing on the undergraduate or graduate level at a school in any state. Selection is based on an essay on their desire to study nursing, character, leadership, scholastic history, and financial need.

Financial data The stipend is $1,000.
Duration 1 year.
Number awarded 1 each year.
Deadline February of each year.

[1087]
MARIA C. JACKSON/GENERAL GEORGE A. WHITE SCHOLARSHIP

Oregon Student Access Commission
Attn: Grants and Scholarships Division
1500 Valley River Drive, Suite 100
Eugene, OR 97401-2146
(541) 687-7395   Toll Free: (800) 452-8807, ext. 7395
Fax: (541) 687-7414   TDD: (800) 735-2900
E-mail: awardinfo@osac.state.or.us
Web: www.oregonstudentaid.gov/scholarships.aspx

Summary To provide financial assistance to veterans and children of veterans and military personnel in Oregon who are interested in attending college or graduate school in the state.

Eligibility This program is open to residents of Oregon who served, or whose parents are serving or have served, in the U.S. armed forces. Applicants or their parents must have resided in Oregon at the time of enlistment. They must be enrolled or planning to enroll at a college or graduate school in the state. College and university undergraduates must have a GPA of 3.75 or higher, but there is no minimum GPA requirement for graduate students or those attending a technical school. Selection is based on scholastic ability and financial need.

Financial data Stipends for scholarships offered by the Oregon Student Access Commission (OSAC) range from $200 to $10,000 but recently averaged $5,200.

Duration 1 year.
Number awarded Varies each year.
Deadline February of each year.

[1088]
MARY ANNE WILLIAMS SCHOLARSHIP

United Daughters of the Confederacy-Virginia Division
c/o Patt Graves, Second Vice President
838 Crymes Road
Keysville, VA 23947-2815
(434) 696-2202   E-mail: thebargthree@aol.com
Web: www.vaudc.org

Summary To provide financial assistance to Confederate descendants from Virginia who are interested in working on an undergraduate or graduate degree in engineering or medicine at a school in the state.

Eligibility This program is open to residents of Virginia who are 1) lineal descendants of Confederates; or 2) collateral descendants and also members of the Children of the Confederacy or the United Daughters of the Confederacy. Applicants must be interested in working on an undergraduate or graduate degree in medicine or engineering at a college or university in Virginia. They must submit proof of the Confederate military record of at least 1 ancestor, with the company and regiment in which he served. They must also submit a personal letter pledging to make the best possible use of the scholarship; describing their health, social, family, religious, and fraternal connections within the community; and reflecting on what a Southern heritage means to them (using the term "War Between the States" in lieu of "Civil

War"). They must have a GPA of 3.0 or higher and be able to demonstrate financial need.

Financial data The amount of the stipend depends on the availability of funds. Payment is made directly to the college or university the recipient attends.

Duration 1 year; may be renewed up to 3 additional years if the recipient maintains a GPA of 3.0 or higher.

Number awarded This scholarship is offered whenever a prior recipient graduates or is no longer eligible.

Deadline March of the years in which the scholarship is available.

[1089]
MARY PAOLOZZI MEMBER'S SCHOLARSHIP

Navy Wives Clubs of America
c/o NSA Mid-South
P.O. Box 54022
Millington, TN 38054-0022
Toll Free: (866) 511-NWCA
E-mail: nwca@navywivesclubsofamerica.org
Web: www.navywivesclubsofamerica.org/scholarships

Summary To provide financial assistance for undergraduate or graduate study to members of the Navy Wives Clubs of America (NWCA).

Eligibility This program is open to NWCA members who can demonstrate financial need. Applicants must be 1) a high school graduate or senior planning to attend college full time next year; 2) currently enrolled in an undergraduate program and planning to continue as a full-time undergraduate; 3) a college graduate or senior planning to be a full-time graduate student next year; or 4) a high school graduate or GED recipient planning to attend vocational or business school next year. Along with their application, they must submit a brief statement on why they feel they should be awarded this scholarship and any special circumstances (financial or other) they wish to have considered. Financial need is also considered in the selection process.

Financial data Stipends range from $500 to $1,000 each year (depending upon the donations from the NWCA chapters).

Duration 1 year.

Additional information Membership in the NWCA is open to spouses of enlisted personnel serving in the Navy, Marine Corps, Coast Guard, and the active Reserve units of those services; spouses of enlisted personnel who have been honorably discharged, retired, or transferred to the Fleet Reserve on completion of duty; and widows of enlisted personnel in those services.

Number awarded 1 or more each year.
Deadline May of each year.

[1090]
MASSACHUSETTS SOLDIERS LEGACY FUND SCHOLARSHIPS

Massachusetts Soldiers Legacy Fund
P.O. Box 962061
Milk Street Post Office
Boston, MA 02196
(508) 630-2382   Toll Free: (866) 856-5533
E-mail: info@mslfund.org
Web: www.mslfund.org

Summary To provide financial assistance for college or professional school to the children of servicemembers from Massachusetts who were killed in Afghanistan or Iraq.
Eligibility This program is open to children of members of the U.S. armed forces who died while deployed on operations Enduring Freedom or Iraqi Freedom. The parent's home of record must have been Massachusetts. Applicants must be enrolled or planning to enroll at a 2- or 4-year college or university, professional school, or trade school in any state. All qualified children receive this assistance; there is no selection process.
Financial data The stipend is $10,000 per year.
Duration 1 year; may be renewed up to 3 additional years.
Additional information This program began in 2004.
Number awarded Varies each year.
Deadline Deadline not specified.

[1091]
MIKE AND GAIL DONLEY SPOUSE SCHOLARSHIPS

Air Force Association
Attn: Manager, Awards and Scholarships
1501 Lee Highway
Arlington, VA 22209-1198
(703) 247-5800, ext. 4807
Toll Free: (800) 727-3337, ext. 4807
Fax: (703) 247-5853　　　　E-mail: awards@afa.org
Web: www.afa.org/donleyspousescholarship
Summary To provide financial assistance for undergraduate or graduate study to spouses of Air Force members.
Eligibility This program is open to spouses of active-duty Air Force, Air National Guard, or Air Force Reserve members. Spouses who are themselves military members or in ROTC are not eligible. Applicants must have a GPA of 3.5 or higher in college (or high school if entering college for the first time) and be able to provide proof of acceptance into an accredited undergraduate or graduate degree program. They must submit a 2-page essay on their academic and career goals, the motivation that led them to that decision, and how Air Force and other local community activities in which they are involved will enhance their goals. Selection is based on the essay and 2 letters of recommendation.
Financial data The stipend is $2,500; funds are sent to the recipients' schools to be used for any reasonable cost related to working on a degree.
Duration 1 year; nonrenewable.
Additional information This program began in 1995.
Number awarded At least 10 each year: 1 to an airman assigned to each of the 10 Air Force Major Commands.
Deadline April of each year.

[1092]
MILDRED RICHARDS TAYLOR MEMORIAL SCHOLARSHIP

United Daughters of the Confederacy
Attn: Second Vice President General
328 North Boulevard
Richmond, VA 23220-4008
(804) 355-1636　　　　　　　　Fax: (804) 353-1396
E-mail: jamieretired@sbcglobal.net
Web: www.hqudc.org/Scholarships/index.htm

Summary To provide financial assistance to female lineal descendants of Confederate veterans who are interested in working on a graduate degree in business.
Eligibility Eligible to apply for these scholarships are female lineal descendants of worthy Confederates or collateral descendants who intend to study business or a business-related field at the graduate level. Applicants must submit certified proof of the Confederate record of 1 ancestor, with the company and regiment in which he served. Preference is given to former members of Children of the Confederacy. They must have a GPA of 3.0 or higher.
Financial data The amount of this scholarship depends on the availability of funds.
Duration 1 year; may be renewed up to 2 additional years.
Number awarded 1 each year.
Deadline April of each year.

[1093]
MILITARY FRIENDS FOUNDATION PATRIOT SCHOLAR PROGRAM

Military Friends Foundation
14 Beacon Street, Suite 706
Boston, MA 02108
(617) 733-7994　　　　　　E-mail: info@militaryfriends.org
Web: www.militaryfriends.org/programs/patriot-scholar
Summary To provide financial assistance for college or graduate school in any state to Massachusetts residents who are the children of National Guard members, Reservists, or deceased servicemembers.
Eligibility This program is open to residents of Massachusetts who are 1) high school seniors or freshmen at a college in any state and the child of an active or honorably discharged member of the Massachusetts National Guard or Reserve component who has been activated overseas after September 11, 2001; and 2) an undergraduate, trade school, or graduate student at a school in any state and the relative of a servicemember who died as a result of military service after September 11, 2001. Selection is based on academic merit and financial need.
Financial data The stipend is $1,000.
Duration 1 year.
Number awarded 10 each year: 1 in each Massachusetts Congressional district.
Deadline Deadline not specified.

[1094]
MILITARY ORDER OF THE STARS AND BARS SCHOLARSHIPS

Military Order of the Stars and Bars
P.O. Box 1700
White House, TN 37188-1700
Web: www.militaryorderofthestarsandbars.org
Summary To provide financial assistance to high school seniors and currently-enrolled college and graduate students who are the descendants of Confederate officers or public servants.
Eligibility This program is open to graduating high school seniors and currently-enrolled undergraduate and graduate students who are the genealogically proven descendants of 1) a Confederate officer; 2) a member of the Confederate executive or legislative branches of government; or 3) a member of the Confederate legislative, judiciary, or executive

branches of state government. Applicants must submit a personal letter of application (describing academic and career aspirations), genealogical proof of Confederate ancestor, a completed and signed application form, and 3 letters of recommendation. Selection is based on academic performance (70%), extracurricular activities (10%), the personal statement (10%), and letters of recommendation (10%).

Financial data The stipend is $1,000.

Duration 1 year; nonrenewable.

Additional information The Military Order of the Stars and Bars is an international genealogical, historical, and patriotic organization that was organized in 1938 and is composed of male descendants of the Confederate officer corps, Confederate civil officials, and state officials. These scholarships are designated the Major General Patrick R. Cleburne Scholarship (for students residing in the area of the Army of Trans-Mississippi), the Lt. General Nathan B. Forrest Scholarship (for students residing in the area of the Army of Tennessee), and the General Robert E. Lee Scholarship (for students residing in the area of the Army of Northern Virginia).

Number awarded Varies each year, but at least 1 in each of the 3 Confederate Army departments.

Deadline February of each year.

[1095]
MINNESOTA G.I. BILL PROGRAM

Minnesota Department of Veterans Affairs
Attn: Programs and Services Division
20 West 12th Street, Room 206
St. Paul, MN 55155
(651) 296-2562 Toll Free: (888) LINK-VET
TDD: (800) 627-3529 E-mail: MNGIBill@state.mn.us
Web: mn.gov/mdva/resources/education/minnesotagibill.jsp

Summary To provide financial assistance for college or graduate school in Minnesota to residents who 1) served in the military after September 11, 2001 or 2) are the family members of deceased or disabled military personnel.

Eligibility This program is open to residents of Minnesota enrolled at colleges and universities in the state as undergraduate or graduate students. Applicants must be 1) a veteran who is serving or has served honorably in a branch of the U.S. armed forces at any time; 2) a non-veteran who has served honorably for a total of 5 years or more cumulatively as a member of the Minnesota National Guard or other active or Reserve component of the U.S. armed forces, and any part of that service occurred on or after September 11, 2001; or 3) a surviving child or spouse of a person who has served in the military at any time on or after September 11, 2001 and who has died or has a total and permanent disability as a result of that military service. Financial need is also considered in the selection process.

Financial data The stipend is $1,000 per semester for full-time study or $500 per semester for part-time study. The maximum award is $3,000 per academic year or $10,000 per lifetime.

Duration 1 year; may be renewed, provided the recipient continues to make satisfactory academic progress.

Additional information This program was established by the Minnesota Legislature in 2007.

Number awarded Varies each year.

Deadline Deadline not specified.

[1096]
MINNESOTA NATIONAL GUARD SURVIVOR ENTITLEMENT TUITION REIMBURSEMENT PROGRAM

Department of Military Affairs
Attn: Education Services Officer
JFMN-J1-ARED
20 West 12th Street
St. Paul, MN 55155-2098
(651) 282-4589 Toll Free: (800) 657-3848
Fax: (651) 282-4694
E-mail: ng.mn.mnarng.mbx.assets-education@mail.mil
Web: www.minnesotanationalguard.org

Summary To provide financial assistance for college or graduate school to survivors of members of the Minnesota National Guard who were killed on active duty.

Eligibility This program is open to surviving spouses and children of members of the Minnesota Army or Air National Guard who were killed while performing military duty. Dependent children are eligible until their 24th birthday; surviving spouses are eligible regardless of age or remarriage; all survivors remain eligible even if they move out of state and become residents of another state. The Guard member's death must have occurred within the scope of assigned duties while in a federal duty status or on state active service. Applicants must be enrolled as undergraduate or graduate students at colleges or universities in Minnesota. Reimbursement is provided only for undergraduate courses completed with a grade of "C" or better or for graduate courses completed with a grade of "B" or better.

Financial data The maximum reimbursement rate is 100% of the tuition rate at the University of Minnesota Twin Cities campus, with a maximum benefit of $13,000 per fiscal year for undergraduate course work or $22,000 per fiscal year for graduate course work.

Duration 1 academic term, to a maximum of 18 credits per term; may be renewed for a total of 144 semester credits or 208 quarter credits.

Additional information This program became effective in 1992.

Number awarded Varies each year.

Deadline Participants must request reimbursement within 90 days of the last official day of the term.

[1097]
NATIONAL GUARD ASSOCIATION OF MINNESOTA SCHOLARSHIPS

National Guard Association of Minnesota
Attn: Executive Director
P.O. Box 47132
Plymouth, MN 55442
(763) 202-2151 E-mail: director@ngamn.org
Web: www.ngamn.org/node/56

Summary To provide financial assistance to current and retired members of the National Guard Association of Minnesota (NGAMN) and their families who are working on an undergraduate or graduate degree at a school in any state.

Eligibility This program is open to active members and retired life members of NGAMN and their spouses, children, and grandchildren. Applicants must be currently enrolled at least half time at an accredited institution of higher learning in any state and working on a 4-year bachelor's or graduate degree. They must have a GPA of 2.75 or higher. Along with their application, they must submit an essay on a topic that describes a value of the Army or Air Force, rotating among loyalty, duty, respect, selfless service, honor, integrity, personal courage, commitment, and excellence. Financial need is not considered in the selection process.

Financial data Stipends are $1,000 or $500. Funds are paid directly to the recipient.

Duration 1 year. Recipients may reapply after 3 years.

Additional information The $1,000 scholarship is sponsored by HiWay Federal Credit Union. This program began in 2008.

Number awarded 3 each year: 1 at $1,000 and 2 at $500 (1 to a member or retired member and 1 to a spouse, child, or grandchild).

Deadline July of each year.

[1098]
NATIONAL GUARD ASSOCIATION OF NEW HAMPSHIRE SCHOLARSHIPS

National Guard Association of New Hampshire
Attn: Scholarship Committee
P.O. Box 22031
Portsmouth, NH 03802-2031
(603) 227-1597   E-mail: nganhscholarship@gmail.com
Web: www.nganh.org/Archive/Scholarship

Summary To provide financial assistance to members of the National Guard Association of New Hampshire and their dependents who are interested in attending college or graduate school in any state.

Eligibility This program is open to current members of the National Guard Association of New Hampshire (officer, enlisted, or retired), their spouses, and their dependent children. Applicants must be enrolled or planning to enroll full or part time in an associate, bachelor's, graduate, professional, or doctoral degree program at an accredited college or university in any state. Along with their application, they must submit a 1-page essay on a topic that changes annually; recently, they were asked to describe what citizen service means to them.

Financial data The stipend is $1,000.

Duration 1 year.

Number awarded 1 each year.

Deadline April of each year.

[1099]
NATIONAL GUARD ASSOCIATION OF NEW JERSEY SCHOLARSHIP PROGRAM

National Guard Association of New Jersey
Attn: Scholarship Committee
P.O. Box 266
Wrightstown, NJ 08562
(973) 541-6776   Fax: (973) 541-6909
E-mail: scholarship@nganj.org
Web: www.nganj.org/benefits.htm

Summary To provide financial assistance to members of the National Guard Association of New Jersey (NGANJ) or their dependents who are interested in attending college or graduate school in any state.

Eligibility This program is open to 1) active members of the NGANJ currently enrolled full time at an approved community college, school of nursing, or 4-year college in any

state; and 2) the spouses, children, and grandchildren of active, retired, or deceased members entering or attending a 4-year college or university in any state. Applicants must submit transcripts, information on the civic and academic activities in which they have participated, and a list of offices, honors, awards, and special recognitions they have received. Selection is based on academic accomplishment, leadership, and citizenship.

Financial data Stipends up to $1,000 are available.

Duration 1 year; nonrenewable.

Number awarded Varies each year; recently, 10 were awarded.

Deadline April of each year.

[1100]
NATIONAL GUARD ASSOCIATION OF SOUTH CAROLINA SCHOLARSHIPS

National Guard Association of South Carolina
Attn: NGASC Scholarship Foundation
132 Pickens Street
Columbia, SC 29205
(803) 254-8456   Toll Free: (800) 822-3235
Fax: (803) 254-3869   E-mail: nginfo@ngasc.org
Web: www.ngasc.org/services-view/scholorships

Summary To provide financial assistance to current and former South Carolina National Guard members and their dependents who are interested in attending college or graduate school in any state.

Eligibility This program is open to undergraduate students who are 1) current, retired, or deceased members of the South Carolina National Guard; 2) their dependents; and 3) members of the National Guard Association of South Carolina (NGASC). Graduate students are also eligible if they are members of the South Carolina National Guard. Applicants must be attending or interested in attending a college or university in any state as a full-time student. Several of the scholarships include additional restrictions on school or academic major; some are granted only for academic excellence, but most are based on both academics and financial need.

Financial data The stipend is $1,500 or $1,000.

Duration 1 year; may be renewed up to 3 additional years.

Number awarded Varies each year; recently, 55 were awarded.

Deadline January of each year.

[1101]
NATIONAL GUARD ASSOCIATION OF TEXAS SCHOLARSHIP PROGRAM

National Guard Association of Texas
Attn: Education Committee
3706 Crawford Avenue
Austin, TX 78731-6803
(512) 454-7300   Toll Free: (800) 252-NGAT
Fax: (512) 467-6803   E-mail: rlindner@ngat.org
Web: www.ngat.org/educate.php

Summary To provide financial assistance to members and dependents of members of the National Guard Association of Texas who are interested in attending college or graduate school in any state.

Eligibility This program is open to annual and life members of the association and their spouses and children (associate members and their dependents are not eligible). Applicants may be high school seniors, undergraduate students, or graduate students, either enrolled or planning to enroll at an institution of higher education in any state. Along with their application, they must submit an essay on their desire to continue their education. Selection is based on scholarship, citizenship, and leadership.

Financial data   Stipends range from $700 to $5,000.

Duration   1 year (nonrenewable).

Additional information   This program includes 1 scholarship sponsored by USAA Insurance Corporation.

Number awarded   Varies each year; recently, 9 were awarded: 1 at $5,000, 2 at $2,000, 1 at $1,500, 1 at $1,250, 3 at $1,000, and 1 at $750.

Deadline   February of each year.

[1102]
NATIONAL GUARD ASSOCIATION OF VERMONT SCHOLARSHIPS

National Guard Association of Vermont
Attn: Scholarships
P.O. Box 694
Essex Junction, VT 05453
(802) 338-3185   E-mail: timothy.gariboldi@us.army.mil
Web: www.ngavt.org/scholarInfo.shtml

Summary   To provide financial assistance to members of the Vermont National Guard (VTNG) or the National Guard Association of Vermont (NGA-VT) and their children or spouses who are interested in attending college or graduate school in any state.

Eligibility   This program is open to current members of the VTNG or the NGA-VT, their spouses, and their unmarried children. Applicants must be working, or planning to work, on an associate, undergraduate, technical, or graduate degree as a full-time student at a school in any state. Along with their application, they must submit an essay on their commitment to selfless public service or their plan for pursuing it in the future. In the selection process, first priority is given to applicants in grades E-1 through E-6, W-1 and W-2, and O-1 through O-3; second to E-7, E-8, and W3; third to E-9, W-4 and W-5, and O-4 and above. Other factors considered include the essay, academic performance, and community service. The program includes the COL James D. Kneeland Memorial Scholarship Award, reserved for a member of the Vermont Army National Guard Aviation Community.

Financial data   Stipends range from $500 to $1,500. Funds are sent directly to the recipient.

Duration   1 year; recipients may reapply.

Number awarded   4 each year: 1 at $1,500 (the COL James D. Kneeland Memorial Scholarship Award), 1 at $1,000, and 2 at $500 (1 for a student affiliated with the Vermont Army National Guard and 1 for a student affiliated with the Vermont Air National Guard).

Deadline   June of each year.

[1103]
NAVAL HELICOPTER ASSOCIATION GRADUATE SCHOLARSHIPS

Naval Helicopter Association
Attn: Scholarship Fund
P.O. Box 180578
Coronado, CA 92178-0578
(619) 435-7139   Fax: (619) 435-7354
Web: nhascholarshipfund.org/scholarships-available.html

Summary   To provide financial assistance for graduate school to students who have an affiliation with the rotary wing activities of the sea services.

Eligibility   This program is open to graduate students who are children, grandchildren, or spouses of active-duty, former, or retired Navy, Marine Corps, or Coast Guard rotary wing aviators, aircrewmen, or support personnel. Applicants must submit a personal statement on their academic and career aspirations. Selection is based on that statement, academic proficiency, scholastic achievements and awards, extracurricular activities, employment history, and letters of recommendation.

Financial data   The stipend is $3,000.

Duration   1 year.

Number awarded   1 each year.

Deadline   January of each year.

[1104]
NAVAL HELICOPTER ASSOCIATION MEMORIAL SCHOLARSHIPS

Naval Helicopter Association
Attn: Scholarship Fund
P.O. Box 180578
Coronado, CA 92178-0578
(619) 435-7139   Fax: (619) 435-7354
Web: nhascholarshipfund.org/scholarships-available.html

Summary   To provide financial assistance for college or graduate school to 1) active-duty personnel who are working or have worked in rotary wing activities of the sea services and 2) members of their families.

Eligibility   This program is open to 1) active-duty Navy, Marine Corps, or Coast Guard rotary wing aviators, aircrewmen, or support personnel; and 2) the children and spouses of those personnel. Applicants must be working on or planning to work on an undergraduate or graduate degree in any field. Along with their application, they must submit a personal statement on their academic and career aspirations. Selection is based on that statement, academic proficiency, scholastic achievements and awards, extracurricular activities, employment history, and letters of recommendation.

Financial data   Stipends are approximately $2,000.

Duration   1 year.

Additional information   This program includes the following named awards: the Edward and Veronica Ream Memorial Scholarship, the CDR Mort McCarthy Memorial Scholarship, the Charles Karman Memorial Scholarship, the LT Christian "Horse" Hescock Memorial Scholarship, and the Captain Mark Starr Memorial Scholarship.

Number awarded   Varies each year; recently, 4 were awarded.

Deadline   January of each year.

[1105]
NAVAL SPECIAL WARFARE DEVELOPMENT GROUP SCHOLARSHIPS

Navy Seal Foundation
Attn: DEVGRU Scholarship Committee
1619 D Street, Building 5326
Virginia Beach, VA 23459
(757) 363-7490   Fax: (757) 363-7491
E-mail: info@navysealfoundation.org
Web: www.navysealfoundation.org

Summary   To provide financial assistance for college or graduate school to the children and spouses of personnel assigned to the Naval Special Warfare Development Group (DEVGRU).

Eligibility   This program is open to the dependent children and spouses of former and present Navy SEAL, Special Warfare Combatant-craft Crewmen (SWCC), or Military Direct Support person who are or have been assigned to DEVGRU. Applicants must be enrolled or planning to enroll at a trade school, technical/vocational institute, or undergraduate college. Spouses may also apply for graduate school. Along with their application, they must submit an essay on their plans as related to their educational and career objectives and long-term goals. Selection is based on merit (as measured by GPA, SAT scores, class rank, extracurricular activities, volunteer community involvement, leadership positions held, military service record, and after school employment, as appropriate) and academic potential.

Financial data   Stipends are $15,000, $7,500, or $5,000 per year.

Duration   1 year; may be renewed.

Number awarded   Varies each year; recently, the Navy Seal Foundation awarded 16 scholarships for all of its programs: 3 for 4 years at $15,000 per year to high school seniors and graduates, 3 for 1 year at $7,500 to high school seniors and graduates, 3 for 1 year at $15,000 to current college students, 3 for 1 year at $7,500 to current college students, and 4 for 1 year at $5,000 to spouses.

Deadline   January of each year.

[1106]
NAVY/MARINE CORPS/COAST GUARD ENLISTED DEPENDENT SPOUSE SCHOLARSHIP

Navy Wives Clubs of America
c/o NSA Mid-South
P.O. Box 54022
Millington, TN 38054-0022
Toll Free: (866) 511-NWCA
E-mail: nwca@navywivesclubsofamerica.org
Web: www.navywivesclubsofamerica.org/scholarships

Summary   To provide financial assistance for undergraduate or graduate study to spouses of naval personnel.

Eligibility   This program is open to the spouses of active-duty Navy, Marine Corps, or Coast Guard members who can demonstrate financial need. Applicants must be 1) a high school graduate or senior planning to attend college full time next year; 2) currently enrolled in an undergraduate program and planning to continue as a full-time undergraduate; 3) a college graduate or senior planning to be a full-time graduate student next year; or 4) a high school graduate or GED recipient planning to attend vocational or business school next year. Along with their application, they must submit a brief

statement on why they feel they should be awarded this scholarship and any special circumstances (financial or other) they wish to have considered. Financial need is also considered in the selection process.

Financial data   The stipends range from $500 to $1,000 each year (depending upon the donations from chapters of the Navy Wives Clubs of America).

Duration   1 year.

Number awarded   1 or more each year.

Deadline   May of each year.

[1107]
NAVY SEAL FOUNDATION SCHOLARSHIPS

Navy Seal Foundation
Attn: Chief Financial Officer
1619 D Street, Building 5326
Virginia Beach, VA 23459
(757) 363-7490   Fax: (757) 363-7491
E-mail: info@navysealfoundation.org
Web: www.navysealfoundation.org

Summary   To provide financial assistance for college or graduate school to Naval Special Warfare (NSW) personnel and their families.

Eligibility   This program is open to active-duty Navy SEALS, Special Warfare Combatant-craft Crewmen (SWCC), and military personnel assigned to other NSW commands. Their dependent children and spouses are also eligible. Applicants must be entering or continuing full or part-time students working on an associate or bachelor's degree. Active-duty and spouses, but not dependent children, may also work on a graduate degree. Selection is based on GPA, SAT scores, class ranking, extracurricular activities, volunteer community involvement, leadership positions held, military service record, and employment (as appropriate).

Financial data   Stipends are $15,000, $7,500, or $5,000 per year.

Duration   1 year; may be renewed.

Number awarded   Varies each year; recently, the Navy Seal Foundation awarded 16 scholarships for all of its programs: 3 for 4 years at $15,000 per year to high school seniors and graduates, 3 for 1 year at $7,500 to high school seniors and graduates, 3 for 1 year at $15,000 to current college students, 3 for 1 year at $7,500 to current college students, and 4 for 1 year at $5,000 to spouses.

Deadline   February of each year.

[1108]
NAVY WIVES CLUBS OF AMERICA NATIONAL SCHOLARSHIPS

Navy Wives Clubs of America
c/o NSA Mid-South
P.O. Box 54022
Millington, TN 38054-0022
Toll Free: (866) 511-NWCA
E-mail: nwca@navywivesclubsofamerica.org
Web: www.navywivesclubsofamerica.org/scholarships

Summary   To provide financial assistance for college or graduate school to the children of naval personnel.

Eligibility   Applicants for these scholarships must be the children (natural born, legally adopted, or stepchildren) of enlisted members of the Navy, Marine Corps, or Coast Guard on active duty, retired with pay, or deceased. Applicants must be attending or planning to attend an accredited college or university as a full-time undergraduate or graduate student. They must have a GPA of 2.5 or higher. Along with their application, they must submit an essay on their career objectives and the reasons they chose those objectives. Selection is based on academic standing, moral character, and financial need. Some scholarships are reserved for students majoring in special education, medical students, and children of members of Navy Wives Clubs of America (NWCA).

Financial data The stipend is $1,500.

Duration 1 year; may be renewed up to 3 additional years.

Additional information Membership in the NWCA is open to spouses of enlisted personnel serving in the Navy, Marine Corps, Coast Guard, and the active Reserve units of those services; spouses of enlisted personnel who have been honorably discharged, retired, or transferred to the Fleet Reserve on completion of duty; and widows of enlisted personnel in those services.

Number awarded 30 each year, including at least 4 to freshmen, 4 to current undergraduates applying for the first time, 2 to medical students, 1 to a student majoring in special education, and 4 to children of NWCA members.

Deadline May of each year.

[1109]
NBCC FOUNDATION MILITARY SCHOLARSHIPS

National Board for Certified Counselors
Attn: NBCC Foundation
3 Terrace Way
Greensboro, NC 27403
(336) 232-0376   Fax: (336) 232-0010
E-mail: foundation@nbcc.org
Web: www.nbccf.applicantstack.com/x/detail/a2ei42lhwwzc

Summary To provide financial assistance to 1) current and former military personnel and 2) spouses of servicemembers who are interested in working on a master's degree in counseling.

Eligibility This program is open to students enrolled in an accredited master's degree counseling program who have completed at least 18 credit hours and are enrolled in at least 6 credit hours during the current semester. Applicants must be prior or current active-duty U.S. military service personnel or the spouse of a servicemember. Veterans must have served in the military within the past 5 years and have received an honorable discharge. Applicants must be able to demonstrate a commitment to apply for the National Certified Counselor credential prior to graduation and to provide counseling services to servicemembers and/or veterans for at least 2 years after graduation.

Financial data The stipend is $5,000.

Duration 1 year.

Additional information This program began in 2010.

Number awarded 5 each year.

Deadline October of each year.

[1110]
NEW JERSEY NATIONAL GUARD TUITION PROGRAM

New Jersey Department of Military and Veterans Affairs
Attn: New Jersey Army National Guard Education Center
3650 Saylors Pond Road
Fort Dix, NJ 08640-7600
(609) 562-0654   Toll Free: (888) 859-0352
Fax: (609) 562-0201
Web: www.state.nj.us/military/education/NJNGTP.htm

Summary To provide financial assistance for college or graduate school to New Jersey National Guard members and the surviving spouses and children of deceased members.

Eligibility This program is open to active members of the New Jersey National Guard who have completed Initial Active Duty for Training (IADT). Applicants must be New Jersey residents who have been accepted into a program of undergraduate or graduate study at any of 31 public institutions of higher education in the state. The surviving spouses and children of deceased members of the Guard who had completed IADT and were killed in the performance of their duties while a member of the Guard are also eligible if the school has classroom space available.

Financial data Tuition for up to 15 credits per semester is waived for full-time recipients in state-supported colleges or community colleges in New Jersey.

Duration 1 semester; may be renewed.

Number awarded Varies each year.

Deadline Deadline not specified.

[1111]
NEW MEXICO CHILDREN OF DECEASED MILITARY PERSONNEL SCHOLARSHIPS

New Mexico Department of Veterans' Services
Attn: Benefits Division
407 Galisteo Street, Room 142
P.O. Box 2324
Santa Fe, NM 87504-2324
(505) 827-6374   Toll Free: (866) 433-VETS
Fax: (505) 827-6372   E-mail: alan.martinez@state.nm.us
Web: www.dvs.state.nm.us/benefits.html

Summary To provide financial assistance for college or graduate school to the children of deceased military personnel in New Mexico.

Eligibility This program is open to the children of military personnel killed in action or as a result of such action during a period of armed conflict. Applicants must be between the ages of 16 and 26 and enrolled in a state-supported school in New Mexico. Selection is based on merit and financial need.

Financial data The scholarships provide full waiver of tuition at state-funded postsecondary schools in New Mexico. A stipend of $150 per semester ($300 per year) provides assistance with books and fees.

Duration 1 year; may be renewed.

Number awarded Varies each year.

Deadline Deadline not specified.

[1112]
PETER CONNACHER MEMORIAL SCHOLARSHIPS

Oregon Student Access Commission
Attn: Grants and Scholarships Division
1500 Valley River Drive, Suite 100
Eugene, OR 97401-2146
(541) 687-7395   Toll Free: (800) 452-8807, ext. 7395
Fax: (541) 687-7414   TDD: (800) 735-2900
E-mail: awardinfo@osac.state.or.us
Web: www.oregonstudentaid.gov/scholarships.aspx

Summary To provide financial assistance for college or graduate school to ex-prisoners of war and their descendants.

Eligibility Applicants must be U.S. citizens who 1) were military or civilian prisoners of war; or 2) are the descendants of ex-prisoners of war. They must be full-time undergraduate or graduate students. A copy of the ex-prisoner of war's discharge papers from the U.S. armed forces must accompany the application. In addition, written proof of POW status must be submitted, along with a statement of the relationship between the applicant and the ex-prisoner of war (father, grandfather, etc.). Selection is based on academic record and financial need. Preference is given to Oregon residents or their dependents.

Financial data Stipends for scholarships offered by the Oregon Student Access Commission (OSAC) range from $200 to $10,000 but recently averaged $5,200.

Duration 1 year; may be renewed for up to 3 additional years for undergraduate students or 2 additional years for graduate students. Renewal is dependent on evidence of continued financial need and satisfactory academic progress.

Additional information This program is administered by the OSAC with funds provided by the Oregon Community Foundation and by the Columbia River Chapter of American Ex-prisoners of War, Inc.

Number awarded Varies each year; recently, 4 were awarded.

Deadline February of each year.

[1113]
PHS COMMISSIONED OFFICERS FOUNDATION DEPENDENT SCHOLARSHIP PROGRAM

Commissioned Officers Association of the U.S. Public
   Health Service
Attn: PHS Commissioned Officers Foundation for the
   Advancement of Public Health
8201 Corporate Drive, Suite 200
Landover, MD 20785
(301) 731-9080   Fax: (301) 731-9084
E-mail: jmcelligott@coausphs.org
Web: www.phscof.org/education/cof-scholarship-program

Summary To provide financial assistance to spouses and descendants of members of the Commissioned Officers Association of the U.S. Public Health Service (COA) who are interested in working on an undergraduate or graduate degree in any of the Public Health Service (PHS) categories.

Eligibility This program is open to high school seniors, undergraduates, and graduate students who are the spouse, child, or grandchild of an active-duty or retired COA member. Applicants must be preparing for a career in a PHS category (e.g., dentist, dietician, engineer, nurse, pharmacist, physician, clinical or rehabilitation therapist, veterinarian).

Financial data The stipend is approximately $1,000.

Duration 1 year.

Number awarded Varies each year; recently, 13 were awarded.

Deadline Deadline not specified.

[1114]
RED RIVER VALLEY FIGHTER PILOTS ASSOCIATION KINSHIP SCHOLARSHIP GRANT PROGRAM

Red River Valley Association Foundation
Attn: Executive Director
P.O. Box 1553
Front Royal, VA 22630-0033
(540) 639-9798   Toll Free: (866) 401-7287
Fax: (540) 636-9776
E-mail: ExecutiveOffice@river-rats.org
Web: www.river-rats.org/about-us/scholarship-program.html

Summary To provide financial assistance for college or graduate school to the spouses and children of selected service personnel and members of the Red River Valley Fighter Pilots Association.

Eligibility This program is open to the spouses and children of 1) servicemembers missing in action (MIA) or killed in action (KIA) in combat situations involving U.S. military forces from August 1964 through the present; 2) U.S. military aircrew members killed in a non-combat aircraft accident in which they were performing aircrew duties; and 3) current members of the association and deceased members who were in good standing at the time of their death. Scholarships are also available to students in fields related to aviation and space, even if they have no kinship relationship to a deceased aviator or member of the association. Applicants must be enrolled or planning to enroll full or part time at an accredited college, university, vocational/technical institute, or career school to work on an undergraduate or graduate degree. They must be 30 years of age or younger, although the age limit is extended to 40 for current and former military personnel. Selection is based on demonstrated academic achievement, SAT or ACT scores, financial need, and accomplishments in school, church, civic, and social activities.

Financial data The amount awarded varies, depending upon the need of the recipient. Recently, undergraduate stipends have ranged from $500 to $3,500 and averaged $1,725; graduate stipends have ranged from $500 to $2,000 and averaged $1,670. Funds are paid directly to the recipient's institution and are to be used for tuition, fees, books, and room and board for full-time students.

Duration 1 year; may be renewed if the recipient maintains a GPA of 2.0 or higher.

Additional information This program began in 1970, out of concern for the families of aircrews (known as "River Rats") who were killed or missing in action in the Red River Valley of North Vietnam.

Number awarded Varies each year; since this program was established, it has awarded more than 1,000 scholarships worth more than $1,700,000.

Deadline June of each year.

[1115]
SFC CURTIS MANCINI MEMORIAL SCHOLARSHIPS

Association of the United States Army-Rhode Island
  Chapter
c/o CSM (Ret) Anthony Ferri, Secretary
47 Spokane Street
Providence, RI 02904
(401) 861-2997   E-mail: afnf458673755@aol.com
Web: www.ausari.org/index.html

Summary To provide financial assistance to members of the Rhode Island Chapter of the Association of the United States Army (AUSA) and their families who are interested in attending college or graduate school in any state.

Eligibility This program is open to members of the AUSA Rhode Island Chapter and their family members (spouses, children, and grandchildren). Applicants must be high school seniors or graduates accepted at an accredited college, university, or vocational/technical school in any state or current undergraduate or graduate students. Along with their application, they must submit a 250-word essay on why they feel their achievements should qualify them for this award. Selection is based on academic and individual achievements; financial need is not considered. Membership in AUSA is open to current and retired Army personnel (including Reserves and National Guard), ROTC cadets, or civilian employees of the Army.

Financial data The stipend is $1,000.

Duration 1 year.

Number awarded 2 each year.

Deadline March of each year.

[1116]
SHIP ISLAND–MRS. J.O. JONES MEMORIAL SCHOLARSHIP

United Daughters of the Confederacy
Attn: Second Vice President General
328 North Boulevard
Richmond, VA 23220-4008
(804) 355-1636   Fax: (804) 353-1396
E-mail: jamieretired@sbcglobal.net
Web: www.hqudc.org/Scholarships/index.htm

Summary To provide financial assistance to lineal descendants of Confederate veterans who are interested in working on a graduate degree in nursing.

Eligibility Eligible to apply for these scholarships are lineal descendants of worthy Confederates or collateral descendants who are members of the Children of the Confederacy or the United Daughters of the Confederacy. Applicants must intend to study nursing at the graduate level and must submit certified proof of the Confederate record of 1 ancestor, with the company and regiment in which he served. They must have a GPA of 3.0 or higher.

Financial data The amount of this scholarship depends on the availability of funds.

Duration 1 year; may be renewed up to 2 additional years.

Number awarded 1 each year.

Deadline April of each year.

[1117]
SSGT. ROBERT V. MILNER MEMORIAL SCHOLARSHIP

American Academy of Physician Assistants-Veterans
  Caucus
Attn: Veterans Caucus
P.O. Box 362
Danville, PA 17821-0362
Fax: (302) 526-7154 E-mail: fbrace@veteranscaucus.org
Web: www.veteranscaucus.org

Summary To provide financial assistance to Air Force veterans and their dependents who are studying to become physician assistants.

Eligibility This program is open to U.S. citizens who are currently enrolled in a physician assistant program. The program must be approved by the Commission on Accreditation of Allied Health Education. Applicants must be honorably discharged members of the United States Air Force or the dependent of an Air Force veteran. Selection is based on military honors and awards received, civic and college honors and awards received, professional memberships and activities, and GPA. An electronic copy of the applicant's DD Form 214 must accompany the application.

Financial data The stipend is $2,000.

Duration 1 year.

Number awarded 1 each year.

Deadline February of each year.

[1118]
STANLEY A. DORAN MEMORIAL SCHOLARSHIPS

Fleet Reserve Association
Attn: FRA Education Foundation
125 North West Street
Alexandria, VA 22314-2754
(703) 683-1400   Toll Free: (800) FRA-1924
Fax: (703) 549-6610   E-mail: scholars@fra.org
Web: www.fra.org

Summary To provide financial assistance for college or graduate school to children of members of the Fleet Reserve Association (FRA).

Eligibility This program is open to the dependent children of FRA members who are in good standing (or were at the time of death, if deceased). Applicants must be working on or planning to work full time on an undergraduate or graduate degree. Along with their application, they must submit an essay on why they want to go to college and what they intend to accomplish with their degree. Selection is based on academic record, financial need, extracurricular activities, leadership skills, and participation in community activities. U.S. citizenship is required.

Financial data Stipends range up to $5,000 per year.

Duration 1 year; may be renewed.

Additional information Membership in the FRA is restricted to active-duty, retired, and Reserve members of the Navy, Marine Corps, and Coast Guard.

Number awarded 3 each year.

Deadline April of each year.

[1119]
SURVIVORS' AND DEPENDENTS' EDUCATIONAL ASSISTANCE PROGRAM

Department of Veterans Affairs
Attn: Veterans Benefits Administration
810 Vermont Avenue, N.W.
Washington, DC 20420
(202) 418-4343   Toll Free: (888) GI-BILL1
Web: www.benefits.va.gov

Summary To provide financial assistance for undergraduate or graduate study to children and spouses of deceased and disabled veterans, MIAs, and POWs.

Eligibility Eligible for this assistance are spouses and children of 1) veterans who died or are permanently and totally disabled as the result of active service in the armed forces; 2) veterans who died from any cause while rated permanently and totally disabled from a service-connected disability; 3) servicemembers listed as missing in action or captured in the line of duty by a hostile force; 4) servicemembers listed as forcibly detained or interned by a foreign government or power; and 5) servicemembers who are hospitalized or receiving outpatient treatment for a service-connected permanent and total disability and are likely to be discharged for that disability. Children must be between 18 and 26 years of age, although extensions may be granted. Spouses and children over 14 years of age with physical or mental disabilities are also eligible.

Financial data Monthly stipends for study at an academic institution are $1,018 for full time, $763 for three-quarter time, or $506 for half-time. Other rates apply for apprenticeship and on-the-job training, farm cooperative training, and special restorative training.

Duration Benefits are provided for up to 45 months (or the equivalent in part-time training). Some beneficiaries who qualify for more than 1 education program may be eligible for up to 81 months. Spouses must complete their training within 10 years of the date they are first found eligible. For spouses of servicemembers who died on active duty, benefits end 20 years from the date of death.

Additional information Benefits may be used to work on associate, bachelor's, or graduate degrees at colleges and universities, including independent study, cooperative training, and study abroad programs. Courses leading to a certificate or diploma from business, technical, or vocational schools may also be taken. Other eligible programs include apprenticeships, on-the-job training programs, farm cooperative courses, and correspondence courses (for spouses only). Remedial, deficiency, and refresher courses may be approved under certain circumstances.

Number awarded Varies each year.

Deadline Applications may be submitted at any time.

[1120]
TENTH MOUNTAIN DIVISION FOUNDATION SCHOLARSHIP PROGRAM

Tenth Mountain Division Foundation, Inc.
133 South Van Gordon Street, Suite 200
Lakewood, CO 80228
(303) 756-8486   Fax: (303) 987-9489
E-mail: admin@10thmdf.ort
Web: www.10thmdf.org/scholarship.htm

Summary To provide financial assistance for college or graduate school to descendants of former members of the Tenth Mountain Division.

Eligibility This program is open to the descendants of veterans who served in the Tenth Mountain Division during World War II. Applicants must have completed at least 2 years of undergraduate study at an accredited college, university, or other comparable institution or be enrolled in a graduate program. Along with their application, they must submit an essay on the military service of their ancestor during World War II. Selection is based on that essay and financial need.

Financial data The stipend is $5,000.

Duration 1 year; nonrenewable.

Number awarded Up to 5 each year.

Deadline April of each year.

[1121]
THOMAS H. MILLER SCHOLARSHIP

Blinded Veterans Association
477 H Street, N.W.
Washington, DC 20001-2694
(202) 371-8880   Toll Free: (800) 669-7079
Fax: (202) 371-8258   E-mail: temanuel@bva.org
Web: www.bva.org/services.html

Summary To provide financial assistance for undergraduate or graduate study, especially of music or the fine arts, to immediate family of blinded veterans and servicemembers.

Eligibility This program is open to dependent children, grandchildren, and spouses of blinded veterans and active-duty blinded servicemembers of the U.S. armed forces. The veteran or servicemember must be legally blind; the blindness may be either service-connected or nonservice-connected. Applicants must have been accepted or be currently enrolled as a full-time student in an undergraduate or graduate program at an accredited institution of higher learning. Preference is given to students of music or the fine arts. Along with their application, they must submit a 300-word essay on their career goals and aspirations. Financial need is not considered in the selection process.

Financial data The stipend is $1,000; funds are intended to be used to cover the student's expenses, including tuition, other academic fees, books, dormitory fees, and cafeteria fees. Funds are paid directly to the recipient's school.

Duration 1 year; recipients may reapply for up to 3 additional years.

Number awarded 1 each year.

Deadline April of each year.

[1122]
TILLMAN MILITARY SCHOLARS PROGRAM

Pat Tillman Foundation
217 North Jefferson Street, Suite 602
Chicago, IL 60661
(773) 360-5277
E-mail: scholarships@pattillmanfoundation.org
Web: www.pattillmanfoundation.org/apply-to-be-a-scholar

Summary To provide financial assistance to active servicemembers, veterans, and their spouses who are interested in working on an undergraduate or graduate degree.

Eligibility This program is open to veterans and active servicemembers of all branches of the armed forces from both the pre- and post-September 11 era and their spouses; children are not eligible. Applicants must be enrolled or planning to enroll full time at a 4-year public or private college or university to work on an undergraduate, graduate, or postgraduate degree. Current and former servicemembers must submit 400-word essays on 1) their motivation and decision to serve in the U.S. military and how that decision and experience has changed their life and ambitions; and 2) their educational and career goals, how they will incorporate their military service experience into those goals, and how they intend to continue their service to others and the community. Spouses must submit 400-word essays on 1) their previous service to others and the community; and 2) their educational and career goals, how they will incorporate their service experiences and the impact of their spouse's military service into those goals, and how they intend to continue their service to others and the community. Selection is based on those essays, educational and career ambitions, record of military service, record of personal achievement, demonstration of service to others in the community, desire to continue such service, and leadership potential.

Financial data The stipend depends on the need of the recipient and the availability of funds; recently, stipends averaged approximately $15,000.

Duration 1 year; may be renewed, provided the recipient maintains a GPA of 3.0 or higher, remains enrolled full time, and documents participation in civic action or community service.

Additional information This program began in 2009.

Number awarded 60 each year. Since the program began, it has awarded more than $6 million to 348 scholars.

Deadline March of each year.

[1123]
TRANSFER OF POST-9/11 GI-BILL BENEFITS TO DEPENDENTS

Department of Veterans Affairs
Attn: Veterans Benefits Administration
810 Vermont Avenue, N.W.
Washington, DC 20420
(202) 418-4343   Toll Free: (888) GI-BILL1
Web: www.benefits.va.gov/gibill/post911_transfer.asp

Summary To provide financial assistance to dependents of military personnel who qualify for Post-9/11 GI Bill benefits and agree to transfer unused benefits to their spouse or child.

Eligibility This program is open to dependents of current military personnel whose parent or spouse 1) has at least 6 years of service in the armed forces (active duty and/or Selected Reserve) and agrees to serve 4 additional years; 2) has at least 10 years of service, is precluded by either standard policy or statute from committing to 4 additional years, but agrees to serve for the maximum amount of time allowed by such policy or statute; or 3) is or becomes retirement eligible during the period following August 1, 2012 and agrees to serve for an additional period up to 4 years, depending on the date of retirement eligibility. The military parent or spouse must agree to transfer unused months of educational benefits to a dependent while still serving on active duty. Dependents must be enrolled or planning to enroll in an educational program, including work on an undergraduate or graduate degree, vocational/technical training, on-the-job training, flight training, correspondence training, licensing and national

testing programs, entrepreneurship training, and tutorial assistance.

Financial data Dependents working on an undergraduate or graduate degree at public institutions in their state receive full payment of tuition and fees. For dependents who attend private institutions in most states, tuition and fee reimbursement is capped at $20,235.02 per academic year. Benefits for other types of training programs depend on the amount for which the spouse or parent qualified under prior educational programs. Dependents also receive a monthly housing allowance that is 1) based on the Department of Defense Basic Allowance for Housing (BAH) for an E-5 with dependents (which depends on the location of the school but ranges from approximately $1,000 per month to approximately $2,500 per month); 2) $1,509 per month at schools in foreign countries; or 3) $754.50 per month for online training classes. They also receive an annual book allowance of $1,000 and (for participants who live in a rural county remote from an educational institution) a rural benefit payment of $500 per year.

Duration Military members may transfer all or a portion of their 36 months of entitlement to a dependent. Spouses may start to use the benefit immediately, but children may use the benefit only after they have completed high school (or equivalency certificate) or reached 18 years of age. They are not subject to the 15-year limit but may not use the benefit after reaching 26 years of age.

Additional information This supplement was added to the Post-9/11 GI Bill program as a result of legislation passed by Congress in 2010.

Number awarded Varies each year.

Deadline Deadline not specified.

[1124]
U.S. ARMY WOMEN'S FOUNDATION LEGACY SCHOLARSHIPS

U.S. Army Women's Foundation
Attn: Scholarship Committee
P.O. Box 5030
Fort Lee, VA 23801-0030
(804) 734-3078   E-mail: info@awfdn.org
Web: www.awfdn.org/programs/legacyscholarships.shtml

Summary To provide financial assistance for college or graduate school to women who are serving or have served in the Army and their children.

Eligibility This program is open to 1) women who have served or are serving honorably in the U.S. Army, U.S. Army Reserve, or Army National Guard; and 2) children of women who served honorably in the U.S. Army, U.S. Army Reserve, or Army National Guard. Applicants must be 1) high school graduates or GED recipients enrolled at a community college or technical certificate program who have a GPA of 2.5 or higher; 2) sophomores or higher at an accredited college or university who have a GPA of 3.0 or higher; or 3) students enrolled in or accepted to a graduate program who have a GPA of 3.0 or higher. Along with their application, they must submit a 2-page essay on why they should be considered for this scholarship, their future plans as related to their program of study, and information about their community service, activities, and work experience. Selection is based on merit, academic potential, community service, and financial need.

Financial data The stipend is $2,500 for college and graduate students or $1,000 for community college and certificate students.
Duration 1 year.
Number awarded 5 to 10 each year.
Deadline January of each year.

[1125]
VADM ROBERT L. WALTERS SCHOLARSHIP

Surface Navy Association
Attn: Scholarship Coordinator
6551 Loisdale Court, Suite 222
Springfield, VA 22150
(703) 960-6800   Toll Free: (800) NAVY-SNA
Fax: (703) 960-6807   E-mail: navysna@aol.com
Web: www.navysna.org

Summary To provide financial assistance for college or graduate school to dependents of members of the Surface Navy Association (SNA).

Eligibility This program is open to the children, stepchildren, wards, and spouses of SNA members. The SNA member must 1) be in the second or subsequent consecutive year of membership; 2) be serving, retired, or honorably discharged; 3) be a Surface Warfare Officer or Enlisted Surface Warfare Specialist; and 4) have served for at least 3 years on a surface ship of the U.S. Navy or Coast Guard. Applicants must be enrolled or planning to enroll full time at an accredited undergraduate or graduate institution; the full-time requirement may be waived for spouses. Along with their application, they must submit a 500-word essay about themselves and why they should be selected to receive this scholarship. High school seniors should also include a transcript of high school grades and a copy of ACT or SAT scores. Current college students should also include a transcript of the grades from their most recent 4 semesters of school. Selection is based on academic proficiency, non-scholastic activities, scholastic and non-scholastic awards, character, and financial need.

Financial data The stipend is $2,000 per year.
Duration 4 years, provided the recipient maintains a GPA of 3.0 or higher.
Number awarded Varies each year.
Deadline February of each year.

[1126]
VETERANS UNITED FOUNDATION SCHOLARSHIPS

Veterans United Home Loans
Attn: Veterans United Foundation
1400 Veterans United Drive
Columbia, MO 65203
(573) 445-7999   Toll Free: (800) 884-5560
E-mail: customer_service@vu.com
Web: www.enhancelives.com/scholarships

Summary To provide financial assistance for college or graduate school to students who have a tie to the military.

Eligibility This program is open to 1) active-duty military personnel with plans to attend college; 2) honorably-discharged veterans of the U.S. military; 3) spouses of military members or veterans; 4) surviving spouses and children of fallen servicemembers; and 5) children of veterans or active-duty military. Applicants must be attending or planning to attend college as a full-time undergraduate or graduate stu-

dent. They must have a GPA of 2.5 or higher. Selection is based primarily on an essay.
Financial data The stipend is $2,000.
Duration 1 year.
Additional information This program began in 2007.
Number awarded Up to 20 each year: 10 each term.
Deadline April or October of each year.

[1127]
VIRGINIA MILITARY SURVIVORS AND DEPENDENTS EDUCATION PROGRAM

Virginia Department of Veterans Services
Attn: VMSDEP Administrator
900 East Main Street
Richmond, VA 23219
(804) 225-2083   Fax: (804) 786-0809
E-mail: melek.sanchez@dvs.virginia.gov
Web: www.dvs.virginia.gov/vmsdep.shtml

Summary To provide educational assistance to the children and spouses of disabled and other Virginia veterans or service personnel.

Eligibility This program is open to residents of Virginia whose parent or spouse served in the U.S. armed forces (including the Reserves, the Virginia National Guard, or the Virginia National Guard Reserves) during any armed conflict subsequent to December 6, 1941, as a result of a terrorist act, during military operations against terrorism, or on a peacekeeping mission. The veterans must have been killed, be missing in action, have been taken prisoner of war, or become at least 90% disabled as a result of such service. Applicants must have been accepted at a public college or university in Virginia as an undergraduate or graduate student. Children must be between 16 and 29 years of age; there are no age restrictions for spouses. The veteran must have been a resident of Virginia at the time of entry into active military service or for at least 5 consecutive years immediately prior to the date of application or death. Surviving spouses must have been residents of Virginia for at least 5 years prior to marrying the veteran or for at least 5 years immediately prior to the date on which the application was submitted.

Financial data The program provides 1) waiver of tuition and all required fees at public institutions of higher education in Virginia; and 2) a stipend (amount not specified) to offset the costs of room, board, books, and supplies at those institutions.

Duration Entitlement extends to a maximum of 36 months (4 years).

Additional information Individuals entitled to this benefit may use it to pursue any vocational, technical, undergraduate, or graduate program of instruction. Generally, programs listed in the academic catalogs of state-supported institutions are acceptable, provided they have a clearly-defined educational objective (such as a certificate, diploma, or degree). This program was formerly known as the Virginia War Orphans Education Program.

Number awarded Varies each year; recently, funding allowed for a total of 1,000 stipends.

Deadline Applications may be submitted at any time, but they must be received at least 30 days prior to the start of the term.

[1128]
VIRGINIA PENINSULA POST SAME SCHOLARSHIPS

Society of American Military Engineers-Virginia Peninsula
Post
c/o James H. King, Jr., Scholarship Chair
129 Andrews Street, Suite 217
Hampton, VA 23665
(757) 764-7570   Fax: (757) 764-3439
E-mail: james.king.45@us.af.mil

Summary To provide financial assistance to high school seniors, undergraduates, and graduate students entering or enrolled at universities in Virginia who have a tie to the Virginia Peninsula Post of the Society of American Military Engineers (SAME) and are majoring in engineering or architecture.

Eligibility This program is open to 1) high school seniors planning to enroll in an engineering or architecture program at an accredited college or university in Virginia; 2) students enrolled as freshmen through graduate students at an accredited college or university in Virginia and working on a bachelor's or higher degree in engineering or architecture; and 3) members and dependents of members of the SAME Virginia Peninsula Post. Applicants must have demonstrated commitment to future military service by enrolling in an ROTC program, a commissioning program, or an extended enlistment. Selection is based on academic standing and accomplishments (50%), involvement in university and community programs, including those with military involvement (30%), and financial need (20%).

Financial data The stipend is $1,500.

Duration 1 year.

Number awarded 4 each year: 1 to a high school senior, 1 to a college freshman or sophomore, 1 to a college junior or senior, and 1 to a graduate student.

Deadline February of each year.

[1129]
WAVES NATIONAL COLLEGE SCHOLARSHIP

Women of the WAVES
c/o Betty Hand, Scholarship Contest Chair
5128 Sammy Street
Virginia Beach, VA 23455
(901) 568-0521   E-mail: hand.craftylady@gmail.com
Web: www.womenofthewaves.com

Summary To provide financial assistance for college or graduate school to relatives of women who served or are serving in the sea services.

Eligibility This program is open to male and female relatives (by birth, legal adoption, or marriage) of women who have served or are currently serving in the Navy, Coast Guard, or Marine Corps. Applicants must be enrolled or planning to enroll at a 2- or 4-year college, university, trade/technical school, or graduate school. They must have a GPA of 3.2 or higher. Along with their application, they must submit an essay of 1,000 to 1,500 words based on an interview with their female sea service relative on how their service changed the lives of others. Financial need is not considered in the selection process.

Financial data The stipend is $1,500.

Duration 1 year.

Number awarded 1 each year.

Deadline March of each year.

[1130]
WILLIAM BODDINGTON SCHOLARSHIP

Tenth Mountain Division Foundation, Inc.
133 South Van Gordon Street, Suite 200
Lakewood, CO 80228
(303) 756-8486   Fax: (303) 987-9489
E-mail: admin@10thmdf.ort
Web: www.10thmdf.org/scholarship.htm

Summary To provide financial assistance for college or graduate school to descendants of former members of the Tenth Mountain Division who demonstrate outstanding character.

Eligibility This program is open to the descendants of veterans who served in the Tenth Mountain Division during World War II. Applicants must have completed at least 2 years of undergraduate study at an accredited college, university, or other comparable institution or be enrolled in a graduate program. They must have a record of strong school and community service. Along with their application, they must submit an essay on how they emulate and put into practice the ideals and character traits valued by William Boddington, who served in the Division during World War II. Selection is based on that essay and financial need.

Financial data The stipend is $5,500.

Duration 1 year; nonrenewable.

Number awarded 1 each year.

Deadline April of each year.

[1131]
WISCONSIN G.I. BILL TUITION REMISSION PROGRAM

Wisconsin Department of Veterans Affairs
201 West Washington Avenue
P.O. Box 7843
Madison, WI 53707-7843
(608) 266-1311   Toll Free: (800) WIS-VETS
Fax: (608) 267-0403   E-mail: WDVAInfo@dva.state.wi.us
Web: www.dva.state.wi.us/Ben-Education.asp

Summary To provide financial assistance for college or graduate school to Wisconsin veterans and their dependents.

Eligibility This program is open to current residents of Wisconsin who 1) were residents of the state when they entered or reentered active duty in the U.S. armed forces; or 2) have moved to the state and have been residents for at least 5 consecutive years after entry or reentry into service. Applicants must have served on active duty for at least 2 continuous years or for at least 90 days during specified wartime periods. Also eligible are 1) qualifying children and unremarried surviving spouses of Wisconsin veterans who died in the line of duty or as the direct result of a service-connected disability; and 2) children and spouses of Wisconsin veterans who have a service-connected disability rated by the U.S. Department of Veterans Affairs as 30% or greater. Children must be between 17 and 25 years of age (regardless of the date of the veteran's death or initial disability rating) and be a Wisconsin resident for tuition purposes. Spouses remain eligible for 10 years following the date of the veteran's death or initial disability rating; they must be Wisconsin residents for tuition purposes but they may enroll full or part time. Students may attend any institution, center, or school within the University of Wisconsin (UW) System or the Wisconsin Technical College System (WCTS). There are no income limits, delimiting periods following military service during which the benefit must be used, or limits on the level of study (e.g., vocational, undergraduate, professional, or graduate).

Financial data Veterans who qualify as a Wisconsin resident for tuition purposes are eligible for a remission of 100% of standard academic fees and segregated fees at a UW campus or 100% of program and material fees at a WCTS institution. Veterans who qualify as a Wisconsin veteran for purposes of this program but for other reasons fail to meet the definition of a Wisconsin resident for tuition purposes at the UW system are eligible for a remission of 100% of non-resident fees. Spouses and children of deceased or disabled veterans are entitled to a remission of 100% of tuition and fees at a UW or WCTS institution.

Duration Up to 8 semesters or 128 credits, whichever is greater.

Additional information This program began in 2005 as a replacement for Wisconsin Tuition and Fee Reimbursement Grants.

Number awarded Varies each year.

Deadline Applications must be submitted within 14 days from the office start of the academic term: in October for fall, March for spring, or June for summer.

[1132]
WISCONSIN JOB RETRAINING GRANTS

Wisconsin Department of Veterans Affairs
201 West Washington Avenue
P.O. Box 7843
Madison, WI 53707-7843
(608) 266-1311   Toll Free: (800) WIS-VETS
Fax: (608) 267-0403   E-mail: WDVAInfo@dva.state.wi.us
Web: www.dva.state.wi.us/Ben-Retraininggrants.asp

Summary To provide funds to recently unemployed Wisconsin veterans or their families who need financial assistance while being retrained for employment.

Eligibility This program is open to current residents of Wisconsin who 1) were residents of the state when they entered or reentered active duty in the U.S. armed forces; or 2) have moved to the state and have been residents for any consecutive 12-month period after entry or reentry into service. Applicants must have served on active duty for at least 2 continuous years or for at least 90 days during specified wartime periods. Unremarried spouses and minor or dependent children of deceased veterans who would have been eligible for the grant if they were living today may also be eligible. The applicant must, within the year prior to the date of application, have become unemployed (involuntarily laid off or discharged, not due to willful misconduct) or underemployed (experienced an involuntary reduction of income). Underemployed applicants must have current annual income from employment that does not exceed federal poverty guidelines (currently $11,490 for a family of 1, rising to $39,630 for a family of 8). All applicants must be retraining at accredited schools in Wisconsin or in a structured on-the-job program. Course work toward a college degree does not qualify. Training does not have to be full time, but the program must be completed within 2 years and must reasonably be expected to lead to employment.

Financial data The maximum grant is $3,000 per year; the actual amount varies, depending upon the amount of the applicant's unmet need. In addition to books, fees, and tuition, the funds may be used for living expenses.

Duration 1 year; may be renewed 1 additional year.

Number awarded Varies each year.

Deadline Applications may be submitted at any time.

[1133]
WISCONSIN LEGION AUXILIARY CHILD WELFARE SCHOLARSHIP

American Legion Auxiliary
Department of Wisconsin
Attn: Education Chair
2930 American Legion Drive
P.O. Box 140
Portage, WI 53901-0140
(608) 745-0124   Toll Free: (866) 664-3863
Fax: (608) 745-1947   E-mail: alawi@amlegionauxwi.org
Web: www.amlegionauxwi.org/Scholarships.htm

Summary To provide financial assistance for graduate training in special education at a school in any state to dependents and descendants of veterans in Wisconsin.

Eligibility This program is open to the children, wives, and widow(er)s of veterans who are college graduates and have a GPA of 3.5 or higher. Grandchildren and great-grandchildren of members of the American Legion Auxiliary are also eligible. Applicants must be residents of Wisconsin and interested in working on a graduate degree in special education at a school in any state; if there are no applicants in the field of special education, applicants in other fields of education are eligible. Along with their application, they must submit a 300-word essay on "Education—An Investment in the Future." Financial need is considered in the selection process.

Financial data The stipend is $1,000.

Duration 1 year; nonrenewable.

Number awarded 1 each year.

Deadline March of each year.

[1134]
WISCONSIN NATIONAL GUARD ENLISTED ASSOCIATION COLLEGE GRANT PROGRAM

Wisconsin National Guard Enlisted Association
Attn: Executive Director
2400 Wright Street
Madison, WI 53704-2572
(608) 242-3112   E-mail: WNGEA@yahoo.com
Web: www.wngea.org/extrasforyou/exfy-scho.htm

Summary To provide financial assistance to members of the Wisconsin National Guard Enlisted Association (WNGEA) and their spouses and children who are interested in attending college or graduate school in any state.

Eligibility This program is open to WNGEA members, the unmarried children and spouses of WNGEA members, and the unmarried children and spouses of deceased WNGEA members. WNGEA member applicants, as well as the parents or guardians of unmarried children who are applicants, must have at least 1 year remaining on their enlistment following completion of the school year for which application is submitted (or they must have 20 or more years of service). Applicants must be enrolled full or part time at a college, university, graduate school, trade school, or business school in any state. Selection is based on financial need, leadership, and moral character.

Financial data   Stipends are $1,000 or $500 per year.

Duration   1 year; recipients may not reapply for 2 years.

Additional information   This program includes 1 scholarship sponsored by the USAA Insurance Corporation.

Number awarded   Varies each year; recently, 5 were awarded: the Raymond A. Matera Scholarship at $1,000 and 4 others (1 reserved for a graduate student) at $500 each.

Deadline   April of each year.

[1135]
WOMEN MARINES ASSOCIATION SCHOLARSHIP PROGRAM

Women Marines Association
P.O. Box 377
Oaks, PA 19456-0377
Toll Free: (888) 525-1943
E-mail: scholarship@womenmarines.org
Web: www.womenmarines.org

Summary   To provide financial assistance for college or graduate school to students with ties to the military who are sponsored by members of the Women Marines Association (WMA).

Eligibility   Applicants must be sponsored by a WMA member and fall into 1 of the following categories: 1) have served or are serving in the U.S. Marine Corps, regular or Reserve; 2) are a direct descendant by blood or legal adoption or a stepchild of a Marine on active duty or who has served honorably in the U.S. Marine Corps, regular or Reserve; 3) are a sibling or a descendant of a sibling by blood or legal adoption or a stepchild of a Marine on active duty or who has served honorably in the U.S. Marine Corps, regular or Reserve; or 4) have completed 2 years in a Marine Corps JROTC program. WMA members may sponsor an unlimited number of applicants per year. High school seniors must submit transcripts (GPA of 3.0 or higher) and SAT or ACT scores. Undergraduate and graduate students must have a GPA of 3.0 or higher.

Financial data   Stipends are $1,500 or $3,000 per year.

Duration   1 year; may be renewed 1 additional year.

Additional information   This program includes the following named scholarships: the WMA Memorial Scholarships, the Lily H. Gridley Memorial Scholarship, the Ethyl and Armin Wiebke Memorial Scholarship, the Maj. Megan Malia McClung Memorial Scholarship, the Agnes Sopcak Memorial Scholarship, the Virginia Guveyan Memorial Scholarship, and the LaRue A. Ditmore Music Scholarships. Applicants must know a WMA member to serve as their sponsor; the WMA will not supply listings of the names or addresses of chapters or individual members.

Number awarded   Varies each year.

Deadline   January of each year.

[1136]
YELLOW RIBBON PROGRAM OF THE POST-9/11 GI BILL

Department of Veterans Affairs
Attn: Veterans Benefits Administration
810 Vermont Avenue, N.W.
Washington, DC 20420
(202) 418-4343   Toll Free: (888) GI-BILL1
Web: www.benefits.va.gov/gibill/yellow_ribbon.asp

Summary   To provide financial assistance to veterans and their dependents who qualify for the Post-9/11 GI Bill and

wish to attend a high cost private or out-of-state public institution.

Eligibility   Maximum Post-9/11 GI Bill benefits are available to veterans who 1) served on active duty for at least 36 aggregate months after September 11, 2001; or 2) were honorably discharged for a service-connected disability and served at least 30 continuous days after September 11, 2001. Military personnel currently on active duty and their spouses may qualify for Post-9/11 GI Bill benefits but are not eligible for the Yellow Ribbon Program. This program is available to veterans who qualify for those benefits at the 100% rate, the children of those veterans to whom they wish to transfer their benefits, and the children and spouses of active-duty personnel who qualify for benefits at the 100% rate to whom they wish to transfer those benefits. Applicants must be working on or planning to work on an undergraduate or graduate degree at a private or out-of-state public institution that charges tuition in excess of the $20,235.02 cap imposed by the Post-9/11 GI Bill and that has agreed with the Department of Veterans Affairs (VA) to participate in this program.

Financial data   Colleges and universities that charge more than $20,235.02 per academic year in tuition and fees agree to waive tuition (up to 50%) for qualifying veterans and dependents. The amount that the college or university waives is matched by VA.

Duration   Most participants receive up to 36 months of entitlement under this program. Benefits are payable for up to 15 years following release from active duty.

Number awarded   Varies each year.

Deadline   Deadline not specified.

Indexes

Program Title Index ●

Sponsoring Organization Index ●

Branch of Service Index ●

Residency Index ●

Tenability Index ●

Subject Index ●

Calendar Index ●

Program Title Index

If you know the name of a particular funding program and want to find out where it is covered in this publication, use the Program Title Index. Here, program titles are arranged alphabetically, word by word. To assist you in your search, every program is listed by all its known names or abbreviations. In addition, we've used a two-character alphabetical code (within parentheses) to help you determine if the program falls within your scope of interest. The first character (capitalized) in the code identifies the level of education supported: U = Undergraduate Studies; G = Graduate Studies. The second character (lower cased) identifies eligible groups: m = Military Personnel; r = ROTC Students; f = Military Family Members. Here's how the code works: if a program is followed by (U–m) 241, the program is described in the Undergraduate Studies chapter under Military Personnel, in entry 241. If the same program title is followed by another entry number—for example, (G–f) 1080—the program is also described in the Graduate Studies chapter, under Military Family Members, in entry 1080. Remember: the numbers cited here refer to program entry numbers, not to page numbers in the book.

100th Infantry Battalion Memorial Scholarship Fund, (U–f) 329, (G–f) 1028

10th Mountain Division Descendant Merit Scholarship, (U–f) 330

10th Mountain Division (Light Infantry) Scholarships, (U–m) 1, (U–f) 331

11th Armored Cavalry Veterans of Vietnam and Cambodia Scholarship, (U–f) 332, (G–f) 1029

25th Infantry Division Association Educational Memorial Scholarship Award, (U–f) 333

28th Infantry Division Scholarship. See Pennsylvania National Guard Scholarship Fund, entries (U–m) 188, (U–f) 775

327th Infantry Regiment Scholarship. See Chappie Hall Memorial Scholarship Program, entry (U–f) 426

37th Division Veterans Scholarship Grant, (U–f) 334

43d Infantry Division Veterans Association Scholarships, (U–f) 335

506th Airborne Infantry Regiment Association Scholarship, (U–f) 336, (G–f) 1030

531 Gray Ghost Squadron Association Scholarship, (U–f) 337

82nd Airborne Division Association Awards, (U–f) 338

A

AAFES Retired Employees Association Scholarships, (U–f) 339

Academy Spouses Club Merit Scholarships for Spouses, (U–f) 340, (G–f) 1031

Acorn Foundation Scholar's Prize. See Daughters of the Cincinnati Scholarship Program, entry (U–f) 463

Ada Mucklestone Memorial Scholarships, (U–f) 341

Adalin Macauley Scholarship. See Wisconsin Legion Auxiliary Merit and Memorial Scholarships, entry (U–f) 893

Adams Prize. See Adelaide Koop Adams Prize, entry (U–f) 342

Adelaide Koop Adams Prize, (U–f) 342

Admiral Mike Boorda Loan Program, (U–m) 2

Admiral Raphael Semmes Memorial Scholarship. See United Daughters of the Confederacy Scholarships, entry (U–f) 845

Adrian and Corena Swanier Education Scholarships, (U–f) 343

Adrienne Alix Scholarship, (U–f) 344

Advanced Civil Schooling Program, (G–m) 908

AECP. See AMEDD Enlisted Commissioning Program (AECP), entry (U–m) 11

AFCEA NOVA Scholarships, (U–m) 3, (U–f) 345, (G–m) 909, (G–f) 1032

AFCEA ROTC Scholarships, (U–r) 248

Afghanistan and Iraq War Veterans Scholarships, (U–m) 4

Aggie Parks Scholarship, (U–f) 346

Agnes Sopcak Memorial Scholarship. See Women Marines Association Scholarship Program, entries (U–m) 244, (U–f) 899, (G–m) 1016, (G–f) 1135

Aileen Webb Tobin Scholarship Program. See Dr. Aileen Webb Tobin Scholarship Program, entry (U–m) 61

Air Force Aid Society Education Loan Program, (U–f) 347

Air Force Aid Society Merit Scholarships, (U–f) 348

Air Force Graduate Law Program, (G–r) 1018

Air Force Health Professions Scholarship Program, (G–m) 910

Air Force Judge Advocate General's Department Funded Legal Education Program, (G–m) 911

Air Force Officers' Wives' Club of Washington, D.C. Current College Student Scholarships, (U–f) 349

Air Force Officers' Wives' Club of Washington, D.C. High School Scholarships, (U–f) 350

Air Force Officers' Wives' Club of Washington, D.C. STEM Scholarships, (U–f) 351

Air Force One-Year College Program (OYCP), (G–r) 1019

Air Force Reserve Tuition Assistance, (U–m) 5, (G–m) 912

Air Force ROTC High School Scholarships, (U–r) 249

Air Force ROTC Nursing Scholarships, (U–r) 250

U–Undergraduate Studies

m–Military Personnel

r–ROTC Students

G–Graduate Studies

f–Military Family Members

353

COL James D. Kneeland Memorial Scholarship Award. *See* National Guard Association of Vermont Scholarships, entries (U—m) 147, (U—f) 707, (G—m) 981, (G—f) 1102

Cold War Veterans Engineering and Science Scholarships, (U—m) 42, (U—f) 439

College Student Pre-Commissioning Initiative, (U—m) 43

Collins, USN (Ret) Scholarship. *See* Navy League Foundation Scholarships, entry (U—f) 719

Colonel Charles L. Schmidt Leadership Scholarship, (U—f) 440

Colonel Harold M. Beardslee Memorial Scholarship Awards, (U—f) 441

Colonel Hazel Elizabeth Benn, USMC Scholarship, (U—f) 442

Colonel Jerry W. Ross Scholarship, (G—m) 943, (G—f) 1050

Colonel Loren J. and Mrs. Lawona R. Spencer Scholarship, (G—m) 944

Colonel Richard Hallock Scholarships, (U—m) 44, (U—f) 443

Colonel Urey Woodson Alexander Memorial Scholarship. *See* Army Scholarship Foundation Scholarships, entry (U—f) 391

Colonel William "Bill" Myers Scholarship. *See* San Antonio Post SAME Scholarships, entry (U—r) 313

Colorado Dependents Tuition Assistance Program, (U—f) 444

Colorado Legion Auxiliary Department President's Scholarship for Junior Auxiliary Members, (U—f) 445

Colorado Legion Auxiliary Department President's Scholarships, (U—f) 446

Colorado Legion Auxiliary Past President's Parley Nurses Training Scholarship, (U—f) 447

Colorado National Guard State Tuition Assistance, (U—m) 45

Comai Scholarships. *See* Dennis Comai Scholarships, entry (U—f) 466

Comer Scholarship PNC. *See* Massachusetts Legion Department General Scholarships, entry (U—f) 652

Commander Daniel J. Christovich Scholarship. *See* Office of Work-Life Scholarships, entry (U—f) 755

Commander Ronald J. Cantin Scholarship. *See* Office of Work-Life Scholarships, entry (U—f) 755

Commander William S. Stuhr Scholarships, (U—f) 448

Commissioned Officers' Association Dependent Scholarships, (U—f) 449

Congressional Medal of Honor Scholarships, (U—r) 263

Congressman David L. Hobson Civil Engineering Scholarship, (U—m) 46, (U—f) 450

Connacher Memorial Scholarships. *See* Peter Connacher Memorial Scholarships, entries (U—f) 777, (G—f) 1112

Connal Education Awards. *See* Robert H. Connal Education Awards, entries (U—m) 199, (U—f) 796

Connecticut Iraq and Afghanistan Service Grants, (U—f) 451

Connecticut National Guard Educational Assistance Program, (U—m) 47

Connecticut National Guard Foundation Scholarships, (U—m) 48, (U—f) 452

Connecticut Tuition Waiver for Veterans, (U—m) 49, (U—f) 453, (G—m) 945, (G—f) 1051

Connie Settles Scholarship, (U—f) 454, (G—f) 1052

Conroy Memorial Scholarship Program. *See* Edward T. Conroy Memorial Scholarship Program, entries (U—f) 484, (G—f) 1058

Cooper Scholarship. *See* Mary Rowena Cooper Scholarship, entry (U—f) 647

Cora Bell Wesley Memorial Scholarship. *See* United Daughters of the Confederacy Scholarships, entry (U—f) 845

Corena Swanier Education Scholarships. *See* Adrian and Corena Swanier Education Scholarships, entry (U—f) 343

Cornelia Branch Stone Scholarship. *See* United Daughters of the Confederacy Scholarships, entry (U—f) 845

Cornelius/Max English Memorial Scholarship Award. *See* John Cornelius/Max English Memorial Scholarship Award, entries (U—m) 96, (U—f) 589, (G—m) 959, (G—f) 1075

Cornett-Huff Scholarships. *See* Loretta Cornett-Huff Scholarships, entries (U—f) 618, (G—f) 1081

Corning Memorial Scholarship. *See* Major General Duane L. "Duke" Corning Memorial Scholarship, entries (U—m) 107, (U—f) 631

Corporal Ernesto "Gooie" Gomez Scholarship. *See* Popasmoke Scholarships, entry (U—f) 784

Costello Memorial Scholarship. *See* Army Scholarship Foundation Scholarships, entry (U—f) 391

Coudret Trust Scholarships, (U—f) 455

Courtney G. Clegg and Mrs. Margaret H. Clegg Scholarship. *See* RADM Courtney G. Clegg and Mrs. Margaret H. Clegg Scholarship, entry (U—f) 787

Cox Prize. *See* Daughters of the Cincinnati Scholarship Program, entry (U—f) 463

CPO Scholarship Fund, (U—f) 456

Create-A-Greeting-Card Scholarship Contest, (U—m) 50

Creech Scholarship. *See* Bill Creech Scholarship, entry (U—f) 401

Cribbins Scholarship. *See* Joseph P. and Helen T. Cribbins Scholarship, entry (U—m) 99

Crow Awards. *See* Association of Aviation Ordnancemen Educational Foundation Scholarships, entry (U—f) 392

Crow Memorial Scholarship. *See* CPO Scholarship Fund, entry (U—f) 456

CSM Harry and Mary Hensell Scholarship Program, (U—m) 51, (U—f) 457

CSM James Nelson Jr. Scholarships, (U—m) 52

CSM Robert W. Elkey Award, (U—m) 53, (G—m) 946

CSM Vincent Baldassari Memorial Scholarships, (U—m) 54, (U—f) 458

CSM Virgil R. Williams Scholarship Program, (U—m) 55, (U—f) 459

Cunningham Scholarship. *See* United Daughters of the Confederacy Scholarships, entry (U—f) 845

Curry Scholarship. *See* Lola B. Curry Scholarship, entry (U—f) 617

Curtis Mancini Memorial Scholarships. *See* SFC Curtis Mancini Memorial Scholarships, entries (U—m) 206, (U—r) 315, (U—f) 812, (G—m) 1004, (G—r) 1026, (G—f) 1115

Curtis Scholarship. *See* Popasmoke Scholarships, entry (U—f) 784

CW4 (Ret) Allnatt Memorial Scholarships. *See* United States Army Warrant Officers Association Scholarship Program, entry (U—f) 846

CW4 (Ret) Calabrese Memorial Scholarship. *See* United States Army Warrant Officers Association Scholarship Program, entry (U—f) 846

CW4 William C. Singletary Scholarship. *See* Virginia National Guard Association Scholarship, entries (U—m) 236, (U—f) 874

D

Daedalian Academic Matching Scholarship Program, (U—r) 264

Daedalian Foundation Descendants' Scholarship Program, (U—f) 460, (G—f) 1053

Daniel E. Lambert Memorial Scholarship, (U—f) 461

Daniel J. Christovich Scholarship. *See* Office of Work-Life Scholarships, entry (U—f) 755

Daniel J. Doherty Scholarship PNC. *See* Massachusetts Legion Department General Scholarships, entry (U—f) 652

Francis P. Matthews and John E. Swift Educational Trust Scholarships, (U—f) 517

Frank R. Kelley Scholarship. *See* Massachusetts Legion Department General Scholarships, entry (U—f) 652

Franklin Memorial Scholarship. *See* United Daughters of the Confederacy Scholarships, entry (U—f) 845

Fred and Susan Augsburg Scholarship, (U—m) 76

Frederick C. Branch Marine Corps Leadership Scholarships, (U—r) 271

Free Tuition for North Dakota Dependents, (U—f) 518

Freedom Alliance Scholarships, (U—f) 519

French Charitable Foundation Scholarships. *See* Ralph S. French Charitable Foundation Scholarships, entry (U—m) 194

French Memorial Scholarship. *See* Naval Officers' Spouses' Club of Washington, D.C. Graduating Senior Scholarship Program, entry (U—f) 716

Frizzell Memorial Scholarships. *See* Donaldson D. Frizzell Memorial Scholarships, entries (U—m) 60, (U—r) 267, (U—f) 471, (G—m) 948, (G—r) 1023, (G—f) 1055

Fry Scholarship. *See* Marine Gunnery Sergeant John David Fry Scholarship, entry (U—f) 640

G

Gail Donley Spouse Scholarships. *See* Mike and Gail Donley Spouse Scholarships, entries (U—f) 660, (G—f) 1091

Gamewardens Association Scholarship, (U—f) 520

Gavenonis Scholarships. *See* Joseph P. Gavenonis Scholarships, entry (U—f) 595

GEN Donald R. Keith Scholarship. *See* United States Field Artillery Association Scholarships, entries (U—m) 225, (U—f) 847

General Edwin Jadwin Scholarship. *See* San Antonio Post SAME Scholarships, entry (U—r) 313

General George A. White Scholarship. *See* Maria C. Jackson/General George A. White Scholarship, entries (U—f) 635, (G—f) 1087

General Henry H. Arnold Education Grant Program, (U—f) 521

General James M. Rockwell, Jr. Scholarship, (U—r) 272

General Jerry Wyatt Memorial Scholarship. *See* National Guard Association of Tennessee Auxiliary Scholarship Program, entry (U—f) 704

General Jim and Pat Boswell Merit Scholarship Program, (U—f) 522

General John Paul Ratay Educational Fund Grants, (U—f) 523

General Mathew B. Ridgeway Scholarship. *See* 82nd Airborne Division Association Awards, entry (U—f) 338

General Robert E. Lee Scholarship. *See* Military Order of the Stars and Bars Scholarships, entries (U—f) 671, (G—f) 1094

General William E. DePuy Memorial Scholarship Program, (U—f) 524

George A. White Scholarship. *See* Maria C. Jackson/General George A. White Scholarship, entries (U—f) 635, (G—f) 1087

George and Rosemary Murray Scholarship Award. *See* 25th Infantry Division Association Educational Memorial Scholarship Award, entry (U—f) 333

George and Vicki Muellner Foundation Scholarships, (U—r) 273

George T. Curtis Scholarship. *See* Popasmoke Scholarships, entry (U—f) 784

Georgia Department American Legion Scholarship, (U—f) 525

Georgia Legion Auxiliary Past Department Presidents Scholarships, (U—f) 526

Georgia Legion Auxiliary Past President Parley Nursing Scholarship, (U—f) 527

Georgia's Helping Educate Reservists and their Offspring Scholarship Program. *See* Georgia's HERO Scholarship Program, entries (U—m) 77, (U—f) 528

Georgia's HERO Scholarship Program, (U—m) 77, (U—f) 528

Gerald R. Guild Memorial Scholarship. *See* CMSGT Gerald R. Guild Memorial Scholarships, entries (U—m) 38, (U—f) 435

Geraldine K. Morris Award, (U—f) 529

Gerard Cook Scholarship. *See* Captain Gerard Cook Scholarship, entry (U—f) 421

Gertrude Botts Saucier Scholarship, (U—f) 530

Getchell and ROTC Scholarships, (U—r) 274

Gillen Memorial Scholarship. *See* Isabella M. Gillen Memorial Scholarship, entry (U—f) 577

Gladys Ann Smith Greater Los Angeles Women's Council Scholarship. *See* Navy League Foundation Scholarships, entry (U—f) 719

Gladys McPartland Scholarships, (U—m) 78, (U—f) 531

Glenn F. Glezen Scholarship. *See* Fleet Reserve Association Graduate Scholarships, entries (G—m) 950, (G—f) 1060

Glezen Scholarship. *See* Fleet Reserve Association Graduate Scholarships, entries (G—m) 950, (G—f) 1060

Goffigan Scholarship. *See* Virginia Division Gift Scholarships, entry (U—f) 872

Gold Star Scholarship Programs, (U—f) 532

Gomez Scholarship. *See* Popasmoke Scholarships, entry (U—f) 784

Gooie Gomez Scholarship. *See* Popasmoke Scholarships, entry (U—f) 784

Grace Fuller Olson Scholarship. *See* Massachusetts Legion Department General Scholarships, entry (U—f) 652

Grant Hirabayashi Memorial Scholarship. *See* Japanese American Veterans Association Memorial Scholarships, entries (U—f) 582, (G—f) 1073

Grant Scholarship Fund. *See* U.S. "Udie" Grant Scholarship Fund, entry (U—f) 851

Gravely, Jr., USN (Ret.) Memorial Scholarships. *See* VADM Samuel L. Gravely, Jr., USN (Ret.) Memorial Scholarships, entry (U—m) 233

Greater Los Angeles Women's Council Scholarship. *See* Navy League Foundation Scholarships, entry (U—f) 719

Greater Omaha Chapter AFCEA AFROTC Scholarship, (U—r) 275

Green Scholarship. *See* Non Commissioned Officers Association Scholarship Fund, entry (U—f) 746

Green to Gold Non-Scholarship Program, (U—m) 79, (U—r) 276

Green to Gold Scholarship Program, (U—m) 80, (U—r) 277

GRFD Scholarships. *See* Guaranteed Reserve Forces Duty (GRFD) Scholarships, entries (U—m) 81, (U—r) 278

Gridley Memorial Scholarship. *See* Women Marines Association Scholarship Program, entries (U—m) 244, (U—f) 899, (G—m) 1016, (G—f) 1135

Griffin/USS Emmons Memorial Scholarship. *See* Lt. John J. Griffin/USS Emmons Memorial Scholarship, entries (U—f) 622, (G—f) 1082

Grimes Physician Assistant Educational Scholarship Award. *See* Captain Sean P. Grimes Physician Assistant Educational Scholarship Award, entries (U—m) 34, (G—m) 937

Grogan Memorial Scholarship, (U—f) 533, (G—f) 1065

Gross Scholarship. *See* Edmund K. Gross Scholarship, entries (U—m) 63, (U—f) 481

Gruber Scholarships. *See* Kathern F. Gruber Scholarships, entries (U—f) 600, (G—f) 1077

Guaranteed Reserve Forces Duty (GRFD) Scholarships, (U—m) 81, (U—r) 278

Hui O'Wahine Merit Scholarship for Continuing Education, (U–f) 552

Hui O'Wahine Merit Scholarship for Traditional Students, (U–f) 553, (G–f) 1072

Human Resources Option of the Seaman to Admiral-21 Program, (U–m) 86, (U–r) 280

I

I. Beverly Lake Scholarship Endowment, (U–f) 554

Ia Drang Scholarship Program, (U–f) 555

Ichiuji Memorial Scholarship. See Japanese American Veterans Association Memorial Scholarships, entries (U–f) 582, (G–f) 1073

Idaho Armed Forces and Public Safety Officer Dependent Scholarships, (U–f) 556

Idaho Enlisted Association Young Patriot Scholarship, (U–m) 87, (U–f) 557

Idaho Legion Auxiliary General Studies Scholarship, (U–f) 558

Idaho Legion Auxiliary Nurses Scholarship, (U–f) 559

Illinois American Legion Auxiliary Past Presidents Parley Nurses Scholarship, (U–f) 560

Illinois AMVETS Junior ROTC Scholarships, (U–f) 561

Illinois AMVETS Service Foundation Scholarships, (U–f) 562

Illinois AMVETS Trade School Scholarships, (U–f) 563

Illinois Children of Veterans Scholarships, (U–f) 564

Illinois Fallen Heroes Scholarship, (U–f) 565

Illinois Legion Scholarships, (U–f) 566

Illinois Legion Trade School Scholarships, (U–f) 567

Illinois MIA/POW Scholarship, (U–f) 568

Illinois National Guard Grant Program, (U–m) 88, (G–m) 956

Illinois Scholarships for Junior Members, (U–f) 569

Illinois SCV/MOS&B Scholarship, (U–f) 570

Imagine America Military Award Program, (U–m) 89

Indiana American Legion Family Scholarship, (U–f) 571

Indiana Children of Veterans Program, (U–f) 572

Indiana Eagle Scout of the Year Scholarships, (U–f) 573

Indiana National Guard Supplemental Grant Program, (U–m) 90

Indiana Sons of the American Legion Scholarship, (U–f) 574

Inouye Scholarship. See Japanese American Veterans Association Memorial Scholarships, entries (U–f) 582, (G–f) 1073

Iowa Eagle Scout of the Year Scholarship, (U–f) 575

Iowa National Guard Education Assistance Program, (U–m) 91

Iraq and Afghanistan Service Grants, (U–f) 576

Irene Rubenstein Memorial Grant. See Jewish War Veterans National Achievement Program, entry (U–m) 94

Isabella M. Gillen Memorial Scholarship, (U–f) 577

Ishio Memorial Scholarship. See Japanese American Veterans Association Memorial Scholarships, entries (U–f) 582, (G–f) 1073

Iverson ROTC Scholarship. See LGS Innovations Lt. General Ronald Iverson ROTC Scholarship, entry (U–r) 285

Iwata Memorial Scholarship. See Florida Navy Nurse Corps Association Scholarships, entries (U–m) 74, (U–f) 512, (G–m) 954, (G–f) 1064

J

Jack and Eileen Anderson Scholarship. See Navy League Foundation Scholarships, entry (U–f) 719

Jack Costello Memorial Scholarship. See Army Scholarship Foundation Scholarships, entry (U–f) 391

Jack E. Barger, Sr. Memorial Nursing Scholarships, (U–m) 92, (U–f) 578

Jackson/General George A. White Scholarship. See Maria C. Jackson/General George A. White Scholarship, entries (U–f) 635, (G–f) 1087

Jackson Scholarship. See United Daughters of the Confederacy Scholarships, entry (U–f) 845

Jadwin Scholarship. See San Antonio Post SAME Scholarships, entry (U–r) 313

Jake Comer Scholarship PNC. See Massachusetts Legion Department General Scholarships, entry (U–f) 652

James D. Kneeland Memorial Scholarship Award. See National Guard Association of Vermont Scholarships, entries (U–m) 147, (U–f) 707, (G–m) 981, (G–f) 1102

James M. Rockwell, Jr. Scholarship. See General James M. Rockwell, Jr. Scholarship, entry (U–r) 272

James Montag, Jr. Scholarship, (U–m) 93, (G–m) 957

James Nelson Jr. Scholarships. See CSM James Nelson Jr. Scholarships, entry (U–m) 52

James Ursano Scholarship Fund. See MG James Ursano Scholarship Fund, entry (U–f) 657

Jan Gwatney Scholarship, (U–f) 579

Jan Pulvermacher-Ryan Scholarship. See Wisconsin Legion Auxiliary Merit and Memorial Scholarships, entry (U–f) 893

Jane Hawkes Liddell Prize, (U–f) 580

Janet B. Seippel Scholarship. See United Daughters of the Confederacy Scholarships, entry (U–f) 845

Janet Russell Whitman Prize, (U–f) 581

Japanese American Veterans Association Memorial Scholarships, (U–f) 582, (G–f) 1073

Jay Smith Memorial Endowment Scholarship. See Lt. Paul (Jay) Smith Memorial Endowment Scholarship, entry (U–r) 290

Jeanne Richter Memorial Scholarship, (U–f) 583

Jeanne Rose Scholarships. See Sergeants Henry and Jeanne Rose Scholarships, entries (U–m) 205, (U–f) 811

Jennie Gunn Ball Scholarship. See Virginia Division Gift Scholarships, entry (U–f) 872

Jennifer Shafer Odom Memorial Scholarship. See Army Scholarship Foundation Scholarships, entry (U–f) 391

Jerry W. Ross Scholarship. See Colonel Jerry W. Ross Scholarship, entries (G–m) 943, (G–f) 1050

Jerry Wyatt Memorial Scholarship. See National Guard Association of Tennessee Auxiliary Scholarship Program, entry (U–f) 704

Jewell Hilton Bonner Scholarship, (U–f) 584

Jewish War Veterans National Achievement Program, (U–m) 94

Jewish War Veterans National Youth Achievement Program, (U–f) 585

Jim and Pat Boswell Merit Scholarship Program. See General Jim and Pat Boswell Merit Scholarship Program, entry (U–f) 522

J.O. Jones Memorial Scholarship. See Ship Island–Mrs. J.O. Jones Memorial Scholarship, entry (G–f) 1116

Joan Bowden Scholarship, (U–r) 281

Joan Katkus Memorial Scholarship, (U–f) 586

Joanne Holbrook Patton Military Spouse Scholarship Program, (U–f) 587, (G–f) 1074

Jodi Callahan Memorial Scholarship. See Captain Jodi Callahan Memorial Scholarship, entry (G–m) 936

Joe King Scholarships, (U–m) 95, (G–m) 958

John A. High Child Welfare Scholarship Endowment Fund, (U–f) 588

John and Alice Egan Multi-Year Scholarships, (U–r) 282

U—Undergraduate Studies　　　**G—Graduate Studies**

m—Military Personnel　　　**r—ROTC Students**　　　**f—Military Family Members**

United States Field Artillery Association Scholarships, (U—m) 225, (U—f) 847

United States Marine Corps Combat Correspondents Association Scholarships. *See* USMCCCA Scholarships, entries (U—m) 227, (U—f) 852

United States Submarine Veterans, Inc. Scholarships. *See* USSVI Scholarships, entry (U—f) 863

University Interscholastic League Patriot Scholarship, (U—f) 848

Urey Woodson Alexander Memorial Scholarship. *See* Army Scholarship Foundation Scholarships, entry (U—f) 391

Ursano Scholarship Fund. *See* MG James Ursano Scholarship Fund, entry (U—f) 657

U.S. Army Ranger Association Legacy Scholarships, (U—f) 849

U.S. Army Women's Foundation Legacy Scholarships, (U—m) 226, (U—f) 850, (G—m) 1008, (G—f) 1124

U.S. Senator Daniel K. Inouye Scholarship. *See* Japanese American Veterans Association Memorial Scholarships, entries (U—f) 582, (G—f) 1073

U.S. Submarine Veterans of World War II Scholarship. *See* Dolphin Scholarships, entry (U—f) 470

U.S. "Udie" Grant Scholarship Fund, (U—f) 851

USMCCCA Scholarships, (U—m) 227, (U—f) 852

USO Desert Storm Education Fund, (U—f) 853

USS America Carrier Veterans Association Merit Scholarship, (U—f) 854

USS Coral Sea Remembrance Scholarships, (U—f) 855

USS Emmons Memorial Scholarship. *See* Lt. John J. Griffin/USS Emmons Memorial Scholarship, entries (U—f) 622, (G—f) 1082

USS Enterprise (CVAN/CVN-65) Association Scholarships, (U—f) 856

USS Kitty Hawk (CV/CVA-63) Veteran's Association Scholarships, (U—f) 857

USS Little Rock Association NROTC Scholarship Program, (U—m) 228, (U—r) 326, (U—f) 858

USS Little Rock Association Scholarship Program for Descendants of Members, (U—f) 859

USS Mahan Scholarship. *See* Navy League Foundation Scholarships, entry (U—f) 719

USS Pittsburgh Fund, (U—m) 229, (U—f) 860

USS Theodore Roosevelt Scholarship, (U—f) 861

USS Yorktown CV-10 Association Scholarship Program, (U—f) 862

USSVI Scholarships, (U—f) 863

Utah ASMC Chapter Scholarships, (U—m) 230, (U—f) 864

Utah National Guard State Tuition Assistance Program, (U—m) 231, (G—m) 1009

Utah National Guard State Tuition Waiver, (U—m) 232

V

VADM Robert L. Walters Scholarship, (U—f) 865, (G—f) 1125

VADM Samuel L. Gravely, Jr., USN (Ret.) Memorial Scholarships, (U—m) 233

Van Deuren Memorial Scholarships. *See* Della Van Deuren Memorial Scholarships, entry (U—f) 465

VAW/VRC Merit Scholarships, (U—f) 866

Veronica Ream Memorial Scholarship. *See* Naval Helicopter Association Memorial Scholarships, entries (U—m) 154, (U—f) 713, (G—m) 983, (G—f) 1104

Veterans Appreciation Scholarship Program, (U—m) 234

Veterans United Foundation Scholarships, (U—m) 235, (U—f) 867, (G—m) 1010, (G—f) 1126

Vice Admiral E.P. Travers Loan Program, (U—f) 868

Vicki K. Heilig Scholarship. *See* United Daughters of the Confederacy Scholarships, entry (U—f) 845

Vicki Muellner Foundation Scholarships. *See* George and Vicki Muellner Foundation Scholarships, entry (U—r) 273

Victor and Teru Matsui Scholarship. *See* Japanese American Veterans Association Memorial Scholarships, entries (U—f) 582, (G—f) 1073

Vietnam Veterans Group of San Quentin Scholarships, (U—f) 869

VII Corps Desert Storm Veterans Association Scholarship, (U—f) 870

Vincent Baldassari Memorial Scholarships. *See* CSM Vincent Baldassari Memorial Scholarships, entries (U—m) 54, (U—f) 458

Vincent Scholarship. *See* ASMC Members' Continuing Education Grants, entries (U—m) 21, (G—m) 929

Virgil R. Williams Scholarship Program. *See* CSM Virgil R. Williams Scholarship Program, entries (U—m) 55, (U—f) 459

Virgin Island National Guard Grants, (U—f) 871

Virginia Division Gift Scholarships, (U—f) 872

Virginia Guveyan Memorial Scholarship. *See* Women Marines Association Scholarship Program, entries (U—m) 244, (U—f) 899, (G—m) 1016, (G—f) 1135

Virginia Military Survivors and Dependents Education Program, (U—f) 873, (G—f) 1127

Virginia National Guard Association Scholarship, (U—m) 236, (U—f) 874

Virginia National Guard Tuition Assistance Program, (U—m) 237, (G—m) 1011

Virginia Peninsula Post SAME Scholarships, (U—m) 238, (U—r) 327, (U—f) 875, (G—m) 1012, (G—r) 1027, (G—f) 1128

Virginia War Orphans Education Program. *See* Virginia Military Survivors and Dependents Education Program, entries (U—f) 873, (G—f) 1127

Viste Scholarship Program. *See* Al and Willamary Viste Scholarship Program, entries (U—f) 356, (G—f) 1034

Vuolo Memorial Scholarship. *See* Dr. Hannah K. Vuolo Memorial Scholarship, entry (U—f) 473

W

Wagner Scholarship. *See* LTC Karen J. Wagner Scholarship, entry (U—f) 625

Waivers of Non-resident Tuition for Dependents of Military Personnel Moving to Texas, (U—f) 876

Waivers of Non-resident Tuition for Dependents of Military Personnel Who Previously Lived in Texas, (U—f) 877

Wallace Kingsbury Scholarship. *See* Elizabeth and Wallace Kingsbury Scholarship, entry (U—f) 487

Walter Beall Scholarship, (U—m) 239, (U—f) 878

Walter Reed Smith Scholarship Program, (U—f) 879

Walters Scholarship. *See* VADM Robert L. Walters Scholarship, entries (U—f) 865, (G—f) 1125

Washington Admiral's Fund Scholarship, (U—r) 328

Washington Legion Children and Youth Scholarships, (U—f) 880

Washington National Guard Scholarship Program, (U—m) 240, (G—m) 1013

Watie Scholarship. *See* Stand Watie Scholarship, entry (U—f) 825

WAVES National College Scholarship, (U—f) 881, (G—f) 1129

Wellington, Jr. Memorial Scholarship. *See* Raymond T. Wellington, Jr. Memorial Scholarship, entry (U—f) 789

Wesley C. Cameron Scholarship. *See* Navy League Foundation Scholarships, entry (U—f) 719

Wesley Memorial Scholarship. *See* United Daughters of the Confederacy Scholarships, entry (U—f) 845

U–Undergraduate Studies **G–Graduate Studies**

m—Military Personnel **r—ROTC Students** **f—Military Family Members**

Sponsoring Organization Index

The Sponsoring Organization Index makes it easy to identify agencies that offer financial aid to military personnel, ROTC, or military family members students. In this index, sponsoring organizations are listed alphabetically, word by word. In addition, we've used a two-character alphabetical code (within parentheses) to help you identify which programs sponsored by these organizations fall within your scope of interest. The first character (capitalized) in the code identifies the level of education supported: U = Undergraduate Studies; G = Graduate Studies. The second character (lower cased) identifies eligible groups: m = Military Personnel; r = ROTC Students; f = Military Family Members. For example, if the name of a sponsoring organization is followed by (U–m) 241, a program sponsored by that organization is described in the Undergraduate Studies chapter under Military Personnel, in entry 241. If that sponsoring organization's name is followed by another entry number—for example, (G–f) 1080—the same or a different program sponsored by that organization is described in the Graduate Studies chapter, under Military Family Members, in entry 1080. Remember: the numbers cited here refer to program entry numbers, not to page numbers in the book.

U–Undergraduate Studies **G–Graduate Studies**

m—Military Personnel **r—ROTC Students** **f—Military Family Members**

American Legion. Nebraska Auxiliary, (U−f) 799

American Legion. New Hampshire Auxiliary, (U−f) 344

American Legion. New Hampshire Department, (U−f) 361, 588

American Legion. New Jersey Auxiliary, (U−f) 434, 472, 729, 732

American Legion. New Jersey Department, (U−f) 730

American Legion. New York Auxiliary, (U−f) 544, 648, 737-739, 789

American Legion. New York Department, (U−f) 473

American Legion. North Carolina Auxiliary, (U−f) 688

American Legion. North Dakota Department, (U−f) 538

American Legion. Ohio Auxiliary, (U−f) 756

American Legion. Oregon Auxiliary, (U−f) 764-767

American Legion. Pennsylvania Department, (U−f) 595

American Legion. South Dakota Department, (U−f) 818

American Legion. Tennessee Department, (U−f) 830

American Legion. Texas Auxiliary, (U−f) 832

American Legion. Washington Auxiliary, (U−f) 507, 634, (G−f) 1086

American Legion. Washington Department, (U−f) 880

American Legion. Wisconsin Auxiliary, (U−f) 465, 551, 627, 892-895, (G−f) 1071, 1133

American Legion. Wisconsin Department, (U−f) 803, 889

American Legion. Wyoming Department, (U−f) 476

American Logistics Association. New York Chapter, (U−f) 663

American Military Retirees Association, Inc., (U−f) 398, 810

American Pharmacists Association, (G−m) 943, (G−f) 1050

American Society of Military Comptrollers, (U−m) 21, (G−m) 929

American Society of Military Comptrollers. Aloha Chapter, (G−m) 918

American Society of Military Comptrollers. Aviation Chapter, (U−m) 76

American Society of Military Comptrollers. National Guard Chapter, (U−m) 148, (U−f) 708

American Society of Military Comptrollers. Utah Chapter, (U−m) 230, (U−f) 864

American Systems, (U−m) 233

America's Child, (U−f) 372

AMVETS. Department of Illinois, (U−f) 561-563, 800

AMVETS National Headquarters, (U−m) 84, 194, (U−f) 373, 375

AMVETS National Ladies Auxiliary, (U−f) 374

Anchor Scholarship Foundation, (U−f) 376

Andrews Spouses' Club, (U−f) 377

Arizona Community Foundation, (U−m) 83, (U−f) 542

Arkansas Community Foundation, (U−f) 384

Arkansas Department of Higher Education, (U−f) 383

Arkansas National Guard, (U−m) 12

Armed Forces Benefit Association, (U−m) 55, (U−f) 427, 459

Armed Forces Communications and Electronics Association, (U−m) 4, 57, 233, (U−r) 248, 268, 272, 281, 285, 287, 293, 295, 298, 312

Armed Forces Communications and Electronics Association. Camp Pendleton Chapter, (U−m) 57

Armed Forces Communications and Electronics Association. Greater Omaha Chapter, (U−r) 275

Armed Forces Communications and Electronics Association. Lexington-Concord Chapter, (U−r) 284

Armed Forces Communications and Electronics Association. Los Angeles Chapter, (U−r) 288

Armed Forces Communications and Electronics Association. Montgomery Chapter, (U−r) 281, 287, 298

Armed Forces Communications and Electronics Association. Northern Virginia Chapter, (U−m) 3-4, (U−f) 345, (G−m) 909, (G−f) 1032

Armed Forces Insurance Company, (U−m) 55, (U−f) 459

Army and Air Force Exchange Service, (U−f) 380

Army Aviation Association of America, (U−m) 13, (U−f) 386, (G−m) 919, (G−f) 1037

Army Aviation Association of America Scholarship Foundation, (U−m) 14, (U−f) 387, (G−m) 920, (G−f) 1038

Army Emergency Relief, (U−f) 388, 657

Army Engineer Association, (U−m) 46, 53, 120, (U−f) 437, 441, 450, (G−m) 946, 971, (G−f) 1049

Army Engineer Spouses' Club, (U−f) 389, 529

Army Nurse Corps Association, (U−m) 17, (U−f) 390, (G−m) 925, (G−f) 1039

Army Officers' Wives' Club of the Greater Washington Area, (U−f) 379

Army Scholarship Foundation, (U−f) 391, 501, 808

Arnold Air Society-Silver Wing, (U−r) 252

Association of Aviation Ordnancemen, (U−f) 392

Association of Former Intelligence Officers, (G−m) 915, 962, (G−f) 1035, 1079

Association of Old Crows, (U−m) 22

Association of Private Sector Colleges and Universities, (U−m) 89

Association of the Century, Inc., (U−m) 119, (U−f) 656

Association of the United States Army, (U−m) 99, 104

Association of the United States Army. Braxton Bragg Chapter, (U−m) 28, (U−r) 257, (U−f) 407, (G−m) 932, (G−r) 1021, (G−f) 1042

Association of the United States Army. Fairfax-Lee Chapter, (U−m) 68, (U−r) 270, (U−f) 497

Association of the United States Army. Major Samuel Woodfill Chapter, (U−m) 108, (U−f) 632

Association of the United States Army. Rhode Island Chapter, (U−m) 206, (U−r) 315, (U−f) 812, (G−m) 1004, (G−r) 1026, (G−f) 1115

Association of the United States Navy, (U−f) 393

Aviation Boatswain's Mates Association, (U−f) 577

B

BAE Systems, (U−f) 391

Belvoir Officers' Spouses' Club, (U−f) 396

Blackhorse Association, (U−f) 402

Blinded Veterans Association, (U−f) 600, 838, (G−f) 1077, 1121

Blinded Veterans Association Auxiliary, (U−f) 792

Boeing Company, (U−m) 168, (U−f) 742

C

California Department of Veterans Affairs, (U−m) 33, (U−f) 411-414, 419, (G−m) 934, (G−f) 1044

California Enlisted Association of the National Guard of the United States, (U−m) 30

California. Office of the Adjutant General, (U−m) 32, (G−m) 933

California Student Aid Commission, (U−m) 32, (G−m) 933

Chase Military Credit Card Services, (U−m) 6, (U−f) 354, (G−m) 913, (G−f) 1033

Children of Fallen Patriots Foundation, (U−f) 431

Children of Fallen Soldiers Relief Fund, (U−f) 432

Church, State and Industry Foundation, (G−m) 940

Civil Service Employees Insurance Group, (U−f) 493

U—Undergraduate Studies **G—Graduate Studies**

m—Military Personnel **r—ROTC Students** **f—Military Family Members**

Branch of Service Index

This index identifies funding programs that are open to applicants with ties to one or more of the five active branches of the Military: Air Force, Army, Coast Guard, Marine Corps, Navy (including their respective Guard and Reserve units). To use this index, look at the branch of service index entry that applies, jot down the entry numbers listed after the educational level and recipient group that describes you, and use those numbers to find the program entries in the directory.

Air Force
  Undergraduate Studies: **Military Personnel,** 3-10, 12, 21-22, 24-26, 29-33, 38, 41-42, 44-45, 47-51, 54-58, 60, 62-66, 69, 73-74, 76-77, 82-85, 87-95, 100-103, 105-107, 110-116, 121, 123-150, 159-160, 162-176, 181-189, 192-194, 196-203, 205, 207, 209, 213, 220-224, 230-238, 240-243, 245-247; **ROTC Students,** 248-252, 256, 258-261, 263-264, 267, 273-275, 279, 281-293, 295-296, 298-299, 305, 310, 312-313, 325, 327; **Military Family Members,** 339-340, 342-343, 345, 347-355, 357-358, 368, 370-373, 375, 377, 380, 383, 395-396, 399-400, 403, 406, 408-410, 412, 415, 418-419, 421, 423, 427, 429-432, 435, 438-439, 443-444, 448, 451-454, 457-459, 463-464, 468, 471, 474-475, 477-479, 481-484, 490-491, 493-495, 503, 512-514, 519, 521, 523, 528, 535-537, 539, 542, 545, 547-550, 552-553, 556-557, 565, 568, 572, 576, 578, 580-583, 587, 592, 595, 598, 600-601, 603, 611, 615-616, 618-619, 621, 625-626, 629, 631, 635, 641, 651, 653-654, 658, 660, 662-663, 665, 667-668, 672-674, 677-680, 684-685, 687, 689, 692-710, 726, 731, 733-735, 740-744, 746, 748-750, 753-754, 757-758, 760-764, 768, 770, 774-776, 779, 781-782, 785, 790-791, 793, 796, 798, 804-805, 811, 817, 819-822, 827-828, 833-836, 838-842, 853, 864, 867, 869, 871, 873-877, 896-897, 902-907
  Graduate Studies: **Military Personnel,** 909-918, 929, 931, 933-936, 939-940, 943-945, 947-949, 953-958, 960-963, 966-968, 972-981, 990-996, 998-1002, 1005-1007, 1009-1015, 1017; **ROTC Students,** 1018-1020, 1023-1024, 1027; **Military Family Members,** 1031-1033, 1035-1036, 1041, 1043-1044, 1047, 1050-1052, 1055-1058, 1064, 1066, 1068-1070, 1072-1074, 1077, 1079, 1081, 1083, 1087, 1090-1091, 1093, 1095-1102, 1109-1111, 1114, 1119, 1121-1123, 1126-1128, 1134, 1136

Army
  Undergraduate Studies: **Military Personnel,** 1, 3-4, 9-22, 24-26, 28-34, 38, 41-42, 44-66, 68, 70, 73-74, 76-77, 79-85, 87-95, 99-108, 110-116, 119-150, 159-160, 162-176, 181-189, 192, 194-202, 205-209, 213, 220-226, 230-238, 240-243, 245-247; **ROTC Students,** 248, 253-261, 263-267, 270, 272, 274, 276-279, 281-284, 286, 288-289, 291-293, 295, 299, 305, 310, 312-313, 315-316, 325, 327; **Military Family Members,** 331, 333, 335, 338-340, 342-343, 345, 357-358, 365, 368, 370-373, 375, 377, 379-380, 383, 386-391, 395-396, 399-400, 402-403, 406-410, 412, 415, 418-419, 421, 423, 427, 430-432, 435, 437-439, 441, 443-444, 448, 450-454, 457-459, 463-464, 468, 471, 474-475, 477-479, 481-484, 486, 490-491, 493-495, 497, 499-501, 503, 512-514, 519, 523, 528-529, 535-537, 539, 542, 545, 547-550, 552-553, 556-557, 565, 568, 572, 576, 578, 580-583, 587, 595, 598, 600-601, 603, 611, 615-616, 618-619, 625-626, 629, 631-632, 635, 641, 651, 653-654, 656-658, 662-663, 665-668, 672-674, 677-680, 684-685, 687, 689, 692-710, 726, 731, 733-735, 740-744, 746, 748-750, 753-754, 757-758, 760-764, 768, 770, 774-776, 779, 781-782, 785, 788, 790-791, 793, 796, 798, 804-805, 808-809, 811-812, 815, 817, 819-822, 827-828, 833-836, 838-842, 846-847, 850, 853, 864, 867, 869, 871, 873-877, 896-897, 900, 902-907
  Graduate Studies: **Military Personnel,** 908-909, 915-929, 931-935, 937, 939-940, 945-949, 953-958, 960-963, 966-968, 971-981, 990-996, 998-1002, 1004-1015, 1017; **ROTC Students,** 1021-1024, 1026-1027; **Military Family Members,** 1031-1032, 1035-1039, 1041-1044, 1047, 1049, 1051-1052, 1055-1058, 1064, 1066, 1068-1070, 1072-1074, 1077, 1079, 1081, 1083, 1087, 1090, 1093, 1095-1102, 1109-1111, 1114-1115, 1119, 1121-1124, 1126-1128, 1134, 1136

Coast Guard
  Undergraduate Studies: **Military Personnel,** 3-4, 21-26, 29, 31, 33, 35, 39-44, 49-50, 57, 60, 63, 66, 71-72, 74, 76-77, 82-84, 89, 92-95, 100, 102, 105, 110-111, 114-115, 123-124, 130, 132-133, 151, 153-154, 160-161, 192, 194, 197, 200-202, 205, 207, 213, 220, 222, 224, 228, 230, 233-235, 238-239, 245; **Military Family Members,** 340, 342-343, 345, 357-359, 364, 368, 370-373, 375, 377, 383, 394-396, 399-400, 403, 406, 408-410, 415, 418-420, 423-424, 427, 431-432, 436, 438-439, 443, 448, 451, 453-454, 463-464, 468, 471, 474, 477, 481, 484, 488, 491, 493-495, 503, 505-506, 512-514, 519, 523, 528, 535-537, 539, 542, 545, 547, 549-550, 552-553, 556, 565, 568, 572, 576, 578, 580-584, 587, 595-596, 598, 600-601, 603, 606-607, 611, 615-616, 618-619, 625-626, 629, 635, 641, 646, 651, 653-654, 658, 662-663, 665, 667-668, 672-674, 678, 684-685, 687, 689, 692, 712-715, 719-720, 724, 726, 731, 734-735, 740, 746, 753, 755, 758, 760, 763-764, 772, 774, 781-783, 790, 793, 798, 801, 804-805, 811, 817, 819-822, 826, 828, 833-836, 838-839, 841-842, 853, 858, 864-865, 867, 869, 873, 875-878, 881, 902-903, 905-907

Residency Index

Some programs listed in this book are restricted to residents of a particular state or region. Others are open to applicants wherever they may live. The Residency Index will help you pinpoint programs available only to residents in your area as well as programs that have no residency restrictions at all (these are listed under the term "United States"). To use this index, look up the geographic areas that apply to you (always check the listings under "United States"), jot down the entry numbers listed after the educational level and recipient group that applies to you, and use those numbers to find the program descriptions in the directory. To help you in your search, we've provided some "see also" references in the index entries. Remember: the numbers cited here refer to program entry numbers, not to page numbers in the book.

A

Alabama
    Undergraduate Studies: **Military Personnel,** 9; **Military Family Members,** 357, 543, 617
    Graduate Studies: **Military Personnel,** 916; **Military Family Members,** 1036
    See also United States

Alaska
    Undergraduate Studies: **Military Personnel,** 10, 25; **Military Family Members,** 346, 358-359, 400, 586, 655
    Graduate Studies: **Military Personnel,** 917, 931; **Military Family Members,** 1041
    See also United States

Alexandria, Virginia
    Undergraduate Studies: **Military Personnel,** 3, 68; **ROTC Students,** 270; **Military Family Members,** 345, 377, 379, 497
    Graduate Studies: **Military Personnel,** 909; **Military Family Members,** 1032
    See also Virginia

Anne Arundel County, Maryland
    Undergraduate Studies: **Military Family Members,** 716-717
    See also Maryland

Arizona
    Undergraduate Studies: **Military Personnel,** 38, 51, 83, 134; **Military Family Members,** 381, 435, 457, 493, 542, 693, 886
    See also United States

Arkansas
    Undergraduate Studies: **Military Personnel,** 12; **Military Family Members,** 382-385, 455, 615-616
    See also United States

Arlington County, Virginia
    Undergraduate Studies: **Military Personnel,** 3, 68; **ROTC Students,** 270; **Military Family Members,** 345, 377, 379, 497, 716-717
    Graduate Studies: **Military Personnel,** 909; **Military Family Members,** 1032
    See also Virginia

B

Berkeley County, South Carolina
    Undergraduate Studies: **Military Family Members,** 862
    See also South Carolina

Berkeley County, West Virginia
    Undergraduate Studies: **Military Personnel,** 3; **Military Family Members,** 345
    Graduate Studies: **Military Personnel,** 909; **Military Family Members,** 1032
    See also West Virginia

Bowie County, Texas
    Undergraduate Studies: **Military Family Members,** 489
    See also Texas

C

California
    Undergraduate Studies: **Military Personnel,** 30-32, 135, 202; **Military Family Members,** 363, 411-418, 454, 469, 493, 636, 694, 869
    Graduate Studies: **Military Personnel,** 933; **Military Family Members,** 1052
    See also United States

Calvert County, Maryland
    Undergraduate Studies: **Military Personnel,** 3; **Military Family Members,** 345, 379, 716-717
    Graduate Studies: **Military Personnel,** 909; **Military Family Members,** 1032
    See also Maryland

Campbellsville, Kentucky. *See* Kentucky

Canada
    Undergraduate Studies: **Military Family Members,** 477
    See also Foreign countries

Charles County, Maryland
    Undergraduate Studies: **Military Personnel,** 3, 68; **ROTC Students,** 270; **Military Family Members,** 345, 377, 379, 497, 716-717
    Graduate Studies: **Military Personnel,** 909; **Military Family Members,** 1032
    See also Maryland

Tenability Index

Some programs listed in this book can be used only in specific cities, counties, states, or regions. Others may be used anywhere in the United States (or even abroad). The Tenability Index will help you locate funding that is restricted to a specific area as well as funding that has no tenability restrictions (these are listed under the term "United States"). To use this index, look up the geographic areas where you'd like to go (always check the listings under "United States"), jot down the entry numbers listed after the educational level and recipient group that applies to you, and use those numbers to find the program descriptions in the directory. To help you in your search, we've provided some "see also" references in the index entries. Remember: the numbers cited here refer to program entry numbers, not to page numbers in the book.

A

Alabama
   Undergraduate Studies: **Military Personnel, 9; ROTC Students,** 281, 287; **Military Family Members,** 357, 617
   Graduate Studies: **Military Personnel,** 916; **Military Family Members,** 1036
   See also United States

Alaska
   Undergraduate Studies: **Military Personnel,** 10, 25; **Military Family Members,** 358, 400
   Graduate Studies: **Military Personnel,** 917, 931; **Military Family Members,** 1041
   See also United States

Albuquerque, New Mexico
   Undergraduate Studies: **Military Personnel,** 178; **ROTC Students,** 260, 297, 306
   See also New Mexico

Arizona
   Undergraduate Studies: **Military Personnel,** 134; **Military Family Members,** 693, 886
   See also United States

Arkansas
   Undergraduate Studies: **Military Personnel,** 12; **Military Family Members,** 383-384, 455
   See also United States

Atlanta, Georgia
   Undergraduate Studies: **ROTC Students,** 271, 297
   See also Georgia

Auburn, Alabama
   Undergraduate Studies: **Military Personnel,** 178; **ROTC Students,** 306
   See also Alabama

Austin, Texas
   Undergraduate Studies: **Military Personnel,** 178; **ROTC Students,** 271, 297, 306
   See also Texas

B

Baton Rouge, Louisiana
   Undergraduate Studies: **Military Personnel,** 178; **ROTC Students,** 271, 297, 306
   See also Louisiana

Bladen County, North Carolina
   Undergraduate Studies: **ROTC Students,** 261
   See also North Carolina

C

California
   Undergraduate Studies: **Military Personnel,** 30-33; **Military Family Members,** 411-419, 454
   Graduate Studies: **Military Personnel,** 933-934; **Military Family Members,** 1044, 1052
   See also United States

Campbellsville, Kentucky. *See* Kentucky

Canada
   Undergraduate Studies: **Military Family Members,** 477, 837
   See also Foreign countries

Champaign, Illinois
   Undergraduate Studies: **Military Personnel,** 178; **ROTC Students,** 306
   See also Illinois

Charleston, South Carolina
   Undergraduate Studies: **Military Personnel,** 178; **ROTC Students,** 306
   See also South Carolina

Chicago, Illinois
   Undergraduate Studies: **ROTC Students,** 297
   See also Illinois

Colorado
   Undergraduate Studies: **Military Personnel,** 45; **Military Family Members,** 444-447, 781
   See also United States

Columbia, South Carolina
   Undergraduate Studies: **Military Personnel,** 178; **ROTC Students,** 271, 297, 306
   See also South Carolina

Subject Index

There are more than 200 different areas of study indexed in this directory. Use the Subject Index when you want to identify a particular major or degree field for a specific educational level (undergraduate or graduate studies) and recipient group (military personnel; ROTC students; military family members). To help you pinpoint your subject search, we've also included numerous "see" and "see also" references. In addition to looking for terms that represent your specific subject interest, be sure to check the "General programs" entry; hundreds of programs are listed there that can be used to support study in *any* subject area (although the programs may be restricted in other ways). Remember: the numbers cited in this index refer to program entry numbers, not to page numbers in the book.

Flight science. *See* Aviation

Flying. *See* Aviation

Food. *See* Nutrition

Foreign affairs. *See* International relations

Foreign language. *See* Language and linguistics

G

General programs
    Undergraduate Studies: **Military Personnel,** 1-2, 5-10, 12-15, 18, 20, 23, 27-33, 35, 38-41, 43-45, 47-49, 51-52, 54-56, 58-62, 64-65, 68-73, 75, 77-85, 87-91, 94-97, 100-101, 103-104, 106-116, 119, 121-147, 149-154, 157-176, 181-199, 201, 203-211, 213, 219-223, 225-226, 228, 230-232, 234-237, 240-247; **ROTC Students,** 249, 251-254, 257-259, 261, 263, 265-267, 270-271, 273, 276-278, 281, 284, 286, 290-293, 295-298, 300, 302-305, 309, 311-312, 314-318, 325-326, 328; **Military Family Members,** 329-341, 343-344, 346-350, 352-355, 357-361, 363-389, 391-394, 396-398, 401-407, 409, 411-416, 418-420, 423-424, 426-437, 440-446, 448-449, 451-459, 461-472, 474-480, 482-494, 496-500, 502-506, 508-511, 513-526, 528, 530-532, 534-542, 544-548, 550-558, 561-577, 579, 582, 584-592, 595-600, 602-610, 612, 614-618, 620, 622-627, 629-632, 635-640, 642, 644-648, 651-675, 677-688, 690-707, 709-731, 733-735, 737-738, 740-763, 766-770, 772-777, 779, 784-799, 801-823, 825-831, 833-837, 839-851, 853-859, 861-874, 876-877, 880-885, 887-893, 896-907
    Graduate Studies: **Military Personnel,** 908, 912-914, 916-917, 919-920, 924, 926, 928, 930, 932-934, 936, 938, 942, 945, 947-953, 955-956, 958-959, 961, 963, 965-967, 972, 974-983, 988-989, 991-1001, 1004-1006, 1008-1011, 1013-1017; **ROTC Students,** 1020-1023, 1026; **Military Family Members,** 1028-1031, 1033, 1036-1038, 1040, 1042-1045, 1047-1049, 1051-1052, 1054-1063, 1066-1068, 1070-1075, 1077-1078, 1081-1085, 1087, 1089-1091, 1093-1108, 1110-1112, 1114-1115, 1118-1120, 1122-1127, 1129-1132, 1134-1136

Geospatial information technology
    Undergraduate Studies: **Military Personnel,** 217; **ROTC Students,** 323
    See also General programs

Government. *See* Political science and politics; Public administration

Graphic arts
    Undergraduate Studies: **Military Personnel,** 50
    See also Art; General programs

Graphic design
    Undergraduate Studies: **Military Family Members,** 410, 736
    See also Design; General programs; Graphic arts

Guidance. *See* Counseling

Gynecology
    Undergraduate Studies: **Military Personnel,** 19
    Graduate Studies: **Military Personnel,** 927
    See also General programs; Medical sciences; Obstetrics

H

Health and health care
    Undergraduate Studies: **Military Personnel,** 66; **Military Family Members,** 495, 894
    See also General programs; Medical sciences

Health and health care, administration
    Undergraduate Studies: **Military Personnel,** 118
    Graduate Studies: **Military Personnel,** 970
    See also Business administration; General programs; Health and health care

High schools. *See* Education, secondary

Hindi language. *See* Language, Hindi

History
    Undergraduate Studies: **Military Family Members,** 342
    Graduate Studies: **Military Personnel,** 985; **Military Family Members,** 1076
    See also General programs; names of specific types of history

History, American
    Undergraduate Studies: **Military Family Members,** 543
    Graduate Studies: **Military Personnel,** 1003
    See also General programs; History

History, English
    Undergraduate Studies: **Military Family Members,** 543
    See also General programs; History

History, military
    Graduate Studies: **Military Personnel,** 1003
    See also History; Military affairs

Home economics
    Undergraduate Studies: **Military Family Members,** 879
    See also General programs

Homeland security. *See* Security, national

Hospitals. *See* Health and health care

Human resources. *See* Personnel administration

Hydrology
    Undergraduate Studies: **Military Personnel,** 217; **ROTC Students,** 323
    See also General programs

I

Indonesian language. *See* Language, Indonesian

Industrial design
    Undergraduate Studies: **Military Family Members,** 410
    See also Design; General programs

Industrial engineering. *See* Engineering, industrial

Industrial hygiene
    Undergraduate Studies: **Military Personnel,** 118; **Military Family Members,** 410
    Graduate Studies: **Military Personnel,** 970
    See also General programs; Health and health care; Safety studies

Industrial relations
    Undergraduate Studies: **Military Family Members,** 410
    See also General programs; Labor unions and members

Information systems
    Undergraduate Studies: **Military Personnel,** 4, 57, 216, 233; **ROTC Students,** 322; **Military Family Members,** 410
    See also Business administration; General programs

Information technology
    Undergraduate Studies: **Military Personnel,** 3-4, 22, 57, 155, 210, 233; **ROTC Students,** 272, 287, 317; **Military Family Members,** 345, 410
    Graduate Studies: **Military Personnel,** 909, 984; **Military Family Members,** 1032
    See also Computer sciences; General programs

Intelligence service
    Undergraduate Studies: **Military Personnel,** 4, 57, 210-211, 233; **ROTC Students,** 248, 317-318
    Graduate Studies: **Military Personnel,** 915, 962; **Military Family Members,** 1035, 1079
    See also General programs; International relations; Military affairs

Calendar Index

Since most financial aid programs have specific deadline dates, some may have already closed by the time you begin to look for funding. You can use the Calendar Index to identify which programs are still open. To do that, go to the educational level (undergraduate or graduate studies) and the recipient group (military personnel; ROTC students; military family members) that applies to you, think about when you'll be able to complete your application forms, go to the appropriate months, jot down the entry numbers listed there, and use those numbers to find the program descriptions in the directory. Keep in mind that the numbers cited here refer to program entry numbers, not to page numbers in the book.

Undergraduate Studies

Military Personnel:
January: 11, 16, 34, 43, 50, 56, 64, 69, 111, 144, 153-154, 171-173, 182-183, 220, 226, 244
February: 3, 26, 88, 101, 114, 127, 146, 148, 157, 172-173, 238, 245-246
March: 1, 21, 27, 29, 31, 48, 56, 59, 62, 76, 79-80, 90, 96, 102-103, 107-108, 137-138, 159, 167-169, 182, 185-186, 199, 201, 206, 219, 222, 225, 237
April: 4, 6, 13-14, 17, 24, 28, 32, 38, 42, 44-45, 51, 57-58, 63, 66, 68, 71-72, 83-84, 92, 100-101, 110, 115, 132, 134, 141-142, 149-150, 165, 187, 194, 205, 213, 220, 223, 229-230, 235, 239, 242
May: 2, 23, 41, 52, 54, 65, 78, 85, 94, 105, 119, 122, 131, 135-136, 143, 145, 155, 195, 200, 202, 207, 227-228, 232-233
June: 37, 45, 53, 55-56, 61, 67, 70, 77, 86, 88-89, 91, 99, 104, 117, 120, 139, 147, 151-152, 159, 161, 165, 170, 178-180, 182, 188, 190, 204, 210-212, 214-218, 221, 237, 240
July: 9, 39, 46, 58, 75, 97, 140, 187
August: 12, 30, 64, 87, 93, 118, 166, 220
September: 56, 79-80, 88, 95, 103, 159, 236
October: 8, 58, 74, 182, 193, 203, 235, 237
November: 4, 45, 57, 91, 139, 165, 175, 181, 213, 221
December: 12, 25, 82, 159, 166, 189, 191
Any time: 5, 10, 18-19, 40, 73, 98, 130, 133, 197, 243
Deadline not specified: 7, 15, 20, 22, 33, 35-36, 47, 49, 60, 81, 106, 109, 112-113, 116, 121, 123-126, 128-129, 156, 158, 160, 162-164, 174, 176-177, 184, 192, 196, 198, 208-209, 224, 231, 234, 241, 247

ROTC Students:
January: 253, 271, 292, 301, 303
February: 248, 252, 256, 259-260, 263, 268, 272, 281, 284-285, 287, 291, 293, 295, 312, 327

March: 258, 266, 275-277, 279, 283, 288, 302, 304, 310-311, 315, 328
April: 257, 270, 286
May: 261, 289, 298-299, 326
June: 250, 262, 269, 280, 294, 297, 300, 306-310, 314, 317-324
July: 264, 282
August: 325
September: 276-277
October: 313
November: 249, 255, 264, 274
December: 254
Deadline not specified: 251, 265, 267, 273, 278, 290, 296, 305, 316

Military Family Members:
January: 448, 482, 510-511, 514, 575, 587, 599, 642, 679, 702-703, 713-714, 718, 745, 748-750, 761, 795, 813, 850, 861, 870, 887, 899
February: 329, 333, 337, 345-346, 349-351, 359-360, 362, 367, 369, 371, 376, 382, 389, 398, 403, 410, 420, 425, 428, 433, 445-446, 454, 480, 485, 491, 498, 507-509, 516-517, 523, 529, 533-534, 544, 546, 561-563, 573, 584, 586, 608, 628, 634-635, 639, 648, 651, 663-664, 670-671, 680, 684, 706, 708, 715, 719, 721, 730, 734, 737-739, 749-752, 766-767, 769-770, 777, 781, 783, 789, 793, 797, 799-800, 803-804, 810, 814, 823-824, 830, 844, 851, 862, 865, 875, 889, 901, 904
March: 331, 335, 339-342, 348, 352-353, 355, 363, 365, 377, 379-381, 384, 396, 399, 402, 404-405, 408, 415, 418, 422-423, 429, 438, 452, 455-456, 462-463, 465, 467, 470, 479, 488, 494, 513, 521, 535-536, 538, 545, 547, 549-553, 566-567, 569-571, 580-581, 583, 589, 594, 597, 601, 603, 609, 611, 615-616, 623, 626-627, 631-633, 641, 643-644, 652, 655, 661, 675-676, 688, 696-697, 716-717, 722-723, 725, 741-743, 746, 755-756, 762-763, 768, 771, 776, 782, 784-785, 796, 807, 809, 812, 816, 829, 839, 847, 855, 880-881, 890, 892-895, 898

Graduate Studies